GALACTIC ARCHAEOLOGY: NEAR-FIELD COSMOLOGY AND THE FORMATION OF THE MILKY WAY

COVER ILLUSTRATION:

A visual color image of the spiral galaxy NGC 2403 obtained with the Subaru Telescope Suprime-Cam. The distance to the galaxy from us is about 3 Mpc. Individual stars including red giants, horizontal branch and main-sequence stars are resolved in the extended structures of this galaxy. See Ferguson (p.265) in this volume.
The image provided by A. Ferguson.

ASTRONOMICAL SOCIETY OF THE PACIFIC
CONFERENCE SERIES

A SERIES OF BOOKS ON RECENT DEVELOPMENTS IN ASTRONOMY AND ASTROPHYSICS

Volume 458

EDITORIAL STAFF

Managing Editor: Joseph Jensen
Associate Managing Editor: Jonathan Barnes
Publication Manager: Pepita Ridgeway
Editorial Assistant: Cindy Moody
LATEX Consultant: T. J. Mahoney

MS 179, Utah Valley University, 800 W. University Parkway, Orem, Utah 84058-5999
Phone: 801-863-8804   E-mail: aspcs@aspbooks.org
E-book site: http://www.aspbooks.org

PUBLICATION COMMITTEE

ASPCS volumes may be found online with color images at http://www.aspbooks.org.
ASP Monographs may be found online at http://www.aspmonographs.org.

For a complete list of ASPCS Volumes, ASP Monographs, and
other ASP publications see http://www.astrosociety.org/pubs.html.

All book order and subscription inquiries should be directed to the ASP at
800-335-2626 (toll-free within the USA) or 415-337-2126,
or email service@astrosociety.org

ASTRONOMICAL SOCIETY OF THE PACIFIC
CONFERENCE SERIES

Volume 458

GALACTIC ARCHAEOLOGY: NEAR-FIELD COSMOLOGY AND THE FORMATION OF THE MILKY WAY

Edited by

Wako Aoki
National Astronomical Observatory of Japan, Mitaka, Tokyo, Japan

Miho Ishigaki
National Astronomical Observatory of Japan, Mitaka, Tokyo, Japan

Takuma Suda
National Astronomical Observatory of Japan, Mitaka, Tokyo, Japan

Takuji Tsujimoto
National Astronomical Observatory of Japan, Mitaka, Tokyo, Japan

Nobuo Arimoto
National Astronomical Observatory of Japan, Mitaka, Tokyo, Japan

SAN FRANCISCO

ASTRONOMICAL SOCIETY OF THE PACIFIC
390 Ashton Avenue
San Francisco, California, 94112-1722, USA

Phone: 415-337-1100
Fax: 415-337-5205
E-mail: service@astrosociety.org
Web site: www.astrosociety.org
E-books: www.aspbooks.org

First Edition
© 2012 by Astronomical Society of the Pacific
ASP Conference Series
All rights reserved.

ISBN: 978-1-58381-798-8
e-book ISBN: 978-1-58381-799-5

Library of Congress (LOC) Cataloging in Publication (CIP) Data:
Main entry under title
Library of Congress Control Number (LCCN): 2012935501

Printed in the United States of America by Sheridan Books, Ann Arbor, Michigan.
This book is printed on acid-free paper.

Contents

Part I. Nucleosynthesis, Supernovae and GRBs

Part II. Early Generations of Stars

Part III. Chemical Evolution

Part IV. Milky Way Galaxy

Part VI. Dark Matter

Part VII. Future Prospects

Part VIII. Closing

Preface

Understanding the formation and evolution of galaxies is one of the major goals of the modern astronomy. The Milky Way and other galaxies in the local group provide us with a unique opportunity to investigate individual stars in galaxies by determining their spatial distributions, ages, and chemical compositions that constrain the formation history of substructures of galaxies. This approach called "Galactic Archaeology" requires detailed knowledge of star formation, stellar evolution, supernova explosions, nucleosynthesis in these objects, dust formation, and chemical processes in interstellar matter. In addition to these individual processes, formations of clusters and substructures of galaxies reflect the nature of dark matter. Galactic Archaeology has an aspect of cosmology.

This book represents the proceedings of the conference "Galactic Archaeology – Near-Field Cosmology and the Formation of the Milky Way" held on November 1-4, 2011 in Shuzenji, Japan. This conference was the third meeting in the Subaru International Conference series organized by the Subaru Telescope of National Astronomical Observatory of Japan (NAOJ) as well as the first NAOJ symposium. In the conference, we had 60 oral talks and 84 poster presentations, widely covering topics related to the Galactic Archaeology, with 141 participants from 23 countries and regions.

In the conference, many exciting results were presented, in particular on the substructures of the Milky Way and galaxies in the local group. Studies of star formation history of individual galaxies and the interaction between galaxies have been making rapid progress by the measurements and analyses of stellar ages and chemical compositions based on wide-field imaging surveys with, e.g., CFHT and Subaru, and spectroscopic surveys of individual stars in local group galaxies with, e.g., SDSS and VLT.

New models and simulations of the Milky Way formation, chemo-dynamics, and nucleosynthesis in stars and supernovae were presented. Investigations of dark matter in laboratory and with observations, as well as their impact on the structure formation were discussed.

The activity of this field will be further accelerated by the currently planned new observational facilities reviewed in the conference. New satellites for astrometry (Gaia and JASMINE) will make major contributions to revealing the substructures of the Milky Way and origins of their stellar components. We will obtain clearer views on the formation of the Milky Way through interactions with surrounding dwarf galaxies by future surveys with wide field of view of, e.g., Subaru Hyper Suprime-Cam, large spectroscopic surveys with, e.g., LAMOST, AAT/HERMES, the Subaru Prime Focus Spectrograph, and more detailed spectroscopic studies with next generation extremely large telescopes.

The meeting was originally scheduled in May 2011, but was postponed because of the large earthquake and tsunami in March in Japan. We would like to thank all participants for the understanding for the schedule change. We would also like to acknowledge the a number of kind messages and encouragements after the disaster. In such situation the speech by Prof. Ken Freeman at the conference banquet on November 3rd was impressive for the LOC members. I would here quote it with his permission:

> I have the pleasant duty to welcome you to the banquet and say a few words to open the occasion. For those of you who have been to Japan

before, I think you will share with me the pleasure of returning to this beautiful and interesting land and meeting again with the wonderful and hospitable people who live here. For those for whom this is the first time, I hope you enjoy it as much as I do.

This is the third Subaru meeting and the first NAOJ symposium. The Subaru meetings celebrate the achievements with the Subaru telescope, one of the best and most productive of the 8-m telescopes. It contributes enormously to our subject of Galactic Archaeology, both through research by Japanese astronomers and through the generous access that Subaru provides to foreign astronomers.

As you know, this meeting was originally scheduled for earlier this year, but was derailed by the earthquake and tsunami disaster. We were all horrified by the scale of the disaster and the personal difficulties and the damage. We are very happy that our friends at Tohoku University survived this disaster, and we all stand in awe of the way that the Japanese people coped with the problems and have recovered.

We are coming up to the final day of our meeting on Galactic Archaeology. The meeting has been very wide ranging and I think it has extended us all into areas in which we are not expert but need to be informed. I have found it very stimulating and I hope you have also found it stimulating and exciting. The SOC certainly had a great response when this meeting was announced, and I would like us to give our thanks and congratulations to Shigeyama-san and his team for putting together such an exciting program.

Congratulations to Aoki-san and his LOC for finding such a wonderful place to hold the meeting. It is a real delight to stand outside the hotel and gaze upon Mt Fuji. Meetings like this do not happen without a huge amount of work and we owe our thanks to the LOC for making this meeting happen and have everything working out so well.

Enjoy the banquet !

Our special thanks go to the Scientific Organizing Committee (N. Arimoto, T. C. Beers, M. Chiba, K. Freeman, G. Gilmore, M. G. Lee, A. Renzini, T. Shigeyama, and E. Tolstoy) for their invaluable commitment for arranging the science program. We are grateful to the venue, Laforet Shuzenji, for the understanding for postponing the conference and careful supports during the meeting. Finally, I would like to thank the LOC members (M. Ishigaki, T. Suda, T. Tsujimoto, N. Arimoto, Y. Takeda, K. Sekiguchi, and F. Yoshida) for their extensive works for organizing the all events, and T. Tajima for taking nice photographs during the conference.

Wako Aoki (LOC Chair), March 2012

Participants

D. AN, Department of Science Education, Ewha Womans University, Seoul 120-750, Republic of Korea ⟨ deokkeun@ewha.ac.kr ⟩

J. ANDERSEN, Niels Bohr Institute, Juliane Maries Vej 30, DK-2100, Copenhagen, Denmark ⟨ ja@astro.ku.dk ⟩

W. AOKI, National Astronomical Observatory of Japan, 2-21-1 Osawa, Mitaka, Tokyo 181-8588, Japan ⟨ aoki.wako@nao.ac.jp ⟩

N. ARIMOTO, National Astronomical Observatory of Japan, 2-21-1 Osawa, Mitaka, Tokyo 181-8588, Japan ⟨ arimoto.n@nao.ac.jp ⟩

M. ASPLUND, Max Planck Institute for Astrophysics, Karl-Schwarzschild-Str. 1, D-85741 Garching, Germany ⟨ asplund@mpa-garching.mpg.de ⟩

T. BENSBY, Lund Observatory, Box 43, SE-221 00 Lund, Sweden ⟨ tbensby@astro.lu.se ⟩

E. J. BERNARD, Institute for Astronomy, University of Edinburgh, Royal Obsertory, Edinburgh, Blackford Hill, Edinburgh EH9 3HJ, UK ⟨ ejb@roe.ac.uk ⟩

J. BLAND-HAWTHORN, Sydney Institute for Astronomy, School of Physics, University of Sydney, NSW 2006, Australia ⟨ jbh@physics.usyd.edu.au ⟩

S. W. CAMPBELL, Monash Centre for Astrophysics, Monash University, VIC 3800, Australia ⟨ simon.campbell@monash.edu ⟩

R. CARLBERG, Department of Astronomy & Astrophysics, University of Toronto, Toronto, ON, M5S 3H4, Canada ⟨ carlberg@astro.utoronto.ca ⟩

J. L. CARLIN, Department of Physics, Applied Physics and Astronomy, Rensselaer Polytechnic Institute, 110 8th Street, Troy, NY 12180, USA ⟨ carlij@rpi.edu ⟩

R. CARRERA, Instituto de Astrofísica de Canarias, La Laguna, Tenerife, Spain ⟨ rcarrera@iac.es ⟩

L. CASAGRANDE, Max Planck Institute for Astrophysics, Postfach 1317, 85741, Garching, Germany ⟨ luca@mpa-garching.mpg.de ⟩

A. R. CASEY, Research School of Astronomy & Astrophysics, Australian National University, Mount Stromlo Observatory, Cotter Road, Weston Creek, Canberra, ACT 2611, Australia ⟨ acasey@mso.anu.edu.au ⟩

J. CHENG, University of California Santa Cruz, Santa Cruz, CA 95064, USA ⟨ jyc@ucolick.org ⟩

M. CHIBA, Astronomical Institute, Tohoku University, Aoba-ku, Sendai 980-8578, Japan ⟨ chiba@astr.tohoku.ac.jp ⟩

M.-Y. CHOU, Institute of Astronomy and Astrophysics, Academia Sinica, Taipei 10617, Taiwan ⟨ cmy@asiaa.sinica.edu.tw ⟩

J. G. COHEN, Palomar Observatory, California Institute of Technology, 1200 E. California Blvd., MC 249-17, Pasadena, CA 91125, USA ⟨ jlc@astro.caltech.edu ⟩

M. COLLINS, Max Planck Institut für Astronomie, Königstuhl 17, Heidelberg, 69117, Germany ⟨ mlmc2@ast.cam.ac.uk ⟩

B. Conn, Max Planck Institut für Astronomie, Königstuhl 17, Heidelberg, 69117, Germany ⟨ conn@mpia-hd.mpg.de ⟩

P. Cottrell, The Beatrice Tinsley Institute, Department of Physics and Astronomy, University of Canterbury, Private Bag 4800, Christchurch, New Zealand ⟨ peter.cottrell@canterbury.ac.nz ⟩

D. Crnojevic, Institute for Astronomy, University of Edinburgh, Blackford Hill, Edinburgh, EH9 3HJ, UK ⟨ dc@roe.ac.uk ⟩

V. D'Orazi, INAF- Osservatorio Astronomico di Padova, vicolo dell'Osservatorio 5, Padova, 35122, Italy ⟨ valentina.dorazi@mq.edu.au ⟩

G. De Silva, Australian Astronomical Observatory, PO Box 296, NSW 1710, Australia ⟨ gdesilva@aao.gov.au ⟩

C. L. Doherty, Monash Centre For Astrophysics (MoCA), School of Mathematical Sciences, Monash University, Victoria 3800, Australia ⟨ carolyn.doherty@monash.edu ⟩

M. Doi, Institute of Astronomy, Graduate School of Science, University of Tokyo, 2-21-1 Osawa, Mitaka, Tokyo181-0015, Japan ⟨ doi@ioa.s.u-tokyo.ac.jp ⟩

A. M. N. Ferguson, Institute for Astronomy, University of Edinburgh, Blackford Hill, Edinburgh, EH9 3HJ, UK ⟨ ferguson@roe.ac.uk ⟩

A. Ferrara, Scuola Normale Superiore, Piazza dei Cavalieri 7, 56126 Pisa, Italy ⟨ andrea.ferrara@sns.it ⟩

C. G. Few, Jeremiah Horrocks Institute for Astrophysics and Supercomputing, University of Central Lancashire, Preston, PR1 2HE, UK ⟨ cgfew@uclan.ac.uk ⟩

C. K. Fishlock, Research School of Astronomy & Astrophysics, Australian National University, Mount Stromlo Observatory, Cotter Road, Weston Creek, Canberra, ACT 2611, Australia ⟨ cherief@mso.anu.edu.au ⟩

K. C. Freeman, Research School of Astronomy & Astrophysics, Australian National University, Mount Stromlo Observatory, Cotter Road, Weston Creek, Canberra, ACT 2611, Australia ⟨ kcf@mso.anu.edu.au ⟩

G. Gilmore, Institute of Astronomy, University of Cambridge, Madingley Road, Cambridge CB3 0HA, UK ⟨ gil@ast.cam.ac.uk ⟩

O. A. Gonzalez, European Southern Observatory, Karl-Schwarzschild-Strasse 2, D-85748 Garching, Germany ⟨ ogonzale@eso.org ⟩

A. Goswami, Indian Institute of Astrophysics, Koramangala, Bangalore 560034, India ⟨ aruna@iiap.res.in ⟩

N. Gouda, National Astronomical Observatory of Japan, 2-21-1 Osawa, Mitaka, Tokyo 181-8588, Japan ⟨ naoteru.gouda@nao.ac.jp ⟩

C. J. Grillmair, Spitzer Science Center, 1200 E. California Blvd., Pasadena, CA 91125, USA ⟨ carl@ipac.caltech.edu ⟩

S. Hamano, Institute of Astronomy, Graduate School of Science, University of Tokyo, 2-21-1 Osawa, Mitaka, Tokyo181-0015, Japan ⟨ hamano@ioa.s.u-tokyo.ac.jp ⟩

T. Handa, Graduate School of Science and Engineering, Kagoshima University, 1-21-35 Korimoto, Kagoshima, Kagoshima 890-0065, Japan ⟨ handa@sci.kagoshima-u.ac.jp ⟩

R. Haschke, Astronomisches Rechen-Institut, Zentrum fuer Astronomie Heidelberg, Mönchhofstrasse 12-14, D-69120 Heidelberg, Germany ⟨ haschke@ari.uni-heidelberg.de ⟩

T. Hasegawa, Gunma Astronomical Observatory, Agatsuma, Gunma 377-0702, Japan ⟨ hasegawa@astron.pref.gunma.jp ⟩

K. Hattori, Institute of Astronomy, Graduate School of Science, University of Tokyo, 2-21-1 Osawa, Mitaka, Tokyo 181-0015, Japan ⟨ khattori@ioa.s.u-tokyo.ac.jp ⟩

K. Hayashi, Astronomical Institute, Tohoku University, Aoba-ku, Sendai 980-8578, Japan ⟨ k.hayasi@astr.tohoku.ac.jp ⟩

A. Heger, University of Minnesota, School of Physics & Astronomy, University of Minnesota, Twin Cities, Minneapolis, MN 55455, USA ⟨ alex@physics.umn.edu ⟩

G. Hensler, Institute of Astronomy, University of Vienna, Trkenschanzstrasse 17, 1180 Vienna, Austria ⟨ gerhard.hensler@univie.ac.at ⟩

S. L. Hidalgo, Instituto de Astrofísica de Canarias, Vía Láctea s/n. E38200 - La Laguna, Tenerife, Canary Islands, Spain ⟨ shidalgo@iac.es ⟩

V. Hill, Laboratoire Lagrange, Universit de Nice Sophia-Antipolis, CNRS, Observatoire de la Côte d'Azur, BP 4229, 06304 Nice cedex 4, France ⟨ Vanessa.Hill@oca.eu ⟩

S. Honda, Kwasan Observatory, Kyoto University, Ohmine-cho Kita Kazan, Yamashina-ku, Kyoto 607-8471, Japan ⟨ honda@kwasan.kyoto-u.ac.jp ⟩

N. Hwang, National Astronomical Observatory of Japan, 2-21-1 Osawa, Mitaka, Tokyo 181-8588, Japan ⟨ narae.hwang@nao.ac.jp ⟩

E. A. Hyde, Department of Physics and Astronomy, Macquarie University, NSW 2109, Australia ⟨ elaina.hyde@mq.edu.au ⟩

S. Inoue, University College London, Department of Space & Climate Physics, Mullard Space Science Laboratory, Holmbury St. Mary, Dorking Surrey RH5 6NT, UK ⟨ inoue@astr.tohoku.ac.jp ⟩

M. Ishigaki, National Astronomical Observatory of Japan, 2-21-1 Osawa, Mitaka, Tokyo 181-8588, Japan ⟨ ishigaki.miho@nao.ac.jp ⟩

H. Ito, The Graduate University for Advanced Studies (Sokendai), 2-21-1 Osawa, Mitaka, Tokyo 181-8588, Japan ⟨ hiroko.ito@nao.ac.jp ⟩

S. Jin, ARI/ZAH, University of Heidelberg, Mönchhofstr. 12–14, D-69120 Heidelberg, Germany ⟨ shoko@ari.uni-heidelberg.de ⟩

R. Joveini, Institute for Research in Fundamental Sciences, Sharif University of Technology, Tehran, Iran ⟨ joveini@physics.sharif.ir ⟩

T. Kajino, National Astronomical Observatory of Japan, 2-21-1 Osawa, Mitaka, Tokyo 181-8588, Japan ⟨ kajino@nao.ac.jp ⟩

A. Karakas, Research School of Astronomy & Astrophysics, Australian National University, Mount Stromlo Observatory, Cotter Road, Weston Creek, Canberra, ACT 2611, Australia ⟨ akarakas@mso.anu.edu.au ⟩

N. Kawai, Department of Physics, Tokyo Institute of Technology, 2-12-1 Ookayama, Meguro-ku, Tokyo 152-8551, Japan ⟨ nkawai@phys.titech.ac.jp ⟩

S. KELLER, Research School of Astronomy & Astrophysics, Australian National University, Mount Stromlo Observatory, Cotter Road, Weston Creek, Canberra, ACT 2611, Australia ⟨ stefan@mso.anu.edu.au ⟩

J. H. KIM, Center for the Exploration of the Origin of the Universe, Astronomy Program, Department of Physics and Astronomy, Seoul National University, Seoul, Republic of Korea ⟨ jhkim@astro.snu.ac.kr ⟩

C. KOBAYASHI, Centre for Astrophysics Research, School of Physics, Astronomy and Mathematics, University of Hertfordshire, Hatfield AL10 9AB, UK ⟨ c.kobayashi@herts.ac.uk ⟩

T. KOGAWA, Astronomical Institute, Tohoku University, Aoba-ku, Sendai 980-8578, Japan ⟨ kogawa@astr.tohoku.ac.jp ⟩

Y. KOMIYA, National Astronomical Observatory of Japan, 2-21-1 Osawa, Mitaka, Tokyo 181-8588, Japan ⟨ yutaka.komiya@nao.ac.jp ⟩

S. KOPOSOV, Institute of Astronomy, University of Cambridge, Madingley Road, Cambridge CB3 0HA, UK ⟨ koposov@ast.cam.ac.uk ⟩

G. KORDOPATIS, Institute of Astronomy, University of Cambridge, Madingley Road, Cambridge CB3 0HA, UK ⟨ Georges.Kordopatis@oca.eu ⟩

O. KRAUSE, Max-Planck Institut for Astronomy, Koenigstuhl 17, 69117 Heidelberg, Germany ⟨ krause@mpia.de ⟩

H. KUNCARAYAKTI, Institute of Astronomy, Graduate School of Science, University of Tokyo, 2-21-1 Osawa, Mitaka, Tokyo 181-0015, Japan ⟨ hanin@ioa.s.u-tokyo.ac.jp ⟩

M. G. LEE, Astronomy Program, Department of Physics and Astronomy, Seoul National University, Gwanak-gu, Seoul 151-742, Republic of Korea ⟨ mglee@astro.snu.ac.kr ⟩

Y. S. LEE, Department of Physics & Astronomy and Joint Institute for Nuclear Astrophysics, Michigan State University, East Lansing, MI 48824, USA ⟨ lee@pa.msu.edu ⟩

S. LIM, Astronomy Program, Department of Physics and Astronomy, Seoul National University, Gwanak-gu, Seoul 151-742, Republic of Korea ⟨ slim@astro.snu.ac.kr ⟩

K. LIND, Max Planck Institute for Astrophysics, Garching bei München, D-857 41 Germany ⟨ klind@mpa-garching.mpg.de ⟩

D. MACKEY, Research School of Astronomy & Astrophysics, Australian National University, Mount Stromlo Observatory, Cotter Road, Weston Creek, Canberra, ACT 2611, Australia ⟨ dougal@mso.anu.edu.au ⟩

K. MAEDA, Institute for the Physics and Mathematics of the Universe (IPMU), Todai Institutes for Advanced Study (TODIAS), University of Tokyo, 5-1-5 Kashiwanoha, Kashiwa, Chiba 277-8583, Japan ⟨ keiichi.maeda@ipmu.jp ⟩

S.R. MAJEWSKI, Department of Astronomy, University of Virginia, P.O. Box 400325, Charlottesville, VA 22904-4325, USA ⟨ srm4n@virginia.edu ⟩

N. MARTIN, Max-Planck-Institut für Astronomie, Königstuhl 17, D-69117 Heidelberg, Germany ⟨ martin@mpia-hd.mpg.de ⟩

G.J. Mathews, Center for Astrophysics, Department of Physics, University of Notre Dame, Notre Dame, Indiana 46556, USA ⟨ gmathews@nd.edu ⟩

K. Matsubayashi, Research Center for Space and Cosmic Evolution, Ehime University, 2-5 Bunkyo-cho, Matsuyama, Ehime 790-8577, Japan ⟨ kazuya@cosmos.phys.sci.ehime-u.ac.jp ⟩

N. Matsunaga, Kiso Observatory, University of Tokyo, 10762-30 Mitake, Kiso, Nagano 397-0101, Japan ⟨ matsunaga@ioa.s.u-tokyo.ac.jp ⟩

A. W. McConnachie, NRC Herzberg Institute of Astrophysics, 5071 West Saanich Road, Victoria, British Columbia, Canada ⟨ alan.mcconnachie@nrc-cnrc.gc.ca ⟩

Y. Miki, Graduate School of Pure and Applied Science, University of Tsukuba, 1-1-1 Tennodai, Tsukuba, Ibaraki 305-8577, Japan ⟨ ymiki@ccs.tsukuba.ac.jp ⟩

T. I. Mori, Department of Astronomy, Graduate School of Science, University of Tokyo, 7-3-1 Hongo, Bunkyo-ku, Tokyo 113-0033, Japan ⟨ morii@astron.s.u-tokyo.ac.jp ⟩

K. Morihana, Japan Aerospace Exploration Agency, Institute of Space and Astronautical Science, 3-1-1 Yoshinodai, Chuo-ku, Sagamihara, Kanagawa 252-5210, Japan ⟨ morihana@astro.isas.jaxa.jp ⟩

S. Moriyama, Kamioka Observatory, Institute of Cosmic Ray Research, University of Tokyo, Higashi-Mozumi, Kamioka, Hida, Gifu 506-1205, Japan ⟨ moriyama@icrr.u-tokyo.ac.jp ⟩

K. Nakamura, National Astronomical Observatory of Japan, 2-21-1 Osawa, Mitaka, Tokyo 181-8588, Japan ⟨ nakamura.ko@nao.ac.jp ⟩

M. Ness, Research School of Astronomy & Astrophysics, Australian National University, Mount Stromlo Observatory, Cotter Road, Weston Creek, Canberra, ACT 2611, Australia ⟨ mkness@mso.anu.edu.au ⟩

H. J. Newberg, Physics Department, Rensselaer Polytechnic Institute, 110 8th Street, Troy, NY 12180, USA ⟨ heidi@rpi.edu ⟩

K. Nomoto, Institute for the Physics and Mathematics of the Universe (IPMU), Todai Institutes for Advanced Study (TODIAS), University of Tokyo, 5-1-5 Kashiwanoha, Kashiwa, Chiba 277-8583, Japan ⟨ nomoto@astron.s.u-tokyo.ac.jp ⟩

B. Nordström, Niels Bohr Institute, Juliane Maries Vej 30, DK-2100, Copenhagen, Denmark ⟨ birgitta@nbi.ku.dk ⟩

T. Nozawa, Institute for the Physics and Mathematics of the Universe (IPMU), Todai Institutes for Advanced Study (TODIAS), University of Tokyo, 5-1-5 Kashiwanoha, Kashiwa, Chiba 277-8583, Japan ⟨ takaya.nozawa@ipmu.jp ⟩

Go Ogiya, Graduate School of Pure and Applied Science, University of Tsukuba, 1-1-1 Tennodai, Tsukuba 305-8577, Japan ⟨ ogiya@ccs.tsukuba.ac.jp ⟩

K. Ohta, Department of Astronomy, Kyoto University, Kyoto 606-8502, Japan ⟨ ohta@kusastro.kyoto-u.ac.jp ⟩

S. Okamoto, Kavli Institute for Astronomy and Astrophysics, Peking University, Yi He Yuan Lu 5, Hai Dian Qu, Beijing 100871, China ⟨ okamoto@pku.edu.cn ⟩

T. Onaka, Department of Astronomy, Graduate School of Science, University of Tokyo, 7-3-1 Hongo, Bunkyo-ku, Tokyo 113-0033, Japan ⟨ onaka@astron.s.u-tokyo.ac.jp ⟩

M. Onodera, Institute for Astronomy, ETH Zürich, Wolfgang-Pauli-Strasse 27, 8093, Zürich, Switzerland ⟨ monodera@phys.ethz.ch ⟩

B. W. O'Shea, Department of Physics and Astronomy and JINA, Michigan State University, East Lansing, MI 48824, USA ⟨ oshea@msu.edu ⟩

M. Otsuka, Institute of Astronomy and Astrophysics, Academia Sinica, P.O. Box 23-141, Taipei 10617, Taiwan ⟨ otsuka@asiaa.sinica.edu.tw ⟩

M. Parthasarathy, National Astronomical Observatory of Japan, 2-21-1 Osawa, Mitaka, Tokyo 181-8588, Japan ⟨ m-partha@hotmail.com ⟩

S. Pasetto, University College London, Department of Space & Climate Physics, Mullard Space Science Laboratory, Holmbury St. Mary, Dorking Surrey RH5 6NT, UK ⟨ spasetto@ari.uni-heidelberg.de ⟩

L. Pasquini, European Southern Observatory, Karl-Schwarzschild-Str. 2, 85748, Garching bei Mnchen, Germany ⟨ lpasquin@eso.org ⟩

R. C. Peterson, Astrophysical Advances and UCO/Lick, 601 Marion Pl, Palo Alto, CA 94301, USA ⟨ peterson@ucolick.org ⟩

K. Pilkington, Jeremiah Horrocks Institute, University of Central Lancashire, Preston, PR1 2HE, UK ⟨ kpilkington@uclan.ac.uk ⟩

G. Piotto, Dipartimento di Astronomia, Universit di Padova, Vicolo dell'Osservatorio 3, Padova, I-35122, Italy ⟨ giampaolo.piotto@unipd.it ⟩

V. M. Placco, Departamento de Astronomia - Instituto de Astronomia, Geofísica e Ciências Atmosféricas, Universidade de São Paulo, São Paulo, SP 05508-900, Brazil ⟨ vmplacco@astro.iag.usp.br ⟩

A. Renzini, INAF - Osservatorio Astronomico di Padova, vicolo dell'Osservatorio 5, Padova, 35122, Italy ⟨ alvio.renzini@oapd.inaf.it ⟩

R. M. Rich, Department of Physics and Astronomy, UCLA, PAB 430 Portola Plaza, Box 951547, Los Angeles, CA 90095-1547, USA ⟨ rmr@astro.ucla.edu ⟩

N. Sakai, The Graduate University for Advanced Studies (Sokendai), 2-21-1 Osawa, Mitaka, Tokyo 181-8588, Japan ⟨ nobuyuki.sakai@nao.ac.jp ⟩

T. Sakamoto, Japan Spaceguard Association, 1716-3 Ookura, Bisei, Ibara, Okayama 714-1411, Japan ⟨ sakamoto@spaceguard.or.jp ⟩

C. M. Sakari, Department of Physics and Astronomy, University of Victoria, Victoria, BC V8W 3P2, Canada ⟨ sakaricm@uvic.ca ⟩

I. Sakon, Department of Astronomy, Graduate School of Science, University of Tokyo, 7-3-1 Hongo, Bunkyo-ku, Tokyo 113-0033, Japan ⟨ isakon@astron.s.u-tokyo.ac.jp ⟩

S. Salvadori, Kapteyn Astronomical Institute, Landleven 12, 9747AD Groningen, the Netherlands ⟨ salvadori@astro.rug.nl ⟩

F. A. Santana, Departamento de Astronomía, Universidad de Chile, Camino el Observatorio 1515, Las Condes, Santiago, Chile ⟨ fsantana@das.uchile.cl ⟩

L. Sbordone, Zentrum für Astronomie der Universität Heidelberg, Landessternwarte, Königstuhl 12, 69117 Heidelberg, Germany ⟨ lsbordon@lsw.uni-heidelberg.de ⟩

T. Shigeyama, Research Center for the Early Universe, Graduate School of Sciecne, University of Tokyo, 7-3-1 Hongo, Bunkyo-ku, Tokyo 113-0033, Japan ⟨ shigeyama@resceu.s.u-tokyo.ac.jp ⟩

T. Shimizu, Insititute of Astromony, Graduate School of Science, University of Tokyo, 2-21-1 Osawa, Mitaka, Tokyo 181-0015, Japan ⟨ shimizu@ioa.s.u-tokyo.ac.jp ⟩

R. Smiljanic, European Southern Observatory, Karl-Schwarzschild-Str. 2, 85748 Garching bei München, Germany ⟨ rsmiljan@eso.org ⟩

M. C. Smith, Kavli Institute for Astronomy & Astrophysics, Peking University, Yi He Yuan Lu 5, Hai Dian Qu, Beijing 100871, China ⟨ dr.mcsmith@me.com ⟩

Y. Sofue, Depertment of Physics, Meisei University, 2-1-1 Hodokubo, Hino, Tokyo 191-8506, Japan ⟨ sofue@ioa.s.u-tokyo.ac.jp ⟩

J. Sohn, Astronomy Program, Department of Physics and Astronomy, Seoul National University, Gwanak-gu, Seoul 151-742, Republic of Korea ⟨ jbsohn@astro.snu.ac.kr ⟩

S. Sotoudeh, Institute for Research in Fundamental Sciences, Sharif University of Technology, Tehran, Iran ⟨ soroushsotoudeh@physics.sharif.edu ⟩

R. J. Stancliffe, Research School of Astronomy & Astrophysics, Australian National University, Mount Stromlo Observatory, Cotter Road, Weston Creek, Canberra, ACT 2611, Australia ⟨ rjs@mso.anu.edu.au ⟩

E. Starkenburg, Kapteyn Astronomical Institute, University of Groningen, PO Box 800, 9700 AV Groningen, the Netherlands ⟨ else@astro.rug.nl ⟩

T. Suda, National Astronomical Observatory of Japan, 2-21-1 Osawa, Mitaka, Tokyo 181-8588, Japan ⟨ takuma.suda@nao.ac.jp ⟩

H. Susa, Department of Physics, Faculty of Science and Engineering, Konan University, 8-9-1 Okamoto, Kobe, Hyogo 658-8501, Japan ⟨ susa@konan-u.ac.jp ⟩

H. Takami, Subaru Telescope, National Astronomical Observatory of Japan, 650 North A'hoku Place, Hilo, HI 96720-2700, USA ⟨ takami@naoj.org ⟩

M. Takada-Hidai, Liberal Arts Education Center, Tokai University, 4-1-1 Kitakaname, Hiratsuka, Kanagawa 259-1292, Japan ⟨ mth_tsc@tsc.u-tokai.ac.jp ⟩

M. Tanaka, Astronomical Institute, Tohoku University, Aoba-ku, Sendai 980-8578, Japan ⟨ mikito@astr.tohoku.ac.jp ⟩

H. Tian, Beijing Normal University, 19 Xinjiekou Wai Street, Beijing 100875, China ⟨ tianhao@mail.bnu.edu.cn ⟩

N. Tominaga, Department of Physics, Faculty of Science and Engineering, Konan University, 8-9-1 Okamoto, Kobe, Hyogo 658-8501, Japan ⟨ tominaga@konan-u.ac.jp ⟩

T. Tsujimoto, National Astronomical Observatory of Japan, 2-21-1 Osawa, Mitaka, Tokyo 181-8588, Japan ⟨ taku.tsujimoto@nao.ac.jp ⟩

M. Van der Swaelmen, Laboratoire Lagrange, UMR7293, Université de Nice Sophia-Antipolis, CNRS, Observatoire de la Côte d'Azur, 06300, Nice, France ⟨ swaelmen@oca.eu ⟩

L. C. VARGAS, Department of Astronomy, Yale University, New Haven, CT 06511, USA ⟨ luis.vargas@yale.edu ⟩

K. VENN, Department of Physics and Astronomy, University of Victoria, Elliott Building, 3800 Finnerty Road, Victoria, BC, V8P 5C2, Canada ⟨ kvenn@uvic.ca ⟩

N. WALTON, Institute of Astronomy, University of Cambridge, Madingley Road, Cambridge CB3 0HA, UK ⟨ naw@ast.cam.ac.uk ⟩

C. C. WORLEY, Laboratoire Lagrange, UMR7293, Université de Nice Sophia-Antipolis, CNRS, Observatoire de la Côte d'Azur, 06300, Nice, France ⟨ cworley@oca.eu ⟩

E. WYLIE DE BOER, Research School of Astronomy & Astrophysics, Australian National University, Mount Stromlo Observatory, Cotter Road, Weston Creek, Canberra, ACT 2611, Australia ⟨ ewylie@mso.anu.edu.au ⟩

R. R. F. WYSE, Department of Physics & Astronomy, Johns Hopkins University, Baltimore, MD 21218, USA ⟨ wyse@pha.jhu.edu ⟩

Y. YAMADA, National Astronomical Observatory of Japan, 2-21-1 Osawa, Mitaka, Tokyo 181-8588, Japan ⟨ yoshihiko.yamada@nao.ac.jp ⟩

M. YAMANAKA, Hiroshima Astrophysical Science Center, Hiroshima University, Higashi-Hiroshima, Hiroshima 739-8526, Japan ⟨ myamanaka@hiroshima-u.ac.jp ⟩

T. YOKOYAMA, Department of Physics, Faculty of Science and Engineering, Konan University, 8-9-1 Okamoto, Kobe, Hyogo 658-8501, Japan ⟨ mn121013@center.konan-u.ac.jp ⟩

D. YONG, Research School of Astronomy & Astrophysics, Australian National University, Mount Stromlo Observatory, Cotter Road, Weston Creek, Canberra, ACT 2611, Australia ⟨ yong@mso.anu.edu.au ⟩

Z. ZHAO, The Graduate University for Advanced Studies (Sokendai), 2-21-1 Osawa, Mitaka, Tokyo 181-8588, Japan ⟨ zhengshi.zhao@nao.ac.jp ⟩

D. ZUCKER, Department of Physics and Astronomy, Macquarie University, NSW 2109, Australia ⟨ daniel.zucker@mq.edu.au ⟩

1. Wako Aoki
2. Kouji Ohta
3. Satoshi Honda
4. Hao Tian
5. David Yong
6. Dougal Mackey
7. Takashi Hasegawa
8. Toshikazu Shigeyama
9. Mei-Yin Chou
10. Carl Grillmair
11. Simon W. Campbell
12. Masahide
    Takada-Hidai
13. Felipe Antonio Santana
14. Takaya Nozawa
15. Luis Vargas
16. Noriyuki Matsunaga
17. Masayuki Yamanaka
18. Masato Onodera
19. Naoteru Gouda
20. Toshihiro Handa
21. Kohei Hattori
22. Tomohiro Yokoyama
23. Kazuya Matsubayashi
24. Nobuo Arimoto
25. Carolyn Doherty
26. Nozomu Tominaga
27. Kohei Hayashi
28. Stefano Pasetto
29. Alvio Renzini
30. Takuma Suda
31. Toshihisa Kogawa
32. Mikito Tanaka
33. Denija Crnojevic
34. Tsuyoshi Sakamoto
35. Masashi Chiba
36. Yoshigaki Sofue
37. Vincius Moris Placco
38. Go Ogiya
39. Tamami I. Mori
40. Blair Conn
41. Stephan Keller
42. Masaaki Otsuka
43. Ko Nakamura
44. Zhengshi Zhao
45. Andrea Ferrara
46. Melissa Ness
47. Thomas Bensby
48. Andrew Casey
49. Hiroko Ito
50. Sakurako Okamoto
51. Nicholas Walton
52. Edouard Bernard
53. Elizabeth
    Wylie de Boer
54. Joss Bland-Hawthorn
55. Cherie Fishlock
56. Rosemary Wyse
57. Martin Smith
58. Kumiko Morihana
59. Yutaka Komiya
60. Grant J. Mathews
61. Ricard Carrera
62. Nicolas Martin
63. Deokkeun An
64. Raoul Haschke
65. Peter Cottrell
66. Alexander Heger
67. Sergey Koposov
68. Yohei Miki
69. Daniel Zucker
70. Shoko Jin
71. Elaina Ann Hyde
72. Hanindyo
    Kuncarayakti
73. Keiichi Maeda
74. Oscar Gonzalez
75. Richard J. Stancliffe
76. Luca Pasquini
77. Michelle Collins
78. Brian O'Shea
79. Oliver Krause
80. Narae Hwang
81. Judith Cohen
82. Nobuyuki Sakai
83. Georges Kordopatis
84. Heidi Jo Newberg
85. Ji Hoon Kim
86. Luca Casagrande
87. Kim Venn
88. C. Clare Worley
89. Sungsoon Lim
90. Ruth C. Peterson
91. Takaharu Shimizu
92. Soroush Sotoudeh
93. Valentina D'Orazi
94. Vanessa Hill
95. Christpher G. Few
96. Jubee Sohn
97. Aruna Goswami
98. Ray Carlberg
99. Birgitta Nordstrom
100. Judy Cheng
101. Else Starkenburg
102. Kate Pilkington
103. Charli Mae Sakari
104. Luca Sbordone
105. Johannes Andersen
106. Mudumba
     Parthasaraty
107. Rodolfo Smiljanic
108. Jeffrey Carlin
109. Rouhollah Joveini
110. Taka Kajino
111. Sebastian L. Hidalgo
112. Shigeki Inoue
113. Stefania Salvadori
114. Myung Gyoon Lee
115. Gerhard Hensler
116. Giampaolo Piotto
117. Amanda Karakas
118. Ken'ichi Nomoto
119. Steven Majewski
120. Mathieu
     Van der Swaelmen
121. Gayandhi De Silva
122. Michael R. Rich
123. Chiaki Kobayashi
124. Alan McConnachie
125. Ken Freeman
126. Gerard Gilmore
127. Martin Asplund
128. Annette Ferguson
129. Takuji Tsujimoto
130. Miho Ishigaki

Part I

Nucleosynthesis, Supernovae and GRBs

Galactic Archaeology: Near-Field Cosmology and the Formation of the Milky Way
ASP Conference Series, Vol. 458
W. Aoki, M. Ishigaki, T. Suda, T. Tsujimoto, N. Arimoto, eds.
© *2012 Astronomical Society of the Pacific*

Nucleosynthesis in Hypernovae and Faint Supernovae and Abundance Patterns of Extremely Metal-Poor Stars

Ken'ichi Nomoto

Institute for the Physics and Mathematics of the Universe (IPMU)
University of Tokyo

Abstract.   With the Subaru telescope, we have been revealing several new properties of various types of supernovae (SNe). Here we report on the properties and nucleosynthesis of the two distinct new classes of massive SNe: 1) very energetic Hypernovae, whose kinetic energy (KE) is more than 10 times the KE of normal core-collapse SNe, and 2) very faint and low energy SNe (Faint SNe). These two new classes of SNe are likely to be "black-hole-forming" SNe with rotating or non-rotating black holes. Nucleosynthesis in Hypernovae is characterized by larger abundance ratios (Zn,Co,V,Ti)/Fe and smaller (Mn,Cr)/Fe than normal SNe, which can explain the observed trends of these ratios in extremely metal-poor (EMP) stars. Nucleosynthesis in Faint SNe is characterized by a large amount of fall-back, which explains the abundance pattern of the most Fe-poor stars. These comparisons suggest that black-hole-forming SNe made important contributions to the early Galactic (and cosmic) chemical evolution. We discuss how nucleosynthetic properties resulted from such unusual supernovae are connected with the unusual abundance patterns of extremely metal-poor stars. Such connections may provide important constraints on the properties of first stars.

1. Introduction

The Subaru telescope has been the powerful tool to reveal new spectroscopic and photometric properties of various types of supernovae. We use the light curve and spectra fitting of individual SN to estimate the mass of the progenitor, explosion energy, and produced ^{56}Ni mass.

One of the most interesting recent developments in the study of supernovae is the discovery of some very energetic supernovae, whose kinetic energy (KE) exceeds 10^{52} erg, more than 10 times the KE of normal core-collapse SNe. These are exceptional class of Type Ic supernovae (SNe Ic) and connected to the gamma-ray bursts (GRBs). These SNe are as luminous at peak as Type Ia supernovae (SNe Ia), indicating that it synthesized $\sim 0.5 M_{\odot}$ of ^{56}Ni, and its KE was estimated at $E_{51} \sim 30$ (Iwamoto et al. 1998). In the present paper, we use the term 'Hypernova (HN)' to describe such a hyper-energetic supernova with $E \gtrsim 10^{52}$ ergs without specifying the explosion mechanism. In terms of brightness, we use "Faint SNe (FSNe)" for low luminosity SNe, and "Superluminous SNe (SLSNe)" for SNe brighter than, say, −20 mag at maximum.

Nucleosynthesis features in such hyper-energetic supernovae must show some important differences from normal supernova explosions. This might be related to the unpredicted abundance patterns observed in the extremely metal-poor (EMP) halo stars. This approach leads to identifying the First Stars in the Universe, i.e., metal-free, Pop-

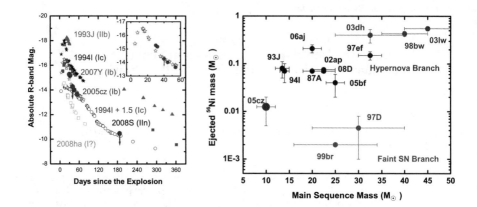

Figure 1.   *(Left)*: The absolute R-band light curve of faint supernovae: SN IIn 2008S (black open circles), SN Ib 2005cz (red circles), SN I 2008ha (orange open squares), and SN Ib 2007Y (green squares) as compared with those of SN IIb 1993J (cyan triangles) and SN Ic 1994I (blue stars). Also shown is the light curve of SN 1994I, but dimmed by 1.5 magnitudes (magenta open stars, Kawabata et al. 2010). *(Right)*: The ejected mass of ^{56}Ni as a function of the main sequence mass M of the progenitors for several supernovae/hypernovae (Kawabata et al. 2010).

ulation III (Pop III) stars which were born in a primordial hydrogen-helium gas cloud. This is one of the important challenges of the current astronomy.

In the following sections, we summarize the final stages of massive star evolution, supernova properties, and their chemical yields for several progenitor's main-sequence mass ranges (Nomoto et al. 2010).

2.   Faint Supernovae from 8 - 13 $M_\odot$ Stars

M_{up} - 10 $M_\odot$ stars: These stars become electron capture SNe because their degenerate O+Ne+Mg cores collapse due to electron capture (Nomoto 1984), where $M_{up} \sim 9 \pm 0.5 M_\odot$ depending on the mass loss rate on the super-AGB phase thus on the metallicity (e.g., Pumo et al. 2009). The SNe are very faint with $M(^{56}$Ni$) \sim 0.002 - 0.004 M_\odot$ (Wanajo et al. 2008).

10 - 13 $M_\odot$ stars: These stars undergo Fe-core collapse to form a neutron star (NS) after the phase of strong Neon-Oxygen flashes (Nomoto & Hashimoto 1988). Their Fe core is relatively small, and the resultant SNe tend to be faint (Smartt et al. 2009).

Among the supernovae from the above mass range, SN 2005cz provides a new clue to the understanding of the SN property-progenitor connection. SN 2005cz is a He-rich Type Ib SN (SN Ib) and appeared in the elliptical galaxy. This is peculiar because SN Ib is a core-collapse explosion of a He star and usually does not appear in elliptical galaxies that contain only old low-mass stars.

Further, SN 2005cz is unusually faint and rapidly fading (Fig. 1, left). The mass of ^{56}Ni is estimated to be $M(^{56}$Ni$) \sim 0.018 M_\odot$. The late-time spectrum of SN 2005cz at $t = +179$ days is very unique; unlike most of other SNe Ibc/IIb SN 2005cz shows much stronger [Ca II] than [O I] (Kawabata et al. 2010; Valenti et al. 2009; Foley et al. 2009).

Oxygen is ejected mostly from the oxygen layer formed during the hydrostatic burning phase. Thus its mass depends sensitively on the progenitor mass and is smaller for lower-mass progenitors. On the other hand, Ca is explosively synthesized during the explosion. Theoretical models predict that the stars having main-sequence masses of M_{ms} = $13M_\odot$ and $18M_\odot$ produce 0.2 and $0.8M_\odot$ of O, and 0.005 and $0.004M_\odot$ of Ca, respectively (Nomoto et al. 2006). Therefore, the Ca/O ratio in the SN ejecta is sensitive to the progenitor mass. To produce the extremely large Ca/O ratio, the mass of the progenitor star of SN 2005cz should be smaller than any other SNe Ib reported to date.

Kawabata et al. (2010) illustrate these unusual facts of SN 2005cz with the properties of SNe from the low-mass end of the core-collapse progenitors (i.e., either 8 - 10 $M_\odot$ or 10 - 13 $M_\odot$) in close binaries (Kawabata et al. 2010).

3. Supernovae from 13 $M_\odot$ - M_{BN} Stars

These stars undergo Fe-core collapse to form a NS, and produce significant amount of heavy elements from α-elements and Fe-peak elements. The boundary mass between the NS and black hole (BH) formation, $M_{BN} \sim 25M_\odot$, is only tentative.

The supernova yields (including the mass of ^{56}Ni) depend on the progenitor's mass M, metallicity, and the explosion energy E (e.g., Kobayashi et al. 2006). From the comparison between the observed and calculated spectra and light curves of supernovae, we can estimate M, E, and the mass of ^{56}Ni as shown in Figure 1 (right) (Nomoto et al. 2006; Kawabata et al. 2010). From this figure, the boundary mass between the NS and BH formation has been estimated to be $M_{BN} \sim 25M_\odot$. As shown in Nomoto et al. (2009), the yields between the three groups (Nomoto et al. 2006; Limo et al. 2000; Heber and Woosley 2010) are in good agreement for $M = 15 - 25M_\odot$, $E = 1 \times 10^{51}$ erg and $Z = 0.00$ - 0.02.

However, theoretical predictions of Zn, Co, Ti/Fe are much smaller than those observed in extremely metal-poor (EMP) stars. The underproduction of these elements relative to Fe is much improved in the hypernova models (Fig. 2, left).

The abundance pattern of EMP stars in the Hercules dwarf spheroidal galaxy is very peculiar (Koch et al. 2008), but can be reproduced by yields of Hypernova model with $M = 25M_\odot$ and $E_{51} = 20$ (Fig. 2, right; Tominaga et al. in prep.). These agreements suggest that hypernovae play an important role in the chemical enrichment during early galactic evolution.

4. Hypernovae and Faint Supernovae from M_{BN} - 90 $M_\odot$ Stars

SNe in this mass range form BHs and seem to bifurcate into the Hypernova branch and the Faint SNe branch (Fig. 1, right). The Hypernova branch include three SNe (1998bw, 2003dh, and 2003lw) that are associated with long Gamma-Ray Bursts (GRBs) (Fig. 1, right).

If the BH has little angular momentum, little mass ejection would take place and be observed as Faint SNe. On the other hand, a rotating BH could eject a matter in a form of jets to make a Hypernova. The latter explosions produce a large amount

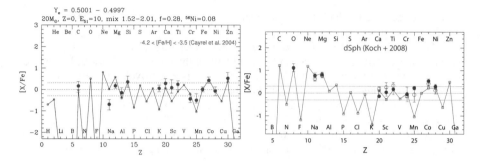

Figure 2. *(Left):* Averaged elemental abundances of stars with [Fe/H] = −3.7 (Cayrel et al. 2004) compared with the hypernova yield (20 $M_\odot$, E_{51} = 10). *(Right):* The peculiar abundance pattern of the EMP stars in the Hercules dwarf spheroidal galaxy (Koch et al. 2008) is compared with the Hypernova yield (Tominaga et al. in prep.).

of heavy elements from α-elements and Fe-peak elements. Nucleosynthesis in these jet-induced explosions is in good agreement with the abundance patterns observed in extremely metal-poor stars.

The fallback SN (e.g., Iwamoto et al. 2005; Fryer et al. 2009) should also undergo mixing of ^{56}Ni before the occurrence of fallback in order to reproduce the observed light curve. Tominaga (2009) has shown that such "mixing and fallback" in spherical explosion is equivalent to the jet-induced nucleosynthesis (Tominaga et al. 2009).

In the jet-induced nucleosynthesis and mass ejection, the important parameter is the energy deposition rate $\dot{E}_{dep}$ (Tominaga et al. 2007). The variation of $\dot{E}_{dep}$ in the range of $\dot{E}_{dep,51} \equiv \dot{E}_{dep}/10^{51} \text{ergs s}^{-1} = 0.3 - 1500$ leads to the following variation of the properties of GRBs and associated SNe. For low energy deposition rates ($\dot{E}_{dep,51} < 3$), the ejected ^{56}Ni masses ($M(^{56}\text{Ni}) < 10^{-3} M_\odot$) are smaller than the upper limits for non-SN GRBs 060505 and 060614 (Iwamoto et al. 2005). For intermediate energy deposition rates ($3 \lesssim \dot{E}_{dep,51} < 60$), the explosions eject $10^{-3} M_\odot \lesssim M(^{56}\text{Ni}) < 0.1 M_\odot$, and the final BH masses are $10.8 M_\odot \lesssim M_{BH} < 15.1 M_\odot$. The resulting SN is faint ($M(^{56}\text{Ni}) < 0.01 M_\odot$) or sub-luminous ($0.01 M_\odot \lesssim M(^{56}\text{Ni}) < 0.1 M_\odot$).

Faint SN as a result of large fallback has been suggested to be responsible to produce the peculiar abundance patterns of extremely metal-poor (EMP) stars (Umeda et al. 2002; Iwamoto et al. 2005). In the jet-induced explosion model, the abundance patterns of EMP stars (esp. [C/Fe]) are related to $\dot{E}_{dep}$ as follows. Lower $\dot{E}_{dep}$ yields larger M_{BH} and thus larger [C/Fe], because the infall reduces the amount of inner core material (Fe) relative to that of outer material (C).

The observed abundance patterns of extremely metal-poor (EMP) stars are classified into three groups according to [C/Fe]:
(1) [C/Fe] ∼ 0, normal EMP stars (−4 < [Fe/H] < −3) (e.g., Cayrel et al. 2004);
(2) [C/Fe] ≳ +1, Carbon-enhanced EMP (CEMP) stars (−4 < [Fe/H] < −3, e.g., CS 22949–37: Depagne et al. 2002);
(3) [C/Fe] ∼ +4, hyper metal-poor (HMP) stars ([Fe/H] < −5, e.g., HE 0107–5240: Christlieb et al. 2002, Bessell and Christlieb 2005; HE 1327–2326: Frebel et al. 2005).

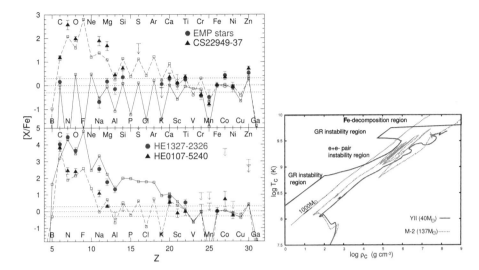

Figure 3.   *(Left)*: A comparison of the abundance patterns between metal-poor stars and models (Tominaga et al. 2007). *Upper*: typical EMP stars *(red dots,* Cayrel et al. 2004) and CEMP *(blue triangles,* CS 22949–37, Depagne et al. 2002) and models with $\dot{E}_{\mathrm{dep},51}$ = 120 *(solid line)* and = 3.0 *(dashed line)*. *Lower*: HMP stars: HE 1327–2326, *(red dots,* e.g., Frebel et al. 2005), and HE 0107–5240, *(blue triangles,* Christlieb et al. 2002, Bessell and Christlieb 2005) and models with $\dot{E}_{\mathrm{dep},51}$ = 1.5 *(solid line)* and = 0.5 *(dashed line)*. *(Right)*: Evolutionary tracks of the central temperature and central density of very massive stars (Ohkubo et al. 2009). The numbers in brackets are the final masses for models YII and M-2. The $1000M_{\odot}$ stars (Ohkubo et al. 2006) are also shown.

Figure 3 (left) shows that the abundance patterns of the averaged normal EMP stars, the CEMP star CS 22949–37, and the two HMP stars (HE 0107–5240 and HE 1327–2326) are well reproduced by the models with $\dot{E}_{\mathrm{dep},51}$ = 120, 3.0, 1.5, and 0.5, respectively. The model for the normal EMP stars ejects $M(^{56}\mathrm{Ni}) \sim 0.2M_{\odot}$, i.e., a factor of 2 less than SN 1998bw. On the other hand, the models for the CEMP and the HMP stars eject $M(^{56}\mathrm{Ni}) \sim 8 \times 10^{-4}M_{\odot}$ and $4 \times 10^{-6}M_{\odot}$, respectively.

To summarize, (1) the explosions with large energy deposition rate, $\dot{E}_{\mathrm{dep}}$, are observed as GRB-HNe, and their yields can explain the abundances of normal EMP stars, and (2) the explosions with small $\dot{E}_{\mathrm{dep}}$ are observed as GRBs without bright SNe and can be responsible for the formation of the CEMP and the HMP stars. We thus propose that GRB-HNe and GRBs without bright SNe belong to a continuous series of BH-forming massive stellar deaths with relativistic jets of different $\dot{E}_{\mathrm{dep}}$.

5.   Superluminous Supernovae from $90 - 140M_{\odot}$ Stars

These massive stars undergo nuclear instabilities and associated pulsations (ϵ- mechanism) at various nuclear burning stages depending on the mass loss and thus metallicity. Eventually, these stars undergo Fe-core collapse. Depending on the angular momentum, Hypernova-like energetic SNe could occur to produce large amount ^{56}Ni. (Because of the large ejecta mass, the expansion velocities may not be high enough to form a broad line features.) Thanks to the large E and ^{56}Ni mass, the SNe could be a super-luminous SNe. The possible presence of circumstellar matter (CM) leads to energetic SNe IIn. Pulsation could also cause luminous event.

Massive Pop III stars are formed through mass accretion, starting from a tiny core through collapse (e.g., Yoshida et al. 2008). Such an evolution with mass accretion starting from $M \sim 1M_\odot$ has recently been studied by Ohkubo et al. (2006, 2009). Figure 3 (right) shows the evolutionary tracks of the central density and temperature in the later phases.

The star M-2, whose final mass is $137M_\odot$, undergoes nuclear instability due to oxygen and silicon burning and pulsates (Nomoto et al. 2005; Woosley et al. 2007; Umeda et al. 2008; Ohkubo et al. 2009). In the extreme case, the pulsation could induce dynamical mass ejection and optical brightening as might be observed in the brightest SN 2006gy (Woosley et al. 2007).

After pulsations, these stars eventually undergo core-collapse to form BHs, which could lead to Pop III GRBs.

If the explosion energy in forming Pop III GRBs is large enough, the mass of ^{56}Ni can be as large as $\sim 6M_\odot$ (Umeda et al. 2008). The resultant light curve can be consistent with superluminous SNe such as SNe 2006gy and 2007bi (Moriya et al. 2010).

6. Pair-Instability Supernovae from 140 - 300 $M_\odot$ Stars

140 - 300 $M_\odot$ stars: SLSNe: If these very massive stars (VMS) do not lose much mass, they become pair-instability supernovae (PISN). The star is completely disrupted without forming a BH and thus ejects a large amount of heavy elements, especially ^{56}Ni. Radioactive decays could produce SLSNe.

Stars with $M \gtrsim 300M_\odot$: SLSNe: These VMSs are too massive to be disrupted by PISN but undergo core collapse (CVMS), forming intermediate-mass black holes (IMBHs). Some mass ejection could be possible, associated with the possible jet-induced explosion, which becomes a superluminous SNe.

These very massive stars (VMS) undergo pair-creation instability and are disrupted completely by explosive oxygen burning, as pair-instability supernovae (PISNe) (e.g., Barkat, Rakavy and Sack, N. 1967; Arnett 1996; Umeda et al. 2002; Heger and Woosley 2002). Their LCs can be consistent with SLSNe 2007bi and 2006gy (Gal-Yam et al. 2009; Moriya et al. 2010).

However the abundance patterns of the ejected material for the 200 $M_\odot$ star (Umeda et al. 2002) are compared with EMP stars. It is clear that PISN ejecta cannot be consistent with the large C/Fe observed in HMP stars and other C-rich EMP stars. Also, the abundance ratios of iron-peak elements ([Zn/Fe] < -0.8 and [Co/Fe] < -0.2) in the PISN ejecta cannot explain the large Zn/Fe and Co/Fe ratios in typical EMP stars.

References

Arnett, W. D. 1996, Supernovae and Nucleosynthesis (Princeton: Princeton Univ. Press)
Barkat, Z., Rakavy, G., & Sack, N. 1967, Physical Review Letters, 18, 379
Bessell, M. S., & Christlieb, N. 2005, in From Lithium to Uranium, edtted by V. Hill et al., vol. 228 of IAU Symposium, 237

Cayrel, R., et al. 2004, A&A, 416, 1117
Christlieb, N., et al. 2002, Nat, 419, 904
Depagne, E., et al. 2002, A&A, 390, 187
Foley, R. J., et al. 2009, AJ, 138, 376
Frebel, A., et al. 2005, Nat, 434, 871
Fryer, C., et al. 2009, ApJ, 707, 193
Gal-Yam, A., et al. 2009, Nat, 462, 624
Heger, A., & Woosley, S.E. 2002, ApJ, 567, 532
Heger, A., & Woosley, S.E. 2010, ApJ, 724, 341
Iwamoto, K., Mazzali, P.A., Nomoto, K., et al. 1998, Nat, 395, 672
Iwamoto, N., Umeda, H., Tominaga, N., Nomoto, K., & Maeda, K. 2005, Science, 309, 451
Kawabata, K., Maeda, K., Nomoto, K., et al. 2010, Nat, 465, 326
Koch, A., et al. 2008, ApJ, 688, L13
Kobayashi, C., Umeda, H., Nomoto, K., Tominaga, N., & Ohkubo, T. 2006, ApJ, 653, 1145
Limongi, M., Straniero, O., & Chieffi, A. 2000, ApJS, 129, 625
Maeda, K., & Nomoto, K. 2003, ApJ, 598, 1163
Moriya, T., Tominaga, N., Tanaka, M., Nomoto, K. Sauer, D.N., Mazzali, P.A., Maeda, K., & Suzuki, T. 2010b, ApJ, 719, 1445
Nomoto, K. 1984, ApJ, 277, 791
Nomoto, K. & Hashimoto, M. 1988, Phys. Rep., 163, 13
Nomoto, K., et al. 2005, in The Fate of Most Massive Stars, editted by R. Humphreys & K. Stanek (ASP Ser. 332), 374 (astro-ph/0506597)
Nomoto, K., et al. 2006, Nuclear Phys A, 777, 424 (astro-ph/0605725)
Nomoto, K., et al. 2009, in The Galaxy Disk in Cosmological Context, editted by J. Andersen, et al., vol. 254 of IAU Symposium, 355 (arXiv: 0901.4536)
Nomoto, K., Moriya, T., & Tominaga, N. 2010a, in Chemical Abundances in the Universe: Connecting First Stars to Planet, editted by K. Cunha, et al., vol.265 if IAU Symposium, 34
Ohkubo, T., Umeda, H., Maeda, K., Nomoto, K., Suzuki, T., Tsuruta, S., & Rees, M. J. 2006, ApJ, 645, 1352
Ohkubo, T., Nomoto, K., Umeda, H., Yoshida, N., & Tsuruta, S. 2009, ApJ, 706, 1184
Pumo, M. L., et al. 2009, ApJ, 705, L138
Smartt, S. J. 2009, ARA&A, 47, 63
Tominaga, N., Maeda, K., Umeda, H., Nomoto, K., Tanaka, et al. 2007, ApJ, 657, L77
Tominaga, N. 2009, ApJ, 690, 526
Umeda, H., & Nomoto, K. 2002, ApJ, 565, 385
Umeda, H., & Nomoto, K. 2008, ApJ, 673, 1014
Valenti, S., et al. 2009, Nat, 459, 674
Wanajo, S., Nomoto, K., Janka, H.-T., Kitaura, F. S., & Müller, B. 2009, ApJ, 695, 208
Woosley, S. E., Blinnikov, S., & Heger, A. 2007, Nat, 450, 390
Yoshida, N., Omukai, K., & Hernquist, L. 2008, Science, 321, 669

Conference room. S. Moriyama talking about dark matter.

Galactic Archaeology: Near-Field Cosmology and the Formation of the Milky Way
ASP Conference Series, Vol. 458
W. Aoki, M. Ishigaki, T. Suda, T. Tsujimoto, N. Arimoto, eds.
©*2012 Astronomical Society of the Pacific*

Nucleosynthesis in Stellar Explosions from Early Stars

Alexander Heger,[1] Stan Woosley,[2] Pamela Vo,[1] Ke-Jung Chen,[1] and Candace Joggerst[3]

[1]*Minnesota Institute for Astrophysics, School of Physics & Astronomy, University of Minnesota, Twin Cities, Minneapolis, MN 55455, U. S. A.*

[2]*Department of Astronomy and Astrophysics, University of California at Santa Cruz, Santa Cruz, CA 95064, U. S. A.*

[3]*Nuclear and Particle Physics, Theoretical Astrophysics and Cosmology (T-2), Los Alamos National Laboratory, Los Alamos, NM 87545, U. S. A.*

Abstract.   The first generation of stars in the universe may have been different from stars in the present-day universe. They may have been typically more massive than stars that form today, or may have rotated faster and hence their evolution, explosion, and overall nucleosynthesis yield could have been quite different. Theoretical models are needed to qualify and quantify these differences. Here we present nucleosynthesis results from the first generations of stars in the universe and how they may be connected to observed abundance patterns from ultra-metal poor stars.

1. Introduction

Our ultimate goal is to understand the history of the universe from the big bang until today, including the history of light - things we can observe like stars and supernovae - and structure - galaxies, clusters, superclusters and the cosmic web, as well as the history of elements from the big bang till today. Often, people refer to the epoch of the universe from recombination until the formation of the first stars the "*Cosmic Dark Ages*" because there were no new sources of light (and though the "light echo" of the big bang was still around). But the physics of what happened in that epoch is reasonably well understood (e.g., Abel et al. 2000; Bromm et al. 1999). Semantically more similar to the historic dark age, perhaps, is what followed then in terms of *our* knowledge of it. How did early structure form, how did the first galaxies form and re-ionize the universe, how did the first stars affect the formation of the first galaxies, and what actually were the first stars like? Most of all, what did the first stars "look like": What were there masses and how did they die? Our approach here is that of a forensic criminologist, looking at the evidence left behind, the nucleosynthesis fingerprint preserved in ultra-metal poor (UMP) stars we find in our galaxy and compare to the nucleosynthesis as predicted by our stellar models.

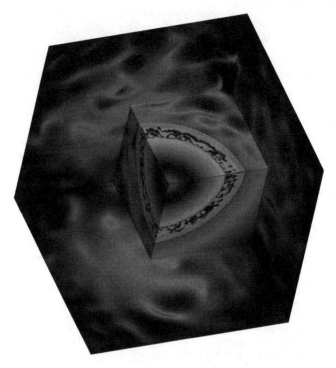

Figure 1.   (color online) Instabilities that develop inside an exploding pair-instability supernova from a 250 $M_\odot$ star (Chen et al. 2011) using the CASTRO code (Almgren et al. 2010).

2. Very Massive Stars

The basic evolution of massive stars has been understood since a long time (e.g., Woosley et al. 2002, for a review), and we also have some general understanding on how we expect them to die (e.g., Heger et al. 2003). What has excited the community over the last dozen years is the prediction from first principle calculations and numerical models that the first stars may have been rather massive, with characteristic masses possibly in the range 30 $M_\odot$ – 300 $M_\odot$ (Bromm et al. 1999, 2002; Abel et al. 2000, 2002; O'Shea & Norman 2006). This is in contrast to the present-day universe where the characteristic mass is around 1 $M_\odot$. The interesting prediction about this was it included the domain of "very massive stars" that can explode as pair-instability supernovae (PSN) (Heger & Woosley 2002; Umeda & Nomoto 2002). The evolution of such stars was also long known and studied in the past history (Barkat et al. 1967; Bond et al. 1984; Glatzel et al. 1985; Woosley 1986), but interestingly, the predicted abundance pattern Heger & Woosley (2002) shows a very strong elemental odd-even effect that does not match any abundance pattern ever observed in any star - no star has formed of the debris of such a star's explosion. A possible ways out is "mixing" inside those big stars (e.g., Heger & Woosley 2005) as found, e.g., by Heger et al. (2000); Woosley et al. (2010); Yoon et al. (2012). We are currently also exploring the effect of multi-dimensional instabilities on the nucleosynthesis in PSN (Chen et al. 2011, Figure 1).

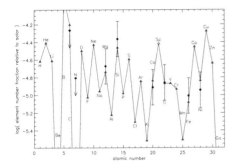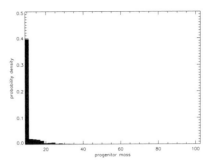

Figure 2. Fit of nucleosynthesis yield from primordial stars Heger & Woosley (2010) to the recent "most primitive" star from Caffau et al. (2011) using the STARFIT package (starfit.org). *Left Panel:* The best fitting supernova out of stars in the range $10\,M_\odot - 100\,M_\odot$ is from a $10.6\,M_\odot$ star. *Right Panel:* Probability distribution of stellar progenitor masses by quality of fit (Vo et al. 2012).

3. Massive Stars

Though there is some observational indication that very massive stars are still born in the universe today (e.g., Eta Car) and some possibly even explode as pair-instability supernovae, they may not be the dominant source of early chemical enrichment; they would, e.g., not be very good at making the r-process to the best of our knowledge. Recently, numerical simulations have found that there may actually be a significant fraction of binary stars among the first stars (Turk et al. 2009) and hence their masses may be lower than we had though. Whereas in the past a minimum metallicity of maybe $[Z] = -3.5$ was considered necessary to have a "normal" Salpeter-like initial mass function (IMF) with low-mass stars, the recent discovery of a star with $[Z] \lesssim -4$ (Caffau et al. 2011) seems to invalidate this picture. So maybe the first stars were not all very massive.

We studied about 120 stellar masses in the mass range $10\,M_\odot - 100\,M_\odot$ and followed a dozen different explosion models (explosion energies) for each model, plus added varying amounts of mixing, and then put all of this into a data base to compare with observations (Heger & Woosley 2010). A first interesting result was that the amount of mixing due to Rayleigh-Taylor instabilities in the supernova explosion needed to be much less than what is needed to explain the supernova light curve of modern stars. And this difference in magnitude of mixing is in very good agreement with multi-dimensional simulations of the mixing in supernova explosions (Joggerst et al. 2009).

A second discovery was that we may obtain rather good fits with low-mass supernovae, maybe not even needing to modify the IMF from Salpeter at all, at least not for massive stars. Figure 2 shows a fitted abundance pattern and probability distribution of progenitor masses (binned) for the star from Caffau et al. (2011). The best fitting model, indeed, is a $10.6\,M_\odot$ star; more massive stars give much worse fits.

In order to reconstruct the IMF from the first generation of stars - or at least of the progenitors of the UMP stars in the halo of our galaxy - we fitted stars from the Cayrel et al. (2004) and Barklem et al. (2005) data sets. The result is shown in Figure 3. We can clearly see that the strong preference for the lowest masses remains; there seems to

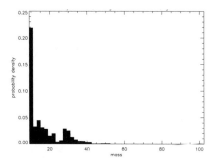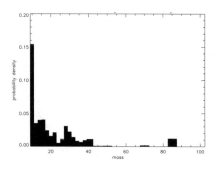

Figure 3.   Probability distribution by mass of best fitting stellar models from primordial nucleosynthesis model yields Heger & Woosley (2010) for the data sets of Cayrel et al. (2004, *Left Panel*) and Barklem et al. (2005, *Right Panel*). Both were fitted using the same selection of elements.

be a gap just above 20 $M_\odot$ and then a secondary peak at 30 $M_\odot$. In both cases we obtain very similar results.

There are limitations, however: The fits do have some sensitivity to the available data and the elements fitted (we tried to make this as homogeneous as possible), and there are large uncertainties in both the observational data and the numerical models.

As a final note, the mixing of ejecta from early supernovae may have been inhomogeneous. In that case, maybe most metals went into not-so-low metallicity stars of, e.g., $[Z] \approx -2$ and very few went into stars of $[Z] \approx -4$: it would require the metals in 100 of the later stars to enrich just one of the former. Koch et al. (2008), e.g., has found stars that may show such abundance patterns, though in the bulge, where we actually do expect material from the regions of first star formation to go. We would like to encourage observers to identify stars with overall primordial abundance pattern but also at high levels of metallicity.

4.   Summary

The IMF of the first stars – and hence how they come to pass – still remains elusive without direct observational data. Major uncertainties in fates of the first stars largely come from uncertainties in their initial properties: mass, rotation, binarity. Significant uncertainty also exists in the modeling of the stellar physics of primordial stars and very massive stars in general. As with all theory, this is particularly true when there is no experimental (observational) constraint as in the case of Pop III stars. Stellar forensics, i.e., determining abundance patterns of what the first stars left behind, may be our best tool in the near future (e.g., to place constraints on PSNe).

Discussion

Nomoto: Could the rotation-induced mixing in the progenitor in pair-instability supernovae reduce the odd-even effect in the abundance pattern of the ejecta?

Heger: Yes, if there is mixing between the core and the envelope during helium burning this would reduce the odd-even effect due to the production of ^{14}N from primary carbon (e.g., Heger & Woosley 2005). Such mixing could be due to rotation (Woosley et al. 2010) but occur even without rotation (Heger et al. 2000).

Nomoto: The [Zn/Fe] ratio is very sensitive to the explosion energy. How good is the agreement between the observed [Zn/Fe] and your model?

Heger: Our Pop III models with spherically symmetric explosion, e.g., using a standard IMF over the entire mass range and a fixed explosion energy of 1.2 B for all masses produces an about solar [Zn/Fe] ratio (Heger & Woosley 2010), which is not in disagreement with Cayrel et al. (2004). Strong super-solar values may require higher entropy or asymmetric explosions. The production of high values of [Zn/Fe] has been predicted already by, e.g., Truran & Arnett (1971).

Kajino: How does the uncertain mass loss along evolutionary track of massive stars change the BH-forming SN rate?

Heger: The mass loss rate and its dependency on metallicity does affect the relation of initial mass to remnant type (Heger et al. 2003; Zhang et al. 2008) and there are major uncertainties in this mass loss rate, in particular for the red supergiant phase in more metal-rich stars. But even for massive stars that do not lose the entire hydrogen envelope, the mass limit for those that make supernovae in contrast to those that may make just black holes without a supernova may be rather low from observational data (Smartt 2009). Hence for single stars the effect may not be as big; an important factor, however, could come from binary star evolution.

O'Shea: Does "normal" IMF imply a Salpeter-like slope, or a normal (1 B) SN explosion?

Heger: Both. Our finding is that we obtain good fits for the abundances of ultra-metal poor stars like the data set from Cayrel et al. (2004) but also individual stars when using a standard Salpeter IMF and "normal" 1 B explosion energies; what we do require, however, is a much lower mixing than what is needed for solar metallicity to reproduce observed light curves (Rauscher et al. 2002; Woosley & Weaver 1995), as predicted by hydro simulations (Joggerst et al. 2009).

O'Shea: What has the low-mass cutoff in progenitors for your fit to observations?

Heger: *I am not sure I understand this question. Let me try to reply as well as I can.* In contrast to the predictions from simulations of first star formation (Bromm et al. 1999, 2002; Abel et al. 2000, 2002; O'Shea & Norman 2006), and possibly even for binary stars (Turk et al. 2009), we do not find a clear indication of a low-mass cutoff in the fits of nucleosynthesis patterns.

Acknowledgments. AH would like to thank the conference organizers for their kind invitation to this outstanding conference, for their financial support, and for their persistent hard work to make this conference happen in a second attempt after the earthquake. We would like to thank Anna Frebel and Maria Bergemann for useful discussions on the fits to stellar abundances. This research was supported by the US Department of Energy (DOE) Program for Scientific Discovery through Advanced Computing (SciDAC; DE-FC02-09ER41618), by the US Department of Energy under grant DE-FG02-87ER40328, by the Joint Institute for Nuclear Astrophysics (JINA; NSF grant PHY02-16783), and by NSF through grant AST-1109394.

References

Abel, T., Bryan, G. L., & Norman, M. L. 2000, ApJ, 540, 39. arXiv:astro-ph/0002135
— 2002, Science, 295, 93. arXiv:astro-ph/0112088
Almgren, A. S., Beckner, V. E., Bell, J. B., Day, M. S., Howell, L. H., Joggerst, C. C., Lijewski, M. J., Nonaka, A., Singer, M., & Zingale, M. 2010, ApJ, 715, 1221. 1005.0114
Barkat, Z., Rakavy, G., & Sack, N. 1967, Physical Review Letters, 18, 379
Barklem, P. S., Christlieb, N., Beers, T. C., Hill, V., Bessell, M. S., Holmberg, J., Marsteller, B., Rossi, S., Zickgraf, F.-J., & Reimers, D. 2005, A&A, 439, 129. arXiv:astro-ph/0505050
Bond, J. R., Arnett, W. D., & Carr, B. J. 1984, ApJ, 280, 825
Bromm, V., Coppi, P. S., & Larson, R. B. 1999, ApJ, 527, L5. arXiv:astro-ph/9910224
— 2002, ApJ, 564, 23. arXiv:astro-ph/0102503
Caffau, E., Bonifacio, P., François, P., Sbordone, L., Monaco, L., Spite, M., Spite, F., Ludwig, H.-G., Cayrel, R., Zaggia, S., Hammer, F., Randich, S., Molaro, P., & Hill, V. 2011, Nat, 477, 67
Cayrel, R., Depagne, E., Spite, M., Hill, V., Spite, F., François, P., Plez, B., Beers, T., Primas, F., Andersen, J., Barbuy, B., Bonifacio, P., Molaro, P., & Nordström, B. 2004, A&A, 416, 1117. arXiv:astro-ph/0311082
Chen, K.-J., Heger, A., & Almgren, A. 2011, ArXiv e-prints. 1108.5234
Glatzel, W., Fricke, K. J., & El Eid, M. F. 1985, A&A, 149, 413
Heger, A., Fryer, C. L., Woosley, S. E., Langer, N., & Hartmann, D. H. 2003, ApJ, 591, 288. arXiv:astro-ph/0212469
Heger, A., & Woosley, S. 2005, in From Lithium to Uranium: Elemental Tracers of Early Cosmic Evolution, edited by V. Hill, P. François, & F. Primas, vol. 228 of IAU Symposium, 297
Heger, A., & Woosley, S. E. 2002, ApJ, 567, 532. (HW02), arXiv:astro-ph/0107037
— 2010, ApJ, 724, 341. 0803.3161
Heger, A., Woosley, S. E., & Waters, R. 2000, in The First Stars, edited by A. Weiss, T. G. Abel, & V. Hill, 121
Joggerst, C. C., Woosley, S. E., & Heger, A. 2009, ApJ, 693, 1780. 0810.5142
Koch, A., McWilliam, A., Grebel, E. K., Zucker, D. B., & Belokurov, V. 2008, ApJ, 688, L13. 0810.0710
O'Shea, B. W., & Norman, M. L. 2006, ApJ, 648, 31. arXiv:astro-ph/0602319
Rauscher, T., Heger, A., Hoffman, R. D., & Woosley, S. E. 2002, ApJ, 576, 323. arXiv: astro-ph/0112478
Smartt, S. J. 2009, ARA&A, 47, 63. 0908.0700
Truran, J. W., & Arnett, W. D. 1971, Ap&SS, 11, 430
Turk, M. J., Abel, T., & O'Shea, B. 2009, Science, 325, 601. 0907.2919
Umeda, H., & Nomoto, K. 2002, ApJ, 565, 385. arXiv:astro-ph/0103241
Vo, P., Heger, A., & Frebel, A. 2012, in preparation
Woosley, S. E. 1986, in Saas-Fee Advanced Course 16: Nucleosynthesis and Chemical Evolution, edited by J. Audouze, C. Chiosi, & S. E. Woosley, 1
Woosley, S. E., Heger, A., Roberts, L., & Hoffman, R. D. 2010, in IAU Symposium, edited by K. Cunha, M. Spite, & B. Barbuy, vol. 265 of IAU Symposium, 3
Woosley, S. E., Heger, A., & Weaver, T. A. 2002, Reviews of Modern Physics, 74, 1015
Woosley, S. E., & Weaver, T. A. 1995, ApJS, 101, 181
Yoon, S.-C., Dierks, A., & Langer, N. 2012, ArXiv e-prints. 1201.2364
Zhang, W., Woosley, S. E., & Heger, A. 2008, ApJ, 679, 639. arXiv:astro-ph/0701083

Galactic Archaeology: Near-Field Cosmology and the Formation of the Milky Way
ASP Conference Series, Vol. 458
W. Aoki, M. Ishigaki, T. Suda, T. Tsujimoto, N. Arimoto, eds.
© 2012 Astronomical Society of the Pacific

Radioactivities from Supernovae and Its Application to Cosmochronology

Ko Nakamura,[1] Takehito Hayakawa,[2] Myung-Ki Cheoun,[3] Satoshi Chiba,[2] Toshitaka Kajino,[1,4] and Grant J. Mathews[5]

[1]*National Astronomical Observatory of Japan, Osawa 2-21-1, Mitaka, Tokyo 181-8588, Japan*

[2]*Japan Atomic Energy Agency, Tokai-mura, Ibaraki 319-1195, Japan*

[3]*Department of Physics, Soongsil University, Seoul 156-743, Korea*

[4]*Department of Astronomy, University of Tokyo, Hongo 7-3-1, Bunkyo-ku, Tokyo 113-0033, Japan*

[5]*Center for Astrophysics, Department of Physics, University of Notre Dame, Notre Dame, IN 46556, USA*

Abstract. An excess of ^{92}Zr observed in meteorites suggests that the solar system was rich in the parent radioactive nuclei ^{92}Nb (half life ~ 34.7 Myr) at its formation epoch. We have investigated the neutrino-induced ^{92}Nb production in core-collapse supernovae and estimated the abundance ratio of ^{92}Nb to ^{93}Nb with newly calculated reaction rates. The isotopic ratio of 10^{-5} from our simulations is supported by the analyses of primitive meteorites (Schönbächler et al. 2002, 2005). We infer the timescale from the last supernova event to the solar system formation to be 30 million years, which is consistent with r-process chronometric study.

1. Introduction

Radioactive isotopes and their residues give us valuable information on nucleosynthetic activities in our Galaxy. For example, ^{26}Al decays to the excited state of ^{26}Mg then to the ground state in the half life of 0.72 million years, emitting a gamma ray with characteristic energy of 1.8 MeV. The sources of the 1.8 MeV gamma rays have been discriminated to be along the Galactic plane and the fact of ongoing ^{26}Al synthesis suggests that these gamma rays originate from massive stars. The total gamma-ray flux combined with theoretical ^{26}Al yields of massive stars is a useful tool to estimate the Galactic supernova rate or star formation rate averaged over the lifetime of radioactive ^{26}Al.

^{92}Nb is also radioactive and decays to the daughter nucleus ^{92}Zr in the half life of 34.7 million years. Some primitive meteorites show anomaly of Zr abundances and the excess of ^{92}Zr is reasonably interpreted as ^{92}Nb incorporation into materials in the early solar system. Harper (1996) estimated the original isotopic ratio ^{92}Nb/^{93}Nb in the context of a simple two timescale molecular cloud self-contamination model to be ~ 10^{-3}. On the other hand, Schönbächler et al. (2002, 2005) inferred the ratio to be

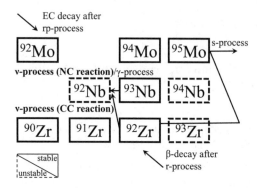

Figure 1.   A part of the nuclear chart around ^{92}Nb and the relevant nucleosynthesis reactions. ^{92}Nb is shielded against decay of r, s, and p-processed elements.

~ 10^{-5} and the exact abundance ratio of ^{92}Nb at the epoch of solar system formation (SSF) is still controversial.

So far the astrophysical production site of ^{92}Nb has been poorly discussed. Figure 1 shows the circumstance of Nb in the nuclear chart with some relevant nucleosynthesis flows. It is attractive that ^{92}Nb is surrounded by stable nuclei and beta (or EC) decay paths of r-processed and rp-processed elements are shielded. This is very similar to the environment of ^{138}La and ^{180}Ta, which are strongly suggested to be coming from "neutrino-process" in core-collapse supernovae. When the core of a massive star collapses and forms a proto-neutron star, a huge number of neutrinos is emitted from the core. Most of the neutrinos pass through the envelope and carry away energy, but a small fraction of them interact with stellar material. The neutrino-matter interaction is very important both for explosion mechanism, in which a shock wave generated after core bounce loses its energy through photodisintegration of iron and then revives by neutrino heating, and for neutrino-induced nucleosynthesis, the neutrino-process such as.

$$(Z, A) + \nu_e \rightarrow (Z, A + 1) + e^-, \tag{1}$$

$$(Z, A) + \nu \rightarrow (Z, A - 1) + \nu' + n. \tag{2}$$

^{92}Nb can be produced via charged current reaction, ^{92}Zr$(\nu_e, e^-)^{92}$Nb, or neutral current reaction, ^{93}Nb$(\nu, \nu'n)^{92}$Nb (see reaction flows in Figure 1).

Supposed that the Nb isotopic ratio at SSF is observationally determined and plausible yield of Nb isotopes from a core-collapse supernova explosion is theoretically estimated, then we could estimate independently the timescale of isolation of the solar system from energetic interstellar medium containing freshly-synthesized supernova products, which is an important factor to understand SSF history. For this purpose, we calculate the ^{92}Nb production in a core-collapse supernova using the state-of-the-art reaction rates (Cheoun et al. 2011) based on the quasi-particle random phase approximation method with neutron-proton pairing as well as neutron-neutron and proton-proton pairing correlations.

2. ^{92}Nb Production in Core-collapse Supernovae

Here we examine the explosion of a 15 solar mass progenitor star with solar metallicity (Rauscher et al., 2002) as a milestone. The explosion energy is set to be 10^{51} erg and released at the center in the form of thermal energy. We trace the temporal evolution of physical quantities by means of 1-dimensional special relativistic hydrodynamic code (Nakamura et al., 2010). The initial abundance of seed nuclei like ^{93}Nb is critical to the current study. We replace the chemical composition in C and O/Ne shells of the original progenitor model with that derived from detailed calculation of carbon-burning weak s-process. Then nuclear reactions including neutrino-induced nucleosynthesis is calculated as a post-process.

The neutrino irradiation is parameterized as follows: Neutrino luminosity is assumed to decay exponentially in the time scale of 5 seconds and the total energy is set to be 3×10^{53} ergs. We take the average neutrino temperatures $kT = 3.2, 4.0,$ and 6.0 MeV for electron neutrino, anti-electron neutrino, and other neutral current neutrinos, respectively, so that the solar abundances of two heavy nuclides ^{138}La and ^{180}Ta can be reproduced as well as a neutron-rich environment necessary to r-process in the neutrino-driven wind around the proto-neutron star.

Our calculations show that a significant amount of ^{92}Nb is produced in C- and O/Ne-rich layers via the neutrino-process. The most dominant process producing ^{92}Nb is the charged current reaction ^{92}Zr(ν_e,e$^-$)^{92}Nb. The neutral current reaction ^{93}Nb(ν, ν'n) also produces ^{92}Nb in the bottom of O/Ne layer, but its contribution in the outer layers is small because of the relative deficiency of seed nuclei ^{93}Nb. Another possible path to ^{92}Nb is gamma-process, photodisintegration of ^{93}Nb. We find that gamma-process can hardly produce ^{92}Nb because it is unstable odd-odd nuclei and the destruction rate is larger than the production rate. In fact the gamma-process plays an important role in destroying, not producing, Nb isotopes in the bottom of O/Ne layer, where newly-synthesized Nb is exposed to strong shock heating. As a result, Nb isotopes are synthesized and survived only in layers far from the center and most of them are expected to be ejected into the interstellar medium after the explosion.

Using the final Nb abundance, combined with its half life of 34.7 million years, we can estimate the initial isotopic ratio at SSF as a function of the timescale of isolation of the solar system from the last SN ejecta. It should be noted that the life time of ^{92}Nb is so short that the accumulation of precursor relic Nb is unlikely and the ratio is predominantly determined by the last supernova nucleosynthesis event just prior to SSF. The isolation timescale has been estimated (Dauphas 2005) to be 0.3-1.0 $\times 10^8$ years from several short-lived r-process elements such as ^{107}Pd, ^{129}I, and ^{182}Hf. If we take this value, our result suggests that the Nb isotopic ratio at SSF should be 0.86-3.5 $\times 10^{-5}$, which is consistent with the value deduced from the analyses of primitive meteorites by Schönbächler et al. (2002, 2005).

3. Conclusions and Discussion

In this paper we argue that core-collapse supernovae may be able to produce radioactive niobium isotope which is useful for chronometer. We investigate neutrino-induced nucleosynthesis in a 15 solar mass model with sophisticated cross sections for nuclear reactions. Our calculations show that this progenitor can produce niobium isotopes including radioactive ^{92}Nb via the neutrino process, in particular the charged current reaction. Although the nucleosynthesis study for other models with different mass is desirable, we expect that other models would show the similar Nb isotopic ratio to our model because the cross sections for neutrino-matter interactions are very small and neutrino-process yields are almost dominated by the abundance of the parent nuclei.

We conclude that the timescale from the last supernova event to the solar system formation to be 30 million years, which is consistent with r-process chronometric study. Note that the neutrino-process elements have some advantages as a chronometer over other elements. First, the neutrino process is direct nuclear reactions. Therefore, estimated abundance at freezeout is more robust than r-process elements which have contributions from many nucleosynthesis paths. Second, the astrophysical site of the neutrino-process is clear (core-collapse supernovae), while the origin of the r-process has not yet been firmly established. Thus, this chronometer can give a robust timescale of isolation of the solar system from energetic interstellar medium containing freshly-synthesized supernova products.

Acknowledgments. This work was partially supported by Grants-in-Aid for Scientific Research of Japan (21340068, 20244035, 20105004) and also by OTKA (NN 83261). G.J.M. was supported by the U.S. Department of Energy under Nuclear Theory Grant DE-FG02-95-ER40934.

References

Cheoun, M.-K., Ha, E., Hayakawa, T., Chiba, S., Nakamura, K., Kajino, T., & Mathews, G. J. 2011, ArXiv e-prints. 1108.4229
Dauphas, N. 2005, Nuclear Physics A, 758, 757. arXiv:astro-ph/0502514
Harper, C., Jr. 1996, ApJ, 466, 1026
Nakamura, K., Yoshida, T., Shigeyama, T., & Kajino, T. 2010, ApJ, 718, L137. 1007.0212
Rauscher, T., Heger, A., Hoffman, R. D., & Woosley, S. E. 2002, ApJ, 576, 323. arXiv:astro-ph/0112478
Schönbächler, M., Lee, D.-C., Rehkämper, M., Halliday, A. N., Hattendorf, B., & Günther, D. 2005, Geochimica et Cosmochimica Acta, 69, 775
Schönbächler, M., Rehkämper, M., Halliday, A. N., Lee, D.-C., Bourot-Denise, M., Zanda, B., Hattendorf, B., & Günther, D. 2002, Science, 295, 1705

Galactic Archaeology: Near-Field Cosmology and the Formation of the Milky Way
ASP Conference Series, Vol. 458
W. Aoki, M. Ishigaki, T. Suda, T. Tsujimoto, N. Arimoto, eds.
©2012 Astronomical Society of the Pacific

Observational Studies of Type Ia Supernovae at High and Intermediate Redshift

Mamoru Doi,[1] Nao Suzuki,[2,3] for Supernova Cosmology Project

[1]*Institute of Astronomy, School of Science, The University of Tokyo, Osawa 2-21-1, Mitaka, Japan, 181-0015*

[2]*E.O. Lawrence Berkeley National Lab, One Cyclotron Rd., Berkeley, CA, 94720*

[3]*Department of Physics, University of California Berkeley, Berkeley, CA, 94720*

Abstract. It was the observations of distant type Ia supernovae (SNe Ia) that revealed the expansion of the universe is now accelerating. The Nobel Prize in Physics 2011 was awarded for this discovery which implied the existence of a mysterious form of energy, dark energy. We briefly review our SNIa observations with Subaru telescope in collaboration with Supernova Cosmology Project (SCP) since 2001 and report the latest results (Suzuki et al. 2012) which doubled the number of SNIa beyond redshift $z = 1$. We found no obvious deviation from a flat ΛCDM model in the era when the expansion of the universe turned from deceleration to acceleration. We discuss the future prospects of high-z SNIa cosmology with Hyper Suprime-Cam.

1. Supernova Cosmology

The Nobel Prize in Physics 2011 was awarded to Saul Perlmutter, Brian Schmidt, and Adam Riess for the discovery of the accelerating expansion of the universe through the observations of distant SNeIa. Two teams competed against each other in 1990s. One is the Supernova Cosmology Project (SCP) led by Saul Perlmutter who pioneered the way to find distant SNeIa in a systematic way (Perlmutter et al. 1998), and the other is High-z supernova search team led by Brian Schmidt and Adam Riess. These two teams reported the calibrated magnitudes of SNIa and reached the same ground breaking conclusion that the expansion of the universe is accelerating (Perlmutter et al. 1999, Schmidt et al. 1998, and Riess et al. 1998). They showed that the distant SNeIa look fainter than those expected in the matter dominated universe model which immediately implied the existence of the unknown form of energy in the universe. This discovery revolutionized our understanding of gravity since Issac Newton and revived Albert Einstein's study of cosmological constant. It has brought excitements not only to the studies of General Relativity but also to the all area of studies in physics.

Although there existed several studies (e.g. galaxy number counts by Fukugita et al. 1990) which suggested the existence of the "cosmological constant" (Caroll et al. 1992 for a review), it was not until the definitive observations of the distant SNeIa when the community began to accept the idea of ΛCDM scenario. The term, "Dark Energy", is introduced as a place holder to explain the cause of the acceleration, but we still do not know the nature of this mysterious form of energy (Perlmutter, Turner, and White 1999). The question today is if this dark energy is constant (namely, vacuum energy) or not over the history of the universe.

To answer this question, many SN Ia cosmology programs have been carried out and being planned. The early supernova programs such as Calan Tololo Supernova search (Hamuy et al. 1993), the Lick Observatory Supernova Search (LOSS; Treffers et al. 1997), and the one by Cappellaro et al. (1999) have played essential roles to establish the templates of SNIa light curves which led the discovery of the accelerating universe. After the revolution of the SNIa cosmology, several large scale surveys have been conducted: the Nearby Supernova Factory (Aldering et al. 2002), Higher-z supernova search program (Strolger et al. 2004), ESSENCE (Matheson et al. 2005), SNLS (Howell et al. 2005), Carnegie Supernova Project (Hamuy et al. 2006), and SDSS-II SN survey (Frieman et al. 2008). The success of these surveys inspired a series of optical transient search programs: the Palomar Transient Factory (PTF; Rau et al. 2009), the Panoramic SurveyTelescope and Rapid Response System (PANSTARRS; Tonry et al. 2002), the SkyMapper Southern Sky Survey (Keller et al. 2007) and the CHilean Automatic Supernova sEarch (CHASE; Pignata et al. 2007).

2.   Cosmological model constraints from SCP UNION 2.1 compilation

Subaru Telescope has joined SNIa cosmology programs with SCP since 1999, and together with Keck, Gemini, VLT and the Hubble Space Telescope, Subaru has been playing a key role for the observations of distant SNeIa (Morokuma et al. 2010). As of today, SCP has carried out nine open use programs of the Subaru telescope (S01A-079, S01B-103, S02A-174, S02B-I04, S03B-227, S05B-137, S06B-085, S08B-092, S10B-141), and in total 34.5 nights have been allocated. Some of those programs were jointly carried out with Subaru "Large Programs (SDF and SXDF)". So far 12 refereed papers have been published, and several more are being prepared.

We would like to report the recent results from our HST Cluster Supernova Survey program. We monitored 25 high-z clusters of galaxies with HST and found SNeIa efficiently in elliptical galaxies. We also conducted a weak lensing study and measured the mass of these high-z clusters and studied the properties of galaxies in the clusters (Jee et al. 2011). The details of the survey are described in Dawson et al. (2009). We successfully discovered and followed 20 new high-z SNeIa ($0.623 < z < 1.415$), and we used them to constrain the cosmological model. Ten of the new SNeIa resulted to double the statistical weight of HST-discovered SNe Ia beyond $z = 1$. The best cosmological parameter fits with or without CMB and BAO results for several cosmological models such as ΛCDM, wCDM, owCDM are presented in Suzuki et al. (2012). We are looking at if the equation of state parameter w equals to -1 or not over the history of the universe to see if the dark energy is vacuum energy. We found the equation of state parameter, $w = -1.013^{+0.068}_{-0.073}$, for a flat universe. We considered the cases for a non-flat universe, time-dependent dark energy, but we have not detected any obvious deviation from the ΛCDM.

In Figure 1, we show the Hubble Diagram of the world's compilation of SNIa, including our latest results (Suzuki et al. 2012) and SNLS three year data (Conley et al. 2011). In the inset, we plot binned the magnitude differences from an "Empty Universe, also known as Milne Universe" ($\Omega_m = 0, \Omega_\Lambda = 0, \Omega_k = 1$). The ΛCMD model gives us the best fit curve ($\Omega_\Lambda = 0.73, \Omega_{matter} = 0.27$) and the detection of the

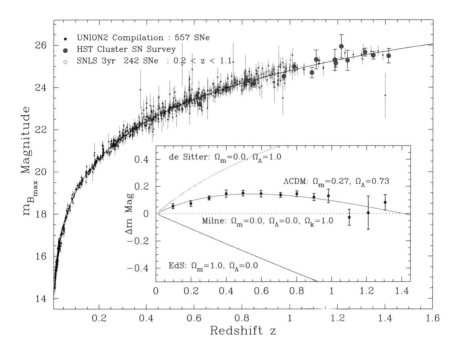

Figure 1.   **Hubble Diagram:** The world's compilation of SNIa (UNION2; Aman-ullah et al. 2010) and our latest results (Suzuki et al. 2012), together it forms UNION2.1 SNIa compilation. We also plot SNLS three year data (Conley et al. 2011). **Inset:** Observed magnitude difference from an empty universe model (dotted line; $\Omega_m = 0, \Omega_\Lambda = 0, \Omega_k = 1$, also known as Milne universe). is shown in binned redshifts. The best fit model to the data is a ΛCDM with $\Omega_m = 0.27, \Omega_\Lambda = 0.73$ in a flat universe. Einstein-de Sitter universe model ($\Omega_m = 1.0, \Omega_\Lambda = 0.0$) and de Sitter universe model ($\Omega_m = 0.0, \Omega_\Lambda = 1.0$) are also shown as a comparison but the data exclude these models with more than 5 sigma level.

cosmological constant is now 5 σ level. We found the universe turned into acceleration from deceleration at $z = 0.752 \pm 0.041$.

3.   SNIa as a standard candle and Future prospects

There are a few key factors for the advancement of SNIa cosmology. It is very im-portant to understand the intrinsic properties of SNIa which are caused by the super-nova itself (Maeda et al. in this conference) and environmental effects (Gallagher et al. 2005, 2008). Various studies have been done (Sullivan et al. 2010, Gupta et al. 2011, D'Andrea et al. 2011, Konishi et al. 2011) to investigate the effect of the environment. Possible significant dependence on the host galaxy mass was found recently, but we have not understood if this dependence is caused by the age or metallicity of the host galaxy. It is natural to believe there exists a profound physics behind this dependence, and it is urgent to resolve it from the observations of nearby supernova where we can resolve the environment of the SNeIa in the host galaxy.

Another key factor is the dust extinction. It is not straightforward to distinguish the intrinsic color diversity of SNIa from the reddening by the dust. One of the obvious solutions is to observe SNeIa in near infrared wavelength in rest frame. The standard extinction law shows that extinction in H−band is about 5% of that of in V−band. Recent studies (Wood-Vasey et al. 2008, Contreras et al. 2010, Burns et al. 2011) show that the properties of SNIa in NIR seem to be more homogeneous than that in optical.

Besides the properties of SNIa, we will need to raise the accuracy of photometric calibration by establishing a new network of standard stars. As of today, the measurements are limited by systematic errors, and the majority of error budget is dominated by heterogeneous calibrations between telescopes and instruments. It is critical to reduce the systematic errors for the future of SNIa cosmology.

The next generation wide-field imager of the Subaru telescope, Hyper Suprime-Cam (HSC, ~1.5 degree FoV), will be commissioned in 2012. With HSC, we expect to find ~500 SNe per night and will revolutionize the studies of transient objects in the next five years before the first light of the Large Synoptic Survey Telescope (LSST) project (the FoV of ~3.5 degree in diameter). In the era of 2020, a planned satellite telescope, wFIRST, may be able to observe distant SNeIa in rest-frame NIR. To make the best use of this facility, we will need to prepare a library of nearby spectral templates of SNIa in NIR. We expect such spectral library can be constructed by a ground-based telescope being planned at the elevation 5640m as TAO (The University of Tokyo Atacama Telescope) where atmospheric windows in NIR is almost continuous.

References

Aldering, G. et al., 2002, SPIE.4836,61A
Amanullah, R. et al., 2010, ApJ, 716, 712
Burns, C. R. et al. 2011, AJ, 141, 19
Cappellaro, E., Evans, R., and Turatto, M., 1999, A&A, 351, 459
Carroll, S. M., Press, W.H., and Turner, E.L., 1992, ARA&A, 30, 499
Conley, A. et al. 2011, ApJS, 192, 1
Contreras, C. et al. 2010, AJ, 139, 519
D'Andrea, C. et al. 2011, ApJ, 743, 172
Dawson, K. S. et al. 2009, AJ, 138, 1271
Frieman, J. A. et al., 2008, AJ, 135, 338
Fukugita, M. et al., 1990, ApJL, 361, L1
Gallagher, J. S. et al. 2005, ApJ, 634, 210
Gallagher, J. S. et al. 2008, ApJ,685,752
Gupta, R. et al. 2011, ApJ, 740, 92
Hamuy, M. et al., 1993, AJ, 106, 2392
Hamuy, M. et al. 2006, PASP, 118, 2
Howell, D. A. et al. 2005, ApJ, 634, 1190
Jee, M. J. et al. 2011, ApJ, 737, 59
Keller, S. et al. 2007, ASPC, 364, 177
Konishi, K. et al. 2011, arXiv1101.4269K
Maeda, K. et al. 2010, Nature, 466, 82
Maeda, K. et al. 2011, MNRAS, 413, 3075
Matheson, T. et al. 2005, AJ, 129, 2352
Meyers, J. et al. 2012, arXiv1201.3989M

Morokuma, T. et al. 2010, PASJ, 62, 19
Perlmutter, S., et al. 1998, Nature, 391, 51
Perlmutter, S., et al. 1999, ApJ, 517, 565
Perlmutter, S., Turner, M.S., and White, M., 1999, PhRvL, 83, 670
Pignata, G. et al. 2007, CBET, 1130, 1
Rau, A. et al. 2009, PASP, 121, 1334
Riess, A. G., et al. 1998, AJ, 116, 1009
Schmidt, B. P., et al. 1998, ApJ, 507, 46
Strolger, L. et al. 2004, ApJ, 613, 200
Sullivan, M. et al. 2010, MNRAS, 406, 782
Suzuki, N. et al. 2012, ApJ, 746, 85
Tonry, J. et al., 2002, Experimental Astronomy, 14, 17
Treffers, R. R., et al. 1997, IAU Circ. 6627
Wood-Vasey, W. M. et al. 2008, ApJ, 689, 377

Mt. Fuji from the conference site in the early morning of November 1st. The mountain was not covered by snow due to the unusually warm weather in that season.

Galactic Archaeology: Near-Field Cosmology and the Formation of the Milky Way
ASP Conference Series, Vol. 458
W. Aoki, M. Ishigaki, T. Suda, T. Tsujimoto, N. Arimoto, eds.
© *2012 Astronomical Society of the Pacific*

Nucleosynthesis in Type Ia Supernovae and Observational Constraints

Keiichi Maeda

Institute for the Physics and Mathematics of the Universe (IPMU), Todai Institutes for Advanced Study (TODIAS), University of Tokyo, 5-1-5 Kashiwanoha, Kashiwa, Chiba 277-8583, Japan

Abstract. Type Ia Supernovae (SNe Ia) are mature cosmological standardized candles, leading to the discovery of the accelerating expansion of the Universe. Although there is a general consensus that they are thermonuclear explosions of a white dwarf, details of the explosion mechanism have not yet been fully clarified. Furthermore, there are observational diversities of SNe Ia whose origins have not yet been specified. In this paper, we argue that asymmetry in the thermonuclear explosion can be a solution on these issues, where the diversity arising from various viewing angles corresponds to various observational diverse properties of SNe Ia. This idea could open up a possibility of using SNe Ia as more precise distance indicators than currently employed.

1. Introduction

It is widely accepted that Type Ia Supernovae (SNe Ia) are thermonuclear explosions of a carbon-oxygen white dwarf (WD) (Nomoto et al. 1994; Branch 1998; Hillebrandt & Niemeyer 2000). In a standard scenario (Nomoto et al. 1984; Khokhlov 1991), thermonuclear runaway is initiated with the ignition of subsonic deflagration bubbles, then the deflagration flame may turn into a supersonic detonation wave (Khokhlov 1991). Such a scenario is called a delayed-detonation model. In this scenario, one key unresolved issue is how the deflagration bubbles are ignited initially.

SNe Ia are mature standardized candles (Riess et al. 1998; Perlmutter et al. 1999). Their luminosities can be estimated using a phenomenological relation between the peak luminosity and the light curve decline rate (i.e., time scale) (Phillips et al. 1999). However, spectral properties of SNe Ia are not uniform unlike the light curve (Branch et al. 1988; Benetti et al. 2004, 2005). In the first few months after the explosion, SNe Ia are at the optically-thick, photospheric phase. Materials moving toward the observer produce blueshifted absorption features. The absorption velocity decreases as time goes by, following the density decrease and the recession of the photosphere. The velocity gradient ($\dot{v}_{Si}$) is defined as a rate of the decrease in the Si II $\lambda 6355$ absorption velocity. SNe that show $\dot{v}_{Si} > 70$ km s^{-1} day^{-1} are classified as the high velocity gradient (HVG) group, while those showing smaller $\dot{v}_{Si}$ are called the low velocity gradient (LVG) SNe Ia. It has been shown that $\dot{v}_{Si}$ is *not* correlated with the decline rate (Benetti et al. 2005). In addition, SNe Ia show a variation in their peak colors beyond the decline rate. The origin of these diversities beyond the 'one-parameter' description (by the decline rate) has not yet been clarified. Thus it has not been clarified if it could introduce any biases in the supernova cosmology.

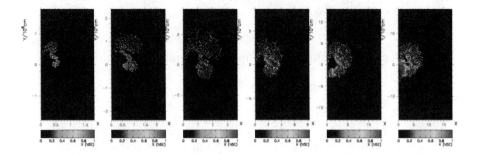

Figure 1.   (color online) Temporal evolution of distribution of Fe-peak elements
(at 0.7, 0.9, 1.1, 1.3, 1.5, 1.7 seconds after the ignition of the deflagration flame, from
left to right), in an offset delayed-detonation model of Maeda et al. (2010b) (see also
Kasen et al. (2009)). Shown here is the mass fraction of iron-peak elements, from 0
(blue/dark) to 1 (red/bright), as indicated by color bars below each panel.

2.   Asymmetry in the Explosion

Once the deflagration is ignited near the center of a WD, the high density ($\sim 10^9$ g
cm^{-3}) leads to the production of neutron-rich Fe-peaks (e.g., ^{58}Ni) through electron
captures. In the delayed-detonation scenario, the transition takes place when the density
encountered by the flame goes down to $\sim 10^7$ g cm^{-3}. The detonation initially produces
radioactive ^{56}Ni (which decays into ^{56}Co and then ^{56}Fe in $\sim$ 100 days powering optical
emissions from SNe), then eventually intermediate mass elements (e.g., Si).

The ignition is possibly started in off-center regions. A perturbation within the
progenitor (e.g., convection) could result in the offset ignition (Kuhlen et al. 2006).
Figure 1 shows such an off-set ignition model (Kasen et al. 2009; Maeda et al. 2010b).
If the ignition is asymmetric, we expect the following features: (1) The distribution of
the deflagration products is highly sensitive to the ignition geometry. If the ignition is
asymmetric, then stable Fe-peaks should be distributed in an asymmetric way. (2) The
detonation propagation is not sensitive to the details of the ignition. The distribution of
the detonation products (e.g., ^{56}Ni) is more or less spherically symmetric.

Deriving the distribution of the deflagration products is thus a key in understanding
the explosion mechanism. We suggest that late-time spectroscopy is a powerful probe.
At > 150 days after the explosion, the whole SN ejecta become transparent because of
the expansion and the density decrease. At this phase, photons from different positions
show different Doppler shifts. In the above model, the deflagration products are ejected
toward a specific direction, thus an emission line from this region should show blueshift
if viewed from the direction of the explosion, but redshift from the opposite direction.

We compiled the late-time spectra of SNe Ia. Figure 2 shows the [Fe III] blend at
4,700Å and [Ni II] λ7378 for 12 SNe Ia. The former is expected to trace the detonation
products and the latter the deflagration products (Maeda et al. 2010a). The [Fe III]
blend does not show evident shift. On the other hand, we discovered that [Ni II] λ7378
does show variations in its central wavelength for different SNe, including both redshift
and blueshift. This suggests that the asymmetric ignition is a generic feature. This can
be further tested for individual SNe with intensive wavelength coverage, using various
lines; see Maeda et al. (2010a) for the case of SN 2003hv.

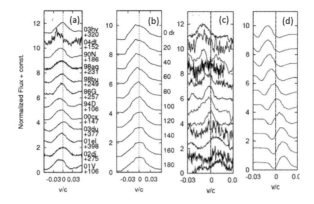

Figure 2.   Late-time spectra of various SNe Ia (Maeda et al. 2010a). (a) Observed and (b) model line profiles of [Fe III] blend at 4700Å, and (c) observed and (d) model line profiles of [Ni II] λ7378. The model profiles are shown for various viewing angles (see Maeda et al. (2010a) for details). The wavelength is corrected for the host galaxy recession velocities.

3.   Observational Diversities and SN Cosmology

If the explosion is asymmetric as argued in §2, it raises an interesting question – whether observed diversities of SN properties (§1) could be related to the diversities arising from the explosion asymmetry and different viewing directions. Figure 3 provides a comparison between the velocity gradient ($\dot{v}_{Si}$; see §1) and the late-time emission-line velocity shift (v_{neb}; measured by the Doppler shift of [Fe II]λ7155 and [Ni II]λ7378) as investigated by Maeda et al. (2010c). These two quantities turned out to be related, with HVG SNe showing redshift in late-time spectra. The correlation indicates that there is no intrinsic difference in HVG and LVG SNe, but the different appearance is merely a consequence of different viewing directions (Fig. 3).

SNe show a variation in their peak $B - V$ color, which is another major issue in SN cosmology. The estimate of extinction (thus distance) relies on the intrinsic color of SNe Ia. By comparing the 'viewing direction' and the color of SNe Ia (Maeda et al. 2011), we have shown that that the intrinsic color variation is at the level of $B - V \sim 0.2$ mag, and the variation within this level can be attributed to the difference in the color depending on different viewing directions.

4.   Concluding Remarks

In this paper, we have argued that an asymmetry is a generic feature of SNe Ia. The scenario provides a unified solution for several major unresolved issues in SNe Ia – the observational diversities of SNe Ia in their spectra and colors are accounted for simply by the random viewing directions. These findings have many implications for SN cosmology. (1) Even if the spectral diversity would be accompanied by a bias in the distance calibration, using a large number of SNe will result in a cancellation of this possible effect. (2) Knowing the origin of the diversity of the color, it provides various possible options so that the intrinsic color can be derived for individual SNe.

30   *Maeda*

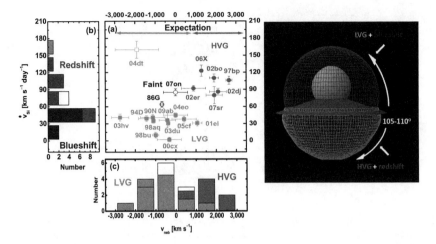

Figure 3.   (color online) (Left:) A comparison between the velocity gradient ($\dot{v}_{Si}$) and the late-time emission-line velocity shift (v_{neb}) (Maeda et al. 2010c). The arrows on top indicate the expected ranges of HVG and LVG SNe Ia based on the relative observed frequencies. (Right:) A schematic picture of SN Ia ejecta (Maeda et al. 2010c). If viewed in the direction $0-110°$, an SN appears as an LVG SN in the early phase and shows blueshift in the late phase. It appears as an HVG SN and shows redshift if viewed from the other directions ($110-180°$).

Acknowledgments.   KM thanks the organizers of the subaru conference. This research has been supported by World Premier International Research Center Initiative (WPI Initiative), MEXT, Japan. KM also acknowledges the support through the Grant-in-Aid for young scientist (20840007, 23740141) of Japanese Society for Promotion of Science (JSPS).

References

Benetti, S., et al. 2004, MNRAS, 348, 261
Benetti, S., et al. 2005, ApJ, 623, 1011
Branch, D., Drucker, W., & Jeffery, D.J. 1988, ApJ, 330, L117
Branch, D. 1998, ARA&A, 36, 17
Hillebrandt, W. & Niemeyer, J.C. 2000, ARA&A, 38, 191
Kasen, D., Röpke, F.K., & Woosley, S.E. 2009, Nature, 460, 869
Khokhlov, A. 1991, A&A, 245, 114
Kuhlen, M., Woosley, S.E., & Glatzmaier, G.A. 2006, ApJ, 640, 407
Maeda, K., et al. 2010a, ApJ, 708, 1703
Maeda, K., et al. 2010b, ApJ, 712, 624
Maeda, K., et al. 2010c, Nature, 466, 82
Maeda, K., et al. 2011, MNRAS, 413, 3075
Nomoto, K., Thielemann, F. -K., & Yokoi, K. 1984, ApJ, 286, 644
Nomoto, K., et al. 1994, in *Supernovae* (Elsevier Science; Netherland), 199
Perlmutter, S., et al. 1999, ApJ, 517, 565
Phillips, M.M., et al. 1999, AJ, 118, 1766
Riess, A.G., et al. 1998, AJ, 116, 1009
Röpke, F.K., Woosley, S.E., & Hillebrandt, W. 2007, ApJ, 660, 1344

Galactic Archaeology: Near-Field Cosmology and the Formation of the Milky Way
ASP Conference Series, Vol. 458
W. Aoki, M. Ishigaki, T. Suda, T. Tsujimoto, N. Arimoto, eds.
© *2012 Astronomical Society of the Pacific*

Supernova Neutrino-Process and Implication in Neutrino Oscillation

T. Kajino,[1,2] W. Aoki,[1] W. Fujiya,[3] G. J. Mathews,[4] T. Yoshida,[2] K. Shaku,[1,2] K. Nakamura,[1] and T. Hayakawa[1,5]

[1] *National Astronomical Observatory of Japan, 2-21-1 Osawa, Mitaka, Tokyo 181-8588, Japan*

[2] *Department of Astronomy, Graduate School of Science, University of Tokyo, 7-3-1 Hongo, Bunkyo-ku, Tokyo 113-0033, Japan*

[3] *Department of Earth and Planetary Science, Graduate School of Science, University of Tokyo, 7-3-1 Hongo, Bunkyo-ku, Tokyo, 113-0033, Japan*

[4] *Center for Astrophysics, Department of Physics, University of Notre Dame, Notre Dame, IN 46556, U.S.A.*

[5] *Japan Atomic Energy Agency, Shirakawa-Shirane 2-4, Tokai, Ibaraki 319-1195, Japan*

Abstract. We studied the supernova nucleosynthesis induced by neutrino interactions and found that several isotopes of rare elements like ^{7}Li, ^{11}B, ^{138}La, ^{180}Ta and many others are predominantly produced by the neutrino-process in core-collapse supernovae. These isotopes are strongly affected by the neutrino flavor oscillation due to the MSW (Mikheyev-Smirnov-Wolfenstein) effect. We here propose a new novel method to determine the unknown neutrino oscillation parameters, θ_{13} and mass hierarchy simultaneously from the supernova neutrino-process, combined with the r-process for heavy-element synthsis and the Galactic chemical evolution on light nuclei.

1. Introduction

Still unknown mass and oscillation properties of neutrinos take the important keys to resolve many fundamental questions in particle physics and astrophysics such as why baryon- and lepton-symmetries are broken in the Universe, why we need unified theory beyond the standard model of elementary particles, why the core-collapse supernovae explode, etc. We here discuss how to determine the unknown neutrino oscillation parameters from the studies of element synthesis in supernovae.

2. Supernova Neutrino-Process

Intensive flux of three flavor neutrinos with total energy $\sim 3.0 \times 10^{53}$ ergs are emitted during the Kelvin-Helmholtz cooling phase in core-collapse supernovae. Neutrino interactions with abundant nuclei like ^{4}He and ^{12}C in carbon-rich helium layer spall them into free neutrons, protons, and other light nuclei. An explosive nucleosynthesis

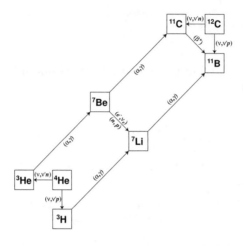

Figure 1.   Nucleosynthesis path of light elements ^{7}Li and ^{11}B in supernova ν-process.

subsequently occurs at high-temperature and density when the shock arrives, which is called the ν-process (Woosley et al. 1990).

In carbon-rich helium layer, two reactions ^{4}He$(\nu, \nu'p)^3$H and ^{4}He$(\nu, \nu'n)^3$He are important for the production of ^{7}Li through ^{3}H$(\alpha, \gamma)^7$Li and ^{3}He(α, γ) ^{7}Be$(e^-, \nu_e)^7$Li, and ^{11}B is produced through ^{7}Li$(\alpha, \gamma)^{11}$B and ^{7}Be$(\alpha, \gamma)^{11}$C$(e^+\nu_e)^{11}$B, as shown in Figure 1. ^{12}C$(\nu, \nu'p)^{11}$B and ^{12}C$(\nu, \nu'n)^{11}$C also contribute to the production of ^{11}B (Yoshida et al. 2006a). The neutral current thus brings about the production of ^{7}Li and ^{11}B from supernovae as well as Galactic cosmic-ray spallation appropriate for the observed Galactic chemical evolution of the light elements (Ryan et al. 2001). The temperature of $\nu_{\mu,\tau}$ and $\bar{\nu}_{\mu,\tau}$ is thus estimated to be $T_{\nu_{\mu,\tau}} = T_{\bar{\nu}_{\mu,\tau}} = 6.0 \pm 1.0$ MeV (Yoshida et al. 2006b). This temperature is also severely constrained from the measured isotopic ratio $(^{11}$B$/^{10}$B$)_{\text{sun}} = 4.5 \pm 0.1$ in the solar system abundance (Yoshida et al. 2005).

^{138}La and ^{180}Ta are produced by the charged current interactions in the ν-process in oxygen-neon-magnesium layer from abundant ^{138}Ba and ^{180}Hf. We can thus use the nucleosynthesis of these isotopes for the estimate of the temperatures of ν_e and $\bar{\nu}_e$. Theoretical model of Heger et al. (2005) however indicated that the calculated abundance of ^{180}Ta is always overproduced by factor ~3 relative to ^{138}La when normalized to the solar abundance whatever neutrino temperatures one might use in the theoretical calculation. This discrepancy is related to an interesting nuclear structure of ^{180}Ta.

In the ν process, low-spin excited states in ^{180}Ta are strongly populated from ^{180}Hf by Gamow-Teller transition and subsequently decay to the ground state 1^+ (half-life 8.15 hr). However, in a high temperature photon bath of exploding supernovae, the meta-stable isomer 9^- is highly excited by (γ, γ') reactions through intermediate states. This meta-stable isomer has a half-life $\geq 10^{15}$ yr which resides until the present Universe. The final isomeric abundance should be evaluated by a time-dependent supernova nucleosynthesis calculation. Our calculation including these quantum transitions shows that the isomeric residual population turns out to be smaller by a factor ≈ 0.39. We thus solved the overproduction of ^{180}Ta and obtain the concordant result with the ob-

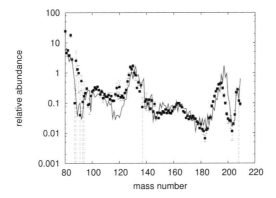

Figure 2.   Abundance pattern (solid line) of the gamma-ray burst r-process (Naka-mura et al. 2012) compared with the solar system r-process abundance (points).

served solar system abundances for both ^{138}La and ^{180}Ta when one sets $T_{\nu_e} \approx T_{\bar{\nu}_e} = 4.0$ MeV (Hayakawa et al. 2010).

Finally, we resolve a weak degeneracy between T_{ν_e} and $T_{\bar{\nu}_e}$ by imposing a neutron-rich condition $0.2 \leq Y_e < 0.5$ for successful *r*-process nucleosynthesis: $T_{\nu_e} = 3.2$ MeV and $T_{\bar{\nu}_e} = 4.0$ MeV (Yoshida et al. 2004; Otsuki et al. 2000). This hierarchy applies also to the r-process as displayed in Figure 2 that occurs in the gamma-ray bursts on the similar condition (Nakamura et al. 2012).

3. Neutrino Oscillation

Neutrino-flavor oscillations affect nucleosynthesis through the charged current interactions, while neutral current interactions do not change for all flavor of neutrinos. We studied the neutrino oscillation effects on nucleosynthesis. The mixing parameters, except 13-mixing angle θ_{13} and the sign of $\Delta m_{31}^2 = m_3^2 - m_1^2$, were precisely determined from recent neutrino experiments: $\Delta m_{21}^2 = 7.9 \times 10^{-5} \text{eV}^2$, $\Delta m_{31}^2 = \pm 2.4 \times 10^{-3} \text{eV}^2$, $\sin^2 2\theta_{12} = 0.816$, and $\sin^2 2\theta_{23} = 1.0$. The sign of Δm_{31}^2 is still unknown, and we consider both of normal ($m_1 < m_2 < m_3$) and inverted ($m_3 < m_1 < m_2$) mass hierarchies. Only an upper limit of $\sin^2 2\theta_{13}$ has been determined: $0 \leq \sin^2 2\theta_{13} \leq 0.1$. See Yoshida et al. (2008) for more details of the neutrino mixing parameters.

Figure 3 shows the predicted $^7\text{Li}/^{11}\text{B}$ ratio as a function of unknown mixing parameter $\sin^2 2\theta_{13}$ for both mass hierarchies (Yoshida et al. 2008). The uncertainty due to neutrino spectra is included as shaded regions. The ratio in the case of adiabatic 13-mixing resonance and normal hierarchy is remarkably larger than that without neutrino oscillations, even with the spectral uncertainties included. Thus, the enhancement or quenching in $^7\text{Li}/^{11}\text{B}$ from supernova matter could constrain θ_{13} and mass hierarchy simultaneously.

Recent T2K (Abe et al. 2011) and MINOS (Adamson et al. 2011) collaborations suggest that θ_{13} is as large as $0.01 \leq \sin^2 2\theta_{13}$ at better than the 90% C.L. There is also a recent suggestion by Fujiya et al. (2011) that some SiC X grains from the Murchison

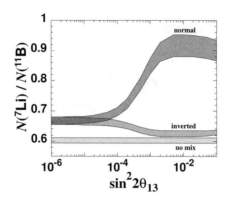

Figure 3.   Predicted ^{7}Li/^{11}B abundance ratio from supernova ν-process for both neutrino mass hierarchies as a function of mixing angle θ_{13} from Yoshida et al. (2008); Mathews et al. (2011).

meteorite indicate the possible existence of ν-process ^{11}B encapsulated in the grains along with an upper limit on ν-process ^{7}Li. These new results suggests marginal preference for an inverted mass hierarchy (Mathews et al. 2011).

Observational efforts (Primas et al. 1998) to obtain Li and B abundances in stars which may have been formed in regions directly affected by prior generations of supernovae, would also detect the signature of the ν-process. The combination of SN nucleosynthesis theory and observations may ultimately provide powerful constraints on neutrino properties.

Acknowledgments.   This work was supported by JSPS Grants-in-Aid for Scientific Research (20244035) and Scientific Research on Innovative Area of MEXT (20105004).

References

Abe, K., et al. 2011, Physical Review Letters, 107, 241801. 1109.1621
Adamson, P. et al. 2011, Physical Review Letters, 107, 181802. 1108.0015
Fujiya, W., Hoppe, P., & Ott, U. 2011, ApJ, 730, L7
Hayakawa, T. et al. 2010, Phys.Rev.C, 81, 052801. 1012.5700
Heger, A. et al. 2005, Physics Letters B, 606, 258. arXiv:astro-ph/0307546
Mathews, G. J., Kajino, T., Aoki, W., & Fujiya, W. 2011, ArXiv e-prints. 1108.0725
Nakamura, K., Sato, S., Harikae, S., Kajino, T. & Mathews, G. J. 2012, submitted to ApJ
Otsuki, K. et al. 2000, ApJ, 533, 424. arXiv:astro-ph/9911164
Primas, F., Duncan, D. K., & Thorburn, J. A. 1998, ApJ, 506, L51
Ryan, S. G. et al. 2001, ApJ, 549, 55. arXiv:astro-ph/0010411
Woosley, S. E., Hartmann, D. H., Hoffman, R. D., & Haxton, W. C. 1990, ApJ, 356, 272
Yoshida, T., Kajino, T., & Hartmann, D. H. 2005, Physical Review Letters, 94, 231101. arXiv:astro-ph/0505043
Yoshida, T. 2006b, ApJ, 649, 319. arXiv:astro-ph/0606042
Yoshida, T. et al. 2006a, Physical Review Letters, 96, 091101. arXiv:astro-ph/0602195
Yoshida, T. et al. 2008, ApJ, 686, 448. 0807.2723
Yoshida, T. et al. 2004, ApJ, 600, 204. arXiv:astro-ph/0305555

Galactic Archaeology: Near-Field Cosmology and the Formation of the Milky Way
ASP Conference Series, Vol. 458
W. Aoki, M. Ishigaki, T. Suda, T. Tsujimoto, N. Arimoto, eds.
© *2012 Astronomical Society of the Pacific*

The Slow Neutron Capture Process at Low Metallicity

A. I. Karakas,[1] M. Lugaro,[2], R. J. Stancliffe,[1,2] and C. Rijs[2]

[1]*Research School of Astronomy & Astrophysics, Mount Stromlo Observatory, Weston Creek ACT 2611, Australia*

[2]*Monash Centre for Astrophysics (MoCA), Monash University, Clayton VIC 3800, Australia*

Abstract. We have performed calculations for the *slow* neutron capture process (the *s* process) in stellar models in the mass range 0.9 to 6 solar masses at a metallicity of [Fe/H]=−2.3. The models were computed with two different stellar evolution codes and our results were compared to the composition of the elements heavier than Fe observed in carbon-enhanced metal-poor (CEMP) stars. Our models provide an explanation for the compositions of CEMP stars showing an *s*-process signature (CEMP-*s*) but not for the composition of CEMP stars showing both *s*-process and *rapid* neutron-capture (*r*-process) signatures (CEMP-*s/r*). To explain the composition of CEMP-*s/r* stars we propose the existence of a "*s/r*" neutron-capture process, which may be a superposition of, or a process in-between, the classical *s* and *r* processes.

1. Introduction

The elements heavier than iron are produced by *s*low and *r*apid neutron captures – the *s* and *r* processes (Meyer 1994). During the *s* process, the timescales for β decay of unstable nuclei are generally shorter than the timescale for neutron capture. During the *s* process neutron densities are typically less than $< 10^8$ n/cm^3. At the other extreme, when neutron densities are 10^{20} n/cm^3 or higher, unstable nuclei will rapidly capture neutrons instead of β decaying and this situation is known as the *r* process. The *s*-process path of neutron captures follows the valley of β stability, while that of the *r* process reaches very neutron-rich highly unstable nuclei, which then decay toward their corresponding stable isobar once the neutron flux is extinguished.

During the *s* process, the total time-integrated neutron flux (neutron exposure, τ) together with the presence of nuclei with magic numbers of neutrons along the *s*-process path determine the final abundance distribution. The magic nuclei have lower neutron-capture cross sections than nuclei far from magic numbers and they act as bottlenecks on the path of neutron captures. Increasing the neutron exposure allows the *s* process to progressively bypass these bottlenecks. For example, a neutron exposure of the order of 0.2 mbarn^{-1} results in the production of nuclei between Fe and the first magic bottleneck at Sr. A neutron exposure of the order of 0.4 mbarn^{-1} results in the production of the elements belonging to the first magic bottleneck (N=50): Sr, Y, and Zr. A neutron exposure of the order of 0.9 mbarn^{-1} favours the production of the elements belonging to the second magic bottleneck (N=82): Ba, La, and Ce. Finally, even higher neutron exposures, e.g., 4 mbarn^{-1}, result in the production of the third magic bottleneck (N=126) at Pb and Bi.

This behaviour explains the presence of abundance peaks at the magic neutron numbers in the Solar System abundance distribution. The *light* [ls/Fe] and *heavy* [hs/Fe] *s*-process indexes, together with [Pb/Fe] are commonly used to characterise the *s*-process distribution observed in stars. They are defined as the arithmetic average of [X/Fe], where X = {Sr, Y, Zr} for [ls/Fe] and X = {Ba, La, Ce} for [hs/Fe], with [X/Fe] representing the common spectroscopic notation [X/Fe] = log[(X/Fe)/(X/Fe)$_\odot$].

The *s* process is responsible for the production of about half the abundances of elements heavier than Fe in the Galaxy. It is well established both observationally and theoretically that the *s*-process component of the elements from Sr to Bi is produced in low-mass asymptotic giant branch (AGB) stars, i.e., stars with initial masses from 1 M$_\odot$ to 3 M$_\odot$ in the final phases of their evolution (Busso et al. 1999).

Roughly 10-20% of old halo stars are C-rich, [C/Fe]> 1 (Cohen et al. 2005; Carollo et al. 2012) and are classified as carbon-enhanced metal-poor (CEMP). Of CEMP stars ~ 2/3 also show large enrichments in the *s*-process elements heavier than Fe, such as Ba (CEMP-*s*) (Aoki et al. 2007). These compositions are interpreted as the result of mass transfer from an initially more massive AGB binary companion. However, about 50% of CEMP-*s* stars also show an enrichment in the *r*-process element Eu (CEMP-*s*/*r*). This class appear to be clearly distinct from the CEMP-*s*, showing an average [Ba/Eu]=0.6 instead of 0.9. It is puzzling how CEMP-*s*/*r* could have formed given that the *s* and *r* processes are thought to occur in independent sites: the *s* process in AGB stars, originating from stars with initial mass < 8 M$_\odot$, and the *r* process in core collapse supernovae, originating from stars with initial mass > 10 M$_\odot$.

2. Low-metallicity AGB models and results

To explain the light and heavy element composition of CEMP-*s* stars as a population and to shed light on the origin of CEMP-*s*/*r* stars we computed theoretical models for the *s* process in AGB stars of metallicity Z = 0.0001 ([Fe/H] =−2.3), in the mass range from 0.9 M$_\odot$ to 6 M$_\odot$. The AGB structure was taken from two different stellar evolution codes: Stromlo (Karakas 2010) and STARS (Stancliffe 2010). The stellar evolutionary sequences were then fed into a post-processing code that computes changes due to nuclear reactions and mixing for 320 nuclear species from H to Bi.

As described in detail in Lugaro et al. (2012), we encountered 4 regimes of neutron-capture nucleosynthesis:

1. The ^{22}Ne(α,n)^{25}Mg neutron source operates during He burning inside convective thermal pulses when the temperature reaches > 300 million K. This is the main regime for stars of initial mass > 3 M$_\odot$.

2. The ^{13}C(α,n)^{16}O neutron source burns radiatively during the periods in-between He-burning thermal pulses, in a very thin layer located below the H-burning ashes. This ^{13}C *pocket* is produced by the inclusion of a proton profile in the He and C-rich region, where the protons react with the abundant ^{12}C to produce ^{13}C. This is the main regime for stars of initial mass between 1.75 M$_\odot$ and 3 M$_\odot$ (see Fig. 1.)

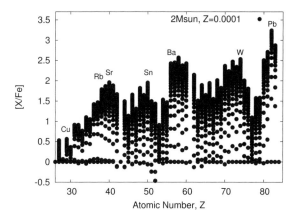

Figure 1.   The evolution of elements [X/Fe] heavier than Fe as a function of atomic number, Z, for the $2M_\odot$, $Z = 0.0001$ Stromlo model with scaled solar initial abundances.

3. The $^{13}C(\alpha,n)^{16}O$ neutron source burns convectively when a significant amount of ^{13}C is left over in the ^{13}C pocket at the end of the interpulse periods and is ingested in the He-burning thermal pulses. This regime applies to the first few thermal pulses of stars of initial mass < 1.75 $M_\odot$.

4. The $^{13}C(\alpha,n)^{16}O$ neutron source is produced and burnt convectively inside the He-burning thermal pulses with ^{13}C produced by the ingestion of a small number of protons in the thermal pulse. This is the main regime for our stellar models of initial mass of 0.9 $M_\odot$ and 1 $M_\odot$ (see Fig. 2).

The final s-process distribution for the different stellar masses depends on the interplay of these four regimes. Neutrons released in radiative as opposed to convective conditions result in higher neutron exposures and produce higher [Pb/Ba]. This is because the free neutrons are released over a mass region which is 10-20 times smaller than the convective thermal pulse, and is void of ^{14}N, a strong neutron poison. Neutrons released in convective conditions produce variable [Ba/Sr], depending on the details of the proton and ^{13}C ingestion.

A detailed comparison of our model predictions to the observations of CEMP stars is presented in Lugaro et al. (2012). In summary, AGB s-process models produce Ba and Eu following the trend of the CEMP-s, however, no models can produce the high [Eu/Fe] seen in the CEMP-s/r. Starting with a high initial [r/Fe] results in high [Eu/Fe], but the same [Ba/Fe]. Thus, the correlation between Ba and Eu observed in CEMP-s/r is not reproduced. Furthermore, all our models produce [hs/ls] < 1, in the range observed in CEMP-s. This is a basic property of any s-process distribution, as it is not possible to increase [hs/ls] above the maximum value determined by the operation of the magic bottlenecks. On the other hand, CEMP-s/r have [hs/ls] values up to +2, on average [hs/ls] values 0.5 higher than CEMP-s, because they have [hs/Fe] on average 0.5 higher. Our models can reproduce the observed [Pb/hs] spread observed in CEMP-s and CEMP-s/r stars, except for the CEMP-s/r stars with high [Pb/hs] and low [Mg/hs].

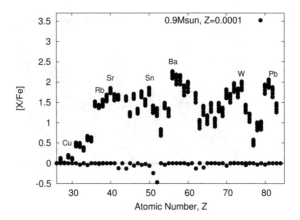

Figure 2.   The evolution of elements [X/Fe] heavier than Fe as a function of atomic number, Z, for the $0.9M_\odot$, $Z = 0.0001$ Stromlo model with scaled solar initial abundances. This model has no ^{13}C pocket included in the post-processing; the neutron-captures are the result of proton ingestion during the first few convective thermal pulses.

Models of intermediate-mass where regime (1) is dominant ($M \geq 3M_\odot$) are excluded as the origin of composition of most CEMP-s and CEMP-s/r stars since they produce [Mg/hs] higher than observed as well as more N than C.

Discussion

Cohen: Qian & Wasserburg introduced accretion induced collapse in a binary to get an r process that might work to produce CEMP-s/r stars; they knew that a modified s-process scenario would not work.

Karakas: Thanks for your comment. We are also trying to point this out.

Renzini: Would convective burning (as opposed to radiative burning) of the ^{13}C pocket help to achieve the high neutron densities that you need?

Karakas: No, we show that in our paper that convective burning does not produce a heavy element distribution compatible with the CEMP-s/r stars.

References

Aoki, W., et al. 2007, ApJ, 655, 492
Busso, M., Gallino, R., & Wasserburg, G. J. 1999, ARA&A, 37, 239
Carollo, D. et al. 2012, ApJ, 744, 195
Cohen, J. et al. 2005, ApJ, 633, L109
Karakas, A. I. 2010, MNRAS, 403, 1413
Lugaro, M., Karakas, A. I., Stancliffe, R. J., & Rijs, C. 2012, ApJ, accepted
Meyer, B. S. 1994, ARA&A, 32, 153
Stancliffe, R. J. 2010, MNRAS, 403, 505

Galactic Archaeology: Near-Field Cosmology and the Formation of the Milky Way
ASP Conference Series, Vol. 458
W. Aoki, M. Ishigaki, T. Suda, T. Tsujimoto, N. Arimoto, eds.

Bridging the Mass Divide: Super and Massive AGB Star Yields

C. L. Doherty,[1] P. Gil-Pons,[2] H. H. B. Lau,[3] and J. C. Lattanzio[1]

[1] *Monash Centre for Astrophysics (MoCA), School of Mathematical Sciences, Monash University, Victoria 3800, Australia*

[2] *Department of Applied Physics, Polytechnical University of Catalonia, 08860 Barcelona, Spain*

[3] *Argelander Institute for Astronomy, University of Bonn, Auf dem Huegel 71, D-53121 Bonn, Germany*

Abstract. Super Asymptotic Giant Branch Stars (Super AGBs) lie in the mass range 6-11 $M_\odot$, which bridges the divide between low/intermediate mass AGB and massive stars. During the thermally pulsing phase of evolution competition between hot bottom burning (HBB) and third dredge up (3DU) events determine the stellar yields. Obtaining these yields is far more computationally demanding than those of most AGB stars because Super AGBs undergo up to a few thousand thermal pulses. We describe results from evolutionary and nucleosynthetic calculations for these stellar models. We examine element production in these Super AGB stars over time, with results from five metallicities spanning the range $Z = 0.02\text{-}10^{-4}$ ([Fe/H] 0 to -2.3). Super AGB star nucleosynthetic yields have hitherto been neglected in galactic chemical evolution modelling.

1. Introduction/Results

There has been a striking gap in stellar yields models in the intermediate 6-11 $M_\odot$ mass range due to their highly computationally demanding nature. This gap has been a source of uncertainty in Galactic chemical evolution modelling. We have computed the evolution of Super and massive AGB models using the Monash version of the Mount Stromlo stellar evolution program (MONSTAR), for current reviews see Campbell & Lattanzio (2008), Doherty et al. (2010). The nucleosynthesis was performed using a post processing code with either a 77 species network (e.g. Karakas 2010) or 475 species network (e.g. Church et al. 2009). The large network allows us to examine s-process element production in detail.

This study of Super AGB stars is the first to find very efficient third dredge up. We can see this in Figure. 1, which plots λ_{max} (the quotient of mass dredged-up by the convective envelope over the mass increase of the core in a thermal pulse) as a function of initial mass.

We examine element production in Super /Massive AGB stars over time, with results from five metallicities spanning the range $Z = 0.02\text{-}10^{-4}$ ([Fe/H]$\approx$ 0 to -2.3) and find that the effects of hot bottom burning dominate over the third dredge up in

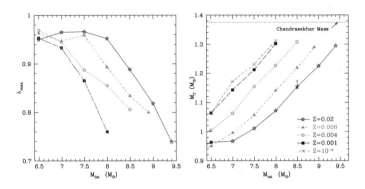

Figure 1.   The left panel details λ_{max}, the maximum dredge up efficiency as a function of initial mass M_{ini}. The right panel relates the initial mass M_{ini} to final core mass M_C for a range of metallicities.

the nucleosynthetic yields for the most metal rich models. We see large production of $^{13}C, ^{14}N, ^{17}O$ as well as ^{25}Mg, ^{26}Mg and ^{26}Al.

In Super AGB stars very large temperatures are attained at the base of the thermal pulse (in excess of 430MK!), which results in a large neutron flux from the ^{22}Ne (α,n) ^{25}Mg reaction. These neutrons facilitate s-process element production. We are currently producing s-process yields for Super and massive AGB stars over a range of metallicities, e.g. Lau et al. (2011). Figure. 1 shows the final core mass as a function of the initial stellar mass for a range of metallicities. Gil-Pons & Doherty (2010) have explored the upper mass limit and the dredge-out phenomenon for metallicities as low as $Z=10^{-5}$. At the high mass tail of Super AGB stars the final fate, either as a white dwarf or as a neutron star remnant is highly contentious.

2.   Conclusions

We have computed the evolution and yields for a grid in mass and metallicity of Super and Massive AGB stars, finding efficient third dredge up. We find that the effects of hot bottom burning dominate over the third dredge-up in the nucleosynthetic yields for the most metal rich models. These stellar models go a long way to bridge the scarcity of yields in this mass range. The final fates and upper mass limits for the formation of Super AGB stars and our produced stellar yields are to be available imminently.

References

Campbell, S. W., & Lattanzio, J. C. 2008, A&A, 490, 769. 0901.0799
Church, R. P. et al. 2009, PASA, 26, 217. 0906.1623
Doherty, C. L. et al. 2010, MNRAS, 401, 1453
Gil-Pons, P., & Doherty, C. L. 2010, MmSAI, 81, 974
Karakas, A. I. 2010, MNRAS, 403, 1413. 0912.2142
Lau, H. H. B. et al. 2011, in Why Galaxies Care about AGB Stars II: Shining Examples and Common Inhabitants, edited by F. Kerschbaum, T. Lebzelter, & R. F. Wing, vol. 445 of Astronomical Society of the Pacific Conference Series, 45

Galactic Archaeology: Near-Field Cosmology and the Formation of the Milky Way
ASP Conference Series, Vol. 458
W. Aoki, M. Ishigaki, T. Suda, T. Tsujimoto, N. Arimoto, eds.
© *2012 Astronomical Society of the Pacific*

Neutron-Capture Nucleosynthesis in AGB Stars and their Connection with Dwarf Spheroidal Galaxies and the Galactic Halo

C. K. Fishlock, A. I. Karakas, and D. Yong

Research School of Astronomy & Astrophysics, Mt Stromlo Observatory, Weston Creek ACT, Australia

Abstract. Using a sample of Galactic halo stars, we will investigate two distinct Galactic halo populations separated by [α/Fe]. The low-α population may be the result of accretion from a dwarf galaxy. Some dwarf galaxies show the signature of asymptotic giant branch (AGB) nucleosynthesis through their neutron-capture element abundance distribution. AGB stars are a known site for the production of heavy elements via the slow neutron-capture process (the s-process). We aim to calculate yields of s-process elements from AGB models. These yields will be used as input into a chemical evolution model for comparison to the high-resolution Magellan data obtained for this investigation.

1. Overview

A study by Nissen & Schuster (2010) found that Galactic halo stars are seen to separate into two populations when looking at [α/Fe] – high-α and low-α stars. The low-α stars are theorised to have been accreted from dwarf galaxies with a slower star formation rate whereas high-α stars are stars that have formed in the Milky Way, either in the disc/bulge and 'heated' to halo kinematics during mergers, or stars that formed as the first stars during the formation of the Milky Way.

There are known elemental abundance differences between stars in the halo and dwarf spheroidal galaxies (dSph; Tolstoy et al. 2009). The [α/Fe] abundance differs for stars in the halo compared to stars located in dSph galaxies. In particular, some dSph galaxies exhibit significant s-process enrichment.

The aim of our work is to extend this analysis to more neutron-capture elements, using the sample of stars from Nissen & Schuster (2010) and data obtained from Magellan and to also calculate s-process yields from stellar models which will enable us to compare populations of AGB stars to the high-α and low-α halo populations via a chemical evolution model.

2. Stellar modelling

We will be calculating an updated grid of s-process element yields from AGB stars covering a range in mass and metallicity applicable to stars in the halo of the Milky Way and in dwarf spheroidal galaxies. One application of these yields will be to interpret any differences in neutron-capture element abundances between the two halo populations. We will be using the Mt Stromlo stellar evolutionary code (Karakas 2010) with up-to-date high- and low-temperature opacity tables. Post-processing nucleosynthesis calculations will provide the *s*-process yields required.

The stellar model grid will cover a mass range of $1M_\odot$ to $6M_\odot$ with a metallicity range [Fe/H] of –3 to –0.8. We have also been testing the effects of an initial alpha-enhancement on the stellar evolution of a $2M_\odot$, $Z = 0.001$ ([Fe/H] = –1.2) model by using α-enhanced opacities tables.

3. Observational work

Using high resolution data taken from the Magellan MIKE echelle spectrograph, we will obtain high-precision measurements of neutron-capture elements in these high-α and low-α halo populations. The observations were taken over two nights with 27 stars observed. The signal-to-noise ratio is 300 per resolution element with $R \approx 83,000$ (blue) and $R \approx 65,000$ (red). See Figure 1 for an example of the data obtained.

We aim to measure 15+ neutron-capture elements with high precision and we shall compare these data to predictions from chemical evolution models which will include our yields from low- and intermediate-mass AGB stars as well as yields from supernovae.

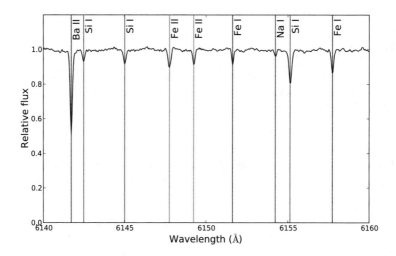

Figure 1.   Example of data obtained from Magellan showing Ba II, an *s*-process element.

References

Karakas, A. I. 2010, MNRAS, 403, 1413.
Nissen, P. E., & Schuster, W. J. 2010, A&A, 511, L10.
Tolstoy, E., Hill, V., & Tosi, M. 2009, ARA&A, 47, 371.

Galactic Archaeology: Near-Field Cosmology and the Formation of the Milky Way
ASP Conference Series, Vol. 458
W. Aoki, M. Ishigaki, T. Suda, T. Tsujimoto, N. Arimoto, eds.
© 2012 Astronomical Society of the Pacific

Supernova Progenitor Mass and Metallicity from Integral Field Spectroscopic Study of the Environment

Hanindyo Kuncarayakti,[1] Mamoru Doi,[1] Greg Aldering,[2] Nobuo Arimoto,[3] Keiichi Maeda,[4] Tomoki Morokuma,[1] Rui Pereira,[5] Tomonori Usuda[6] and Yasuhito Hashiba[1]

[1] *Institute of Astronomy, Graduate School of Science, the University of Tokyo, 2-21-1 Osawa, Mitaka, Tokyo 181-0015 Japan (hanin@ioa.s.u-tokyo.ac.jp)*

[2] *Physics Division, Lawrence Berkeley National Laboratory, 1 Cyclotron Road, Berkeley, CA 94720, USA*

[3] *National Astronomical Observatory of Japan, 2-21-1 Osawa, Mitaka, Tokyo 181-0015, Japan*

[4] *Institute for the Physics and Mathematics of the Universe (IPMU), the University of Tokyo, 5-1-5 Kashiwanoha, Kashiwa, Chiba 277-8583, Japan*

[5] *CNRS/IN2P3, Institut de Physique Nucleaire de Lyon, 4 Rue Enrico Fermi, 69622 Villeurbanne Cedex, France*

[6] *Subaru Telescope, National Astronomical Observatory of Japan, 650 North A'ohoku Place, Hilo, HI 96720, USA*

Abstract. We present preliminary results of our investigation of core-collapse supernova (SN) progenitors by studying its immediate environment. We have obtained integral field spectroscopy of 27 SN explosion sites using UH88/SNIFS and Gemini-N/GMOS. This technique enables us to obtain both spatial and spectral information of the stellar populations present at the sites. Metallicity of the stellar population was estimated using strong-line method, while comparison with simple stellar population (SSP) models yields age. This age and metallicity were then adopted for the SN progenitor star since it is assumed to be coeval with the stellar population at the explosion site. We then determined the initial mass of the SN progenitor, whose lifetime corresponds to the age of the parent stellar population. With this strategy we envision to present the first sample of type-IIP/IIL/Ib/Ic SNe with reliable mass and metallicity determination.

1. Introduction

Observational constraint on supernova progenitor mass and metallicity is still inadequate. In the other hand, theoretical predictions suggest that a particular SN explosion type is produced by progenitor star located within a specific region in mass-metallicity space (e.g. Georgy et al. 2009). Therefore, it is necessary to constrain progenitor mass and metallicity reliably and confront theoretical predictions with observational data. We employ integral field spectroscopy to investigate SN explosion sites spatially and spectrally and provide useful constraints on progenitor mass and metallicity.

2. Observation and data analysis

Twenty-three SN sites have been observed using SNIFS integral field spectrograph (Aldering et al. 2002) attached to University of Hawaii 2.2 m telescope (UH88) at Mauna Kea in two observing runs in August 2010 and March 2011. SNIFS covers 6.4"×6.4" field with 0.4" spatial resolution, producing spectra of 3300-9700 Å at $R \sim 1000$. Four more targets were observed using 8.1 m Gemini-N/GMOS in IFU mode (Hook et al. 2004; Allington-Smith et al. 2002) in September 2011 and data reduction is currently underway. GMOS observation covers 5"×3.5" area on the sky at 0.2" resolution, with 4000-6800 Å spectral coverage at $R \sim 1700$.

The SNIFS data were reduced using a dedicated pipeline, then analyzed using IRAF. For each target we extracted the spectrum of the detected objects in the field of view, which are star clusters or HII regions at the explosion sites. The resulting spectra were then analyzed to determine metallicity via strong line method (Pettini & Pagel 2004), and compared to simple stellar population (SSP, Starburst99 (Leitherer et al. 1999)) models to derive age. Based on apparent association we assume the detected star cluster as the parent population of the SN progenitor. The cluster age corresponds to the lifetime of the SN progenitor, and this translates into its initial mass via Padova stellar evolution models (Bressan et al. 1993). An example is presented in Figure 1.

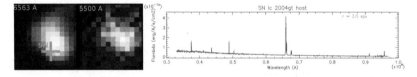

Figure 1.   IFU maps of SN 2004gt host cluster, and the spectrum. Derived metallicity of 12+log(O/H) = 8.72 and age of 5.8 Myr implies a 33.5 $M_\odot$ progenitor.

3. Summary

Using integral field spectroscopy we have obtained spatial and spectral information of 27 core-collapse SN explosion sites in nearby galaxies. Employing strong line method and SSP model comparison, we derive metallicity and age (hence mass) of the progenitor star by analyzing the parent stellar population. While data analysis is still ongoing, we expect to put reliable constraints on type-IIP/IIL/Ib/Ic SN progenitor mass and metallicity using this unique dataset.

References

Aldering, G. et al. 2002, Proc. SPIE, 4836, 61
Allington-Smith, J. et al. 2002. PASP, 114, 892
Bressan, A. et al. 1993, A&AS, 100, 647
Georgy, C. et al. 2009, A&A 502, 611
Hook, I. et al. 2004, PASP, 116, 425
Leitherer, C. et al. 1999, ApJS, 123, 3
Pettini, M., & Pagel, B.E.J. 2004, MNRAS, 348, L59

Galactic Archaeology: Near-Field Cosmology and the Formation of the Milky Way
ASP Conference Series, Vol. 458
W. Aoki, M. Ishigaki, T. Suda, T. Tsujimoto, N. Arimoto, eds.
© *2012 Astronomical Society of the Pacific*

3D Hydrodynamical Simulations of Proton Ingestion

Richard J. Stancliffe,[1] David S. P. Dearborn,[2] John C. Lattanzio,[3]
Stuart A. Heap[3] and Simon W. Campbell[3]

[1]*Research School for Astronomy and Astrophysics, Mount Stromlo Observatory, Cotter Road, Weston Creek, ACT 2611, Australia.*

[2]*Lawrence Livermore National Laboratory, 7000 East Avenue, Livermore, CA 94551, U.S.A.*

[3]*Monash Centre for Astrophysics, Monash University, VIC 3800, Australia*

Abstract.   We use the 3D stellar structure code Djehuty to model the ingestion of protons in a low-mass, low-metallicity asymptotic giant branch star. We find significant differences between the predictions of our 1D stellar evolution code and the results of our hydrodynamic simulations. The hydrodynamic simulations show that protons are rapidly transported from the tail of the hydrogen burning shell by fast, downward flowing plumes and burning does not take place until the protons are in close proximity to the helium burning shell. We find hydrogen burning luminosities many orders of magnitude in excess of those in the 1D model, but there is no splitting of the convective region. We caution that 1D mixing length theory with diffusive mixing does not give an accurate representation of proton ingestion events.

1. Introduction

At low metallicity, convection driven by helium burning can penetrate into hydrogen-rich regions (e.g. Fujimoto et al. 1990), a phenomenon referred to as proton ingestion. 1D stellar models suggest that as protons are dragged down into the convective region, they burn at high temperatures and the convective region becomes split into two: the lower region contintues to be driven by helium burning, while the upper one is powered by hydrogen burning. However, this conclusion rests on shaky foundations, namely the treatment of convection and mixing in 1D. Is our use of the mixing length theory and diffusive mixing correct in such situations? To answer this question, we have simulated a proton ingestion episode during the asymptotic giant branch for a 1 solar mass star of metallicity $Z=10^{-4}$ with the 3D stellar structure code Djehuty (Dearborn et al. 2006), taking a 1D model from the STARS evolution code as the input (Stancliffe & Eldridge 2009). Djehuty is able to model the whole of the convective intershell and possesses a nuclear burning network of 21 species. We are able to follow the convective motions for about 4 hours, a total of 4 convective turnover times.

We find that protons are drawn into the convective regions in fast, downward flowing plumes. These plumes are very fast moving, with maximum speeds of over 100 km/s. The transport process is anything but diffusive in nature! This means that protons can be transported to the helium burning shell before they have time to burn. Significant energy generation only takes place in close proximity to the helium burning shell, so there is no possibility for the convective region to split into two. The proton burning leads to significant production of ^{13}C which becomes mixed throughout the in-

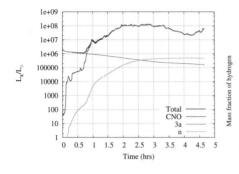

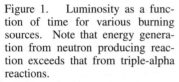

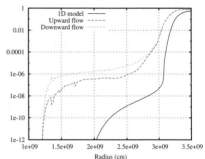

Figure 1. Luminosity as a function of time for various burning sources. Note that energy generation from neutron producing reaction exceeds that from triple-alpha reactions.

Figure 2. Hydrogen abundance by mass fraction as a function of radius for the 1D model (solid black line) and the up- and downstream flows in the 3D model.

tershell. The ^{13}C subsequently burns via the ^{13}C$(\alpha,n)^{16}$O reaction, liberating neutrons. We plan to investigate the nucleosynthetic consequences in future work.

2. Comparison to 1D models

Fig. 1 shows the luminosity from various burning sources for the 3D model. The energy generated by CNO burning reaches 10^8 L$_\odot$, in contrast to the 1D input model which was generating 5.5×10^2 L$_\odot$ from the same reactions. The reason for this difference is evident from Fig. 2. In the 1D model, diffusive mixing of protons only permits a small quantity of protons to get into the intershell and these do not get more than half-way across to the He-burning shell before they are consumed. In contrast, the advective flows seen in the 3D simulation can efficiently transport large amounts of protons through out the intershell. The high intershell abundance of hydrogen results in a much higher hydrogen burning luminosity.

Another major difference between the 1D model and the 3D simulations is the convective velocities. Mixing length theory gives a mixing velocity of around 1-2 km/s. The speeds obtained in the 3D simulations are much higher, with an average speed of around 30-40 km/s. Peaks flow speeds can be much higher than this, reaching over 100 km/s. In addition, the downflows tend to be faster but narrower than the upflows.

These simulations suggest that the treatment of convective mixing via a diffusion equation - something that is commonly done in stellar evolution codes - does not give an accurate representation of the physics underlying the proton ingestion phenomenon. We suggest that the use of a two-stream advective mixing scheme may be better. We are currently in the processes of implementing such a scheme into the Monash stellar evolution code.

A complete discussion of this work can be found in Stancliffe et al. (2011).

References

Dearborn, D. S. P., Lattanzio, J. C., & Eggleton, P. P. 2006, ApJ, 639, 405
Fujimoto, M. Y., Iben, I., Jr., & Hollowell, D. 1990, ApJ, 349, 580
Stancliffe, R. J., Dearborn, D. S. P., Lattanzio, J. C., et al. 2011, ApJ, 742, 121
Stancliffe, R. J., & Eldridge, J. J. 2009, MNRAS, 396, 1699

Galactic Archaeology: Near-Field Cosmology and the Formation of the Milky Way
ASP Conference Series, Vol. 458
W. Aoki, M. Ishigaki, T. Suda, T. Tsujimoto, N. Arimoto, eds.
© *2012 Astronomical Society of the Pacific*

Nucleosynthesis in Gamma-Ray Bursts and Supernovae: Constraints of Extremely Metal-Poor Stars

Nozomu Tominaga[1,2]

[1]*Department of Physics, Faculty of Science and Engineering, Konan University, 8-9-1 Okamoto, Kobe, Hyogo 658-8501, Japan*

[2]*Institute for the Physics and Mathematics of the Universe, University of Tokyo, 5-1-5 Kashiwanoha, Kashiwa, Chiba 277-8569, Japan*

Abstract. I present nucleosynthesis in explosions with relativistic jets or non-relativistic mildly aspherical components, assuming gamma-ray bursts (GRBs) or supernovae (SNe), and compare the abundance ratios of their yields with those of the extremely metal-poor (EMP) stars. The explosion with non-relativistic mildly aspherical energy deposition can explain [Mg/Fe], [Ca/Fe], and [Zn/Fe] but not [Ti/Fe], while the explosion with relativistic jets can explain [Ca/Fe], [Ti/Fe], and [Zn/Fe] but not [Mg/Fe]. This illustrates that the explosion with relativistic jets or non-relativistic mildly aspherical components cannot fully reproduce the EMP stars and implies that the explosion with relativistic jets and non-relativistic mildly aspherical components as in GRB-SNe could explain the abundance ratios of EMP stars simultaneously.

1. Introduction

The photometric and spectroscopic observations indicate that gamma-ray bursts (GRBs) involve relativistic narrow jets with an opening angle $\theta_{jet} \sim 15°$ at the launch site (Frail et al. 2001; Zhang et al. 2003) and that supernovae (SNe) are elliptical explosions with mild asphericity, which is characterized by a ratio of energy deposition between major and minor axes $BP \sim 2 - 8$ (Maeda et al. 2008). Since the asphericities of GRBs and SNe are inconsistent, it is important to clarify which kind of asphericity is favorable for other astronomical objects. In this presentation, I focus on the nucleosynthesis outcome of the aspherical explosions by comparing them with the extremely metal-poor (EMP) stars and present the aspherical explosions with relativistic jets or mildly aspherical energy injection ("elliptical" explosion, hereafter).

2. Method & Results

I investigate aspherical SN explosions of a Pop III $40M_\odot$ star (Umeda & Nomoto 2005; Tominaga et al. 2007a) by means of a two-dimensional relativistic Eulerian hydrodynamic and nucleosynthesis calculation with the Newtonian gravity (Tominaga 2009). Since the explosion mechanism of GRBs and SNe are still uncovered, I do not consider how the explosion is triggered. Instead, the explosion energy is parametrically injected from the inner boundary (Tominaga et al. 2007b; Tominaga 2009). I show the jet-

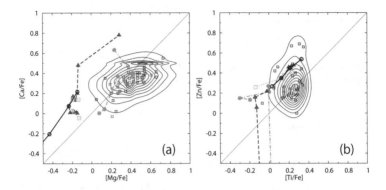

Figure 1.   Abundance ratios (a) [Mg/Fe] and [Ca/Fe] and (b) [Ti/Fe] and [Zn/Fe] of observations (*contours* and *open squares*, e.g., Cayrel et al. 2004; Honda et al. 2004), jet-induced explosion models with different E_{dep} (*solid line*), $\dot{E}_{dep}$ (*dashed line*), and θ_{jet} (*dotted line*), and elliptical explosion models with different *BP* (*dot-dashed line*).

induced explosion models with different total deposited energy E_{dep}, energy deposition rate $\dot{E}_{dep}$, and θ_{jet}, and the elliptical explosion models with different *BP*.

In Figures 1ab, the abundance ratios of the jet-induced explosion models and the elliptical explosion models are compared with the observations of EMP stars. [Mg/Fe] and [Ca/Fe] of the jet-induced and elliptical models with variations of E_{dep}, $\dot{E}_{dep}$, and *BP* are correlated roughly linearly.   This is consistent with the observational trend (Fig. 1a).   However, the jet-induced explosion models show low [Mg/Fe] due to the extended fallback along the equatorial plane, while the ratios [Mg/Fe] and [Ca/Fe] of the elliptical explosion models are consistent with the EMP stars. On the other hand, some of the elliptical explosion models can reproduce well [Zn/Fe] but all of them show low [Ti/Fe] (Fig. 1b). Since Ti and Zn syntheses are activated in the high-entropy environment, the ratios [Ti/Fe] and [Zn/Fe] are enhanced in the jet-induced explosion and the models with high $\dot{E}_{dep}$ and narrow θ_{jet} locate in the contours.

The result illustrates that the explosion with relativistic jets or non-relativistic mildly aspherical components cannot fully reproduce the EMP stars and implies that an explosion with relativistic jets and non-relativistic component as in GRB-SNe could explain the overall abundance patterns of EMP stars, including [Mg/Fe], [Ca/Fe], [Ti/Fe], and [Zn/Fe]. Such a hybrid explosion model will be presented in future work.

References

Cayrel, R., et al. 2004, A&A, 416, 1117.
Frail, D. A., et al. 2001, ApJ, 562, L55.
Honda, S., et al. 2004, ApJ, 607, 474.
Maeda, K., et al. 2008, Science, 319, 1220.
Tominaga, N. 2009, ApJ, 690, 526.
Tominaga, N., et al. 2007a, ApJ, 657, L77.
Tominaga, N., Umeda, H., & Nomoto, K. 2007b, ApJ, 660, 516.
Umeda, H., & Nomoto, K. 2005, ApJ, 619, 427.
Zhang, W., Woosley, S. E., & MacFadyen, A. I. 2003, ApJ, 586, 356.

Galactic Archaeology: Near-Field Cosmology and the Formation of the Milky Way
ASP Conference Series, Vol. 458
W. Aoki, M. Ishigaki, T. Suda, T. Tsujimoto, N. Arimoto, eds.
©2012 Astronomical Society of the Pacific

Late-Phase Observations of a Super-Chandrasekhar SN Ia

M. Yamanaka,[1] K. S. Kawabata,[1] K. Maeda,[2] M. Tanaka,[2]
M. Yoshida,[1] T. Hattori,[3] K. Nomoto,[2] T. Komatsu[4] & T. Okushima[4]

[1] *Hiroshima Astrophysical Science Center, Hiroshima University, Higashi-Hiroshima, Hiroshima 739-8526, Japan*

[2] *Institute for the Physics and Mathematics of the Universe, University of Tokyo, Kashiwa, Japan*

[3] *Subaru Telescope, National Astronomical Observatory of Japan, Hilo, HI, USA*

[4] *Department of Physical Science, Hiroshima University, Kagamiyama 1-3-1, Higashi-Hiroshima 739-8526, Japan*

Abstract. A super-Chandrasekhar (SC) supernova (SN) has an extremely high luminosity and a slow decline rate of the light curve in the early-phase. We present late-phase observations of a SC SN 2009dc. We find that optical luminosity at a year after maximum is much fainter than that expected from its early luminosity. We attempt to fit the analytic light curve model to the observations using Arnett's rule. The model successfully explains the light curves until 120 days. This suggests that the extremely high luminosity originates from the ^{56}Ni decay. We suggest that the late-phase decline would be caused by the dust formation. The existence of strong carbon features in early-phase spectra would support this scenario. We also find the blend of [Ca II] and [Ni II] in its late-phase spectrum. This indicates that the calcium is distributed in the inner layer as nickel and iron. We conclude that the mixing may occur in inner-part of the ejecta.

SN 2009dc exhibits an extremely high luminosity ($M_V = -20.3$) and a very slow decline rate ($\Delta m_{15}(B)=0.65$) in its early-phase Yamanaka et al. (2009); Silverman et al. (2011); Taubenberger et al. (2011). Spectra show the deep C IIλ6580 absorption line, which is unseen in those of typical SNe Ia. The observational properties of SN 2009dc are similar to those of SN 2006gz. The ^{56}Ni mass is calculated to be 1.8 $M_\odot$ from the peak quasi-bolometric luminosity, assuming that the extinction is $A_V = 0.43$ and the rising time is 20 days (Yamanaka et al. 2009). The presence of large amounts of carbon supports that the total ejected mass is much more. Low polarization degree of the continuum also support this (Tanaka et al. 2010). From these observational facts, Yamanaka et al. (2009) conclude that SN 2009dc is a super-Chandrasekhar SN Ia (see also Silverman et al. 2011; Taubenberger et al. 2011).

A late-phase spectrum is a useful tool to understand the inner structure of SN ejecta. As SN expands, the ejecta become optically thin. Thus, late-phase observations of a SN inform us of the inner structure of ejecta. We perform the optical photometric and spectroscopic observations using 8.2m Subaru telescope attached with FOCAS (Kashikawa et al. 2002) on May 13, 2010 (383 days after *B*-band maximum).

We constructed the quasi-bolometric light curves using B, V, R_C and I_C-band light curves (figure 1). The early-phase light curves are from Yamanaka et al. (2009). The quasi-bolometric light curves indicate that the late-phase luminosity is fainter than that expected from early-phase luminosity (Yamanaka et al. 2009). We attempt to fit to the light curve using Arnett's rule (Arnett 1982). The analytic model (Arnett 1982) successfully explains the light curves until 120 days after B-band maximum. Thus, we conclude that the early-phase luminosity originates from ^{56}Ni decay. We suggest that the late-phase luminosity is decreased by dust formation. The presence of carbon supports this scenario. The much redder color at late-phase than a typical SN Ia also supports it. We discuss about possibly identifying [Ca II]$\lambda7299$ in the late-phase spectrum (figure 2). We compare the spectrum of SN 2009dc with typical SNe Ia, SC SN 2006gz (Maeda et al. 2009) and core-collapse SN 1993J. This calcium line shows redshift of 300km s^{-1}, while the nickel and iron emission lines do blueshift of 600km s^{-1}. This indicates that the calcium distributed in inner layer than iron-group elements. This situation would be reproduced by the mixing in the ejecta.

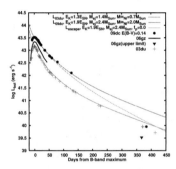

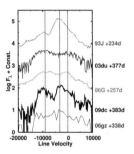

Figure 1. The quasi-bolometric light curve of SN 2009dc compared with those of typical SN Ia 20003du and another SC SN 2006gz. Analytic light curves are constructed based on Arnett's rule (Arnett 1982) for the total ejected mass of 2.4M$_\odot$ and kinetic energy of 1.9×10^{51} erg, denoted in pink line.

Figure 2. Emission line of SC SN 2009dc compared with another SC SN 2006gz (Maeda et al. 2009), typical SN Ia 2003du (Stanishev et al. 2007), subluminous SN 1986G and core-collapse Type IIb SN 1993J. The two vertical gray lines denote the rest frame velocity of [Fe II]$\lambda7155$ and [Ni II]$\lambda7379$. On the other hand, the vertical red line denotes that of [Ca II]$\lambda7299$.

References

Yamanaka, M., et al. 2009, ApJ, 707, L118
Tanaka, M., et al. 2010, ApJ, 714, 1209
Maeda, K., et al. 2009, ApJ, 690, 1745
Silverman, J. M et al. 2011, MNRAS, 410, 585
Taubenberger, S., et al. 2011, MNRAS, 61
Kashikawa, N., et al. 2002, PASJ, 54, 819
Arnett, W. D. 1982, ApJ, 253, 785
Stanishev, V. et al. 2007, A&A, 469, 645

Galactic Archaeology: Near-Field Cosmology and the Formation of the Milky Way
ASP Conference Series, Vol. 458
W. Aoki, M. Ishigaki, T. Suda, T. Tsujimoto, N. Arimoto, eds.
©2012 Astronomical Society of the Pacific

Contribution of Very Massive Population III Stars to the Chemical Enrichment

Tomohiro Yokoyama,[1] and Nozomu Tominaga[1,2]

[1]*Department of Physics, Faculty of Science and Engineering, Konan University, Okamoto 8-9-1, Kobe, Hyogo 658-8501, Japan*

[2]*Institute for the Physics and Mathematics of the Universe, Todai Institutes for Advanced Study, University of Tokyo, Kashiwanoha 5-1-5, Kashiwa, Chiba 277-8583, Japan*

Abstract. The first chemical enrichment has been made by supernovae (SNe) of metal-free Population (Pop) III stars. The first generation stars predicted to be as massive as $> 300 M_\odot$. Although such very massive stars (VMSs) had been considered to directly collapse to black holes, the VMSs are suggested to be able to explode as gamma-ray bursts (GRBs). In order to clarify whether such VMSs can contribute to the chemical enrichment, we present explosive nucleosynthesis in VMS explosions and compare the abundance patterns of their yields with those of the extremely metal-poor (EMP) stars. It is shown that the yields of VMS explosions with explosion energy of 6.3×10^{54} erg cannot reproduce [C/Fe], [Mg/Fe], and [Zn/Fe] simultaneously. This implies that the VMSs are likely not to dominantly contribute to the chemical enrichment in the early universe.

1. Introduction

First stars formed from the primeval density fluctuation, called population III.1 stars (Pop III.1 stars), are predicted to be very massive stars (VMSs) being more massive than $300 M_\odot$ (Omukai & Palla 2003). Assuming an ad hoc jet injection, the abundance patterns of SN yields of VMS calculated by two-dimentional Newtonian calculation show lower [C/Fe] than those of EMP stars (Ohkubo et al. 2006).

Recently, it is suggested that the gravitational energy released by the collapse of VMS can trigger a gamma-ray burst (GRB) due to a high mass accretion rate kept for a long time by the extended envelope (Suwa & Ioka 2011). Relativistic jets powered by the long-standing high mass accretion rate can penetrate the stellar envelope. The explosion with such weak and long-lived jet ejects C-rich matter which could solve low [C/Fe] problem (Tominaga et al. 2007a).

2. Method, results, discussion, and conclusion

We perform hydrodynamics and nucleosynthesis calculation of an explosion of $1000 M_\odot$ star (Ohkubo et al. 2006) with explosion energy $E = 6.3 \times 10^{54}$ erg in spherical symmetry. In order to approximately take into account aspherical effects, we adopt a mixing-fallback model parameterizing the aspherical SN explosions with three parameters, i.e.,

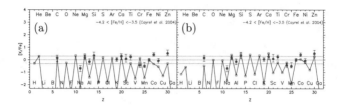

Figure 1.   (a,b) Comparisons of abundance patterns of EMP stars (filled circles, Cayrel et al. 2004) and SN yields of (a) model A and (b) model B (lines).

the initial mass cut M_{cut}(ini), the outer boundary of the mixing region M_{mix}(out), and the ejection factor f (Umeda & Nomoto 2002; see also the Appendix in Tominaga et al. 2007b for detail). It is shown that the model well reproduces the overall abundance pattern of the jet-induced explosion (Tominaga 2009).

We focus on three ratios [C/Fe], [Mg/Fe], and [Zn/Fe]. The EMP stars typically show [C/Fe] ~ 0.2, [Mg/Fe] ~ 0.4, and [Zn/Fe] ~ 0.6 (Cayrel et al. 2004). In this paper, we present two models providing [Mg/Fe] ~ 0.4: model A with M_{cut}(ini) = $359M_\odot$, M_{mix}(out) = $476M_\odot$ and f = 0.03, and model B with M_{cut}(ini) = $267M_\odot$, M_{mix}(out) = $408M_\odot$ and f = 0.06.

In model A, the C enhancement is realized by an explosion with strong fallback up to the O layer. However, [Mg/Fe] ~ 0.4 is obtained by the ejection of matter only above the complete Si burning layer. As a result, the ejected amount of Zn synthesized by the complete Si burning is small and [Zn/Fe] in model A is lower than that in the EMP stars.

On the other hand, model B explosion ejects a matter synthesized by the complete Si burning and realizes high [Zn/Fe]. However, the explosion yields the large amount of Fe so that all the matter above the Si burning layer should be ejected to obtain [Mg/Fe] ~ 0.4. As a result, the [C/Fe] ratio of the explosion is lower than that of the EMP stars.

The comparisons indicate that the nucleosynthesis yields of VMS SNe can not be in agreement with the abundance patterns of the EMP stars within the framework of the explosion. However, there is a caveat that a jet-induced explosion with weak jets could yield high [C/Fe] and [Zn/Fe] simultaneously (Tominaga et al. 2007a; Tominaga 2009).

References

Cayrel, R., Depagne, E., Spite, M., Hill, V., Spite, F., François, P., Plez, B., Beers, T., Primas, F., Andersen, J., Barbuy, B., Bonifacio, P., Molaro, P., & Nordström, B. 2004, A&A, 416, 1117. arXiv:astro-ph/0311082

Ohkubo, T. e. a., Umeda, H., Maeda, K., Nomoto, K., Suzuki, T., Tsuruta, S., & Rees, M. J. 2006, ApJ, 645, 1352. arXiv:astro-ph/0507593

Omukai, K., & Palla, F. 2003, ApJ, 589, 677. arXiv:astro-ph/0302345

Suwa, Y., & Ioka, K. 2011, ApJ, 726, 107. 1009.6001

Tominaga, N. 2009, ApJ, 690, 526. 0711.4815

Tominaga, N., Maeda, K., Umeda, H., Nomoto, K., Tanaka, M., Iwamoto, N., Suzuki, T., & Mazzali, P. A. 2007a, ApJ, 657, L77. arXiv:astro-ph/0702471

Tominaga, N., Umeda, H., & Nomoto, K. 2007b, ApJ, 660, 516. arXiv:astro-ph/0701381

Umeda, H., & Nomoto, K. 2002, ApJ, 565, 385. arXiv:astro-ph/0103241

Part II

Early Generations of Stars

Galactic Archaeology: Near-Field Cosmology and the Formation of the Milky Way
ASP Conference Series, Vol. 458
W. Aoki, M. Ishigaki, T. Suda, T. Tsujimoto, N. Arimoto, eds.
© *2012 Astronomical Society of the Pacific*

Extremely Metal-Poor Stars in the Milky Way Halo

Wako Aoki

National Astronomical Observatory of Japan
2-21-1 Osawa, Mitaka, Tokyo 181-8588, Japan
email: aoki.wako@nao.ac.jp

Abstract. Elemental abundances of the chemically most primitive stars are believed to record the nucleosynthesis yields of the first generations of stars, their mass distribution, evolution, and nature of their supernova explosions. This paper reviews recent progresses in searches for extremely metal-poor stars ([Fe/H]< −3) in the Milky Way halo and studies of their chemical abundances, in particular our recent efforts of follow-up spectroscopy with the Subaru Telescope for candidate metal-poor stars discovered with SDSS/SEGUE. The metallicity distribution of extremely metal-poor stars ([Fe/H]< −3) and fraction and nature of carbon-enhanced stars among them are discussed.

1. Introduction

The continuing efforts of surveys in the past few decades have been finding a number of metal-poor stars in the Milky Way (MW) Galaxy (Beers & Christlieb 2005). In particular, detailed studies have been made for Extremely Metal-Poor (EMP) stars ([Fe/H]< −3.0) among them, although they are very rare objects around the solar-system. Their chemical abundances are usually regarded as records of the nucleosynthesis of the first generation massive stars and supernova explosions. This interpretation is supported by the large scatter of chemical abundance ratios found in EMP stars. Supernova nucleosythesis models are compared not only with the averaged chemical abundance patterns of EMP stars (e.g. Tominaga et al. 2007), but also with those of individual objects.

Remarkable examples are Carbon-Enhanced Metal-Poor (CEMP) stars with no excess of neutron-capture elements (CEMP-no stars: Beers & Christlieb 2005), which are frequently found in EMP stars, including the Hyper Metal-Poor (HMP) stars with [Fe/H]< −5 (Christlieb et al. 2002; Frebel et al. 2005). Detailed chemical abundances have been recently determined for a bright CEMP-no star BD+44°493 ([Fe/H]= −3.7) by Ito et al. (2009), providing a strong constraint on nucleosynthesis models for the progenitors of such objects.

Abundance patterns of elements heavier than iron determined for EMP stars are also useful constraints on nucleosynthesis models of neutron-capture processes. While heavy neutron-capture elements (e.g., Ba, Eu, Th) in such metal-poor stars are well explained by the r-process, there are number of EMP stars showing excesses of light neutron-capture elements (e.g., Sr, Zr). The origins of these elements are in controversy at present, and the measurements for the bright metal-poor stars HD 122563 and HD 88606, which show clear excesses of light neutron-capture elements, by Honda et al. (2006) and Honda et al. (2007) have provided the "template" of the abundance patterns of the process.

With increasing the sample of EMP stars studied in detail, the data also become useful as probes of low-mass star formation and evolution at very low metallicity, as well as of the MW formation. In the ΛCDM scenarios, very metal-poor stars have formed in smaller systems and have accreted forming the MW halo. Dwarf galaxies are suggested to have connections with such small stellar systems, that is, building blocks of the Galaxy. However, there are some significant differences between dwarf galaxies currently observed and the MW halo, including the abundance ratios of α elements and metallicity distribution function (Tolstoy et al. 2009).

While the abundance data for dwarf galaxy stars have been increasing by great efforts using 8-m class telescopes, the statistics of MW halo stars are still insufficient, in particular for the metallicity range of [Fe/H]< -3.0. One reason for this limitation is that EMP stars are very rare among nearby stars. Another reason is that high resolution spectroscopy is required even to determine the metallicity, because spectral lines of such objects are extremely weak.

In order to improve this situation, we have been conducting follow-up high resolution spectroscopy for candidate metal-poor stars in the field halo found by the Sloan Digital Sky Survey (SDSS) and its extension program SEGUE (Yanny et al. 2009). The abundance measurements and derived metallicity distribution function are discussed in this paper.

2. Chemical Abundance Studies for SDSS/SEGUE Sample

Candidates for metal-poor stars are selected from medium-resolution ($R \sim 1800$) spectra obtained in SDSS. The metallicity is estimated from the SDSS spectra by several indicators, including the strength of the Ca II K line (Lee et al. 2008).

High resolution ($R \sim 30,000$) spectra are obtained with the Subaru Telescope High Dispersion Spectrograph (Subaru/HDS) for about 150 stars selected from the SDSS spectra. The typical S/N ratio is 25–30, which is useful to determine the metallicity based on Fe lines and abundance ratios for several important elements (e.g., Mg, Ca, Ba). We call such observing "snap-shot spectroscopy". The Fe abundances are determined for 137 objects.

We set the criterion of [Fe/H]$= -2.7$ in our target selection from the SDSS sample before the Subaru program that was carried out in 2008. We found, however, significant scatter and some offset (by about 0.3 dex) in Fe abundances between the estimates from our high resolution spectra and those from SDSS data before 2008. The offset almost disappears in the comparison with the new estimates from SDSS using the latest version of the analysis pipeline SSPP (see series of papers including Lee et al. 2008). However, large scatter in the comparison for EMP stars remains, indicating that high resolution spectroscopy is required to determine accurate metallicity for EMP stars because of the weakness of metal lines, though such stars are efficiently selected from the medium-resolution spectra of SDSS.

Chemical abundance ratios are determined from atomic lines (e.g. Mg, Ca, Ti, Ba) and CH molecular features in the high resolution spectra by the standard LTE analyses. Effective temperatures estimated by SSPP from SDSS data are adopted in the final analysis, comparing with estimates from colors.

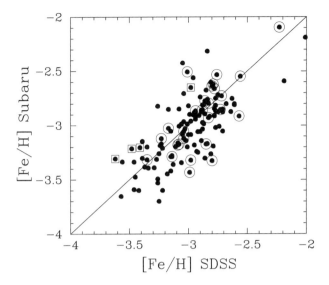

Figure 1. Fe abundances estimated from the Subaru/HDS high resolution spectra and those from the SDSS medium-resolution spectra using the latest version of the analysis pipeline. Red giants and cool main-sequence stars (T_{eff} <5500 K) are indicated by the over-plotted circles and squares, respectively.

3. Metallicity Distribution of EMP Stars

The metallicity distribution function (MDF) of metal-poor stars should contain important information on low-mass star formation in the early Galaxy, and has been studied in the past few decades. The studies in 1990s based on photometry and low-resolution spectroscopy for kinetically selected halo samples (Ryan & Norris 1991; Carney et al. 1994) still provide important data-set, but the sample size is too small at lowest metallicity range ([Fe/H]$\lesssim$ −3). Recent studies based on medium-resolution spectra obtained by the Hamburg/ESO survey (Schörck et al. 2009; Li et al. 2010) determined the MDF for sufficiently large sample in this metallicity range. They emphasized the sharp cutoff of the MDF at [Fe/H]= −3.5, suggesting the existence of the metallicity criterion of low-mass star formation around this Fe abundance (Salvadori et al. 2007). However, we recall that the metallicity estimates for such low-metallicity range from medium-resolution spectroscopy is uncertain and confirmation by high resolution spectroscopy is required. High resolution spectra are also useful to check the excess of other elements (e.g., C, Mg) to discuss the "total metallicity".

The left panel of Figure 3 shows a histogram of the Fe abundances of our snap-shot sample. The metallicity criterion in our sample selectron from the SDSS estimates is [Fe/H]= −2.7 (in the estimates before 2008). Given the ∼ 0.3 dex offset in metallicity estimate between the previous SDSS estimates and our high resolution study is found (high resolution spectroscopy results in lower Fe abundances), the data in the metallicity range [Fe/H]< −3.0 should be incomplete. For the lower metallicity, there is no explicit selection bias in our sample. We confirm that there is no correlations between metallicity and the apparent magnitude nor the effective temperature.

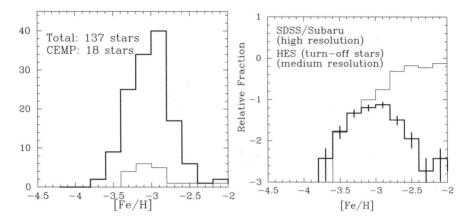

Figure 2.   Left: Metallicity distribution of our sample for the whole sample (thick line) and for carbon-enhanced objects (thin line). Right: Metallicity distribution function of our sample (thick line) compared to that of Li et al. (2010) from the Hamburg/ESO sample (thin line). Our sample is incomplete in [Fe/H]$\gtrsim$ −3.

The MDF estimated from our sample is compared with that obtained by Li et al. (2010) from the Hamburg/ESO survey in the right panel of Figure 3. Our MDF is normalized at the bin of [Fe/H]= −3.3. The lower values in [Fe/H]> −3.2 in our result would be due to the incompleteness of the sample in this metallicity range. The distribution at the lower metallicity agrees with that of Li et al. (2010), and confirms the rapid decrease of the distribution at [Fe/H]= −3.5. However, we found a tail of the distribution in [Fe/H]< −3.5, which is not found by the HES studies. If such a tail really exists, MDF models other than that assumes metallicity criterion for low-mass star formation (e.g. Salvadori et al. 2007) is not excluded (e.g., Prantzos 2008).

The existence of the low metallicity tail might also be suggested by the recent discovery of the ultra metal-poor star SDSS J102915+172927 ([Fe/H]∼ −5) with no carbon-excess (Caffau et al. 2011). Further investigations for the range [Fe/H]< −4 will be particularly important to understand the tail structure of the MDF.

4.   Carbon-Enhanced Objects

The carbon abundance is estimated from the CH molecular bands at 4315 Å and 4322 Å. The quality of our snap-shot spectra is sufficient for detecting the bands for cool giants if the object has carbon-excess (e.g., [C/Fe]> +0.7 at [Fe/H]∼ −3). We found eight carbon-enhanced stars ([C/Fe]> +0.7) among 25 giants, indicating the fraction of CEMP stars is about 30%. This value agrees well with the recent estimate by Carollo et al. (2012) for [Fe/H]∼ −3. It should be noted that we did not give any priority to carbon-enhanced stars in our target selection from SDSS data.

Interestingly, only three stars among the above eight CEMP giants show excesses of Ba even if our spectrum has sufficient quality for detecting the Ba II resonance lines if Ba is enhanced. Hence, AGB stars yielding heavy neutron-capture elements (e.g. Ba) are not the dominant source of the carbon-enhanced objects in the lowest metallicity range, but other objects (e.g. rotating massive stars, faint supernovae: see discussion by Ito et al. 2009) had important contributions to chemical compositions of EMP stars.

Carbon abundances can be measured for main-sequence turn-off stars by our spectra only when the carbon is significantly enhanced (e.g. [C/Fe]> +1.5), because the molecular features are weaker in warmer stars. The fraction of carbon-enhanced objects in our sample of turn-off stars is 9% (10 CEMP stars among 109 objects). Eight of them show Ba-excesses, suggesting that they are CEMP-s stars. The fraction of CEMP-s stars is significantly higher than that found for CEMP giants in our sample. This would be due to the fact that moderately carbon-enhanced stars (0.7 <[C/Fe]< 1.5) can not be identified for turn-off stars by the snap-shot spectra. Previous studies have revealed that the distributions of carbon abundances ([C/H] values) are different between CEMP-s and CEMP-no stars: most of CEMP-s stars have very large carbon-excesses, while CEMP-no stars show a wide distribution in [C/H] (Aoki et al. 2007). Indeed, our sample of CEMP giants include moderately carbon-enhanced objects. Therefore, we suggest that there are many (~20) moderately carbon-enhanced stars in our sample of turn-off stars which are yet to be confirmed by higher quality spectroscopy.

The metallicity distribution of CEMP stars (known at present by our spectra) is shown in the left panel of Figure 3. The fraction of these stars in the whole sample is not large, and the metallicity distribution is not significantly changed if these CEMP stars are excluded. It should be noted, however, that, if several stars with [Fe/H]< −3.5 are identified to be CEMP stars (having moderate excesses of carbon), the impact is not small because the sample size in this metallicity range is still small.

5. Summary and Future Prospect

We have been conducting high resolution follow-up spectroscopy with Subaru/HDS for candidate EMP stars found by SDSS/SEGUE. The snap-shot spectroscopy provides useful sample to discuss the statistics of EMP stars (e.g., metallicity distribution function, fraction of carbon-enhanced object), which are indispensable information for understanding the low-mass star formation and evolution at low metallicity and the formation of the MW halo.

The high resolution spectroscopy also contributes to the calibration of the estimate for metallicity and chemical abundance ratios (e.g., C/Fe) from medium-resolution spectroscopy. SDSS is currently providing a large and homogeneous data-set. The Subaru Telescope has a plan to install a wide-field, multi-object spectrograph at its prime focus (PFS: see Chiba 2012). A deeper survey of metal-poor stars in the MW halo and satellite galaxies will become possible using this instrument. For the follow-up high resolution spectroscopy for metal-poor stars found with Subaru/PFS, we will need the Thirty Meter Telescope (TMT) with its high resolution spectrograph, which will appear also in Hawaii in early 2020s.

Discussion

Cohen: How big is the tail in [Fe/H] below −3.5?

Aoki: The sample includes several objects in this metallicity range and the existence of the tail is certain, but the size is still uncertain. In particular, measurements of the carbon abundances of turn-off stars in this range is important.

Peterson: Can you capitalize on the snapshot approach to reproduce any residual selection bias?

Aoki: Objects with [Fe/H]< −2.7 are efficiently selected from the SDSS spectra, while the exact values of the metallicity for individual objects are not well determined. As a result, the metallicity distribution of our EMP sample in [Fe/H]< −3 is free from the selection bias.

Acknowledgments. The author is supported by the JSPS Grant-in-Aid for Scientific Research (23224004).

References

Aoki, W., Beers, T. C., Christlieb, N., Norris, J. E., Ryan, S. G., & Tsangarides, S. 2007, ApJ, 655, 492. arXiv:astro-ph/0609702

Beers, T. C., & Christlieb, N. 2005, ARA&A, 43, 531

Caffau, E., Bonifacio, P., François, P., Sbordone, L., Monaco, L., Spite, M., Spite, F., Ludwig, H.-G., Cayrel, R., Zaggia, S., Hammer, F., Randich, S., Molaro, P., & Hill, V. 2011, Nat, 477, 67

Carney, B. W., Latham, D. W., Laird, J. B., & Aguilar, L. A. 1994, AJ, 107, 2240

Carollo, D., Beers, T. C., Bovy, J., Sivarani, T., Norris, J. E., Freeman, K. C., Aoki, W., Lee, Y. S., & Kennedy, C. R. 2012, ApJ, 744, 195. 1103.3067

Christlieb, N., Bessell, M. S., Beers, T. C., Gustafsson, B., Korn, A., Barklem, P. S., Karlsson, T., Mizuno-Wiedner, M., & Rossi, S. 2002, Nat, 419, 904. arXiv:astro-ph/0211274

Frebel, A., Aoki, W., Christlieb, N., Ando, H., Asplund, M., Barklem, P. S., Beers, T. C., Eriksson, K., Fechner, C., Fujimoto, M. Y., Honda, S., Kajino, T., Minezaki, T., Nomoto, K., Norris, J. E., Ryan, S. G., Takada-Hidai, M., Tsangarides, S., & Yoshii, Y. 2005, Nat, 434, 871. arXiv:astro-ph/0503021

Honda, S., Aoki, W., Ishimaru, Y., & Wanajo, S. 2007, ApJ, 666, 1189. 0705.3975

Honda, S., Aoki, W., Ishimaru, Y., Wanajo, S., & Ryan, S. G. 2006, ApJ, 643, 1180. arXiv:astro-ph/0602107

Ito, H., Aoki, W., Honda, S., & Beers, T. C. 2009, ApJ, 698, L37. 0905.0950

Lee, Y. S., Beers, T. C., Sivarani, T., Allende Prieto, C., Koesterke, L., Wilhelm, R., Re Fiorentin, P., Bailer-Jones, C. A. L., Norris, J. E., Rockosi, C. M., Yanny, B., Newberg, H. J., Covey, K. R., Zhang, H.-T., & Luo, A.-L. 2008, AJ, 136, 2022. 0710.5645

Li, H. N., Christlieb, N., Schörck, T., Norris, J. E., Bessell, M. S., Yong, D., Beers, T. C., Lee, Y. S., Frebel, A., & Zhao, G. 2010, A&A, 521, A10. 1006.3985

Prantzos, N. 2008, A&A, 489, 525. 0807.1502

Ryan, S. G., & Norris, J. E. 1991, AJ, 101, 1865

Salvadori, S., Schneider, R., & Ferrara, A. 2007, MNRAS, 381, 647. arXiv:astro-ph/0611130

Schörck, T., Christlieb, N., Cohen, J. G., Beers, T. C., Shectman, S., Thompson, I., McWilliam, A., Bessell, M. S., Norris, J. E., Meléndez, J., Ramírez, S., Haynes, D., Cass, P., Hartley, M., Russell, K., Watson, F., Zickgraf, F.-J., Behnke, B., Fechner, C., Fuhrmeister, B., Barklem, P. S., Edvardsson, B., Frebel, A., Wisotzki, L., & Reimers, D. 2009, A&A, 507, 817. 0809.1172

Tolstoy, E., Hill, V., & Tosi, M. 2009, ARA&A, 47, 371. 0904.4505

Tominaga, N., Umeda, H., & Nomoto, K. 2007, ApJ, 660, 516. arXiv:astro-ph/0701381

Yanny, B. et al. 2009, AJ, 137, 4377. 0902.1781

Galactic Archaeology: Near-Field Cosmology and the Formation of the Milky Way
ASP Conference Series, Vol. 458
W. Aoki, M. Ishigaki, T. Suda, T. Tsujimoto, N. Arimoto, eds.

Outliers in the 0Z Survey

Judith G. Cohen,[1] Norbert Christlieb,[2] Ian Thompson,[3] Andrew McWilliam,[3] and Stephen Shectman[3]

[1]*Palomar Observatory, California Institute of Technology, Pasadena, CA, USA*
[2]*Zentrum fur Astronomie der Universitt Heidelberg, Germany*
[3]*Observatories of the Carnegie Institution of Washington, Pasadena, CA, USA*

Abstract. We have now completed detailed abundance analyses of more than 100 stars selected as candidate extremely metal-poor stars with [Fe/H] < −3.0 dex. Of these 18 are below −3.3 dex on the scale of the First Stars VLT project led by Cayrel, and 57 are below −3.0 dex on that scale. Ignoring enhancement of carbon which ranges up to very large values, and two C-rich stars with very high N as well, there are 0 to 3 high or low *strong* outliers for each abundance ratio tested from Mg to Ni. The outliers have been checked and they are real. Ignoring the outliers, the dispersions are in most cases approximately consistent with the uncertainties, except those for [Sr/Fe] and [Ba/Fe], which are much larger. Approximately 6% of the sample are strong outliers in one or more elements between Mg and Ni. This rises to ~15% if minor outliers for these elements and strong outliers for Sr and Ba are included. There are 6 stars with extremely low [Sr/Fe] and [Ba/Fe], including one which has lower [Ba/H] than Draco 119, the star found by Fulbright, Rich & Castro to have the lowest such ratio known previously. There is one extreme *r*-process star.

1. Outliers in Abundance Ratio Trends

Extremely metal poor (EMP) stars were presumably among the first stars formed in the Galaxy, and hence represent in effect a local high-redshift population. Such stars provide important clues to the chemical history of our Galaxy, the role and type of early SN, the mode of star formation in the proto-Milky Way, and the formation of the Galactic halo. Beers & Christlieb (2005) compiled the small sample of EMP stars known as of 2005. The goal of our 0Z Project is to increase this sample substantially.

Our sample selection is based on mining the database of the Hamburg/ESO Survey (Wisotzki et al 2000) for candidate EMP stars with [Fe/H] < −3.0 dex (Christlieb 2003). Our abundance determination procedures are described in Cohen et al (2004). The determination of stellar parameters, measurement of equivalent widths, and detailed abundance analyses were all carried out by J. Cohen.

Our data in general follow the well established trends from numerous studies of Galactic halo stars between abundance ratios [X/Fe] and overall metallicity as measured by [Fe/H] (see e.g. Cayrel et al 2004; Cohen et al 2004). The interesting question is whether in the low metallicity regime studied here we can detect the effect of only a small number of SN contributing to a star's chemical inventory or inhomogeneous mixing within the ISM at these early stages of formation of the Galaxy. Thus the size of the scatter around these trends and whether there are major outliers is of great interest.

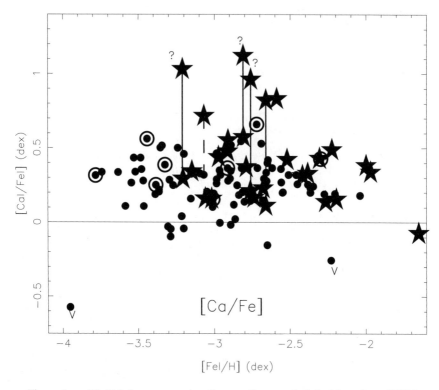

Figure 1.   [Ca/Fe] for our sample. Stars = C-stars, circled objects have [C/Fe] > 1.0 dex but no C_2 bands. Objects marked V are outliers that have been checked. Vertical lines connect the initial and final [Ca/Fe] for four C-stars which were high outliers. The initial high values were rated as uncertain (marked by ?) during the checking process. New spectra for these four C-stars were obtained that reach to the 6160 Å region with strong Ca I lines that is clear of molecular bands. The resulting Ca abundances for each of these C-stars is substantially lower; they now lie with the main distribution and are no longer outliers.

After all the abundance analyses were completed, we looked for *strong* outliers, either high or low, in plots of [X/Fe] vs [Fe/H]. We checked these in detail. The Ca abundance turned out to be problematical in those very C-rich stars whose spectra were obtained prior to HIRES detector upgrade in mid-2004 and thus included only a limited wavelength range. In an effort to derive Ca abundances from these early HIRES spectra, we ended up using lines which were crowded/blended, presumably by molecular features. This was only realized fairly recently when we obtained additional C-star HIRES spectra extending out to 8000 Å which covered key isolated Ca I lines in the 6160 Å region. We found much lower Ca abundances from the additional Ca lines in these carbon stars. Our earlier claims in Cohen et al (2006) of high Ca/Fe for some C-rich stars are not correct.

These abundance analyses were carried out over a period of a decade, and some updates were made in J. Cohen's master list of adopted gf values during that period.

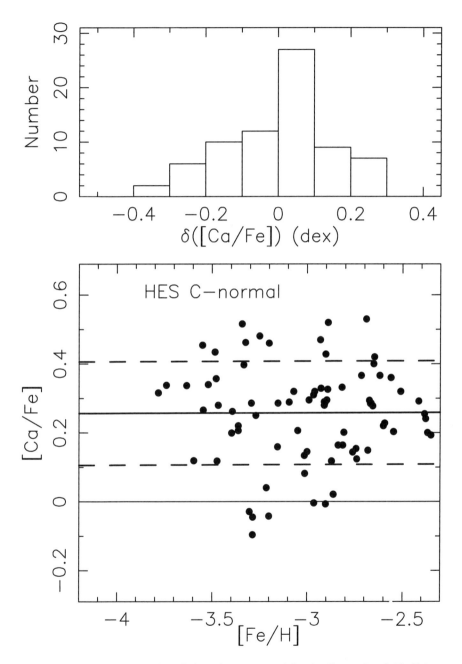

Figure 2. Lower panel: [Ca/Fe] for stars used in the linear fit of [Ca/Fe] with [Fe/H] for the 100 EMP candidates with high dispersion HIRES/Keck or MIKE/Magellan specra and with detailed abundance analyses. The linear fit is the thick solid line. Dashed lines are the fit ±0.15 dex. Upper panel: histogram of deviations around the linear fit. Note the assymetric tail towards low [Ca/Fe] ratios.

The next step, completed in Dec 2011 after the conference, was to homogenize the gf values.

2. Linear Fits to Abundance Ratios

Fig. 1 shows [Ca/Fe] vs [Fe/H] for our sample. Linear fits to the abundance ratios vs [Fe/H] where there is adequate data for the species X were calculated, excluding C-rich stars and a small number of *strong* outliers. An example of these fits is shown for Ca in Fig 2, where in the lower panel the included stars are shown together with the fit (thick solid line) and the fit ±0.15 dex (dashed lines). Note that the fit for [Ca/Fe] vs [Fe/H] is constant, [Ca/Fe] = 0.26 dex. In the upper panel the histogram of deviations from the linear fit is shown. Although a number of very deviant low outliers were excluded, an assymetric distribution of δ([Ca/Fe]) still remains, suggesting the presence of a small tail of stars with low [Ca/Fe], though not so extreme that the stars were rejected as strong outliers. This is also apparent in the lower panel, where there are four stars with [Ca/Fe] < 0; these values were not low enough for them to be rejected as strong outliers. Current work focuses on determining whether the dispersion about these fits is larger than the expected uncertainties.

There are six stars which are very deviant low outliers in [Ba/Fe]. One of these has [Ba/H] below that of Draco 119, the star with the lowest Ba abundance previously known (Fulbright, Rich & Castro 2004).

Acknowledgments.   We are very grateful to the Palomar, Las Campanas, and Keck time allocation committees for their long-term support of this effort. J. Cohen acknowledges partial support from NSF grants AST–0507219 and AST–0908139. I. Thompson acknowledges partial support from NSF AST-0507325. We are grateful to the many people who have worked to make the Keck Telescopes and their instruments, and the Magellan Telescopes and their instruments, a reality and to operate and maintain these observatories.

References

Beers, T. C. & Christlieb, N., 2005, ARA&A, 43, 531
Cayrel, R. et al, 2004, A&A, 416, 1117
Christlieb, N., 2003, Rev. Mod. Astron., 16, 191
Cohen, J. G.,et al, 2004, ApJ, 612, 1107
Cohen, J., McWilliam, A., Shectman, S., Thompson, I., Christlieb, N., Ramírez, S., Swenson, A. & Zickgraf, F. J., 2006, AJ, 132, 137
Fulbright, J., Rich, R. M. & Castro, S., 2004, ApJ, 612, 447
Wisotzki, L., Christlieb, N., Bade, N., Beckmann, V., Köhler, T., Vanelle, C. & Reimers, D., 2000, A&A, 358, 77

Galactic Archaeology: Near-Field Cosmology and the Formation of the Milky Way
ASP Conference Series, Vol. 458
W. Aoki, M. Ishigaki, T. Suda, T. Tsujimoto, N. Arimoto, eds.
© 2012 Astronomical Society of the Pacific

Star Formation History of Our Galaxy Explored with AGB Star Evolution Models

Takuma Suda,[1] Yutaka Komiya,[1] Wako Aoki,[1] Shimako Yamada,[2] Yutaka Katsuta,[2] and Masayuki Y. Fujimoto[2]

[1]*National Astronomical Observatory of Japan, Osawa 2-21-1, Mitaka, Tokyo, 181-8588, Japan*

[2]*Hokkaido University, Kita 10 Nishi 8, Kita-ku, Sapporo, 060-0810, Japan*

Abstract. We discuss the characteristics of known extremely metal-poor (EMP) stars in the Galaxy using stellar evolution models and the Stellar Abundances for Galactic Archaeology (SAGA) database. We compare the observed characteristics of carbon-enhanced EMP (CEMP) stars with the evolution and nucleosynthesis in EMP AGB stars. In particular, we focus on the transition of the initial mass function (IMF) during the early evolution of the Galaxy based on the statistics of CEMP stars. This work is devoted to the explanation for the sharp drop of the CEMP star frequency at [Fe/H] ~ −2 by considering the efficiency of carbon dredge-up during the AGB phase. We conclude that high-mass IMF is favored at low-metallicity, although there are still some uncertainties in the results affected by stellar models and binary nature.

1. CEMP star frequency

Extremely metal-poor (EMP) stars are important tracer of the chemical enrichment of the Galaxy, although these stars constitute minor population in the Galactic halo as inferred from the metallicity distribution function (Suda et al. 2008). High resolution spectroscopy of these stars reveals that carbon-enhanced stars are common to EMP stars compared with CH stars (Rossi et al. 1999). The large frequncy of carbon-enhanced EMP (CEMP) stars, defined by [C/Fe] $\geq$ 0.7 and [Fe/H] $\leq$ −2.5 in this paper, was argued to be a consequence of stellar evolution at low-metallicity (Fujimoto et al. 2000), i.e., hydrogen in the bottom of hydrogen burning shell mix into the helium-flash driven convective zones (Suda & Fujimoto 2010, and references therein). However, larger efficiency or larger channels to become CEMP stars is not enough to explain such large frequency of CEMP stars among EMP stars (Komiya et al. 2007; Izzard et al. 2009; Suda et al. 2011). It is also pointed out by Carollo et al. (2012) that the frequency of CEMP stars increases with decreasing metallicity. In this paper, we explore the possibility of changing the IMF accoring to the idea of high-mass IMF proposed by Komiya et al. (2007), by our numerical model of binary population in a similar approach to the paper by Izzard et al. (2009).

2. Models and assumptions

We modeled stochastic formation of binary system subject to the IMF, mass ratio function, and binary period distribution function. The basic model parameters for binary population is the same as in Komiya et al. (2007); The IMF is a log-normal distribution and has a peak at $10M_\odot$ with an appropriate dispersion to generate low-mass stars with $M \lesssim 0.8M_\odot$. Binary frequency is assumed to be 50 %. Mass ratio function is assumed to be constant for all model data sets throughout this paper. Our model adopts additional period distribution function proposed by Rastegaev (2010) where the sharp peak in the distribution appears at ∼ 100 days.

AGB evolution models are taken from Suda & Fujimoto (2010). Binary mass transfer is followed by wind accretion or Roche-Lobe overflow depending on masses and separation of the system. The channel of mass transfer is determined by the Roche radius prescribed by Eggleton (1983). If a separation of the binary system is larger than the sum of the Roche radius of primary and the raidus of secondary at the main sequence phase, wind accretion is assumed to be at play. Otherwise, the Roche lobe overflow applies to the system. For wind accretion, we assumed abrupt mass loss at the end of the dredge-up of carbon by heium-flash driven deep mixing (Suda et al. 2004) or the third dredge-up in the last model, since mass loss is not taken into account in the AGB models by Suda & Fujimoto (2010). The amount of mass lost from the envelope is calculated from initial-mass final-mass relations for white dwarfs (Han et al. 1994). The accretion process is approximated by Bondi-Hoyle accretion onto the secondary by assuming constant mass loss velocity ($20km/s$). The primary stars are assumed to have $[C/H] = -1$ by the helium-flash driven deep mixing (He-FDDM) and $[C/H] = 0$ by the third dredge-up. If a separation of binary system is smaller than the Roche radius, we assume that the envelope of a primary is stripped off to the extent that the sum of the radii of two stars are identical to the separation. Accretion efficiency is assumed to be 10 % of the mass transferred. The accretion onto a secondary is approximated by steady state process with the amount of dilution in the surface convection taken into account. The mass of the convective envelope is set at $0.0035M_\odot$ for dwarfs and $0.35M_\odot$ for giants.

In our models, the occurrence of the third dredge-up and the hot bottom burning is treated as free parameters. In the fiducial model, we set the lower boundary for the third dredge-up and the hot bottom burning at $1.5M_\odot$ and $5M_\odot$, respectively, indepent of metallicity. The He-FDDM is assumed to occur for models with $0.8 \leq M/M_\odot \leq 3.5$ and with $[Fe/H] \leq -2.5$ throughout the paper.

With regards to the detectablity of secondaries, we set lower mass boundary at $0.7M_\odot$ and upper boundary at $8.3M_\odot$. The former comes from apparent detection limit to determine carbon abundance of dwarf stars in the Galactic halo. The latter is determined by the lifetime of stars. We assume that typical lifetime of halo stars is 13 Gyrs and that stars with $8.2 \leq M/M_\odot < 8.3$ can be detected as red giants.

3. Results and discussion

Figures 1 shows the comparisons of the frequency of CEMP stars as a function of metallicity for different period distribution function. The choice of different period distribution has a strong impact on the frequency of CEMP stars. From the observational point of view, the CEMP frequency increases with decreasing metallicity according to the compilation of the observations of EMP stars using the SAGA database (Suda et al. 2008) as already shown by Suda et al. (2011). We should note that the number of stars at the metallicity range of [Fe/H] $\lesssim$ -4 is small and the CEMP frequency is not statistically reliable. We also plot the result by Carollo et al. (2012) who estimate the CEMP frequency from kinematically selected sample in the SDSS data.

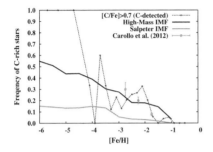 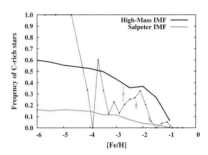

Figure 1.   CEMP star frequency as a function of metallicity. The period distribution function is taken from Duquennoy & Mayor (1991) (left panel) and from Rastegaev (2010) (right panel).

We plot the predicted frequency of CEMP stars by generating 5×10^5 - 2×10^6 binary systems at given metallicity with 0.5 dex step in [Fe/H] from -6 to -1. As expected from the definition of CEMP stars, CEMP frequency increases with decreasing metallicity with reasonable agreement with observations. This means that carbon enhancement in primary AGB stars are almost independent of metallicity, which is confirmed for the numerical simulations of He-FDDM in AGB stars. On the other hand, it is reported that the third dredge-up efficiency decreases with decreasing metallicity (Suda & Fujimoto 2010). Therefore, consideration of metallicity dependence in models will be important for future works.

Figure 2 shows a parameter dependence of our model with Rastegaev's period distribution function. The lower mass boundary for hot bottom burning during the AGB phase are varied from 4 to $7 M_\odot$ for model with high-mass IMF. This change also has a strong impact on CEMP frequency especially for models with high-mass IMF. However, large frequency of NEMP stars is not supported observationally. Therefore, smaller mass range for hot bottom burning is favored, or nitrogen-enhanced AGB stars may suppress mass loss and decrease the production of NEMP stars, probably due to decreased efficiency of dust driven mass loss by decreased carbon abundance in the surface.

We also tried to find a solution to enhance CEMP frequency at [Fe/H] $\lesssim$ -2.5 for low-mass IMF by changing free parameters. For low-mass IMF, increasing the binary frequency results in larger CEMP frequency by nearly a factor of two by assuming that all the stars are born in binary. As an another extreme assumption, we set carbon yield from AGB at solar value for the mass range of $0.8 \leq M/M_\odot \leq 5$. This model agrees with observations at low-metallicity, but results in an overproduction of carbon-enhanced stars at [Fe/H] $\gtrsim$ -1.5. We conclude that the transition of the IMF can account for the entire trend of CEMP frequency. This work supports the previous results by Suda et al. (2011) that the IMF change should occur at [Fe/H] $\sim$ -2, although the

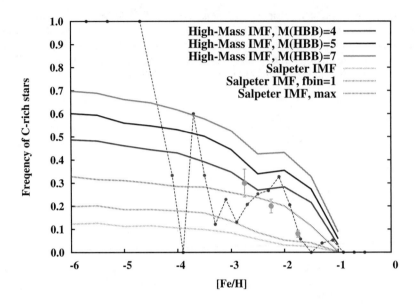

Figure 2.   The same as in Fig. 1, but with different parameters. Solid lines show
the dependence on the choice of lower boundary mass for the hot bottom burning.
Dotted line represents our maximization of CEMP frequency with Salpeter IMF. See
text for more detail.

models have some uncertainties affected by stellar models and characteristcs of binary
system.

Acknowledgments.   This work has been supported by Grant-in-Aid for Scientific
Research (23224004), from Japan Society of the Promotion of Science.

References

Carollo, D. et al. 2012, ApJ, 744, 195
Duquennoy, A., & Mayor, M. 1991, A&A, 248, 485
Eggleton, P. P. 1983, ApJ, 268, 368
Fujimoto, M. Y., Ikeda, Y., & Iben, I., Jr. 2000, ApJ, 529, L25
Han, Z., Podsiadlowski, P., & Eggleton, P. P. 1994, MNRAS, 270, 121
Izzard, R. G., Glebbeek, E., Stancliffe, R. J., & Pols, O. R. 2009, A&A, 508, 1359
Komiya, Y., Suda, T., Minaguchi, H., Shigeyama, T., Aoki, W., & Fujimoto, M. Y. 2007, ApJ,
    658, 367
Rastegaev, D. A. 2010, AJ, 140, 2013
Rossi, S., Beers, T. C., & Sneden, C. 1999, in The Third Stromlo Symposium: The Galactic
    Halo, edited by B. K. Gibson et al. vol. 165 of ASP Conference Series, 264
Suda, T., Aikawa, M., Machida, M. N., Fujimoto, M. Y., & Iben, I., Jr. 2004, ApJ, 611, 476
Suda, T., & Fujimoto, M. Y. 2010, MNRAS, 405, 177
Suda, T., Katsuta, Y., Yamada, S., Suwa, T., Ishizuka, C., Komiya, Y., Sorai, K., Aikawa, M., &
    Fujimoto, M. Y. 2008, PASJ, 60, 1159
Suda, T., Yamada, S., Katsuta, Y., Komiya, Y., Ishizuka, C., Aoki, W., & Fujimoto, M. Y. 2011,
    MNRAS, 412, 843

Galactic Archaeology: Near-Field Cosmology and the Formation of the Milky Way
ASP Conference Series, Vol. 458
W. Aoki, M. Ishigaki, T. Suda, T. Tsujimoto, N. Arimoto, eds.
©*2012 Astronomical Society of the Pacific*

Detailed Abundances in Extremely Metal Poor Dwarf Stars Extracted from SDSS

L. Sbordone,[1,2] P. Bonifacio[2], E. Caffau,[1,2] and H.-G. Ludwig[1,2]

[1]*Zentrum für Astronomie der Universität Heidelberg, Landessternwarte, Königstuhl 12, 69117 Heidelberg, Germany*

[2]*GEPI, Observatoire de Paris, CNRS, Univ. Paris Diderot, Place Jules Janssen, 92190 Meudon, France*

Abstract. We report on the result of an ongoing campaign to determine chemical abundances in extremely metal poor (EMP) turn-off (TO) stars selected from the Sloan Digital Sky Survey (SDSS) low resolution spectra. This contribution focuses principally on the largest part of the sample (18 stars out of 29), observed with UVES@VLT and analyzed by means of the automatic abundance analysis code MyGIsFOS to derive atmosphere parameters and detailed compositions. The most significant findings include i) the detection of a C-rich, strongly Mg-enhanced star ([Mg/Fe]=1.45); ii) a group of Mn-rich stars ([Mn/Fe]>-0.4); iii) a group of Ni-rich stars ([Ni/Fe]>0.2). Li is measured in twelve stars, while for three upper limits are derived.

1. Introduction

Since many years we are conducting a campaign to select EMP candidates from the Sloan Digital Sky Survey (SDSS York et al. 2000). Candidate TO stars are selected among SDSS spectroscopic targets on the basis of $(g - z)_0$ color, and their SDSS low resolution spectra are screened by means of an automatic procedure to derive a metallicity estimate (Ludwig et al. 2008). A number of candidates have been so far observed by means of the X-Shooter (D'Odorico et al. 2006) and UVES (Dekker et al. 2000) spectrographs at VLT, and partial results have appeared in the literature. Behara et al. (2010) presented 3 carbon enhanced metal poor stars observed with UVES, and Bonifacio et al. (2011) and Caffau et al. (2011a) described 7 stars observed with X-Shooter. The most striking result so far has been the discovery of SDSS J1029151+172927 (Caffau et al. 2011b), an ultra metal poor (UMP)[1]

TO star ([Fe/H]$_{3D}$=-5.0) with an abundance pattern typical of Halo stars for all measured elements. The CNO elements are not measured, but strong enhancements can be excluded ([C/Fe]<0.7, [N/Fe]<0.2).

This characteristic, unique among the 4 UMP stars known to date, sets the current record of the star with the lowest metal content (Z<4.5 $10^{-5}Z_\odot$). The discovery of this object challenges the Bromm & Loeb (2003) theory of low metallicity star formation, which implies that a higher C and O abundance would be necessary to form a star of such low mass. On the other hand, it favors theories predicting a lower critical

---

[1]EMP / UMP and similar designations were initially established as being based on [Fe/H] only (Beers & Christlieb 2005). As such, they are misleading due to the extreme CNO enrichment often seen in stars of extremely low iron content. However, we keep using them here in the usual meaning for consistency.

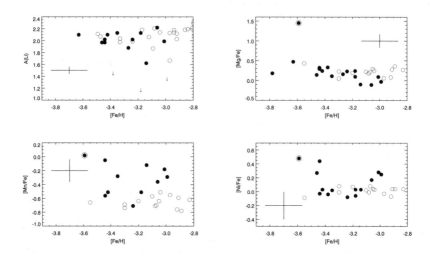

Figure 1.   Abundance determinations for Li, Mg, Mn and Ni plotted against [Fe/H] for the stars in the UVES SDSS sample (filled circles, the encircled point indicates the preliminary results for SDSS J134922+140736). Open circles represent literature data. Upper left panel: A(Li) measurements or upper limits, against Sbordone et al. (2010a) results (3D temperature scale parameters and A(Li)$_{3D,NLTE}$); other panels [Mg/Fe], [Mn/Fe], [Ni/Fe] against Bonifacio et al. (2009) data for EMP TO stars. Typical error bars superimposed.

metallicity for the formation of low mass stars (e.g. Schneider et al. 2012) or even the absence of a critical metallicity (Greif et al. 2011).

In this contribution we will focus on the bulk of the sample of stars observed with UVES@VLT (18 stars) about which a more extensive paper is in preparation (Bonifacio et al. 2012).

2.   Observations and analysis

The observations were performed with UVES set in 380+580nm dichroic mode, 1.4" slit and 2×2 pixel binning. Reduction was carried out by means of the standard ESO UVES pipeline. The analysis was performed with the MyGIsFOS code (Sbordone et al. 2010b, 2012a). This is an evolution of the code of Bonifacio & Caffau (2003), with a number of improvements, most notably a loop to determine surface gravity from the iron ionization equilibrium. The grid of synthetic spectra was computed from a grid of ATLAS 12 (Kurucz 2005; Castelli 2005; Sbordone et al. 2004; Sbordone 2005) model atmospheres.

The effective temperature was considered a prior and was derived from the $(g - z)_0$ color using the calibration presented in Ludwig et al. (2008). Surface gravity was determined from the iron ionization equilibrium. If no Fe II lines were retained in the analysis, the surface gravity was held fixed at $\log g = 4.0$.

One star (SDSS J134922+140736) turned out to be C-rich (qualitative estimate, from G-band strength), and the MyGIsFOS analysis determines an extreme Mg enrichment ([Mg/Fe]=1.45). The whole analysis technique employed was not designed to handle C-rich stars. Moreover, MyGIsFOS is potentially prone to systematic deviations when measuring abundances strongly deviating from the ones assumed in the grid (such as is the case of Mg in this star). As a consequence, until an better adapted analysis is performed for this star (Sbordone et al. 2012b), results for SDSS J134922+140736 are to be considered preliminary.

Lithium abundance was measured using the same technique employed in Sbordone et al. (2010a): the 670.7nm doublet equivalent width was estimated by fitting a grid of synthetic profiles, and the Sbordone et al. (2010a) fitting function was applied to derive a 3D, NLTE Li abundance measurement.

One additional star was observed (SDSS J153110+095255) but resulted to be a double-lined spectroscopic binary: it is thus excluded from the analysis.

3. Results and discussion

In fig. 1 we show some of the most interesting results of the present analysis. A more through analysis is to appear in Bonifacio et al. (2012) and Sbordone et al. (2012b).

Lithium: in Sbordone et al. (2010a) we identified a progressive disruption of the Spite plateau, taking place below [Fe/H]~-2.8. We referred to this observed feature as a "meltdown": an increasing number of stars show some variable degree of Li depletion. The new observations reinforce this picture. Meléndez et al. (2010) suggested that convective Li depletion should be expected in stars as warm as ~6100 K in the EMP range. This is partially compatible with the results in Sbordone et al. (2010a), where every star below 6000 K is Li depleted. However, the new sample contains one object (SDSS J090733+024608) whose Li abundance places it on the Spite plateau despite a T_{eff}=5934 K, and both the Sbordone et al. (2010a) sample and the new one contain a number of Li-poor objects of relatively high temperature. Moreover, SDSS J1029151+172927, otherwise a very inconspicuous star, shares the same deep Li depletion as HE 1327–2326 (Frebel et al. 2008, [Fe/H]=-5.96,[C/Fe]=+3.78). This leads us to believe that a fundamental understanding of the low metallicity Li behavior is still eluding us.

Mg, and the chemically peculiar SDSS J134922+140736: the new sample presents for the most part the usual pattern of α-enhancement expected in the metal poor Halo. However, three α-poor stars are found, similar, but at lower metallicity, to the two stars described in Bonifacio et al. (2011). The extreme Mg overabundance is the most striking anomaly of SDSS J134922+140736, but it is interesting to notice that the star appears anomalous in Ni and Mn too, as well as C-rich. Two similarly Mg-rich stars have been detected also by the 0Z survey (Cohen et al. 2011, and J. Cohen's contribution at this conference), and a possibly similar star was detected by the "First Stars" ESO Large Program (Depagne et al. 2002). Li is not detected due to the low S/N in the red region of the spectrum, but if measured should provide a diagnostic of the amount of high-temperature processed gas that polluted the star.

Mn and Ni rich populations: while the detection of a Ni rich subsample is not highly significant due to the associated error, a Mn overabundant subsample is evident also by comparing the Mn line strengths in stars with otherwise very close parameters and metallicities. Both anomalies are reported also in J. Cohen's contribution to this conference, as detected by the 0Z survey. There is a hint of a correlation between Ni and Mn enrichment: of the seven stars with [Mn/Fe]>-0.4, four have [Ni/Fe]>0.2.

The size of the errors and the limited sample, however, prevent us from deriving more stringent conclusions.

Discussion

Cohen: How do the SDSS pipeline parameters estimate compare with yours?

Sbordone: Comparisons between our method for deriving T_{eff} and metallicity from SDSS and the one coming from the SDSS pipeline are shown in Ludwig et al. (2008) Fig. 1 and 2.

Asplund: Do you have an estimate of the Li depletion expected from models for SDSS J1029151+172927?

Sbordone: No estimates exist at such low metallicity. At a much higher metallicity, Richard et al. (2005) derives A(Li)=2.05 for a MS star of similar temperature ("T6.25" model).

Acknowledgments.   PB acknowledges support from the Programme National de Physique Stellaire (PNPS) and the Programme National de Cosmologie et Galaxies (PNCG) of the Institut National de Sciences de l'Universe of CNRS.

References

Beers, T., & Christlieb, N., 2005, ARA&A, 43, 531
Behara, N. T. et al. 2010, A&A, 513, A72
Bonifacio, P., & Caffau, E. 2003, A&A, 399, 1183
Bonifacio, P., et al. 2009, A&A, 501, 519
Bonifacio, P., et al. 2011, Astronomische Nachrichten, 332, 251
Bonifacio, P., et al., 2012, in prep.
Bromm, V., & Loeb, A. 2003, Nat, 425, 812
Caffau et al. 2011a, A&A, 534, A4
Caffau et al. 2011b, Nature, 477, 67
Castelli, F. 2005, Memorie della Società Astronomica Italiana Supplementi, 8, 25
Cohen, J. G. et al. 2011, RR Lyrae Stars, Metal-Poor Stars, and the Galaxy, 239
Dekker, H. et al. 2000, Proc. SPIE, 4008, 534
Deliyannis, C. P., Demarque, P., & Kawaler, S. D. 1990, ApJS, 73, 21
Depagne, E., Hill, V., Spite, M., et al. 2002, A&A, 390, 187
D'Odorico, S., et al. 2006, Proc. SPIE, 6269
Frebel, A., Collet, R., Eriksson, K., Christlieb, N., & Aoki, W. 2008, ApJ, 684, 588
Greif, T. H., Springel, V., White, S. D. M., et al. 2011, ApJ, 737, 75
Kurucz, R. L. 2005, Memorie della Società Astronomica Italiana Supplementi, 8, 14
Ludwig, H.-G. et al. 2008, Physica Scripta Volume T, 133, 014037
Meléndez, J., Casagrande, L., Ramírez, I., Asplund, M., & Schuster, W. J. 2010, A&A, 515, L3
Richard, O., Michaud, G., & Richer, J. 2005, ApJ, 619, 538
Sbordone, L. et al. 2004, Memorie della Società Astronomica Italiana Supplementi, 5, 93
Sbordone, L. 2005, Memorie della Società Astronomica Italiana Supplementi, 8, 61
Sbordone, L., et al. 2010a, A&A, 522, A26
Sbordone, L., Bonifacio, P., Caffau, E., & Ludwig, H.-G. 2010b, arXiv:1009.5210
Sbordone, L. eta al., 2012a, in preparation
Sbordone, L. eta al., 2012b, in preparation
Schneider, R., Omukai, K., Bianchi, S., & Valiante, R. 2012, MNRAS, 419, 1566
York, D. G., et al. 2000, AJ, 120, 1579

Galactic Archaeology: Near-Field Cosmology and the Formation of the Milky Way
ASP Conference Series, Vol. 458
W. Aoki, M. Ishigaki, T. Suda, T. Tsujimoto, N. Arimoto, eds.
© 2012 Astronomical Society of the Pacific

Binaries in r-Process Enhanced Extremely Metal-Poor Stars: Chemical Tagging in the Early Galactic Halo

J. Andersen[1,2], B. Nordström[1], T. Hansen[1], L. Buchhave[1], T.C. Beers[3]

[1]*Niels Bohr Institute, Juliane Maries Vej 30, DK-2100 Copenhagen, Denmark*

[2]*Nordic Optical Telescope, Apartado 474, ES-38700 Santa Cruz de La Palma, Canarias, Spain*

[3]*Dept. of Physics & Astronomy and JINA, Michigan State University, East Lansing, MI 48824-1116, USA*

Abstract. This poster showed that the frequency and orbital properties of binaries among r−process enhanced EMP stars is normal. Thus, the r−process enhancement has nothing to do with binary evolution or mass exchange, but was imprinted preferentially on some star-forming clouds in the early ISM.

The project described in this poster used precise long-term radial-velocity monitoring to assess the frequency and orbital properties of spectroscopic binaries among r−process enhanced extremely metal-poor (EMP) giant stars. We find both the frequency and the orbital periods and eccentricities of the binaries to be indistinguishable from those of normal giants. This is in contrast to the properties of s-process enhanced metal-poor stars, which are generally found to be long-period binaries with former AGB secondaries.

We conclude from this evidence that the r−process enhancement did not arise locally (i.e. from a binary companion), but was due to strongly non-uniform enrichment in a clumpy, early ISM. This is consistent with the SN II models also discussed at this conference, which were capable of ejecting freshly produced r−process nuclei in strongly collimated jets. This would explain the existence of stars that are enhanced in r−process elements by factors up to ~60 relative to iron and lighter elements, as well as stars that are r−element *poor*, and provides another clue to the astrophysical site of the r process. Further, the r−process enhanced EMP stars trace their birth places in the early Galaxy and demonstrate that binary stars formed already then in a clumpy and chemically inhomogeneous ISM, but with properties just like those of binaries with giant primaries observed today in open clusters of Population I.

This work has now been published in full by Hansen et al. (2011), and we refer to that paper for details.

Acknowledgments. This work is based on observations made with the Nordic Optical Telescope, operated on the island of La Palma jointly by Denmark, Finland, Iceland, Norway, and Sweden, in the Spanish Observatorio del Roque de los Muchachos of the Instituto de Astrofísica de Canarias. We thank the NOT staff and students for help with the observations, and the Danish Natural Science Foundation, the US National Science Foundation, and the Carlsberg Foundation for financial support.

References

Hansen, T., Andersen, J., Nordström, B., Buchhave, L. A., & Beers, T. C. 2011, ApJ, 743, L1

Galactic Archaeology: Near-Field Cosmology and the Formation of the Milky Way
ASP Conference Series, Vol. 458
W. Aoki, M. Ishigaki, T. Suda, T. Tsujimoto, N. Arimoto, eds.
© *2012 Astronomical Society of the Pacific*

Molybdenum Abundances in Metal-Poor Stars

R. C. Peterson

Astrophysical Advances and UCO/Lick

Abstract.   Peterson (2011) has analyzed HST spectra near 2000Å of five metal-poor turnoff stars with mild enhancements of heavy *r*-process elements. Two stars, HD 94028 and HD 160617, are unique in showing an extreme overabundance of the light trans-ironic element molybdenum (Z = 42), but less extreme enhancements of Zr (Z = 40) and Ru (Z = 44). Of several nucleosynthesis scenarios that can produce nuclei in this mass range in the oldest stars, a high-entropy wind (HEW) acting in a core-collapse supernova seems uniquely capable of a high overproduction confined to a narrow mass range. That this unusual elemental distribution is achieved only under very limited physical conditions suggests that very few individual nucleosynthesis events were responsible for the synthesis of the light trans-ironic elements in these stars, even though both are only moderately metal-poor.

Table 1.   Stellar Parameters and Light-Element Abundances Found in This Work

HD	T_{eff}, log g	[Fe/H]	[Eu/Fe]	[Y/Fe]	[Zr/Fe]	[Mo/Fe]	[Ru/Fe]	[La/Fe]
140283	5700, 3.6	−2.6	< −0.9	−0.4	−0.1	+0.2	< +1.0	...
160617	6000, 3.8	−1.8	+0.6	+0.0	+0.4	+0.8	+0.6	+0.24
94028	6050, 4.3	−1.4	+0.3	+0.2	+0.5	+1.0	+0.7	+0.30
76932	5900, 4.1	−0.9	+0.4	+0.0	+0.2	+0.6	+0.4	+0.14
211998	5300, 3.1	−1.5	+0.2	+0.2	+0.5	+0.5	+0.5	−0.06

Units: T_{eff}, K; Z: Eu, 63 (*r*); Zr, 40; Mo, 42; Ru, 44; La, 57 (*s*). From Peterson (2011).

Existing Mo abundance determinations for >20 field and cluster giants with [Eu/Fe] < 0.6 all show [Mo/Fe] < +0.5. To confirm how unusual the HD 94028 and HD 160617 Mo abundances are, we will analyze archival spectra for metal-poor dwarfs cooler than these, in which the same optical Mo I and Ru I lines seen in giants become detectable.

Stellar parameters and abundances were derived by matching each stellar spectral observation to theoretical spectra calculated for each star using the Kurucz SYNTHE program with the stellar models of Castelli & Kurucz. The input line list is founded on Kurucz molecular and laboratory *gfhy* atomic lines, modified by matching calculations such as these to echelle spectra of observed stars over a range of temperature and metallicity. "Missing" lines were added where stars showed additional line absorption, but this is still seriously incomplete below 2000Å. Once this can be addressed, we will assess abundances in the same stars for As, Se, and Sn (Z = 33, 34, and 50) to further constrain HEW and other nucleosynthesis models for light trans-ironic elements.

We are similarly measuring carbon abundances in five turnoff stars with −3.5 < [Fe/H] < −2.2, obtaining HST COS spectra (R ~ 15,000) of the very strong C I 1930.9Å line. Its low excitation (1.26 eV) renders it very insensitive to non-LTE and convective effects. The latter will be assessed from the CH lines near 3144Å in the same stars.

The figure shows comparisons between observed (heavy) and calculated (light) spectra in nine UV and optical regions, indicated by wavelength in Å at the bottom. Each vertically-offset stellar plot shows the star's HD number. Y-axis ticks indicate 10% of the total continuum. The strongest lines are identified at the top. First are the digits following the decimal place of the line center wavelength (in air, except for the first plot). Next is the line species; a colon indicates a "missing" line, here assumed to be Fe I. Following this are the lower excitation potential of the line in eV, and indicator of its strength, and its log gf-value. Three calculations are shown near Mo and Ru lines, adopting the abundance determinations in the table, and 0.3 dex larger/smaller. Red arcs highlight a few calculations in which the line indicated was the only line calculated.

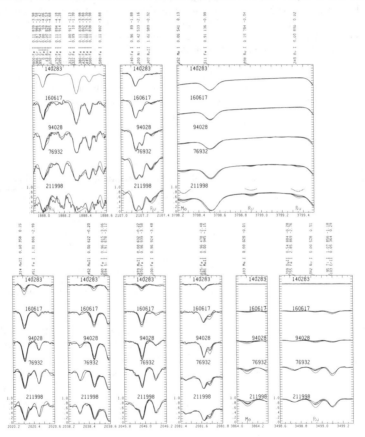

Figure 1.   Comparisons between observed (heavy) and calculated (light) spectra.

References

Peterson, R. C. 2011, ApJ, 742, 21

Galactic Archaeology: Near-Field Cosmology and the Formation of the Milky Way
ASP Conference Series, Vol. 458
W. Aoki, M. Ishigaki, T. Suda, T. Tsujimoto, N. Arimoto, eds.
© *2012 Astronomical Society of the Pacific*

Making Good Use of Bad Weather: Finding Extremely Metal-Poor Stars in the Clouds

Vinicius Placco,[1] Timothy C. Beers,[2,3] Silvia Rossi,[1] Catherine Kennedy,[4] Norbert Christlieb,[5] Young Sun Lee,[2] and Thirupathi Sivarani[6]

[1]*Departamento de Astronomia - Instituto de Astronomia, Geofísica e Ciências Atmosféricas, Universidade de São Paulo, São Paulo, SP 05508-900, Brazil.*

[2]*Department of Physics & Astronomy and JINA: Joint Institute for Nuclear Astrophysics, Michigan State University, East Lansing, MI 48824, USA.*

[3]*National Optical Astronomy Observatory, Tucson, AZ 85719, USA.*

[4]*Research School of Astronomy & Astrophysics, The Australian National University, Mt. Stromlo Observatory, Weston, ACT 2611, Australia.*

[5]*Zentrum für Astronomie der Universität Heidelberg, Landessternwarte, Königstuhl 12, 69117, Heidelberg, Germany.*

[6]*Indian Institute of Astrophysics, Koramangala, Bangalore 560034, India.*

Abstract.
Current results are presented for a new survey effort to search for Extremely Metal-Poor (EMP) and Carbon Enhanced Metal-Poor (CEMP) stars from the Hamburg / ESO objective-prism survey (HES). These stars are important probes of Galactic Chemical Evolution, as they require specific scenarios and conditions for their formation. Recent results infer that their distribution among the various structural components of the Milky Way can also help describe the dynamical process(es) that led to the assembly of our Galaxy.

We have developed a new method to search for metal-poor stars, based on identifying stars with apparently strong molecular CH G-band strengths for their colors. The hypothesis we exploit is that large over-abundances of carbon are common among metal-poor stars, as has been found by numerous studies over the past two decades. Estimates of the stellar atmospheric parameters, as well as carbon abundances, are now available for about 250 of the first candidates, based on follow-up medium-resolution spectra obtained with bad weather GMOS proposals on the Gemini 8m telescopes, and also with the Goodman HTS on the SOAR 4.1m telescope. We have over 5000 candidates, they are reasonably bright ($10<B<16$), and they cover most of the southern sky. Thus, they are perfect to switch to when weather or seeing prevents the execution of other programs. There are 13 newly discovered stars with [Fe/H]<-3.0 in our sample, including four with [Fe/H]<-3.5 and one with [Fe/H]~-4.0. This work is important to provide reliable targets suitable for high-resolution spectroscopy on 8m class telescopes such as Subaru, to determine the detailed abundance patterns of these objects.

1. Background

A number of recent studies have shown that carbon abundance ratios increase for decreasing values of stellar metallicity. This work has made use of this fact in order to identify metal-poor stars based on their level of carbon enhancement, contrasting with earlier studies that used the Can K line strength as a proxy for metallicity.

2. Results and Future Work

To date, our observational effort achieved a ~70% success ratio on the identification of CEMP stars in a wide range of metallicity, aiming to sample the disk and halo systems of the Milky Way. The survey has yielded, so far, ~300 (and counting) new metal-poor stars. Among those, there are 18 EMP stars ([Fe/H] < −3.0) with [C/Fe] > +1.0 and 3 ultra metal-poor ([Fe/H]< −4.0) star candidates, as seen in Figure 1.

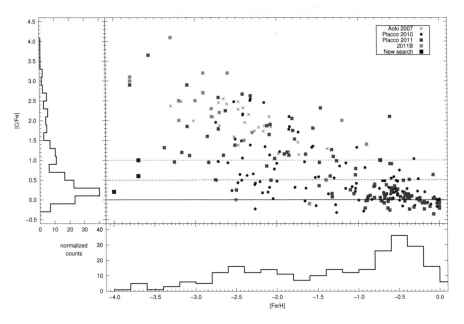

Figure 1.   Carbonicity, [C/Fe], as a function of metallicity for the observed candidates.

This survey is a flexible program, which fits well with bad weather queues, and has the advantage of covering most of the southern sky. As a result, reliable targets are now available for high-resolution follow-up spectroscopy.

Acknowledgments.   V.P. acknowledges hospitality at the Zentrum für Astronomie der Universität Heidelberg, Landessternwarte, during which the visual inspection of the new CEMP candidates took place. V.P. and S.R. acknowledge CNPq, CAPES and FAPESP funding (2010/08996-0). T.C.B., C.K., Y.S.L., and T.S. acknowledge partial support for this work from grants AST 07-07776, PHY 02-15783 and PHY 08-22648; Physics Frontier Center/JINA, awarded by US National Science Foundation.

Galactic Archaeology: Near-Field Cosmology and the Formation of the Milky Way
ASP Conference Series, Vol. 458
W. Aoki, M. Ishigaki, T. Suda, T. Tsujimoto, N. Arimoto, eds.
© *2012 Astronomical Society of the Pacific*

The Scatter of Be Abundances in Extremely Metal-Poor Stars

Rodolfo Smiljanic,[1] Luca Pasquini,[1] and Piercarlo Bonifacio[2]

[1] *ESO, Karl-Schwarzschild-Str. 2, 85748 Garching bei München, Germany*
[2] *GEPI, Observatoire de Paris, CNRS, 92125 Meudon Cedex, France*

Abstract. Beryllium and Fe abundances show a linear relation with a slope very close to one in metal-poor stars. Towards [Fe/H] $\sim$ -3.00, however, there is some evidence that the relation flattens out. This might be an increase in the dispersion or a sign of a possible plateau. We are redetermining Be in a sample of extremely metal-poor stars and preliminary results seem to support an increased scatter below [Fe/H] $\sim$ -3.00. We speculate that in the scenario where Be is a good tracer of time this scatter is an expected feature and reflects the early inhomogeneity of star formation in the Galaxy.

1. Introduction

Beryllium has one stable isotope (^{9}Be) produced by cosmic-ray spallation (Reeves et al. 1970). In the early-Galaxy, it is produced in the collision of accelerated CNO nuclei with protons and α-particles of the ISM. In metal-poor stars, Be abundances show a linear relation with [Fe/H] (see e.g. Smiljanic et al. 2009; Tan et al. 2009).

Considering that cosmic-rays are globally transported across the Galaxy, then the Be production is a widespread process. At a given time, its abundance should have a smaller scatter than the products of stellar nucleosynthesis (such as Fe and O). Thus, Be could be used as a time scale for the early Galaxy (see e.g. Pasquini et al. 2005).

However, at the extremely metal-poor regime the scenario seems to change. Detection of Be in two stars, LP 815-43 and G64-12, with [Fe/H] $\sim$ -3.00 (Primas et al. 2000a,b) suggests a possible flattening of the relation between log(Be/H) and [Fe/H]. Some authors, however, do not find evidence of the flattening (Rich & Boesgaard 2009).

2. Analysis

In this work, we present preliminary Be abundances of 12 stars with [Fe/H] $<$ -2.50, expanding the sample of 73 stars from Smiljanic et al. (2009). We are investigating if the linear relation between Be and Fe breaks down at lower metallicities.

The spectra were obtained with UVES/VLT and reduced with the UVES pipeline within EsoRex. Atmospheric parameters were adopted from the literature or recalculated using $T_{\rm eff}$ obtained with the IRFM (González Hernández & Bonifacio 2009).

Beryllium abundances were derived using spectrum synthesis, with the same codes and line lists used in Smiljanic et al. (2009). For some stars, only upper-limits could be derived. We also derived a (relatively high) upper limit of the Be abundance of star HE1327-2326 with [Fe/H] $=$ -5.40 (Frebel et al. 2005), log(Be/H) $<$ -12.10.

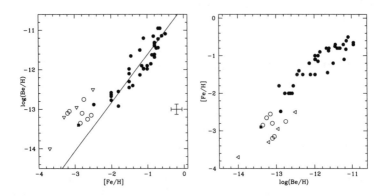

Figure 1.   *Left:* [Fe/H] vs. Be including the metal-poor stars from this work, from Smiljanic et al. (2009) and the star with [Fe/H] = −3.70 from Ito et al. (2009). *Right:* same stars in a plot of [Fe/H] as a function of Be (time). Triangles are upper limits.

3. Discussion

The [Fe/H] vs. log(Be/H) diagram is shown on the right panel of Figure 1. The same plot from a different point of view is seen on the left panel. An increased scatter (or flattening) of the linear relation is seen at low metallicities. At a given Fe these stars have more Be than expected by extending the linear relation to lower metallicities.

We caution however, that the abundances derived here are not in the same scale as the abundances from Smiljanic et al. (2009). A definite answer of whether the scatter is real or not should await the reanalysis of the complete sample in a consistent way.

Nevertheless, in the scenario where Be is time a scatter is easily understood. At a given time in the early-Galaxy, the ISM was enriched in Fe in a non-homogeneous way and stars with different metallicities could be formed simultaneously, therefore with different Fe but similar Be abundances (tracer of time). The linear relation at higher metallicities, with a smaller scatter, seems to indicate that at a later time the ISM became more homogeneous. In this scenario, the flattening/scatter of the relation between [Fe/H] vs. log(Be/H) is nothing but an expected feature.

Acknowledgments.   This research has received funding from the European Community's 7th Framework Programme (FP7/2007-2013) under grant agreement 229517.

References

Frebel, A., Aoki, W., Christlieb, N., et al., 2005, Nat, 434, 871.
González Hernández, J. I., & Bonifacio, P. 2009, A&A, 497, 497.
Ito, H., Aoki, W., Honda, S., & Beers, T. C. 2009, ApJ, 698, L37.
Pasquini, L., Galli, D., Gratton, R. G., et al., 2005, A&A, 436, L57
Primas, F., Asplund, M., Nissen, P. E., & Hill, V. 2000a, A&A, 364, L42.
Primas, F., Molaro, P., Bonifacio, P., & Hill, V. 2000b, A&A, 362, 666.
Reeves, H., Fowler, W. A., & Hoyle, F. 1970, Nat, 226, 727
Rich, J. A., & Boesgaard, A. M. 2009, ApJ, 701, 1519.
Smiljanic, R., Pasquini, L., Bonifacio, P., et al., 2009, A&A, 499, 103.
Tan, K., & Zhao, G. 2011, ApJ, 738, L33+.
Tan, K. F., Shi, J. R., & Zhao, G. 2009, MNRAS, 392, 205.

Galactic Archaeology: Near-Field Cosmology and the Formation of the Milky Way
ASP Conference Series, Vol. 458
W. Aoki, M. Ishigaki, T. Suda, T. Tsujimoto, N. Arimoto, eds.
©2012 Astronomical Society of the Pacific

Effects of Photodissociation on the Fragmentation of Accretion Disk around Proto First Stars

Hajime Susa

Department of Physics, Konan University

Abstract. Very recently, the final stages of the first star formation have been investigated intensively. At such stages, an accretion disk is formed around the very first seed of a proto-star, and they seem to fragment inevitably. As a result, it might be possible for sub-solar mass first stars to form from such fragments. However, most of the previous numerical studies did not include the effects of photodissociating radiation from the first proto-stars, which could suppress the fragmentation of the disk. In this paper we include the transfer of Lyman-Werner photons to assess the effects of photodissociation on the fragmentation of the accretion disk. Consequently, we find that the dissociating radiation tends to suppress the mass accretion, but it cannot quench the fragmentation process.

1. Mass of First Stars

The typical mass and the initial mass function of the first stars are the key quantities to understand the cosmic dawn. Theoretical efforts in the last decade revealed that those stars are more massive than the stars forming in the present-day galaxies. A few years before, it was believed that they are very massive ($> 100 M_\odot$), however, recent numerical simulations using the sink particle technique claim that they could be $O(10) M_\odot$, and they form as a member of a multiple stellar system (Clark et al. 2011). On the other hand, recent two dimensional radiative hydrodynamics simulations revealed that radiative feedback from the proto-first stars are quite important to quench the mass accretion onto the proto-star (Hosokawa et al. 2011). In paper, we combine the radiative feedback effects and the three dimensional effects, in order to find the physical effects these processes on the fragmentation of the accreting gas disk and the final mass of the first stars. For this purpose, we perform numerical experiments using RSPH code develpoed by ourselves (Susa 2006, 2011). We set the the initial condition of the collapsing cloud to be the Bonner-Evert sphere with $10^4 \mathrm{cm}^{-3}$ / 200K, at the "loitering" phase of the collapsing primordial prestellar cloud. We add rigid rotation with $\Omega = 10^{-14} \mathrm{s}^{-1}$ or $2 \times 10^{-14} \mathrm{s}^{-1}$, those are comparable to the rotation in cosmological simulations.

2. Numerical Results

Two panels in Figure 1 show the edge-on views of the gas disk around the proto-stars at two epochs with $\Omega = 10^{-14} \mathrm{s}^{-1}$. At later epoch (right panel), the polar region of the gas disk is highly dissociated by the radiation from the sink particles. It is also

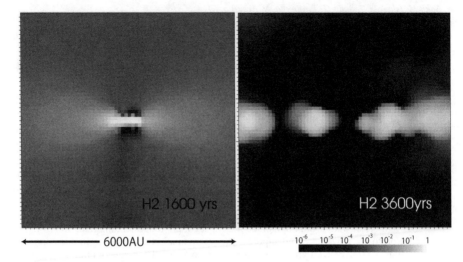

Figure 1.   (color online) Edge-on view of the gas disk around the first sink at two
epochs. Contour shows the fraction of H_2 molecules.

worth noting that dissociated region is heated up to $7000 - 8000$K, due to the accretion
shocks and the chemical heating. We emphasize the importance of the H_2 formation
heating in the photodissociated region, since H_2 dissociation cooling is negligible in
such environments, which almost cancels the H_2 formation heating in the absence of
photodissociating radiation.

The "heated bubble" by the absence of coolant and chemical heating by photodissociation reduces the mass accretion onto the sink particles. In fact, the total accreted
mass after 6000 yrs is $\sim 30\%$ smaller than the mass without radiative feedback. Thus,
the photodissociation is one of the important effects to control the final mass of the first
stars. However, we also found that it cannot quench the fragmentation of the gas disks.
We observe the fragmentation of the disk for all runs we perform, and the numbers of
the sink particles are several$\sim$ 10. We also found that a few sinks are kicked away from
the central part of the host gas cloud via the gravitational three-body interaction. As a
result, the mass accretion onto these sinks basically shut-off. We find that the some of
these sinks do not grow larger than $0.8 M_\odot$. If we regard these sink particles as "stars",
we might be able to find the "real first stars" in our Galactic halo.

Acknowledgments.   This work was supported by Ministry of Education, Science,
Sports and Culture, Grant-in-Aid for Scientific Research (C), 22540295.

References

Clark, P. C., Glover, S. C. O., Smith, R. J., Greif, T. H., Klessen, R. S., & Bromm, V. 2011,
        Science, 331, 1040. 1101.5284
Hosokawa, T., Omukai, K., Yoshida, N., & Yorke, H. W. 2011, Science, 334, 1250. 1111.3649
Susa, H. 2006, PASJ, 58, 445. arXiv:astro-ph/0601642
— 2011, in Computational Star Formation, edited by J. Alves, B. G. Elmegreen, J. M. Girart,
        & V. Trimble, vol. 270 of IAU Symposium, 195

Galactic Archaeology: Near-Field Cosmology and the Formation of the Milky Way
ASP Conference Series, Vol. 458
W. Aoki, M. Ishigaki, T. Suda, T. Tsujimoto, N. Arimoto, eds.
©*2012 Astronomical Society of the Pacific*

Behavior of [S/Fe] Obtained from Near-IR S I Lines at 10456–9 Å

Masahide Takada-Hidai,[1] and Yoichi Takeda[2]

[1]*Liberal Arts Education Center, Tokai University, Hiratsuka, Japan*

[2]*NAOJ, Mitaka, Tokyo, Japan*

Abstract.   Behavior of [S/Fe] was examined based on near-IR S I 10456–9 Å lines observed with the Subaru IRCS+AO188. We found that the behavior of their [S/Fe] shows a flat trend in the range of [Fe/H]< −1, which is consistent with that of [S/Fe] obtained from 9212–28–37 Å lines. The full papers of this presentation are published in Takeda & Takada-Hidai (2011, 2012).

1. Introduction

Sulfur (S) is one of α elements, whose abundances in very metal-poor stars play a key role for the Galactic chemical evolution. S is also one of volatile elements with its low condensation temperature $T_c = 650$ K, which deplete very little into dust, so that S abundances may be more reliable probe for the α-chemistry than other refractory α elements. Behaviors of [S/Fe] have been studied for the past decade based on two indicators of S I (6) 8694 Å and S I (1) 9212–28–37 Ålines: the former suggests an increasing trend with decreasing [Fe/H] (cf. Israelian & Rebolo 2001, Takada-Hidai et al. 2002), but the latter shows a flat trend with supersolar value in the range [Fe/H]< −1 (eg. Nissen et al. 2007).

2. Purpose

To clarify the [S/Fe] behavior of the third indicator of S I (3) 10456–9 Å lines, and try to settle the controversial situation of S behavior, S I (3) lines are analyzed based on the spectra observed with IRCS) + AO188 system of the Subaru telescope.

3. Observations

Our observations were carried out for the sample stars with metallicity of −4 <[Fe/H] < +0.5: 33 stars observed in 2009 July 29–30 (UT) and 13 stars and the minor planet Vesta in 2011 August 17–18 (UT). High dispersion spectra were obtained in the *zJ*-band with the echelle spectrograph mode of IRCS by using a slit width of 0.14" to accomplish a resolution of $R \simeq 20000$. The $S/N = 100 - 500$ were achieved around S I 10456 Å lines, and some examples of observed spectra are shown in Figure 1.

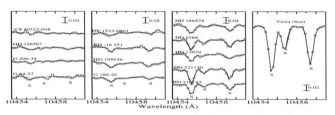

Figure 1.   Examples of observed spectra (red curve) and synthetic spectra (blue curve) of S I lines.

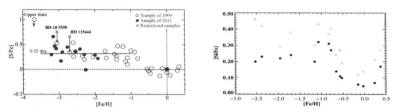

Figure 2.   *Left*: Fig. 2a. Behavior of [S/Fe]. *Right*: Fig. 2b. Behaviors of [Si/Fe] derived from LTE (o) and Non-LTE (•) analyses.

4.   Abundance Analysis

Non-LTE spectrum synthesis (Takeda 1995) was applied to abundance analyses, based on model atmospheres of ATLAS9 (Kurucz 1993). S abundances were derived by fitting synthetic spectra to observed ones as shown in Fig.1.

5.   Results and Discussion

The [S/Fe] values obtained for the samples are demonstrated in Figure 2a. Figure 2a reveals the following results: (1) In the range of -1 <[Fe/H]< 0, [S/Fe] increases with decreasing [Fe/H], which is consistent with the behaviors of [α/Fe] of other refractory elements. As an example, the behavior of [Si/Fe] is shown in Figure 2b, which was analyzed for a part of our sample stars, based on Non-LTE analysis of near-IR Si I lines by Shi et al.(2012). (2) In the range of [Fe/H] < -1, [S/Fe] shows a flat trend with a supersolar value of 0.32 dex, which is consistent with that observed in [S/Fe] based on S I (1) 9212–37 lines in the previous studies (eg. Nissen et al 2007; Spite et al. 2011).

References

Israelian, G. & Rebolo, R. 2001, ApJ, 557, L43
Kurucz, R.L. 1993, CD-Rom No. 13
Nissen, P.E. et al. 2007, A&A, 469, 319
Shi, J.R. et al. 2012 submitted to ApJ
Spite, M. et al. 2011, A&A, 528, A9
Takada-Hidai, M. et al. 2002, ApJ, 573, 614
Takeda, Y. 1995, PASJ, 47, 287
Takeda, Y. & Takada-Hidai, M. 2011, PASJ, 63, S537; 2012, PASJ, 64, No.3 in press.

Part III

Chemical Evolution

Galactic Archaeology: Near-Field Cosmology and the Formation of the Milky Way
ASP Conference Series, Vol. 458
W. Aoki, M. Ishigaki, T. Suda, T. Tsujimoto, N. Arimoto, eds.
©*2012 Astronomical Society of the Pacific*

Stellar-Mass Metallicity Relation at $z \sim 1.4$

K. Ohta,[1] K. Yabe,[1] F. Iwamuro, [1] S. Yuma,[1] M. Akiyama, [2] N. Tamura,[3] and FMOS team

[1]*Department of Astronomy, Kyoto University, Kyoto 606-8502, Japan*

[2]*Astronomical Institute, Tohoku University, Sendai 980-8578, Japan*

[3]*Subaru Telescope, National Astronomical Observatory of Japan, Hilo, HI 96720, USA*

Abstract. With Fibre Multi-Object Spectrograph on the Subaru Telescope, we obtained gas metallicity for $\sim$ 70 star-forming galaxies at $z \sim 1.4$. The sample galaxies are selected from objects with $K < 23.9(\text{AB})$ mag in the SXDS/UDS field. Among them, galaxies with $M_{\text{star}} > 10^{9.5} M_{\odot}$ at $1.2 < z_{\text{ph}} < 1.6$ and with expected Hα flux larger than 1×10^{-16} erg s^{-1} cm^{-2} were observed. We derived a mass-metallicity relation at the redshift and found the relation locates between those previously obtained at $z \sim 0.8$ and at $z \sim 2.2$. The shape of the relation is similar to those at other redshifts, showing a smooth evolution of mass-metallicity relations from $\sim$ 3 to $\sim$ 0.1, except for a very massive part at $z \sim 0.1$. The metallicity distribution of the galaxies at a fixed stellar mass, however, shows a significant scatter around the relation. The estimated intrinsic scatter is $\sim$ 0.1 dex or larger. We examined the cause for the scatter and found the trends that the metallicity is lower for the galaxies with larger star-formation rates and larger sizes. Our data points show a large scatter with respect to the Fundamental Metallicity Relation (FMR) obtained at $z \sim 0.1$, but the average metallicity is close to the FMR with a small offset.

1. Introduction

Tracing cosmological chemical evolution of galaxies is one of keys to understand evolution of galaxies as well as the Milky Way galaxy. For example, Lilly et al. (2003) confronted a cosmological chemical evolution of galaxies up to $z \sim 3$ (at $z \sim 0$, $\sim 0.5 - 1.0$, and ~ 3) with age-metallicity relation for the Galactic disk stars(Twarog 1980). The shape of the evolution track is similar each other with lower metallicity for the Galactic stars.

Meanwhile, gas metallicity depends on a galaxy stellar mass, which is known as 'mass-metallicity relation'; i.e., more massive (in stellar mass) galaxies tend to show higher gas metallicity. The relation is established at $z \sim 0.1$ with $\sim$53,000 star-forming galaxies obtained with SDSS (Tremonti et al. 2004). After that, a mass-metallicity relation was obtained at $z \sim 0.7$ with $\sim$56 star-forming galaxies (Savaglio et al. 2005), at $z \sim 2.2$ with $\sim$ 90 galaxies (Erb et al. 2006), and at $z \sim 3$ with $\sim$ 20 galaxies (Maiolino et al. 2008; Mannucci et al. 2009). These relations show smooth evolution of the mass-metallicity relation.

The mass-metallicity relation has an intrinsic scatter around the relation. The scatter is about 0.1 dex at $z \sim 0.1$ (Tremonti et al. 2004). This intrinsic scatter should reflect processes of galaxy evolution (star-formation history, gas inflow/outflow in a galaxy, etc), and thus studying the amount of scatter and its cause(s) is very important to understand how galaxy evolves and how mass-metallicity relation evolves. However, to examine the amount and dependence of the scatter, a large number of sample galaxies is required and it is very hard to achieve it at high redshifts, hence almost no such works have been made.

The cosmic star-formation history is recently considered to be the highest at $z \sim 2$. Since metals are produced through star formation, studies of chemical evolution at the epoch and slightly later epoch are indispensable. This epoch is further intriguing, because AGN activity also showed its peak around at $z \sim 2$, and galaxy morphology such as Hubble sequence was emerged in the period. Therefore, the redshift of $1 \sim 2$ was the most violent epoch of the galaxy evolution. Although studies of galaxies at the epoch with respect to stellar mass and star-formation rate (or specific star-formation rate) have been made extensively, revealing chemical properties of star-forming galaxies is not progressed so much. In order to know chemical properties of galaxies in the violent epoch, a large spectroscopic survey for star-forming galaxies is necessary. However, the redshift range is so called 'redshift desert', and it is almost impossible to conduct an optical spectroscopic survey. NIR spectroscopy is inevitable for the studies. The multiplicity of NIR spectrographs currently available are, however, still very limited. Fibre Multi-Object Spectrograph (FMOS) on the Subaru telescope now enables us to make a large NIR spectroscopic survey thanks to its very large multiplicity; 400 fibres in a 30′ field of view (Kimura et al. 2010). Here we report initial results obtained mainly during FMOS GTO runs. Full details will be published (Yabe et al. 2011), and we are enlarging the sample.

2. Sample

The primary sample is selected as galaxies with $K_{AB} < 23.9$ mag and $M_{star} > 10^{9.5} M_{\odot}$ at $1.2 < z_{ph} < 1.6$ in the SXDS/UDS field. The redshift range is set to detect Hα and [NII]6548/6584 emission lines as well as Hβ and [OIII]4959/5007 emission lines simultaneously with FMOS. The number of the sample galaxies is huge and a certain fraction of them would not show an Hα emission line strong enough to be detected. Thus a spectroscopic survey with this sample is unrealistic. Thus we introduce a criterion: the expected Hα emission flux is larger than 1×10^{-16} erg s^{-1} cm^{-2}. The expected Hα flux is calculated as follows: intrinsic Hα luminosity is derived from a star-formation rate based on its UV luminosity after correcting for the extinction from UV continuum slope, then with the extinction for the nebular emission line an apparent Hα luminosity is calculated. This obviously introduces a bias to the sample; we examined this effect based on the results obtained and found that the bias does not affect significantly and does not change conclusions. The sample constructed (secondary sample) is still very large and thus we randomly selected target galaxies from the secondary sample. The final number of galaxies observed was about 300.

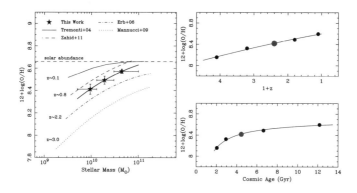

Figure 1.   *Left:* Mass-metallicity relation derived by stacking analysis (stars). Also shown are the relations derived at other redshifts: solid curve at $z \sim 0.1$ (Tremonti et al. 2004), dashed curve at $z \sim 0.8$ (Zahid et al. 2011), dot-dashed curve at $z \sim 2.2$. (Erb et al. 2006), and dotted curve at $z \sim 3$ (Mannucci et al. 2009). *Right:* Cosmological chemical evolution traced at $M_{star} = 10^{10}M_{\odot}$. Solid curve shows $12+\log(O/H)= 8.69 - 0.086(1 + z)^{1.3}$.

3. Observations and Data Reduction

Observations were mostly carried out during the period from September 2010 to December 2010 as GTO runs with FMOS. We used the low-resolution mode ($R = 500 \sim 800$) covering a wavelength region from $\sim 1\mu$m to $\sim 1.8\mu$m, and employed the cross-beam switch mode (up to 200 objects can be observed simultaneously). A typical exposure time on each target was about 3 hours in total.

The data reduction was made by using 'FIBRE-pac', which was developed as the reduction tool for FMOS data based on IRAF (Iwamuro et al. 2011).

For 71 objects, we detected Hα emission lines significantly. After extracting spectrum for each object, we determined a redshift, flux, and line width for the emission lines detected by considering the effect of OH masks in the spectrograph. We use spectroscopic redshifts hereafter and all the quantities (stellar mass, luminosity, etc) are calculated using z_{spec}.

4. Metallicity and Mass-Metallicity Relation

Gas metallicity (12+log O/H) was derived from the ratio of the Hα emission and [NII]6584 emission based on a calibration by Pettini & Pagel (2004). Before getting gas metallicity, we excluded objects showing AGN nature by inspecting [OIII]5007/Hβ and [NII]6584/Hα for some objects for which these lines were detected. We only obtained upper limits on [NII] lines (and Hβ and [OIII]5007) for a fraction of the galaxies. Thus we also examined the stacked spectrum of all the objects and confirmed the line ratios are consistent with those for star-forming galaxies. (X-ray sources were already discarded before the sample selection.)

Resulting mass-metallicity relation obtained by stacking analysis is shown in Figure 1 together with those at other redshifts. Differences of the metallicity calibrations were corrected following the method by Kewley & Ellison (2008), and the stellar

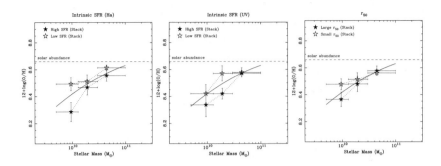

Figure 2.   Mass-metallicity relations for two subsamples. *Left:* Subsample with larger SFR derived from Hα luminosity after correcting for the extinction at each mass bin is shown by filled stars, while with smaller SFR with open stars. *Middle:* The same as left panel, but SFR is derived from rest-UV luminosity density (extinction corrected). *Right:* Subsample with larger half-light radius at each mass bin is shown by filled stars, while with smaller size with open stars.

masses were converted to base the same IMF. The mass-metallicity relation we obtained locates between $z \sim 0.8$ and ~ 2.2, and the smooth cosmological evolution can be seen from $z \sim 3$ to ~ 0.1 without changing shape, except for the massive part at $z \sim 0.1$, where this metallicity indicator may saturate.

Motivated by this smooth evolution, we quantify the cosmic evolution of the metallicity at $M_{\rm star} = 1.0 \times 10^{10} M_{\odot}$. The chemical evolution is described as $12+\log(\mathrm{O/H})= 8.69 - 0.086(1+z)^{1.3}$, and shown in Figure 1 with solid curve. The gas metallicity grew rapidly from $z \sim 2.2$ (cosmic age of ~ 2 Gyr) to $z \sim 1.4$ (cosmic age of ~ 4 Gyr), then the evolution became very slow. We should note here although we corrected for the differences of metallicity calibration and IMF, the sample selection at each redshift is not necessarily the same and hence we cannot rule out the possibility that the sample selection causes a systematic difference in metallicity distribution. Nevertheless, we try to plot a data point at $z \sim 5$ (cosmic age of ~ 1 Gyr) in Figure 1. If we take an average location for $z \sim 5$ LBGs in mass-metallicity relation by Ando et al. (2007), the metallicity comes at ~ 7.5, suggesting a very rapid increase at the higher redshifts. (But the metallicity calibration is not based on Hα/[NII]6584 ratio, and no correction was applied.)

5.   The Second Parameter for the Mass-Metallicity Relation

The gas metallicity against stellar mass of individual object shows significant scatter around the mass-metallicity relation, even if we consider the errors. We estimated an intrinsic scatter at each mass bin and found the scatter of ~ 0.1 dex. The values are comparable to those at $z \sim 0.1$ and the scatter is getting smaller in the more massive part. The values calculated here, however, include upper limits on the metallicity. Therefore the scatters estimated should be regarded as lower limits and it is very likely that the real scatters are larger at $z \sim 1.4$ than those at $z \sim 0.1$.

In order to investigate cause(s) of the scatter, we divided the sample into two subsamples according to a parameter such as an extinction corrected star-formation

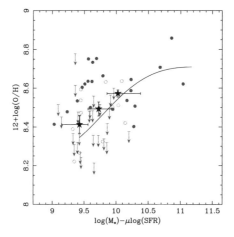

Figure 3.   Data points of our sample in three dimensional space of stellar mass, metallicity, and SFR with a viewing angle proposed by Mannucci et al. (2010) (FMR). An arrow refers to an upper limit on metallicity. Filled stars indicate stacking analysis. Solid curve shows FMR by Mannucci et al. (2010).

rate(SFR). No clear trend against the metallicity is seen with respect to SFR; galaxies with larger SFR tend to show larger stellar-mass, but this is a reflection that larger SFR is seen in more massive galaxies and massive galaxies tend to show higher metallicity. Thus we divided the sample at each stellar-mass bin. Then, it is found that galaxies with larger SFR derived from $H\alpha$ luminosity tend to show lower metallicity in a stellar-mass bin as shown in Figure 2 (left panel). This trend can also be seen if we use SFR from UV luminosity density (Figure 2 (middle panel)). Similar trend is seen among $z \sim 0.1$ galaxies from SDSS data (Mannucci et al. 2010; Yates et al. 2011), though the range of SFR covered is different; our sample covers much larger SFRs than those in SDSS sample.

Mannucci et al. (2010) claimed the presence of the fundamental metallicity relation (FMR) at $z \sim 0.1$. When the galaxy data points in the three-dimensional space with respect to stellar mass, gas metallicity, and SFR, are seen with a certain viewing angle, they make a smooth curved surface. We plot our data points at $z \sim 1.4$ in Figure 3 with the same viewing angle by Mannucci et al. (2010). (An arrow shows an upper limit on metallicity.) As seen in the figure, the data points do not make a clear surface, but show a large scatter even if we consider the error for the metallicity; no fundamental surface can be seen. If we see the stacked data points shown by filled stars, the points are close to the proposed surface (FMR) shown as solid curve with a slight offset. We note again the SFRs of our sample are larger than those covered with SDSS galaxies.

We also examined the size dependence on the metallicity. Half-light radii of the sample galaxies were measured with K-band images; we confirmed the measurement is accurate within $\sim 10\%$ using a sub-sample resides in CANDELS FoV in UDS. We found a trend that a larger galaxy shows lower metallicity at a fixed stellar mass as shown in Figure2 (right panel). This trend is also reported in local galaxies (e.g., Ellison et al. (2008)).

Although our results have firstly indicated the presence of such trends at high redshift, the significance is not very clear (especially at some mass bins), and we need to confirm these trends with a larger sample. But it is interesting to discuss the origin of these trends. One possibility is that infall of pristine gas onto a galaxy or a merge of a metal poor galaxy. These could dilute the metallicity of the gas presented in the galaxy. Meanwhile since a large amount of gas is supplied to the galaxy, star formation could activate. Then it is likely a galaxy with a larger SFR tends to show lower metallicity. The infall and/or merge could also affect the kinematic structure of the galaxy; the galaxy could be turbulented with these events and its size may increase. We inspected the sign of interaction or merge for the target galaxies, but at this moment we could not find any clear evidence that galaxies with larger SFR and larger size tend to show sign of galaxy interaction.

Acknowledgments.   We appreciate coauthors of the paper by Yabe et al. (2011). KO's activity is supported by the grant-in-aid for Scientific Research on Priority Areas (19047003).

References

Ando, M., Ohta, K., Iwata, I., Akiyama, M., Aoki, K., & Tamura, N. 2007, PASJ, 59, 717
Ellison, S. L., Patton, D. R., Simard, L., & McConnachie, A. W. 2008, ApJ, 672, L107
Erb, D. K., et al. 2006, ApJ, 644, 813
Iwamuro, F., et al. 2011, PASJ, in press. arXiv:1111.6746
Kewley, L. J., & Ellison, S. L. 2008, ApJ, 681, 1183
Kimura, M., et al. 2010, PASJ, 62, 1135
Lilly, S. J., Carollo, C. M., & Stockton, A. N. 2003, ApJ, 597, 730
Maiolino, R., et al. 2008, A&A, 488, 463
Mannucci, F., Cresci, G., Maiolino, R., Marconi, A., & Gnerucci, A. 2010, MNRAS, 408, 2115
Mannucci, F., et al. 2009, MNRAS, 398, 1915
Pettini, M., & Pagel, B. E. J. 2004, MNRAS, 348, L59
Savaglio, S., et al. 2005, ApJ, 635, 260
Tremonti, C. A., et al. 2004, ApJ, 613, 898
Twarog, B. A. 1980, ApJ, 242, 242
Yabe, K., et al. 2011, in press. arXiv:1112.3704
Yates, R. M., Kauffmann, G., & Guo, Q. 2011. arXiv:1107.3145
Zahid, H. J., Kewley, L. J., & Bresolin, F. 2011, ApJ, 730, 137

Galactic Archaeology: Near-Field Cosmology and the Formation of the Milky Way
ASP Conference Series, Vol. 458
W. Aoki, M. Ishigaki, T. Suda, T. Tsujimoto, N. Arimoto, eds.
© *2012 Astronomical Society of the Pacific*

Dust Lifecycle and Processing in the Interstellar Medium

Takashi Onaka,[1] Hidehiro Kaneda,[2] Itsuki Sakon,[1] Ryou Ohsawa,[1]
Tamami I. Mori,[1] Bon-Chul Koo,[3] and Ji Yeon Seok[3]

[1]*Department of Astronomy, University of Tokyo, Tokyo 113-0033, Japan*

[2]*Graduate School of Science, Nagoya University, Nagoya 464-8602, Japan*

[3]*Department of Physics and Astronomy, Seoul National University, Seoul 151-742, Korea*

Abstract.   Material circulation in the interstellar space plays a crucial role in the evolution of the universe. Recent space infrared observations have revolutionized the view of interstellar dust grains and their lifecycle. The presence of dust grains outside of the galactic disk has been indicated for several galaxies. Dust formation and processing in supernovae becomes an important topic for the understanding of dust sources in the early universe. This presentation reviews processing of dust grains in the various environments in the ISM of our Galaxy and external galaxies based on recent infrared observations with the Japanese infrared satellite *AKARI* .

1. Introduction

Interstellar matter evolves through a phase transition between gas and solid (e.g., Tielens 2005; Onaka et al. 2009a). Heavy elements are synthesized in stellar interior and ejected to the interstellar medium (ISM) via mass-loss from evolved low-mass stars or supernova explosions. Part of the ejected elements condense into dust grains. Grains are processed in the ISM and become seeds for next-generation stars in dense clouds. Dust grains are incorporated into newly-born stars or evaporated in protoplanetary disks as young stars grow. In every process of this material circulation in the ISM, dust grains play crucial roles and thus infrared observations of their emission are the key means to understand the material evolution in the universe. However, only very limited information has been obtained observationally for the dust lifecycle until recently.

In the last 10 years several infrared satellites, such as *Spitzer* (Werner et al. 2004), *AKARI* (Murakami et al. 2007), and *Herschel* (Pilbratt et al. 2010), have been put on orbits and have been giving us new insights into the dust lifecycle. This paper reviews latest results of the dust processing based on observations with the *AKARI* satellite.

AKARI is the first Japanese satellite mission fully dedicated to infrared astronomy (Murakami et al. 2007). It was launched in February, 2006. It had a 70-cm cooled telescope and two focal-plane instruments, Far-Infrared Surveyor (FIS: Kawada et al. 2007) and the Infrared Camera (IRC: Onaka et al. 2007). It was cooled by 180-liter liquid helium and mechanical coolers. The cryogen lasted until August, 2007. During the cold mission phase, an all-sky survey was carried out at 9, 18, 65, 90, 140, and 160 μm together with a number of deep pointed observations. The mid-infrared (MIR) part of the all-sky survey is described in Ishihara et al. (2010). Even after the exhaustion of the cryogen, the telescope system was kept at temperatures low enough to continue near-infrared (NIR) imaging and spectroscopic observations (Onaka et al. 2010a). Some of the early results of *AKARI* observations are reported in Onaka et al. (2009c).

2. Processing of Carbonaceous Dust

The Unidentified Infrared (UIR) bands are emission bands ubiquitously seen in the ISM. The major features appear at 3.3, 3.4, 6.2, 7.7, 8.6, and 11.3 μm (e.g., Onaka et al. 2008). The band carriers are thought to be materials related to polycyclic aromatic hydrocarbons (PAH; Tielens 2008) or carbonaceous materials with aromatic and aliphatic bonds (Kwok & Zhang 2011). Since they are conspicuous features in the IR and each band feature is assigned to a specific vibration mode of C-C or C-H, the physical properties and conditions of the carriers can be investigated efficiently with IR spectroscopy of the UIR bands. The carriers are thought to be the smallest members of dust grains and should be very vulnerable to harsh conditions in the ISM. Hence their spectral appearance is a good indicator of dust processing. However the formation sites and detailed processing of the carriers in various environments still remain uncertain.

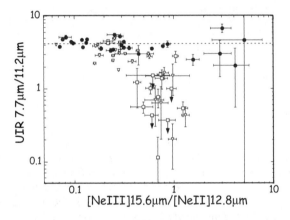

Figure 1.   Band intensity ratio of the UIR 7.7 to 11.3 μm against the line ratio of [NeIII]15.6 μm/[NeII]12.8 μm (Onaka et al. 2008). The SINGS galaxy data are taken from Smith et al. (2007). The filled circles indicate those with HII-dominated nuclei and the open triangles plot those with low-luminosity AGNs. Elliptical galaxies from Kaneda et al. (2008) are indicated by the open squares. The dotted line shows the median of the HII-dominated galaxies.

The ratios of the UIR band intensities have been known to stay relatively constant in the diffuse Galactic radiation (Onaka 2000). Very recently Mori et al. (2012, and this volume) show variations in the ratios of the NIR to MIR UIR bands in the diffuse emission from the Large Magellanic Cloud, suggesting the paucity or possible destruction of small band carriers in ionized regions. The amplitudes of the variations in the LMC are, however, still only a factor of several. The extreme case of the variation is seen in elliptical galaxies (Kaneda et al. 2005, 2008), which show very weak or almost absent 6.2 and 7.7 μm bands relative to the 11.3 μm band. Figure 1 shows the 7.7 to

11.3 µm band ratio against the [NeIII]15.6 µm/[N2II]12.8 µm for star-forming and elliptical galaxies (Onaka et al. 2008), which clearly indicates that elliptical galaxies have different ratios of 7.7 to 11.3 µm band intensities from star-burst galaxies.

Recent *Spitzer* and *AKARI* observations reveal the presence of dust grains in the outflow or halo of galaxies (e.g., Engelbracht et al. 2006; Kaneda et al. 2009, 2010). Onaka et al. (2010b) indicate the presence of the UIR bands in a Hα filament of the dwarf star-burst galaxy NGC1569 based on its 7 µm (S7) band image ,which covers the strong 6.2 and 7.7 µm UIR bands entirely and thus is efficient to trace the UIR band emission (Fig. 2, Onaka et al. 2009b). The presence of the UIR bands in the filament has been confirmed by subsequent spectroscopic observations. The filament is thought to be formed by the outflow triggered by strong star-burst activity in the galaxy disk. Its age is estimated from the flow velocity and the size of the filament as 5.3 Myr, while the expected life time of the band carriers against thermal sputtering is less than 1×10^3 yr according to the latest theoretical estimate (Micelotta et al. 2010). Since there are no efficient stellar sources that supply the band carriers, we suggest that the band carriers may be formed *in situ* in the filament by the fragmentation from large carbonaceous grains. The UIR band spectrum of the filament taken with the IRC is compared with that of the galaxy disk taken with the Infrared Spectrograph (IRS) onboard *Spitzer*, indicating that the 7.7 to 11.3 µm band ratio in the disk is 3.5 ± 0.2, being in agreement with those of the star-burst galaxies, while that of the filament is 1.5 ± 0.3, clearly small and in the range of elliptical galaxies (Fig. 1). Whether or not the low band ratios in the filament and elliptical galaxies have the same origin is an interesting question, which needs to be addressed by future investigations.

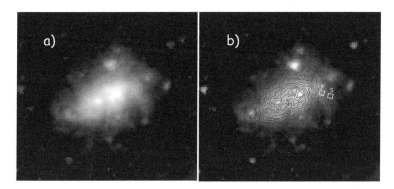

Figure 2.   (color online) a) Artificial 3-color image of NGC1569 taken with the IRC onboard *AKARI* (Onaka et al. 2010b): N4 (4.1 µm) band in in blue, S7 (7 µm) in green, and L15 (15 µm) in red. b) S7 image of NGC1569 superimposed with contours of the Hα emission. The Hα data (Hunter & Elmegreen 2004) were taken from the NASA/IPAC Extragalactic Database (NED). The white boxes indicate the positions where the IRC spectroscopy was carried out (Onaka et al. 2010b).

The *AKARI*/IRC provides sensitive spectroscopy in 2–5 µm and enables detailed studies of the UIR bands in the 3 µm region (e.g., 3.3, 3.4, and 3.5 µm bands) in various objects for the first time. Seok et al. (2012) report detection of the 3.3 µm UIR band in the supernova remnant (SNR) N49 based on the IRC spectroscopy (Fig. 3). This is the first detection of the 3.3 µm band in SNRs. The band is expected to originate from the smallest members of the band carriers (e.g., Mori et al. 2012) and thus is thought to be destroyed quickly in harsh environments, such as SNRs (e.g., Micelotta et al. 2010). N49 is an old SNR ($\sim$ 6600 yr) and the shock velocity with which it interacts with the surrounding ISM is not large ($\sim$ 100 km s^{-1}). With this velocity small band carriers are not preferentially destroyed (Micelotta et al. 2010), and we again suggest that the carriers may rather be formed by the fragmentation of large carbonaceous grains in the interacting ISM. This result suggests that SNRs not only destroy dust grains, but also produce the UIR band carriers, contributing significantly to processing of dust grains.

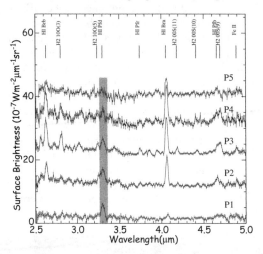

Figure 3.   IRC NIR spectra of the SNR N49 at various positions (see Seok et al. (2012) for details). The UIR band at 3.3 μm (indicated by a hatch) is seen in the spectra of most positions. The identification of the detected lines are indicated.

3. Processing of Silicate Grains

Very little is known observationally about processing of silicate dust compared to small carbonaceous grains in the ISM. Silicates have characteristic bands at 10 and 18 μm. In the ISM and circumstellar regions of stars, they show broad profiles without fine structures, suggesting the amorphous nature of silicate grains in the ISM (e.g., Onaka et al. 1989; Kemper et al. 2004). Crystalline silicates, characterized by fine structures, have been detected in dusty AGB stars, comets, Herbig Ae/Be stars, and luminous blue variables (LBVs) by observations with the *Infrared Space Observatory* (Waters et al. 1996; Crovisier et al. 1997; Malfait et al. 1998; Voors et al. 1999). Crystalline silicates are thought to be amorphized by cosmic-ray hits in the ISM (Bringa et al. 2007), while amorphous silicate grains are crystallized in protoplanetary disks (e.g., Ábrahám et al. 2009). Crystallization is an important sign of processing of silicate grains.

Recently Koo et al. (2011) report *AKARI* and *Spitzer* observations of the SNR MSH15-52, which show very prominent extended structures in the MIR (Fig. 4). Further spectroscopic observations of the central source IRAS 15099–5856 with the IRS clearly indicate the presence of crystalline silicates. This is the first detection of crystalline silicates associated with SNRs. Since the SNR is associated with intense extended X-ray emission and the SN blast wave efficiently destroys dust grains, Koo et al. (2011) propose a scenario that the crystalline silicates originate in a mass outflow from the progenitor of the SNR MSH15-52, which is in a close binary system and shielded from the SN blast wave by the companion. The results indicate that SNe or their progenitors could be an important source of crystalline silicates in the ISM.

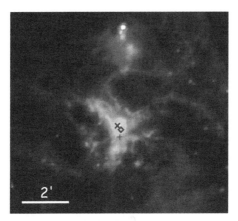

Figure 4.   (color online) Three-color artificial image of IRAS 15099-5856 produced from *AKARI*/IRC observations (Koo et al. 2011). The S7 (7 μm) band is in blue, L15 (15 μm) in green, and L24 (24 μm) in red. North is up and east is left. The cross indicates the central compact infrared source IRS1, the plus marks the pulsar B1509-58, and the diamond shows the O star Muzzio 10. See Koo et al. (2011) for details.

4.   Summary

Recent space infrared observations give us a quite new view of interstellar dust grains and their lifecycle. *AKARI* and *Spitzer* observations reveal the presence of dust grains outside of the galactic disk in several galaxies. In particular, *AKARI* detects effciently the UIR band emission in these regions owing to its IRC 7 μm (S7) filter band. These results suggest the fragmentation of large carbonaceous grains in shocks as a possible formation mechanism of the band carriers. The IRC NIR spectroscopy also provides sensitive data for the study of the UIR bands in the 3 μm region, which gives us information on the smallest members of the band carriers. The IRC NIR spectra indicate the variation in the size distribution of the band carriers in HII regions (Mori et al. 2012) and the formation of the band carriers in a SNR (Seok et al. 2012) in the LMC.

SNe are thought to play significant roles in the dust lifecycle in the ISM. However, the amount and composition of dust grains formed associated with a SN explosion are still largely controversial (e.g. Sakon et al. 2009; Matsuura et al. 2011). The results presented here indicate that SNe could also be a significant source of the UIR band carriers and crystalline silicates. We are beginning to see variations in the dust signature and processing. Further investigations with *JWST* (Gardner et al. 2006) and *SPICA* (Nakagawa 2010) are certainly needed to fully understand the dust lifecycle in the universe.

Acknowledgments. This work is based on observations with *AKARI*, a JAXA project with the participation of ESA, and with the *Spitzer Space Telescope* operated by the Jet Propulsion Laboratory, California Institute of Technology under a contract with NASA. We thank all the members of the *AKARI* project and the *AKARI* interstellar medium in our Galaxy and nearby galaxies (ISMGN) team. This work is supported in part by a Grant-in-Aid for Scientific Research from the Japan Society of Promotion of Science.

References

Ábrahám, P., et al. 2009, Nature, 459, 224
Bringa, E. M., et al. 2007, ApJ, 662, 372
Crovisier, J., et al. 1997, Science, 275, 1904
Engelbracht, C. W., et al. 2006, ApJL, 642, L127
Gardner, J. P., et al. 2006, Sp. Sci. Rev., 123, 485
Hunter, D. A., & Elmegreen, B. G. 2004, AJ, 128, 2170
Ishihara, D., et al. 2010, A&A, 514, A1
Kaneda, H., Onaka, T., & Sakon, I. 2005, ApJL, 632, L83
Kaneda, H., et al. 2008, ApJ, 684, 270
— 2009, ApJL, 698, L125
— 2010, A&A, 514, A14
Kawada, M., et al. 2007, PASJ, S59, 389
Kemper, F., Vriend, W. J., & Tielens, A. G. G. M. 2004, ApJ, 609, 826
Koo, B.-C., et al. 2011, ApJ, 732, 6
Kwok, S., & Zhang, Y. 2011, Nature, 479, 80
Malfait, K., et al. 1998, A&A, 332, L25
Matsuura, M., et al. 2011, Science, 333, 1258
Micelotta, E. R., Jones, A. P., & Tielens, A. G. G. M. 2010, A&A, 526, A52
Mori, T. I., et al. 2012, ApJ, 744, 68
Murakami, H., et al. 2007, PASJ, S59, 369
Nakagawa, T. 2010, Proc. of SPIE, 7731, 77310O
Onaka, T. 2000, Adv. Sp. Res., 25, 2167
Onaka, T., de Jong, T., & Willems, F. J. 1989, A&A, 218, 169
Onaka, T., et al. 2007, PASJ, S59, 401
— 2008, in Organic compounds in galaxies, edited by S. Kowk, & S. Sandford (Cambridge: Cambridge University Pres), IAU Symp. 251, 229
— 2009a, in SPICA joint European/Japanese Workshop, edited by A. Heras, B. Swinyard, K. Isaak, & J. Goicoechea (Les Ulis: EDP Sciences), 03007
— 2009b, in Cosmic Dust - Near and Far, edited by T. Henning, E. Grün, & J. Steinacker (San Francisco: Astron. Soc. Pacific), ASP Conf. ser. 414, 227
Onaka, T., et al. (eds.) 2009c, AKARI, a Light to Illuminate the Misty Universe, ASP Conf. ser. 418. (San Francisco: Astron. Soc. Pacific)
Onaka, T., et al. 2010a, Proc. of SPIE, 7731, 77310M
— 2010b, A&A, 514, A15
Pilbratt, G. L., et al. 2010, A&A, 518, L1
Sakon, I., et al. 2009, ApJ, 692, 546
Seok, J.-Y., Koo, B.-C., & Onaka, T. 2012, ApJ, 744, 160
Smith, J. D., et al. 2007, ApJ, 656, 770
Tielens, A. G. G. M. 2005, The Physics and Chemistry of the Interstellar Medium (Cambridge: Cambridge University Press)
— 2008, ARA&A, 46, 289
Voors, R. H. M., et al. 1999, A&A, 341, L67
Waters, L. B. F. M., et al. 1996, A&A, 315, L361
Werner, M. W., et al. 2004, ApJS, 154, 1

Galactic Archaeology: Near-Field Cosmology and the Formation of the Milky Way
ASP Conference Series, Vol. 458
W. Aoki, M. Ishigaki, T. Suda, T. Tsujimoto, N. Arimoto, eds.
© *2012 Astronomical Society of the Pacific*

The Infant Milky Way

Stefania Salvadori[1] and Andrea Ferrara[2]

[1]*Kapteyn Astronomical Institute, Landleven 12, 9747AD Groningen, NL*

[2]*Scuola Normale Superiore, Piazza dei Cavalieri 7, 56126 Pisa, IT*

Abstract. We investigate the physical properties of the progenitors of today living Milky Way-like galaxies that are visible as Damped Lyα Absorption systems and Lyα Emitters at higher redshifts ($z \approx 2.3, 5.7$). To this aim we use a statistical merger-tree approach that follows the formation of the Galaxy and its dwarf satellites in a cosmological context, tracing the chemical evolution and stellar population history of the progenitor halos. The model accounts for the properties of the most metal-poor stars and local dwarf galaxies, providing insights on the early cosmic star-formation. Fruitful links between Galactic Archaeology and more distant galaxies are presented.

1. Background

One of the most popular methods to identify high-redshifts galaxies ($z \approx 2 - 7$) is by detecting their strong Lyα line. These Lyman Alpha Emitters (LAEs) are mainly associated to *star-forming galaxies*, and they have been extensively used to probe both the ionization state of the Inter Galactic Medium and the early galaxy evolution. At lower redshifts, $z < 5$, galaxies with *high neutral hydrogen column densities*, $N_{HI} > 10^{20.3} \mathrm{cm}^{-2}$, can be identified in the spectra of more distant quasars by means of their strong Lyα absorption line. The most metal-poor among these Damped Lyα Absorption systems (DLAs), can provide insights on the initial metal-enrichment phases of galaxy formation. Recently a DLA with [Fe/H]≈ -3 observed at $z_{abs} \approx 2.3$, has indeed revealed strong carbon-enhancement and evident odd-even effect (Cooke et al. 2011b), consistent with the chemical imprint by $Z = 0$ faint supernovae (Kobayashi et al. 2011). Furthermore, all others DLAs with [Fe/H]< -2 observed at high-resolution show chemical abundance ratios consistent with those of very metal-poor Galactic halo stars (Cooke et al. 2011a), thus suggesting possible connections between these absorbers and the early building blocks of Milky Way (MW) -like galaxies.

We determine the physical properties of the progenitors of the MW and its dwarf companions by using the merger-tree code GAMETE (GAlaxy MErger Tree & Evolution), which reconstructs the possible star-formation and chemical evolution histories of the MW system. The observed Lyα luminosity and Lyα line equivalent width are computed using the LAE model by Dayal and collaborators (Dayal et al. 2008, 2010) that reproduces a number of important observations for high-z LAEs. Adopting the canonical observational criteria we identify the progenitors visible as DLAs and LAEs at redshifts respectively equal to $z \approx 2.3$ and $z \approx 5.7$. The observable properties of the MW Galaxy and its neighboring companions are presented below, from present days back to the time when the Universe was only 1 Gyr old.

2.   The Milky Way system at $z = 0$: Galactic Archaeology

Very metal-poor stars represent the living fossils of the first stellar generations. Their chemical abundance patterns and Metallicity Distribution Functions (MDFs) observed in both the stellar halo and in nearby dSph galaxies can provide fundamental insights on the properties of the first cosmic sources.

2.1.   First stars and their Cosmic Relics

Cosmological simulations suggest that first stars formed at $z \approx 15 - 20$ in primordial H_2-cooling minihaloes and that were possibly more massive than typical stars forming today (Hosokawa et al. 2011). The transition from massive to normal stars is expected to be driven by metals *and* dust cooling, becoming important when the metallicity of the star-forming gas exceeds the critical value, $Z_{cr} = 10^{-4\pm1}Z_\odot$ (Schneider et al. 2002). We use our cosmological model to interpret the observed Galactic halo MDF. We find that the low-metallicity tail of the MDF strongly depends on the assumed Z_{cr} value (Fig. 1). If the observed cut-off (Schörck et al. 2009) suggests $Z_{cr} \approx 10^{-4}Z_\odot$, the presence of the four stars at [Fe/H]< -4.5 can only be accounted if $Z_{cr} < 10^{-5}Z_\odot$. In particular, the existence of the most metal-deficient star ever, which has *total* metallicity $Z \approx 10^{-4.5}Z_\odot$ (Caffau et al. 2011) clearly requires $Z_{cr} < 10^{-4}Z_\odot$. Such a recent discovery definitely proves that dust strongly governs the transition from massive to normal stars in the low-Z regimes (Schneider et al. 2002).

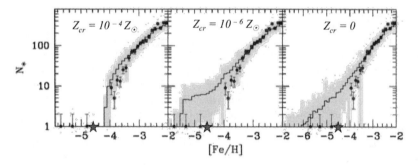

Figure 1.   The Galactic halo MDF: observations (points (Beers & Christlieb 2005)) vs simulations averaged over 100 possible MW merger histories (histograms and shaded area). The starred symbol indicates the most metal-deficient star.

The chemical abundance patterns of halo stars with $-4.5 <$[Fe/H]< -2.7 (Cayrel et al. 2004; Caffau et al. 2011), do not show any peculiar imprint from very massive primordial stars, and have small chemical abundance scatter unlikely resulting from individual supernovae (SN) ejecta. According to our cosmological model (Salvadori et al. 2007) the number of stars formed out of gas polluted *only* by $Z < Z_{cr}$ stars is extremely small, and thus negligible in current data sample. These "second-generation" stars can either have low or high [Fe/H] (Fig. 2) if they form in halos that accreted metal-enriched gas from the MW environment or that are self-enriched by the first stars. To have the chance to detect the chemical imprint by first stars an higher number of [Fe/H]< -2 stars is clearly needed. To this aim it is useful to survey the stellar halo between 20 kpc $\lesssim r \lesssim 40$ kpc, where the contribution of [Fe/H]< -2 stars with respect to the overall stellar population is expected to be maximal (Salvadori et al. 2010b).

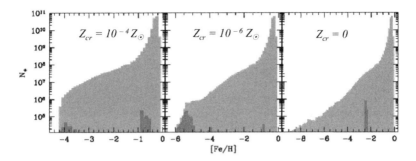

Figure 2.   (color online) Number of stars predicted to exist at $z = 0$ as a function of their [Fe/H] for different Z_{cr} models. The magenta histograms show second-generation stars, the cyan histograms the overall stellar populations.

2.2.   First Galaxies and their Cosmic Relics

An alternative way to find very metal-poor stars is by surveying dSph galaxies and in particular ultra-faint dSphs ($L < 10^5 L_\odot$, Fig. 2), in which [Fe/H]< -3 stars represent the 25% of the total stellar mass. These faint dwarfs are predicted to be among the first star-forming galaxies in the MW system, left-overs of H_2-cooling minihaloes formed at $z > 8.5$ (Salvadori & Ferrara 2009), i.e. before the end of reionization ($z_{rei} = 6$). In these galaxies the higher fraction of [Fe/H]< -3 stars with respect to the more luminous "classical dSphs" reflects both the lower star-formation rate, caused by ineffective H_2 cooling, and the lower metal (pre-)enrichment of the MW-environment at their further formation epoch. Indeed classical dSphs are find to finally assemble at $z < 7$ when the pre-enrichment of the MW environment was [Fe/H]≈ -3. The few stars at [Fe/H]< -3 observed in classical dSphs (Starkenburg et al. 2010) are predicted to form in progenitor minihaloes at $z > 8.5$ (Salvadori & Ferrara 2009), some of which might host first stars. The unusual composition of two stars at [Fe/H]≈ -2 observed in Hercules (Koch et al. 2008) might be the result of self-enrichment by first stars in early progenitor halos.

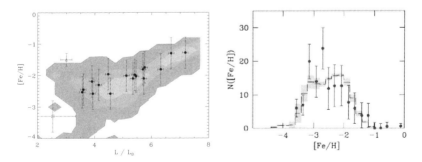

Figure 3.   Observed (points with error-bars, (Kirby et al. 2008)) vs simulated (contours/histograms) properties of dSph galaxies at $z = 0$. *Left:* the iron-luminosity relation. The colored shaded areas correspond to regions including the $(99, 95, 68)\%$ of the total number of dSph candidates in 50 MW merger histories (Salvadori & Ferrara 2011). *Right:* MDF of ultra-faint dSph galaxies (Salvadori & Ferrara 2009).

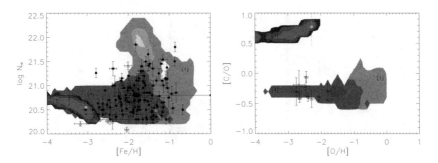

Figure 4.   (color online) MW progenitors visible as DLAs at $z \approx 2.3$ (contours), with color intensity corresponding to regions containing the $(99, 95, 68)\%$ of DLAs in 50 merger histories (Salvadori & Ferrara 2011). Points with error-bars are observations: circles (Prochaska et al. 2007), triangles (Cooke et al. 2011a), square (Cooke et al. 2011b).

3.   The Milky Way system at $z \approx 2.3$: DLAs

The predicted N_{HI} vs [Fe/H] values of the MW progenitors visible as DLAs at $z \approx 2.3$ follows the observed relation (Fig. 4). In our picture very metal-poor DLAs, [Fe/H]< -2, are associated to starless $M \approx 10^8 M_\odot$ minihaloes that virialize from metal-enriched regions of the MW environment before the end of reionization and passively evolve down to $z \approx 2.3$. These sterile absorbers retain the chemical imprint of the dominant stellar populations that pollute the MW environment at their formation epoch: low-Z SN type II (Salvadori et al. 2007). This finding agrees with the observational results by Becker et al. (2012) that show that the gas chemical abundance ratios in very metal-poor DLAs/sub-DLAs do not significantly evolve between $2 < z < 5$. The recently discovered C-enhanced DLA is instead pertaining to a new class of absorbers hosting first stars along with second-generation of long-living low-mass stars. These peculiar DLAs are descendants of $M \approx 10^7 M_\odot$ minihaloes, that virialize at $z > 8$ in neutral primordial regions of the MW environment and passively evolve after a short *initial period of star formation*. These conditions are only satisfied by $\approx 0.01\%$ of the total amount of DLAs, making these absorbers extremely rare. The peculiar abundance pattern observed in the C-enhanced DLA results from the enrichment by low-metallicity SN typeII and AGB stars, which may start to form as soon as $Z > Z_{cr}$. While SNII nucleosynthetic products are mostly lost in winds, AGB metals are retained in the ISM, causing a dramatic increase of [C/Fe]. The amount of N produced by $Z < 5 \times 10^{-4} Z_\odot$ AGB stars is very limited (Meynet & Maeder 2002), resulting in a gas abundance [N/H]$= -3.8 \pm 0.9$ (see Fig. 5). The mass of relic stars in C-enhanced DLAs is $M_* \approx 10^{2-4} M_\odot$, making them the gas-rich counterpart of the faintest dwarfs.

4.   The Milky Way system at $z \approx 5.7$: LAEs

At $z \approx 5.7$ the star-forming progenitors of MW-like galaxies cover a wide range of observed Lyα luminosity, $L_\alpha = 10^{39-43.25}$ erg s^{-1}. The probability to have at least one progenitor observable as LAE ($L_\alpha \geq 10^{42}$, $EW \geq 20$ Å) is therefore very high $P \geq 68\%$. Such visible progenitors are mainly associated with the most massive halos

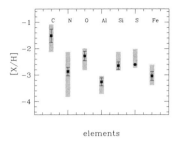

Figure 5.   Gas chemical abundances in the C-enhanced DLA: observations (points, Cooke et al. (2011a)) vs simulations (average value $\pm 1\sigma$, shaded areas).

of the hierarchy, i.e. the major branch, with total mass $M > 10^{9.5} M_\odot$. On average the identified LAEs have star-formation rates $\dot{M}_* \approx 2.3 M_\odot/\mathrm{yr}$ and $L_\alpha \approx 10^{42.2} \mathrm{erg/s}$. They are populated by intermediate age stars, $t_* \approx 150 - 400$ Myr, which have average metallicities $Z \approx (0.3-1) Z_\odot$ (Fig.6). Interestingly these visible MW progenitors provide more than the 10% of the very metal-poor stars that are observed today in the Galactic halo. Indeed, most of these [Fe/H]< -2 stars formed at $z > 6$ in newly virializing halos, accreting metal-enriched gas from the MW environment. By $z \approx 5.7$ many of these premature building blocks have already merged into the major branch of the hierarchy, i.e. the visible progenitor (Salvadori et al. 2010a).

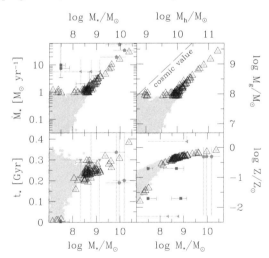

Figure 6.   (color online) Physical properties of MW progenitors (yellow circles) at $z \approx 5.7$. Blue triangles identify the objects visible as LAEs. Points with error-bars are data by Ono et al. (2010) (magenta squares, 4 models for 1 LAE), Pirzkal et al. (2007) (blue triangles) and Lai et al. (2007) (green circles). As a function of the total stellar mass the panels show: the instantaneous star formation rate (a), the average stellar age (c) and (d) metallicity (d). Panel (b) shows the relation between the halo and the gas mass, with the cosmic value pointed out by the dashed line.

5. Conclusions

The MW system is a powerful laboratory to study early galaxy formation. On the one hand the properties of the first cosmic sources can be studied by exploiting the observations of today living metal-poor stars and galaxies. From the other hand the early evolutionary stages of different MW progenitors can be investigated using complementary observations of high-z galaxies. In particular, by identifying the MW progenitors among the faintest LAEs observed at $z \approx 5.7$ it will be possible to observe the MW in its infancy, when it was only 1 Gyr old.

Acknowledgments. We thank R. Schneider and P. Dayal for their contribution to the works on Galactic Archaeology and MW-LAE connection.

References

Becker, G. D., Sargent, W. L. W., Rauch, M., & Carswell, R. F. 2012, ApJ, 744, 91
Beers, T. C., & Christlieb, N. 2005, ARA&A, 43, 531
Caffau, E., Bonifacio, P., François, P., Sbordone, L., Monaco, L., Spite, M., Spite, F., Ludwig, H.-G., Cayrel, R., Zaggia, S., Hammer, F., Randich, S., Molaro, P., & Hill, V. 2011, Nat, 477, 67
Cayrel, R., Depagne, E., Spite, M., Hill, V., Spite, F., François, P., Plez, B., Beers, T., Primas, F., Andersen, J., Barbuy, B., Bonifacio, P., Molaro, P., & Nordström, B. 2004, A&A, 416, 1117
Cooke, R., Pettini, M., Steidel, C. C., Rudie, G. C., & Jorgenson, R. A. 2011a, MNRAS, 412, 1047
Cooke, R., Pettini, M., Steidel, C. C., Rudie, G. C., & Nissen, P. E. 2011b, MNRAS, 417, 1534
Dayal, P., Ferrara, A., & Gallerani, S. 2008, MNRAS, 389, 1683
Dayal, P., Ferrara, A., & Saro, A. 2010, MNRAS, 402, 1449
Kirby, E. N., Simon, J. D., Geha, M., Guhathakurta, P., & Frebel, A. 2008, ApJ, 685, L43
Kobayashi, C., Tominaga, N., & Nomoto, K. 2011, ApJ, 730, L14
Koch, A., McWilliam, A., Grebel, E. K., Zucker, D. B., & Belokurov, V. 2008, ApJ, 688, L13
Lai, K., Huang, J.-S., Fazio, G., Cowie, L. L., Hu, E. M., & Kakazu, Y. 2007, ApJ, 655, 704
Meynet, G., & Maeder, A. 2002, A&A, 390, 561
Ono, Y., Ouchi, M., Shimasaku, K., Dunlop, J., Farrah, D., McLure, R., & Okamura, S. 2010, ApJ, 724, 1524
Pirzkal, N., Malhotra, S., Rhoads, J. E., & Xu, C. 2007, ApJ, 667, 49
Prochaska, J. X., Wolfe, A. M., Howk, J. C., Gawiser, E., Burles, S. M., & Cooke, J. 2007, ApJS, 171, 29
Salvadori, S., Dayal, P., & Ferrara, A. 2010a, MNRAS, 407, L1
Salvadori, S., & Ferrara, A. 2009, MNRAS, 395, L6
— 2011, MNRAS, L388
Salvadori, S., Ferrara, A., Schneider, R., Scannapieco, E., & Kawata, D. 2010b, MNRAS, 401, L5
Salvadori, S., Schneider, R., & Ferrara, A. 2007, MNRAS, 381, 647
Schneider, R., Ferrara, A., Natarajan, P., & Omukai, K. 2002, ApJ, 571, 30
Schörck, T., Christlieb, N., Cohen, J. G., Beers, T. C., Shectman, S., Thompson, I., McWilliam, A., Bessell, M. S., Norris, J. E., Meléndez, J., Ramírez, S., Haynes, D., Cass, P., Hartley, M., Russell, K., Watson, F., Zickgraf, F.-J., Behnke, B., Fechner, C., Fuhrmeister, B., Barklem, P. S., Edvardsson, B., Frebel, A., Wisotzki, L., & Reimers, D. 2009, A&A, 507, 817
Starkenburg, E., Hill, V., Tolstoy, E., González Hernández, J. I., Irwin, M., Helmi, A., Battaglia, G., Jablonka, P., Tafelmeyer, M., Shetrone, M., Venn, K., & de Boer, T. 2010, A&A, 513, A34

Galactic Archaeology: Near-Field Cosmology and the Formation of the Milky Way
ASP Conference Series, Vol. 458
W. Aoki, M. Ishigaki, T. Suda, T. Tsujimoto, N. Arimoto, eds.
© 2012 Astronomical Society of the Pacific

Abundance Trends in the Milky Way Disk as Observed by SEGUE

Judy Y. Cheng,[1] Constance M. Rockosi,[1,2] Heather L. Morrison,[3]
Ralph A. Schönrich,[4] Young Sun Lee,[5] and Timothy C. Beers[5,6]

[1] *University of California Santa Cruz, Santa Cruz, CA 95064, USA*

[2] *UCO/Lick Observatory, Santa Cruz, CA 95064, USA*

[3] *Case Western Reserve University, Cleveland, OH 44106, USA*

[4] *Max-Planck-Institute für Astrophysik, Karl-Schwarzschild-Str. 1, D-85741
Garching, Germany*

[5] *Department of Physics and Astronomy/Joint Institute for Nuclear
Astrophysics, Michigan State University, E. Lansing, MI 48824, USA*

[6] *National Optical Astronomy Observatory, Tucson, AZ 85719, USA*

Abstract.   Detailed observations of the Galaxy can be used to test predictions made
by models of disk formation and evolution, and they serve to complement large surveys
that study galaxies at high redshift. The observed radial and vertical metallicity distribution of old stars in the Milky Way disk provides powerful constraints on the chemical
enrichment and dynamical history of the disk. We present trends in [Fe/H] and [α/Fe]
as a function of Galactocentric radius R and height above the plane |Z| using 7010 main
sequence turnoff stars observed by the Sloan Extension for Galactic Understanding and
Exploration (SEGUE) survey. The sample consists of mostly old thin and thick disk
stars, with a minimal contribution from the stellar halo, in the region $6 < R < 16$ kpc,
$0.15 < |Z| < 1.5$ kpc. We find that the radial metallicity gradient Δ[Fe/H]/ΔR becomes
flat at heights $|Z| > 1$ kpc. In addition, we find that the high-α population, which dom-
inates at large heights |Z| in the inner disk ($R < 10$ kpc), makes up a small fraction of
stars in the outer disk ($R > 10$ kpc). The chemical and kinematic properties of high-α
stars in the outer disk differ from those in the inner disk, consistent with the high-α
population having a short scale length. Our observations are consistent with the predictions for a thick disk formed in situ at high redshift, and the lack of high-α stars at
large R and |Z| provides a strong constraint on the strength of radial migration induced
by transient spiral arms.

1. Introduction

Abundance gradients in the Milky Way disk can be used to distinguish between proposed scenarios of thick disk formation, such as early gas accretion (Brook et al. 2005),
minor merger activity (Bird et al. 2012), and radial migration (Loebman et al. 2011).
Because thick disks are a common feature of disk galaxies (Dalcanton & Bernstein
2002), understanding how the Galactic thick disk formed will elucidate the relative
importance of each of these processes in forming the Galaxy. We use a large homogeneous sample of 7010 main sequence turnoff (MSTO) stars from the Sloan Extension

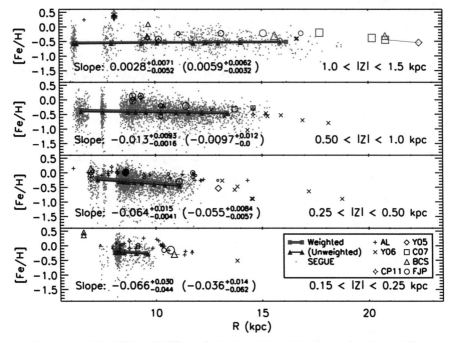

Figure 1.   **Metallicity [Fe/H] vs. Galactocentric radius R as a function of distance from the plane $|Z|$ in SEGUE.** The radial metallicity gradient (thick red lines) of SEGUE MSTO stars (blue points) is flat at $|Z| > 1.0$ kpc. Forty-eight open clusters with high-resolution spectroscopic observations (open symbols; Paper I, Table 4) roughly follow the trends seen in the SEGUE stars. Reproduced from Paper I.

for Galactic Understanding and Exploration (SEGUE; Yanny et al. 2009; Eisenstein et al. 2011) survey to examine trends in [Fe/H] and [α/Fe] as a function of Galactocentric radius R and distance from the plane $|Z|$ in the Milky Way disk (Cheng et al. 2012a,b, hereafter Papers I and II). Careful work has been done to correct for selection biases and to account for Galactic extinction; see Paper I for details.

2.   Trends in [Fe/H]: A flat radial gradient at $|Z| > 1.0$ kpc

In Paper I, we examine the distribution of [Fe/H] as a function of R and $|Z|$ and show that the radial metallicity gradient of field stars from SEGUE is flat far from the plane of the disk (Figure 1). While at $|Z| < 0.5$ kpc (bottom two panels), the gradient is consistent with literature values (e.g., Friel et al. 2002), at $|Z| > 1.0$ kpc (top panel), the gradient is flat. The lack of a radial gradient at large $|Z|$ is consistent with the findings of previous studies (e.g., Allende Prieto et al. 2006; Jurić et al. 2008).

3.   Trends in [α/Fe]: A short scale length for the high-α population

Stars with thick disk kinematics typically have high [α/Fe], making α-abundance ratios a useful discriminant of thin and thick disk stars in the solar neighborhood (Bensby

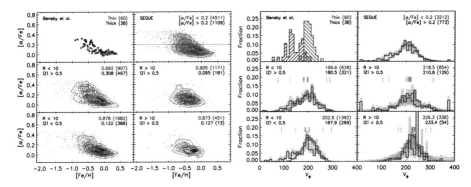

Figure 2.   **Left: [Fe/H] vs. [α/Fe]. Right: Rotational velocity distributions.** In each plot, the top two panels show a solar neighborhood sample (Bensby et al. 2005) and the total SEGUE sample. The bottom four panels show the SEGUE sample divided into four regions in R and $|Z|$. The numbers in the top right of each panel indicate the weighted fraction (left plot) and the mean rotational velocity (right plot) of high- and low-α stars in blue and red, respectively. Reproduced from Paper II.

et al. 2003, 2005). In Paper II, we examine the distribution of [α/Fe] as a function of R and $|Z|$ in the disk and find evidence that the high-α population has a short scale length, in agreement with recent work by Bensby et al. (2011).

First, the lack of high-α stars in the outer disk suggests that the high-α component of the disk has a short radial extent. The fraction of high-α stars ([α/Fe] > 0.2) falls dramatically at $R > 10$ kpc (Figure 2, left). At $R < 10$ kpc, the fraction of high-α stars increases with $|Z|$, as we expect if the high-α population is associated with the thick disk (left panels). At $R > 10$ kpc, however, the fraction of high-α stars is low at all $|Z|$ (right panels). Second, the rotational velocities of high- and low-α stars suggest that the correlation between kinematics and chemistry seen in the solar neighborhood disappears in the outer disk (Figure 2, right). At $R < 10$ kpc, high-α stars (blue) rotate more slowly and are kinematically hotter than low-α stars (red) at all $|Z|$ (left panels), consistent with the kinematic properties of thin and thick disk stars in the solar neigh borhood (e.g., Bensby et al. 2003, 2005). At $R > 10$ kpc, high- and low-α stars have similar kinematic properties, which indicates that [α/Fe] and thick disk membership are not correlated in the outer disk (right panels).

4.   Summary: Implications for Thick Disk Formation

The lack of radial metallicity gradients and the short scale length of the high-α population are consistent with the predictions of a scenario in which the thick disk forms during a clumpy disk phase at early times. This phase has been studied in simulations (Brook et al. 2005) and seen in observations of high redshift disks (Förster Schreiber et al. 2009). The stars observed at large $|Z|$ in the outer disk have properties unlike thick disk stars in the solar neighborhood, and their presence, as well as the flattening of the radial metallicity gradient in low-α stars, may be explained by recent minor merger activity (e.g., Bird et al. 2012). The lack of high-α stars at large R and $|Z|$ also places strict constraints on some models of radial migration (e.g., Loebman et al. 2011).

Discussion

Bland-Hawthorn: Do you have an SDSS example for the bulge? Do you find your high-α, thick disk stars are distinct or similar?

Cheng: Our stars are all at $R > 6$ kpc, so we should not have any bulge stars in our data.

Rich: We see that bulge giants tend to have a low [La/Eu] r-process-like ratio. This is lower than for the thick disk.

Chiba: What is the dependence of the scale height with R for high-α stars? (This issue is related to the heating mechanism for thick disk formation.)

Cheng: We have only tried to fit the scale length and assumed a constant scale height.

Wyse: An early gas-rich disk would be expected to have higher gas densities in the inner regions and higher star formation rates. This gradient of star formation history will lead naturally to a gradient in mean [α/Fe]. Have you modeled?

Cheng: No, we haven't done any modeling.

Pasetto: How much can the errors in α-enhancement or distance influence the slope of low-α/high-α trends?

Cheng: We have analyzed a series of Monte Carlo realizations of the data to account for the errors and we find that our results are robust.

Acknowledgments. J.Y.C. thanks the organizing committee for planning a great conference. C.M.R. gratefully acknowledges funding from the David and Lucile Packard Foundation, and thanks the Max-Planck-Institute für Astronomie (MPIA), Heidelberg for hospitality. Y.S.L. and T.C.B. acknowledge partial funding of this work from grants PHY 02-16783 and PHY 08-22648: Physics Frontier Center/Joint Institute for Nuclear Astrophysics (JINA), awarded by the U.S. National Science Foundation. Funding for SDSS-III has been provided by the Alfred P. Sloan Foundation, the Participating Institutions, the National Science Foundation, and the U.S. Department of Energy Office of Science. The SDSS-III web site is http://www.sdss3.org/.

References

Allende Prieto, C. et al. 2006, ApJ, 636, 804.
Bensby, T. et al. 2011, ApJ, 735, L46+
Bensby, T., Feltzing, S., & Lundström, I. 2003, A&A, 410, 527
Bensby, T. et al. 2005, A&A, 433, 185
Bird, J. C., Kazantzidis, S., & Weinberg, D. H. 2012, MNRAS, 420, 913
Brook, C. B. et al. 2005, ApJ, 630, 298
Cheng, J. Y. et al. 2012a, ApJ, 746, 149
Cheng, J. Y. et al. 2012b, ApJ, in prep, Paper II
Dalcanton, J. J., & Bernstein, R. A. 2002, AJ, 124, 1328
Eisenstein, D. J. et al. 2011, AJ, 142, 72
Förster Schreiber, N. M. et al. 2009, ApJ, 706, 1364
Friel, E. D. et al. 2002, AJ, 124, 2693
Jurić, M. et al. 2008, ApJ, 673, 864
Loebman, S. R. et al. 2011, ApJ, 737, 8
Yanny, B. et al. 2009, AJ, 137, 4377

Galactic Archaeology: Near-Field Cosmology and the Formation of the Milky Way
ASP Conference Series, Vol. 458
W. Aoki, M. Ishigaki, T. Suda, T. Tsujimoto, N. Arimoto, eds.
© *2012 Astronomical Society of the Pacific*

3D and NLTE Effects on Spectroscopic Parameters of Late-Type Stars

Karin Lind,[1] Maria Bergemann,[1] Remo Collet,[2] Martin Asplund,[3] and Zazralt Magic[1]

[1]*Max Planck Institute for Astrophysics, Garching bei München, D-857 41 Germany*

[2] *Niels Bohr Institute, Juliane Maries Vej 30, DK-2100 Copenhagen, Denmark*

[3] *Research School of Astronomy & Astrophysics, Mount Stromlo Observatory, Cotter Road, Weston Creek, ACT 2611*

Abstract. We investigate the impact on spectroscopic effective temperatures ($T_{\rm eff}$), surface gravities (log (g)), and metallicites ([Fe/H]) of metal-poor stars, when departures from LTE are taken into account and the atmospheric model is constructed from realistic 3D, hydrodynamical simulations. We demonstrate that traditional 1D, LTE analysis underestimates the values for all three parameters in the metal-poor subgiant HD140283.

1. Introduction

The fundamental stellar parameters, $T_{\rm eff}$, $\log(g)$, and [Fe/H], constitute the basis of all spectroscopic abundance analysis. The iron content is commonly adopted as single proxy for the entire content of metals in the stellar atmosphere. With the knowledge of the three stellar parameters, we can acquire further information about the evolution of the star itself, i.e. determine its mass and age, and the evolution of the stellar population it resides in.

A common approach is to determine stellar parameters spectroscopically, using the wealth of Fe lines present in late-type star spectra. In particular, a spectroscopic temperature is determined by selecting the $T_{\rm eff}$ of the atmospheric model such that the abundances inferred from Fe I lines exhibit no significant slope with the excitation potential of the lower level of the line transition. This method exploits the different temperature-sensitivity of the level populations of different excitation potential, the lowest excited lines being most sensitive. Further, a spectroscopic surface gravity, is determined by adjusting the model gravity such that Fe I and Fe II lines give consistent abundances. When the stellar parameters are constrained in this fashion, along with the microturbulence, one may derive a highly precise value of the metallicity.

However, the success of the method hinges on the realism of the atmospheric structure. Even if high precision may be obtained with a very simplistic model, the answer may be inaccurate. Traditional methods rely on model atmospheres calculated under the assumptions of hydrostatic equilibrium and a one-dimensional (1D) geometry. The most critical approximation is the mixing-length description of the convective energy transport. The development of 3D, radiation-hydrodynamical simulations has uncovered systematic uncertainties introduced by these simplifying assumptions. In particular, metal-poor stars have been demonstrated to have much cooler line-forming layers than previously thought (see Collet et al. 2011, and references therein).

A second critical assumption is that spectral line formation can be well modelled in local thermodynamic equilibrium (LTE). The atomic level populations of minority species, such as Fe I, may react very sensitively on the super-thermal ultra-violet (UV) radiation field, in the shortage of thermalizing collisional processes. For these species, statistical equilibrium (NLTE) is a more realistic assumption (e.g. Mashonkina et al. 2011). We have tested the influence of NLTE and 3D models on stellar parameters derived for a sample of benchmark metal-poor stars. For this purpose we adopt atmospheric models determined with MARCS (Gustafsson et al. 2008), a state-of-the-art 1D code, and STAGGER, a 3D radiation-hydrodynamical code (e.g. Nordlund et al. 2009). The convection simulations are averaged temporally and spatially on surfaces of equal optical depth, so that spectrum synthesis can be carried out in one dimension. For this study we thus neglect the potential impact of existing temperature and density inhomogeneities. Line formation calculations for 1D and <3D> models are performed in LTE and NLTE with the radiative transfer code MULTI2.3 (Carlsson 1986).

2. Results

Figure 1 illustrates schematically how the Fe abundances derived for a famous metal-poor subgiant, HD140283, are affected by the assumptions of LTE and 1D atmospheres. The adopted stellar parameters ($T_{\rm eff}$ = 5777 ± 55 K and $\log(g)$ = 3.70 ± 0.08) have been determined by the infra-red flux method (Casagrande et al. 2010) and measurement of the parallax (van Leeuwen 2007). 1D modelling produces a negative slope of Fe I line abundances with excitation potential that corresponds to approximately 300 K, in LTE as well as NLTE. The <3D> model exhibits an equally strong but positive slope in LTE, while the the combination of NLTE and <3D> successfully establishes the excitation balance at this effective temperature. The inferred metallicity is [Fe/H] = −2.35.

Also evident from the figure is that ionization balance between Fe I and Fe II lines is achieved simultaneously. In the 1D, LTE case, the surface gravity would have to be lowered by 0.42 dex to achieve ionization balance at the spectroscopic temperature. The star would thus be moved from its location in the HR diagram close to a point further along the same isochrone ($T_{\rm eff}$ = 5450 K, $\log(g)$ = 3.25 and [Fe/H] = −2.70), turning HD140283 into a red giant at the base of the branch. More details about this star and the rest of the benchmark star sample will be presented in Bergemann et al. and Lind et al. (in prep.). The latter paper will present an extensive 1D, NLTE grid for late-type stars.

Discussion

Q.: The disparity of Fe abundances with excitation potential can be reduced for 1D models in two ways: 1) Models with convective overshoot reduce the temperature gradient in line forming regions. 2) Transition probabilities for high-excitation lines may have large errors and choices can be made that essentially eliminate these trends over all wavelengths from UV to NIR.

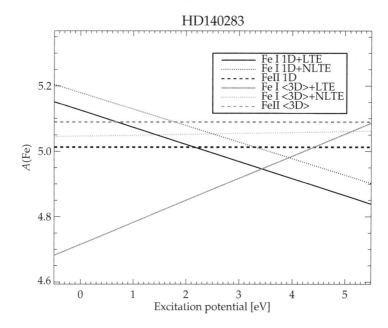

Figure 1. The figure illustrates the excitation equilibrium for 1D and <3D> models of HD140283. *Solid:* Linear regression to LTE abundances inferred from Fe I lines. *Dotted:* Same as solid, but in the NLTE case. *Dashed:* Mean abundances inferred from Fe II lines.

Lind: For our benchmark star sample, models with convective over-shoot (Kurucz 1992) bear no greater resemblance to the temperature structure recovered from hydrodynamical simulations than models without overshoot. Like the mixing-length description in itself, the implementation of overshoot is not based on first principles but governed by free parameters that require calibration. It is also important to realise that all 1D models in radiative equilibrium, including those with overshoot, will inevitably overestimate the temperatures in shallow optical layers of metal-poor stars.

As shown in Figure 1 the modelling technique may have very dramatic impact on the excitation equilibrium irrespectively of which transition probabilities are adopted. We have made a critical selection of lines for this analysis, and estimate that the uncertainty in atomic data propagates into no more than $\sim$ 50 K in the case of HD140283, which is small compared to the differences between 1D and <3D> models (Bergemann et al. in prep).

Q.: When spectroscopic stellar parameters are unreliable they can be replaced by parameters derived from photometric colours.

Lind: Our analysis demonstrates that 1D LTE spectroscopic stellar parameters are not accurate for metal-poor stars. Low excitation lines in particular require a combined 3D and NLTE treatment to be modelled correctly. With those caveats in mind, spectroscopy is an excellent tool to extract information about fundamental stellar parameters, with the considerable advantage of being insensitive to foreground extinction. Depending on the latitude of the stars, reddening uncertainties may well amount to hundreds of Kelvin, especially for optical colours. One should also bear in mind that synthetic color-temperature calibrations are similarly model dependent (e.g. Önehag et al. 2009). The infra-red flux method (González Hernández & Bonifacio 2009; Casagrande et al. 2010) offers a low sensitivity to the atmospheric model, but is dependent on the reddening and the photometric zero-point. With a tight constraint on the reddening, the uncertainty on temperatures derived with this method is small.

Q.: Your results show that spectroscopic 1D LTE stellar parameters are too cool compared to interferometric measurements, which contradicts e.g. Baines et al. (2010), who argue that the reverse is true.

Lind: Baines et al. report angular diameter measurements and inferred effective temperatures for a sample of solar-metallicity K giants. At these low temperatures (T_{eff} < 4800K) and high metallicities, NLTE and 3D effects for Fe I lines are small. These are probably not the reason for the discrepancy between 1D LTE spectroscopic temperatures and the interferometric results. More likely to blame is missing opacity, as suggested by the authors, or the presence of unresolved blends in the line-rich spectra, possibly skewing the results. Another possibility is that the interferometric measurements are subjected to systematic errors in the adopted limb-darkening coefficients (Chiavassa et al. 2010).

References

Baines, E. K., Döllinger, M. P., Cusano, F., Guenther, E. W., Hatzes, A. P., McAlister, H. A., ten Brummelaar, T. A., Turner, N. H., Sturmann, J., Sturmann, L., Goldfinger, P. J., Farrington, C. D., & Ridgway, S. T. 2010, ApJ, 710, 1365. 0912.5491

Carlsson, M. 1986, Uppsala Astronomical Observatory Reports, 33

Casagrande, L., Ramírez, I., Meléndez, J., Bessell, M., & Asplund, M. 2010, A&A, 512, A54+. 1001.3142

Chiavassa, A., Collet, R., Casagrande, L., & Asplund, M. 2010, A&A, 524, A93. 1009.1745

Collet, R., Magic, Z., & Asplund, M. 2011, ArXiv e-prints. 1110.5475

González Hernández, J. I., & Bonifacio, P. 2009, A&A, 497, 497. 0901.3034

Gustafsson, B., Edvardsson, B., Eriksson, K., Jørgensen, U. G., Nordlund, Å., & Plez, B. 2008, A&A, 486, 951. 0805.0554

Kurucz, R. L. 1992, in The Stellar Populations of Galaxies, edited by B. Barbuy & A. Renzini, vol. 149 of IAU Symposium, 225

Mashonkina, L., Gehren, T., Shi, J.-R., Korn, A. J., & Grupp, F. 2011, A&A, 528, A87. 1101.4570

Nordlund, Å., Stein, R. F., & Asplund, M. 2009, Living Reviews in Solar Physics, 6, 2

Önehag, A., Gustafsson, B., Eriksson, K., & Edvardsson, B. 2009, A&A, 498, 527

van Leeuwen, F. 2007, A&A, 474, 653. 0708.1752

Galactic Archaeology: Near-Field Cosmology and the Formation of the Milky Way
ASP Conference Series, Vol. 458
W. Aoki, M. Ishigaki, T. Suda, T. Tsujimoto, N. Arimoto, eds.
© 2012 Astronomical Society of the Pacific

Elemental and Isotopic Abundances and Chemical Evolution of Galaxies

Chiaki Kobayashi

Centre for Astrophysics Research, School of Physics, Astronomy and Mathematics, University of Hertfordshire, UK

Abstract. Elemental and isotopic abundances are the fossils of galactic archaeology. The observed [X/Fe]-[Fe/H] relations in the Galactic bulge and disk and the mass-metallicity relation of galaxies are roughly reproduced with chemodynamical simulations of galaxies under the standard Λ-CDM picture and standard stellar physics. The isotopic ratios such as ^{17,18}O and ^{25,26}Mg may require a refinement of modelling of supernova and asymptotic giant branch stars. The recent observation of the Carbon-rich damped Lyman α system can be reproduced only with faint core-collapse supernovae. This suggests that chemical enrichment by the first stars in the first galaxies is driven not by pair-instability supernovae but by core-collapse supernovae ($\sim 20-50M_\odot$). The observed F abundances can be reproduced with the neutrino processes of core-collapse supernovae. As in F, the observations of elemental abundances in small systems may requires further complications of chemical enrichment. In globular clusters the relative contribution from low-mass supernovae is likely to be smaller than in the field, while the contribution from massive supernovae seems smaller in dwarf spheroidal galaxies than in the solar neighborhood.

1. Introduction

Elemental and isotopic abundances are the fossils of galactic archaeology. Different elements are produced from stars on different timescales, therefore elemental and isotopic abundance ratios provide independent information on the "age" of a system and can be used as a form of "cosmic clock". The formation and evolutionary history of galaxies can be constrained in theoretical models by using the observed abundances of stars. The space astrometry missions (e.g., GAIA) and large-scale surveys (e.g., HERMES on the AAT) will produce unprecedented information on the chemodynamical structure of the Milky Way Galaxy. Theoretically Kobayashi et al. (2006) succeeded in reproducing the average evolution of major elements (except for Ti) in the solar neighbourhood including normal Type II Supernovae (SNe II) and hypernovae (HNe). In this paper we extend the discussion to isotope ratios (§2) and more realistic chemodynamical simulations (§3). From the observed abundances, we discuss the possibility of non-standard chemical enrichment in the very metal-poor damped Lyman α system (DLA, §4), globular clusters (GCs, §5), and dwarf spheroidal galaxies (dSphs, §6).

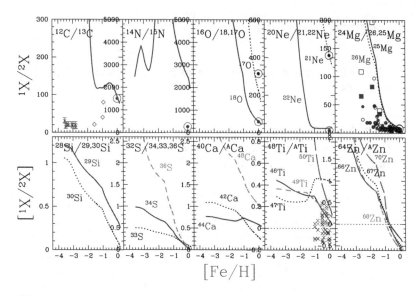

Figure 1.   (color online) Evolution of isotope ratios against [Fe/H] for the solar
neighbourhood with AGB yields. See Kobayashi et al. (2011a) for the observational
data sources for C, Mg, and Ti (dots). The solar ratios are shown with the solar
symbols at [Fe/H] = 0 in the upper panels.

2. Isotope Ratios

We include the latest chemical enrichment input into our chemical evolution models,
which are summarised in Kobayashi et al. (2011a). The basic equations of galactic
chemical evolution are described in Kobayashi et al. (2006). Figure 1 shows the evolution of the isotope ratios against [Fe/H] for the solar neighbourhood. In general,
core-collapse supernovae are the main producers of the major isotopes with more minor isotopes synthesized at higher metallicity. For this reason, the evolution of major
to minor isotope ratios continuously decreases toward higher metallicity. The slope
changes at [Fe/H] ∼ −2.5 and ∼ −1.5 are due to the onset of intermediate- and low-
mass asymptotic giant branch (AGB) stars, respectively. The rapid change in the slope
at [Fe/H] ∼ −1 is caused by Type Ia Supernovae (SNe Ia).

     The time evolution of isotope ratios depends on the star formation and chemical
enrichment histories of the system. See Kobayashi et al. (2011a) for the models of
bulge, thick disk, and halo. In general, the ratios between the major and minor isotopes
such as $^{24}Mg/^{25,26}Mg$ are smaller in the bulge and thick disk, and are larger in the halo
because of the metallicity effect of supernovae. However, the $^{16}O/^{17}O$ ratio in the halo
is low due to the production of ^{17}O from low-mass AGB stars, as also seen in the high
[(C, F)/Fe] abundances. Therefore, the isotopic ratios can be used as a tool to pick out
the stars that form in a system with a low chemical enrichment efficiency. This may be
possible in our halo, but more likely in small satellite galaxies that were accreted onto
our Milky Way Galaxy.

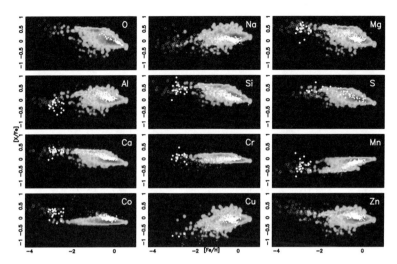

Figure 2.   (color online) [X/Fe]-[Fe/H] relations in the solar neighborhood at $z =$ 0. The contours show the frequency distribution of stars in the simulated galaxies, where red is for the highest frequency. See Kobayashi & Nakasato (2011) for the observational data sources.

3.   Chemodynamical Simulations

In a real galaxy, the star formation history is not so simple and the interstellar medium (ISM) is not homogeneous. In chemodynamical simulation (Kobayashi & Nakasato 2011), hydrodynamics and chemical enrichment are solved self-consistently through the galaxy formation. Star formation and chemical enrichment depend on the local density and mixing due to dynamical effects such as merging and migration are also naturally included. Figure 2 shows the frequency distribution of stars in the solar neighborhood at present. See Kobayashi & Nakasato (2011) for the bulge and the thick disk.

In our simulations, the metallicity of the first enriched stars reaches [Fe/H] ~ −3. At later times, the star forming region becomes denser, and both metal richer and poorer stars than [Fe/H] ~ −3 appear. Different from one-zone chemical evolution models, the following phenomena occur in the case of inhomogeneous enrichment: i) The age-metallicity relation is weak. In other words, the most metal-poor stars are not always the oldest stars. ii) SNe Ia can affect the elemental abundance ratios at [Fe/H] $\lesssim$ − 1 even with the metallicity inhibition of SNe Ia. The SN Ia contribution is characterised by low [α/Fe] and high [Mn/Fe]. iii) The scatter of elemental abundance ratios becomes large if the supernova yield depends on progenitor metallicity such as Na and iv) Some of CEMP/NEMP stars can be explained with the local enrichment from AGB stars even without the binary effect. In fact, the observed [N/O]-[O/H] trend can be reproduced with our simulation without including the effect of rotating massive stars.

4.   Carbon-Enhanced Dampled Lyman α (DLA) System

The observations of very metal-poor DLAs have opened a new window to study the chemical enrichment of the Universe by the first generations of stars. Figure 3 shows the

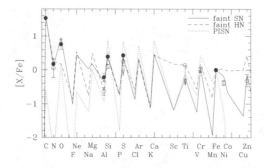

Figure 3.   The elemental abundance pattern of the metal-poor C-rich DLA (filled circles) and peculiar DLA (open circles). The solid and short-dashed lines show the nucleosynthesis yields of faint core-collapse supernovae from $25M_\odot$ stars with mixing-fallback. The dotted line is for PISNe from $170M_\odot$ stars.

elemental abundance ratios from C to Zn relative to Fe. We implement two cases with different explosion energies: 1×10^{51} erg (SN, solid line) and 20×10^{51} erg (HN, short-dashed line) for an initial mass of $M = 25M_\odot$ and metallicity $Z = 0$ (see Kobayashi et al. 2011b for the details). An efficient mixing-fallback is adopted in both models, black hole masses are as large as $\sim 6M_\odot$, and thus the ejected iron mass is much smaller than "normal" SNe/HNe in Kobayashi et al. (2006) that are responsible for the chemical enrichment in the Galaxy. Since C is synthesized in the outermost region of the ejecta, [C/Fe] ratio is higher for faint SNe/HNe than "normal" SNe/HNe.

We then compare these model calculations with the available abundance measurements in the extremely metal-poor DLA reported by Cooke et al. (2010b, filled circles). This DLA was originally identified in the SDSS spectrum of the QSO J0035−0918. Follow-up high resolution spectroscopy indicated $z_{abs} = 2.3400972$, log N(HI) $/\text{cm}^{-2} = 20.55 \pm 0.1$, and [Fe/H] $\simeq -3.04$. 1) A pronounced carbon enhancement [C/Fe] $\simeq +1.53$ is found, which is well reproduced with our faint SN/HN models. Low-mass AGB stars $(1 - 4M_\odot)$ can also provide such high [C/Fe]. However, such low-mass stars are unlikely to contribute at the redshift of the C-rich DLA. With the star formation history in the solar neighborhood, [C/Fe] reaches the maximum value at $z = 1.8$ due to the AGB contribution (Kobayashi et al. 2011a). 2) The [O/Fe] ratio is higher than for non-faint supernovae ([O/Fe] $\sim 0.5 - 0.6$ for $25M_\odot$) and is consistent with the faint SN model because of the smaller ejected Fe mass. 3) The [(Si,S)/Fe] ratios are similar to those of non-faint supernovae, and also consistent with the faint SN/HN models. 4) The low Al abundance strongly suggests that the enrichment source is not Pop II supernovae but primordial supernovae. 5) The low N abundance is also consistent with the faint SN/HN models, and the high [C/N] ratio cannot be explained with mass loss from rotating massive stars or intermediate-mass AGB stars ($>4M_\odot$).

In order to discuss the detailed explosion mechanism of the supernova, it is necessary to obtain the elemental abundances of iron-peak elements. For the C-rich DLA, because of the low metallicity, it is impossible to detect heavier elements than S except for Fe. In Fig. 3 we overplot the element abundances recently reported by Cooke et al. (2010a, open circles) for the $z_{abs} = 1.62650$ DLA in front of the gravitationally lensed quasar UM637A. This abundance pattern can also be explained with faint supernovae.

The dotted line is for the nucleosynthesis yields of the pair instability supernova (PISN) of a $170M_\odot$ star (Umeda & Nomoto 2002). Compared with core-collapse supernovae, the abundance pattern of PISNe can be summarized as follow: 1) The odd-Z effect is much larger than ~ 1 dex. 2) [(Si, S, Ar, Ca)/Fe] are much larger than [(O, Mg)/Fe] because of more extensive explosive oxygen burning. 3) [Cr/Fe] is much larger because of the larger incomplete Si-burning region. 4) [(Co, Zn)/Fe] are much smaller because of the much larger ratio between the complete and incomplete Si-burning regions. All of these characteristics disagree with the observed elemental abundances of these metal-poor DLAs. Even at high-redshift, there is no signature of the existence of PISNe. The [Si/C] for PISNe is as large as +1.5, which is also inconsistent with the observational estimate in the intergalactic medium (IGM, [Si/C] ~ 0.77). The IGM abundance looks more consistent with normal (non-faint) core-collapse supernovae with [C/Fe] ~ 0 and [Si/Fe] ~ 0.7 (Kobayashi et al. 2006).

In the early stages of chemical enrichment, the ISM is supposed to be highly inhomogeneous, so that the properties of the first objects can be directly extracted from the comparison between the observed elemental abundances and nucleosynthesis yields. Since the DLA abundances reflect the chemical enrichment in gas-phase, the binary or accretion scenarios of the EMP stars do not work. To explain the abundance pattern of the C-rich DLA, enrichment by primordial supernovae is the best solution. It is interesting that the observed DLA abundance is very similar to those of EMP stars in the solar neighborhood including the ultra metal-poor star HE0557-4840 ([Fe/H] = −4.75, [C/Fe] = +1.6) and BD+44°493. Some of EMP stars in dSphs and the Galactic outer halo also show similar carbon enhancement at [Fe/H] $\lesssim -3$. Chemical enrichment by the first stars in the first galaxies is likely to be driven by core-collapse supernovae from $\sim 20 - 50M_\odot$ stars, which may be consistent with the latest simulations of primordial star formation (e.g., Greif et al. 2011).

5.   Fluorine Problem and Globular Clusters (GCs)

Fluorine is an intriguing, though currently poorly studied element. ^{19}F is mainly produced by core and shell He-burning at $T \gtrsim 1.5 \times 10^8$ K in low-mass and massive stars. The production of F in AGB stars is highly mass dependent, where F production peaks at $\sim 3M_\odot$ at solar metallicity; in higher mass models F is destroyed by α-captures caused by the higher temperatures reached during He-burning. In Kobayashi et al. (2011c), we have calculated the nucleosynthesis yields of core-collapse supernovae (SNe and HNe) including the ν-process. Most of the energy from core-collapse supernovae is released as neutrinos and anti-neutrinos ($>10^{53}$ erg). The ν-process does not affect the yields of major elements such as Fe and α elements, but it increases those of some elements such as B, F, K, Sc, V, Mn, and Ti.

Figure 4 shows the evolution of [F/O] against [O/H]. Without the AGB yields and the ν-process (short-dashed line), the predicted F abundance is too low to meet the observational data at all metallicities. With the AGB yields (long-dashed line), [F/O] shows a rapid increase from [O/H] $\gtrsim -1.2$ toward higher metallicities, which corresponds to the timescale of $2 - 4M_\odot$ stars in the solar neighborhood. At [O/H] ~ 0, [F/O] reaches −0.14, which is 0.26 dex larger than the case without the AGB yields. However, the present [F/O] ratio is still significantly lower than the observations at

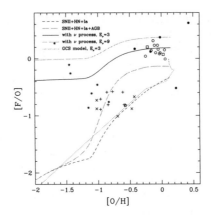

Figure 4.   (color online) Evolution of the [F/O] ratio against [O/H] for the solar neighbourhood with SNe II, HNe, and SNe Ia only (short-dashed lines), with AGB stars (long-dashed lines), with the ν-process of SNe II and HNe (solid line and dot-dashed line for $E_\nu = 3 \times 10^{53}$ and 9×10^{53} erg, respectively). The dotted line is for the model for GCs. See Kobayashi et al. (2011c) for the observational data sources.

[O/H] ~ 0. Note that the F yields from AGB stars were increased with updated reaction rates.

The timescale of supernovae is much shorter than AGB stars, which means that the [F/O] ratio at low metallicities can be strongly enhanced by the ν-process occurring in core-collapse supernovae. With the standard neutrino luminosity $E_\nu = 3 \times 10^{53}$ erg (solid line), the [F/O] ratio shows a plateau of [F/O] ~ -0.4 at [O/H] $\lesssim -1.2$, and reaches [F/O] $\sim +0.19$ at [O/H] $\gtrsim 0$. This is consistent with the observational data of field stars at $-0.5 \lesssim$ [O/H] $\lesssim 0$. If we adopt a larger $E_\nu = 9 \times 10^{53}$ erg (dot-dashed line), [F/O] can be as large as $\sim +0.37$ at [O/H] ~ 0. In the bulge the star formation timescale is shorter and the average metallicity is higher than the solar neighborhood, but the [F/O] ratio is not so different at [O/H] ~ 0. The observations for the bulge stars (filled circles) might suggest that the initial mass function is also different, although the number of observations is too small to make a conclusion.

At $-1 \lesssim$ [F/O] $\lesssim -0.5$ the observational data are for stars in GCs, which seem to be more consistent with the models with the AGB yields only than with the ν-process. However, it is unlikely that the existence of the ν-process depends on the environment or metallicity. The neutrino luminosity may be small in the case of faint supernovae with a large black hole, which give high [α/Fe], but there is no significant difference seen in the [α/Fe] ratio between field halo stars and GC stars. One possible scenario is as follows: in GCs, the contribution from low-mass supernovae is smaller than in the filed. Since the star formation occurs in a baryon dominated cloud with very high density, the initial star burst can be very intense. After the initial star burst, because of the small gravitational potential, galactic winds are generated immediately after the explosion of massive supernovae, which may remove the contribution from low-mass supernovae. The small production of α elements from low mass supernovae means that the [F/O] ratio can reach values as large as ~ 0. In contrast, massive supernovae produce more α elements which results in [F/O] ratios of ~ -0.5, consistent with the observational data.

The dotted line shows an example of such a GC model (see Kobayashi et al. 2011c for the details).

At low metallicities ($[O/H] \lesssim -1.2$) F is produced only from supernovae, and thus the observations of field stars at low-metallicities are important for constraining the neutrino luminosity released from a core-collapse supernova. If the neutrino luminosity is specified, the F abundance along with C could be a good clock in the study of galactic archaeology to distinguish the contribution from AGB stars and supernovae.

6. Dwarf Spheroidal Galaxies (dSphs)

The F observations of stars in GCs suggest that the star formation and chemical enrichment histories of GCs are different from those of field stars and that low-mass supernova played a smaller role in shaping the chemical evolution of these systems. This is the opposite to the situation for dSphs. DSphs show low $[\alpha/Fe]$ and low $[Mn/Fe]$ (Romano et al. 2011), of which elemental abundance pattern is more consistent with the enrichment from low-mass SNe II than that from the SN Ia enrichment (Kobayashi et al. 2006, see also Figure 20 of Kobayashi & Nakasato 2011). There is no strong metallicity dependence on Mn yields of SNe Ia (Ohkubo, Nomoto et al, in prep.). In dSphs, the dark matter component is large, the gas density is low, the star formation rate is low, and thus the contribution from massive supernovae is expected to be smaller than in the Milky Way halo. The elemental abundance pattern (low $[(Cu, Zn)/Fe]$) of anomaly stars in the Galactic halo (Nissen & Shuster 2011) is also consistent with low-mass SNe II.

References

Cooke, R., Pettini, M., Steidel, C. C., et al. 2010a, MNRAS, 409, 679
Cooke, R., Pettini, M., Steidel, C. C., et al. 2010b, MNRAS, 412, 1047
Greif, T. H. et al. 2011, ApJ, 737, 75
Kobayashi, C., Karakas, I. A., & Umeda, H. 2011a, MNRAS, 414, 3231
Kobayashi, C., & Nakasato, N. 2011, ApJ, 729, 16
Kobayashi, C., Tominaga, N., & Nomoto, K. 2011b, ApJ, 730, L14
Kobayashi, C., Umeda, H., Nomoto, K., Tominaga, N., & Ohkubo, T. 2006, ApJ, 653, 1145
Kobayashi, C., Izutani, N., Karakas, A. I. et al, 2011c, ApJ, 739, L57
Nissen, P. E. & Shuster, W. J. 2011, A&A, 530, 15
Romano, D., Cescutti, G., & Matteucci, F. 2011, MNRAS, 418, 696
Umeda, H. & Nomoto, K. 2002, ApJ, 565, 385

Poster session on November 1st. A. Goswami (left) and K. Nomoto.

Galactic Archaeology: Near-Field Cosmology and the Formation of the Milky Way
ASP Conference Series, Vol. 458
W. Aoki, M. Ishigaki, T. Suda, T. Tsujimoto, N. Arimoto, eds.
© 2012 Astronomical Society of the Pacific

From the Solar Neighbourhood to the Galactic Disc(s)

Luca Casagrande

Max Planck Institute for Astrophysics, Garching, Germany

Abstract. We present a re-analysis of the Geneva-Copenhagen Survey (GCS), based on improved effective temperature and metallicity scales, which also provide a better match to theoretical isochrones. The latter are used for a Bayesian investigation on stellar ages. With respect to previous analyses, our stars are on average 100 K hotter and 0.1 dex more metal rich, which shifts the peak of the metallicity distribution function (MDF) around the solar value. From Strömgren photometry we are able to derive for the first time a proxy for alpha elements, which enables us to perform a tentative dissection of the chemical thin and thick disc. We find evidence for the latter being composed of an old, mildly but systematically alpha-enhanced population that extends to super solar metallicities. These findings help to constrain different processes potentially relevant in the build-up of the Milky Way disc.

1. Introduction

Late-type dwarf stars are long-lived objects and can be regarded as snapshots of the stellar populations that are formed at different times and places over the history of our Galaxy. Therefore, they have been historically used to study various aspects of the chemical evolution of the Milky Way, and the solar neighbourhood in particular (e.g. Edvardsson et al. 1993; Nordström et al. 2004). While spectroscopic studies allow detailed abundance investigations, currently they are still limited to small samples of a few hundred or about a thousand stars at most, and must use sophisticated kinematic selections to sample significant numbers of members belonging to different Galactic subpopulations. On the contrary, photometric catalogues have access to several thousands of stars –such as the GCS (Nordström et al. 2004)– and thus are largely free from selection biases, but have to pay for this by being only able to derive one single parameter for metallicity (and no detailed elemental abundances) from photometry.

We present a revision of the astrophysical parameters in the GCS with the new effective temperature (T_{eff}) scale presented in Casagrande et al. (2010) as a starting point to derive new metallicities and ages. We improve not only on the accuracy, i.e. reduce zeropoint systematics, but also the precision by avoiding photometric transformations. These improvements are crucial to provide more stringent observational constraints on Galactic chemical evolution theories and hence on the history of the Milky Way. Among other things (e.g. Chiappini et al. 2001), a knowledge of the MDF together with Galactic abundance gradients can improve our understanding of the impact and shape of the stellar migration process in the Galactic disc (Schönrich & Binney 2009a,b). Because models including radial migration relax the classical tight correlation between age and metallicity, this relation becomes an additional constraint independent from the

MDF. Furthermore, being able for the first time to derive an estimate for α-elements from Strömgren photometry allows for a tentative dissection of the chemical thin and thick disc with a sample exceeding the largest spectroscopic studies available so far.

2. Determination of astrophysical parameters

The GCS provides the ideal database for studies dealing with Galactic chemical and dynamical evolution: it is kinematically unbiased, all its stars have Hipparcos parallaxes and highly homogeneous photometry (Strömgren, Tycho2 and 2MASS).

Effective temperatures: the infrared flux method described in Casagrande et al. (2006, 2010) not only improves the accuracy of the zeropoint of the derived stellar parameters, but also their precision by employing Tycho2 and 2MASS photometry to simultaneously recover the bolometric flux and the effective temperature of each star. Thus, it is well suited to be applied to the GCS catalogue directly, avoiding the use of colour calibrations as well as transformations among different photometric systems. Compared to previous GCS calibrations, our effective temperatures are on average hotter by about 80 – 100 K. The HR diagram constructed using our newly derived T_{eff} scale matches very well that predicted by stellar models for evolved F and G dwarfs (VandenBerg et al. 2010; Brasseur et al. 2010), and the uncertainties which might still affect the cool end of the main sequence (Casagrande et al. 2007; Portinari et al. 2010) are thus of no concern for the sake of the GCS analysis.

Metallicities: since the adopted T_{eff} scale has immediate consequences on abundances, we recalibrated Strömgren indices versus stellar metallicities using a sample of nearly 1500 stars with high-resolution spectroscopic abundances derived adopting T_{eff} consistent with ours. For the first time we are able to derive rough estimates for alpha elements (αFe) from Strömgren photometry. The method becomes less reliable for increasingly hotter objects and also for metal-poor stars ($\lesssim -1$ dex), but focusing on disc stars gives a reasonable guidance on the *relative* alpha enhancements for the whole sample. The new metallicity scale was then checked against open clusters and a moving group, showing indeed a high degree of internal consistency with a suggested intrinsic scatter below 0.10 dex. The recently measured Strömgren solar colours (Meléndez et al. 2010) finally corroborate the agreement between the temperature and metallicity scales.

Ages: revising metallicities and effective temperatures also affects age and mass estimates for the stars. Compared to previous studies, our improved effective temperatures are hotter and the large systematic discrepancies between theoretical isochrones and observed data that plagued e.g., Nordström et al. (2004) almost entirely disappear, without having to introduce metallicity–dependent temperature shifts to reconcile isochrones with data. This greatly reduces the risk of introducing an artificial age–metallicity relationship. Naïve fits to isochrones lead to severe biases, e.g. the terminal age bias. This happens because some places on isochrones are more densely populated than others; just looking for the closest match ignores these facts and might erroneously place too many stars into sparsely populated regions of the HR diagram. Biases of this kind can be accounted for by taking a Bayesian approach as described e.g. in Pont & Eyer (2004). Here we implement the same technique, where isochrones provide a grid for calculating the probability distribution function of the parameters of any given star. In order to study differences between different isochrones, we used grids of the BASTI (Pietrinferni et al. 2009) and Padova (Bertelli et al. 2008) isochrones, obtaining similar results.

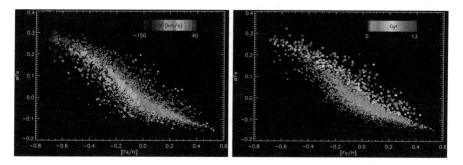

Figure 1.   (color online) *Left:* photometric alpha estimates αFe versus [Fe/H] according to the V velocities of the stars (represented by different tones). *Right:* same as in left panel, with different tones now representing stars of different ages. Ages are derived using the Bayesian isochrone fitting described in Section 2.

3. Observational constraints: classical and new

Classical: given its nearly volume complete nature, the GCS is well suited for the study of the MDF in the solar neighbourhood. As a consequence of our revised metallicity scale, the peak of the MDF is only slightly subsolar, thus making the Sun a completely average star given its metallicity. The MDF has been historically used to constrain the gas infall rate (Lynden-Bell 1975), but slicing it into different age intervals suggests that old stars are also a relevant ingredient in describing the wings of the MDF. A natural explanation to this is provided by radial migration, where the solar neighbourhood is not only assembled from local stars, following a local age-metallicity relation, but also originating from the inner (more metal-rich) and outer (more metal-poor) Galactic disc that have migrated to the present position on different timescales (Roškar et al. 2008; Schönrich & Binney 2009a).

The GCS has a small spatial extent, but in principle its large number of stars would still allow for an estimate of the radial metallicity gradients in the Galactic disc. This can mostly be achieved by using the azimuthal velocities (V) of stars which give the abundance gradient in angular momentum, which is by the flat rotation curve of the Milky Way disc directly related to the Galactocentric radius they stem from. However, its exact value depends on the adopted kinematic or metallicity cuts to avoid halo contamination, as well as the age interval considered. Difficulties in estimating e.g. the interdependence between age and kinematic cuts (as stars with increasing asymmetric drift are preferentially older, see also Fig. 1) as well as the increasing scatter in the age-metallicity and in the age-dispersion relation further complicate the picture (Casagrande et al. 2011). Thus, despite being extremely powerful in constraining chemical models for the disc, metallicity gradients should always be taken *cum grano salis*.

New: the Milky Way is usually dissected into two-component disc, which was first proposed to fit the vertical density profile derived from star counts (Yoshii 1982; Gilmore & Reid 1983). Disentangling the nature and origin of these components is therefore highly relevant for understanding galaxy formation. Though limited to the solar neighbourhood, the GCS can provide important insights, because it is essentially free from kinematic selections. Our metallicities and alpha estimates provide for the first time a way to investigate this with a more complete sample. Fig. 1 shows the αFe vs. [Fe/H] using our revised GCS sample, where stars with different rotation velocities (V) and ages are depicted by different tones. Clearly, this is only a rough criterion for the division and this selection is not stringent in targeting single disc "components", yet a striking difference appears. At each metallicity, the stars with highly negative V velocities, or at high/large asymmetric drift (graymost tones in the left panel) have higher average αFe. This can be expected because stars with such a large asymmetric drift should be significantly older than the remaining population (because of the asymmetric drift–dispersion and the age–dispersion relations), which is confirmed by their ages in the right panel, which are indeed older (lightmost tones). Our analysis thus confirms a similar result drawn by Haywood (2008) from a smaller spectroscopic sample. Because of the tight age–metallicity relation in chemical evolution models without radial migration, older and more alpha-enhanced stars are expected to be more metal-poor. Yet Fig. 1 rather tells the opposite, at a given alpha value the the old stars are on average more metal-rich than the population with positive rotation velocities. The emergence of a metal-rich, old thick disc was already noticed in the spectroscopic study of Feltzing & Bensby (2008), and a metal-rich alpha-rich population has also been recently confirmed by Adibekyan et al. (2011). This apparently surprising behaviour is however readily explained if there is no strong age–metallicity dependence and if the lagging metal-rich population comprises –to some extent at least– objects from the inner disc, which are more metal-rich thanks to the Galactic metallicity gradient.

Acknowledgments. The author wishes to acknowledge the organizers for financial support, a stimulating conference and an outstanding selection of wines.

References

Adibekyan, V. Z., Santos, N. C., Sousa, S. G., & Israelian, G. 2011, A&A, 535, L11.
Bertelli, G., Girardi, L., Marigo, P., & Nasi, E. 2008, A&A, 484, 815.
Brasseur, C. M., Stetson, P. B., VandenBerg, D. A., Casagrande, L., Bono, G., & Dall'Ora, M. 2010, AJ, 140, 1672.
Casagrande, L., Portinari, L., & Flynn, C. 2006, MNRAS, 373, 13.
Casagrande, L., Flynn, C., Portinari, L., Girardi, L., & Jimenez, R. 2007, MNRAS, 382, 1516.
Casagrande, L., Ramírez, I., Meléndez, J., Bessell, M., & Asplund, M. 2010, A&A, 512, A54+.
Casagrande, L., Schönrich, R., Asplund, M., Cassisi, S., Ramírez, I., Meléndez, J., Bensby, T., & Feltzing, S. 2011, A&A, 530, A138.
Chiappini, C., Matteucci, F., & Romano, D. 2001, ApJ, 554, 1044.
Edvardsson, B., Andersen, J., Gustafsson, B., et al., 1993, A&A, 275, 101
Feltzing, S., & Bensby, T. 2008, Physica Scripta Volume T, 133, 014031.
Gilmore, G., & Reid, N. 1983, MNRAS, 202, 1025
Haywood, M. 2008, MNRAS, 388, 1175.
Lynden-Bell, D. 1975, Vistas in Astronomy, 19, 299
Meléndez, J., Schuster, W. J., Silva, J. S., Ramírez, I., Casagrande, L., & Coelho, P. 2010, A&A, 522, A98+.
Nordström, B., Mayor, M., Andersen, J., et al., 2004, A&A, 418, 989.
Pietrinferni, A., Cassisi, S., Salaris, M., Percival, S., & Ferguson, J. W. 2009, ApJ, 697, 275.
Pont, F., & Eyer, L. 2004, ApJ, 351, 487
Portinari, L., Casagrande, L., & Flynn, C. 2010, MNRAS, 406, 1570.
Roškar, R., Debattista, V. P., Quinn, T. R., Stinson, G. S., & Wadsley, J. 2008, ApJ, 684, L79.
Schönrich, R., & Binney, J. 2009a, MNRAS, 396, 203.
— 2009b, MNRAS, 399, 1145.
VandenBerg, D. A., Casagrande, L., & Stetson, P. B. 2010, AJ, 140, 1020
Yoshii, Y. 1982, PASJ, 34, 365

Galactic Archaeology: Near-Field Cosmology and the Formation of the Milky Way
ASP Conference Series, Vol. 458
W. Aoki, M. Ishigaki, T. Suda, T. Tsujimoto, N. Arimoto, eds.
© *2012 Astronomical Society of the Pacific*

RAMSES-CH: A New Chemodynamics Code

C. Gareth Few,[1] Stéphanie Courty,[2] and Brad K. Gibson[1]

[1]*Jeremiah Horrocks Insitute, University of Central Lancashire, Preston, PR1 2HE, UK*

[2]*Centre de Recherche Astrophysique de Lyon, Ecole Normale Supérieure de Lyon, Lyon, F-69007, France*

Abstract. We present a new chemodynamical code based on the adaptive mesh refinement code RAMSES. The new code uses Eulerian hydrodynamics and N-body dynamics in a cosmological framework to trace the production and advection of several chemical species. It is the first such code to follow the self-consistent evolution of chemical elements in cosmological volumes while maintaining sub-kiloparsec resolution. The code will be used to simulate disk galaxies and explore the influence of chemical evolution models and star formation on galactic abundance ratios.

There are numerous cosmological codes on the market but studies of chemical evolution (CE) are limited to smoothed particle hydrodynamics with a dearth of Eulerian implementations that include a detailed chemical evolution model. With the aim of providing a complementary approach to existing CE codes we present a fully cosmological, CE code with an adaptive mesh refinement hydrodynamics scheme that traces the formation and subsequent evolution of H, He, C, N, O, Ne, Mg, Si and Fe. The model presented here uses a Kroupa et al. (1993) initial mass fraction (IMF), a SNIa delayed time distribution inspired by Kawata & Gibson (2003). Stellar lifetimes are taken from Kodama & Arimoto (1997), SNIa yields from Iwamoto et al. (1999), SNII yields from Woosley & Weaver (1995) and AGB stellar wind yields from van den Hoek & Groenewegen (1997).

1. Results

Our code is applied to cosmological simulations of disk galaxies achieving a resolution of 436 pc. The galaxy presented is a field spiral galaxy of total mass $6.8 \times 10^{11} M_\odot$. This galaxy will be used as a fiducial model for a series of test runs using different IMFs and SNIa models to ascertain the influence that each of these ingredients has on the abundance ratios, metallicity gradients, morphology and kinematics of the galaxy. A degree of success is achieved in fitting observations of the Milky Way disk (however we stress that this galaxy is by no means a Milky Way clone) but most parameter combinations are too α-rich at the high metallicity end of the distribution. It is believed that this can be traced to the relatively low SNIa rate and future runs will explore this in more detail.

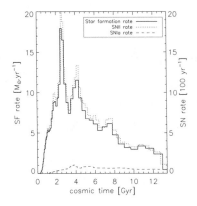 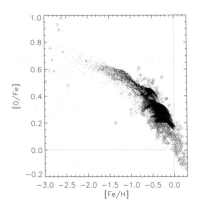

Figure 1.   Star formation and SN rates (left panel).   The z=0 SN rates are
SNII=0.763$S\,NuM$ and SNIa=0.096$S\,NuM$ (SN per century per $10^{10}M_\odot$) and com-
pare favourably with those observed by Mannucci et al. (2008) of $0.652^{+0.164}_{-0.134}S\,NuM$
(SNII) and $0.140^{+0.045}_{-0.035}S\,NuM$ for (SNIa) in field Sbc/d galaxies. An example of
[O/Fe] vs. [Fe/H] (right panel) for the particular CE model used in this run. Ob-
servational data is plotted in grey, Cayrel et al. (2004) (crosses), F/G/K dwarfs from
Ramírez et al. (2007) (diamonds) and solar neighborhood F/G stars from Bensby
et al. (2004) (triangles).

2. Summary

We present the first of what will become a suite of Eulerian cosmological disk galaxy
simulations with CE and sub-kpc resolution. The first simulations show a good agreement of the SN rates with observations and an improved rotation curve with respect to
their counterparts created with the standard feedback mechanism. A great deal of variation in abundance ratios is seen under changes in initial mass function slope, upper
mass limit and SNIa delayed time distribution. Future work will explore a full range in
parameter space to constrain the CE of disk galaxies.

Acknowledgments.   We would like to acknowledge contributions to this work from
Daisuke Kawata, Romain Teyssier and Francesco Calura. We also acknowledge the
STFC programmes (ST/F007701/1;ST/F002432/1;ST/G003025/1), the CC-IN2P3 Com-
puting Center and the HPC resources of CINES under the allocation 2010-c2011046642.

References

Bensby, T., Feltzing, S., & Lundström, I. 2004, A&A, 415, 155
Cayrel, R. et al. 2004, A&A, 416, 1117
Iwamoto, K. et al. 1999, ApJS, 125, 439
Kawata, D., & Gibson, B. K. 2003, MNRAS, 340, 908
Kodama, T., & Arimoto, N. 1997, A&A, 320, 41
Kroupa, P., Tout, C. A., & Gilmore, G. 1993, MNRAS, 262, 545
Mannucci, F. et al. 2008, MNRAS, 383, 1121
Ramírez, I., Allende Prieto, C., & Lambert, D. L. 2007, A&A, 465, 271
van den Hoek, L. B., & Groenewegen, M. A. T. 1997, A&A, 123, 305
Woosley, S. E., & Weaver, T. A. 1995, ApJS, 101, 181

Galactic Archaeology: Near-Field Cosmology and the Formation of the Milky Way
ASP Conference Series, Vol. 458
W. Aoki, M. Ishigaki, T. Suda, T. Tsujimoto, N. Arimoto, eds.
©*2012 Astronomical Society of the Pacific*

Contribution of HdC Stars to the Galactic Enrichment: The Sr-rich HdC Star HE 1015-2050

Aruna Goswami[1] and Wako Aoki[2]

[1]*Indian Institute of Astrophysics, Koramangala, Bangalore 560034, India*

[2]*NAOJ, 2-21-1, Osawa, Mitaka, Tokyo 181-8588, Japan*

Abstract. A fraction of the rare class of Hydrogen-deficient carbon (HdC) stars in our Galaxy are known to exhibit strong features of light neutron-capture elements such as Sr, Y and Zr usually attributed to the weak component of the s-process. Believed to be in a very short-lived evolutionary phase, their ejecta could have significantly contributed to chemical enrichment in the Galaxy. The origin of these stars have long been disputed and poorly understood due to a lack of statistically significant sample. From medium-resolution spectral analyses of a sample of 250 faint high latitude carbon (FHLC) stars, Goswami et al. (2010) have added a new member HE 1015-2050 to this rare class that is found to exhibit anomalously strong features of Sr in its spectrum. Possible scenarios that might have led to the formation of this object are discussed in the light of existing scenarios of HdC star formation.

1. Introduction

HdC stars form a rare class of objects. Only five HdC stars that are non-variable and fifty five HdC stars of R Coronae Borealis (RCB) type are known so far in our Galaxy. The rarity of these objects is a primary constraint for understanding the origin of these objects. Each addition to this rare group is therefore important for population studies which will help better understanding of the origin of these mysterious stars. HE 1015−2050, a recent addition to this rare class is thus quite significant. This object and a previously known HdC star of RCB type U Aquarii (U Aqr, HE 2200−1652) are the only two HdC stars found in the sample of 403 FHLC stars offered by Christlieb et al. (2001) from Hamburg/ESO survey covering a survey area of ~ 6400 deg^2. The surface density of HdC stars is quite low, ~ 0.0003 deg^{-2}. However, newly discovered HdC stars are mostly cool objects ($T_{eff} < 6000$ K). This indicates that observational bias may have precluded their discovery and that the over all contribution of these objects to Galactic enrichment of heavy elements may not be negligible.

2. Spectral characteristics of HE 1015−2050

The spectrum of HE 1015−2050 is characterized by strong C_2 molecular bands. H_α feature is not detected. The G-band of CH at about 4300 Å is also weak or absent indicating that it is a hydrogen-deficient star. The spectrum exhibits extraordinarily strong features of Sr at 4077 Å and 4215 Å but no significant enhancement of Ba II features at 4554 Å and 6495 Å. These features are also characteristics of U Aqr.

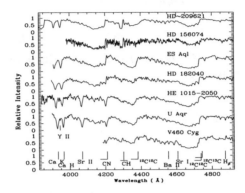

Figure 1.   Absence or a weak-detection of G-band of CH at about 4310 Å indicates hydrogen deficient nature of HE 1015–2050. Strong features of Sr II at 4077 Å and 4215 Å are indicated. (Ref Figure 1 of Goswami et al. (2010) for details)

3.   Discussion and conclusions

The stellar atmosphere of HE 1015–2050 has an effective temperature of 5263 K, similar to those of cool Galactic RCB stars such as S Aps, WX CrA and U Aqr. The strong Sr II features observed in HE 1015–2050 indicate that its atmosphere is enriched with material resulting from weak s-process. Three possibilities can give rise to such enhancement. The object may have been in a binary system with a companion that had undergone unusual s-process enrichment and transferred mass to this object. At present, this scenario is not directly applicable as there is no evidence that the star is a binary. A second possibility is that the object is formed out of material which is already enriched with s-process material. As the spectrum of HE 1015–2050 does not show enhancement in heavy s-process elements such as Ba, it seems necessary for the s-process to produce only light s-process material. This requires a low neutron density. Assuming all other parameters same higher neutron-densities produce larger amounts of heavier elements than the lighter ones (Smith 2005). Thirdly, as suggested for U Aqr (Bond et al. 1979) HE 1015–2050 could also be a He-C core of an evolved star of near-solar initial mass that ejected its H-rich envelope at the He core flesh. A single neutron exposure occurred at the flash, resulting in a brief neutron irradiation producing only the light s-process elements. These possible contributions of s-process elements to the Galactic enrichment are unique to HdC stars and are quite evidently different from the contributions of usual Asymptotic Giant Branch (AGB) stars, in particular metal-poor AGB stars. Thus with regard to the heavy elements HdC stars could make unique contributions to the Galactic chemical evolution.

Acknowledgments.   AG gratefully acknowledes the LOC for local hospitality.

References

Bond, H. E., Luck, R. E. & Newman, M. J., 1979, ApJ, 233, 205
Christlieb N., Green, P. J., Wisotzki, L., Reimers, D., 2001, A&A, 375, 366
Goswami, A., Karinkuzhi, D., Shantikumar, N. S. 2010, ApJ, 723, L238
Smith, V. V. 2005, ASP Conf. Ser. 336, p 165

Galactic Archaeology: Near-Field Cosmology and the Formation of the Milky Way
ASP Conference Series, Vol. 458
W. Aoki, M. Ishigaki, T. Suda, T. Tsujimoto, N. Arimoto, eds.
©2012 Astronomical Society of the Pacific

Type-Ia SNR-Shell at z=3.5 Seen in the Three Sightlines toward the Gravitationally Lensed QSO B1422+231

Satoshi Hamano,[1] Naoto Kobayashi,[2] Sohei Kondo,[3] Takuji Tsujimoto,[4] Katsuya Okoshi,[5] and Toshikazu Shigeyama[6]

[1,2]*Institute of Astronomy, University of Tokyo, 2-21-1 Osawa, Mitaka, Tokyo 181-0015, Japan*

[3]*Facility of Science, Kyoto-Sangyo University, Motoyama, Kamigamo, Kita-Ku, Kyoto 603-8555, Japan*

[4]*National Astronomy Observatory of Japan, 2-21-1 Osawa, Mitaka, Tokyo 181-0015, Japan*

[5]*Tokyo University of Science, 102-1 Tomino, Oshamanbe, Hokkaido, 049-3514, Japan*

[6]*Research Center for the Early Universe, University of Tokyo, 7-3-1 Hongo, Bunkyo, Tokyo 113-0033, Japan*

Abstract. By making use of high spatial resolution of Subaru 8.2m Telescope and IRCS Echelle spectrograph, we obtained high-resolution near-infrared spectra of images A and B (AB ~ 0".5) of the gravitationally lensed QSO B1422+231 ($z = 3.628$) consisting of four known lensed images. We detected MgII and FeII absorption lines at $z = 3.54$, which show a large variance of column densities and velocities between the sightlines A and B with a projected separation of only $8.4h_{70}^{-1}$ pc at the redshift. The observed systematic variances between images A and B imply that the absorbing gas cloud is an expanding shell of a supernova remnant (SNR) as originally suggested by Rauch et al. for images A and C. Along with the Fe richness of the gas cloud, we conclude that the SNR is produced by a SNIa explosion.

1. Variances of Absorption Lines at z=3.54

We obtained near-infrared (1.01 - 1.38 μm) high-resolution (R=10,000) spectra of images A and B of gravitationally lensed QSO B1422+231 with Subaru 8.2 m telescope and IRCS echelle spectrograph. We detected MgII $\lambda\lambda2796, 2803$ absorption lines of the z=3.54 system, which had been found in images A and C in optical spectra by Rauch et al.(1999) (Figure 1). The projected separation between A and B images at z=3.54 is just $8.4h_{70}^{-1}$ pc and we found considerable differences of column density ($\Delta(\log N)$ ~ 0.3 dex) and velocity shear (Δv ~ 10 km s^{-1}) between both images on such a small scale (Figure 1).

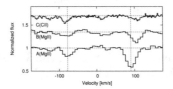

Figure 1.   The velocity profiles of the z=3.54 system for images A (MgII, R=10,000), B (MgII, R=10,000), and C (CII from Rauch et al. 1999, R=70,000) from bottom to top. The velocity is relative to z = 3.53850. Velocity intervals, which become large from image A to C, indicate the expanding kinematics of a gas cloud.

2.   Discovery of Type-Ia SNR remnant

Considering the physical origin of the differences of α-elements absorption lines among three images A, B and C, we conclude that the z=3.54 system is an expanding shell as originally suggested by Rauch et al.(1999). The information of *three images* enable us to analyse the three-dimensional structure of the absorbing gas cloud for the first time and we constrain the expanding velocity and radius of the z = 3.54 system as ~ 130 km s^{-1} and 50-100 pc, respectively (Figure 2). Therefore, we concluded that this z=3.54 system is a supernova remnant (SNR) shell.

We also found that the FeII absorption lines of the z=3.54 system have much larger column density and Doppler width than those of the weak MgII systems in the literature. The small column density ratio logN(MgII)/N(FeII) (=0.31±0.07) is indicative of the richness of the iron of the z=3.54 system. We also estimated the mass of FeII as 0.07-0.29 $M_\odot$ which is roughly consistent with the yield of observed SNe Ia. Moreover, the large Doppler width of FeII, which is interpreted as the existence of one more velocity component that is blueshifted and extremely Fe-rich, suggests that the Fe-rich gas cloud is localized in the expanding shell of the SNR. From these results, we conclude that the SNR shell at the z=3.54 is produced by SN Ia explosion.

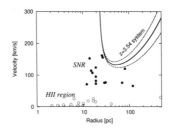

Figure 2.   The relation of radius and expansion velocity of the expanding shell model of the z = 3.54 system. The dotted lines along the solid line show 1σ uncertainty of our calculation. The filled and open circles show the radius and expansion velocity of the observed SNRs and HII regions in our Galaxy.

References

Rauch, M., Sargent, W. L. W., & Barlow, T. A. 1999, ApJ, 515, 500

Galactic Archaeology: Near-Field Cosmology and the Formation of the Milky Way
ASP Conference Series, Vol. 458
W. Aoki, M. Ishigaki, T. Suda, T. Tsujimoto, N. Arimoto, eds.
© *2012 Astronomical Society of the Pacific*

Hierarchical Chemical Evolution and R-process Elements of Extremely Metal-Poor Stars

Yutaka Komiya,[1] Shimako Yamada,[2] Takuma Suda,[1] and
Masayuki Y. Fujimoto[2]

[1]*National Astronomical Observatory of Japan*

[2]*Hokkaido University*

Abstract. We present results of the new chemical evolution model which focus on extremely metal-poor (EMP) stars and discuss r-process element abundances. We built a merger tree of the Galaxy and follow the enrichment of the chemical abundance along the tree. We also follow the inhomogeneous metal enrichment process of intergalactic matter and surface pollution of EMP stars by accretion of interstellar matter (ISM). Our model well reproduces observed abundance distributions. O-Ne-Mg supernovae with 9-10 $M_\odot$ are the most plausible source of the r-process elements.

1. Introduction

In the concordance cosmology, galaxies are formed hierarchically through recurrent mergers of small galaxies. Extremely metal poor (EMP; [Fe/H] < -2.5 in this paper) stars as living fossils of the early universe are thought to be formed in these small galaxies. To investigate element abundances of EMP stars, the hierarchical nature of the galaxy formation should be taken into account in chemical evolution studies.

Observationally, it is known that neutron capture element abundances of EMP stars show very large scatter (e.g. McWilliam et al. 1995). For EMP stars, r-process is the dominant source for all the neutron capture elements. Some stars with very large r-process element enhancement ([Eu/Fe]$> +1.0$) are referred to as r-II stars.

R-process thought to be associated with a supernova (SN) explosion or a neutron-star merger but astronomical site of r-process is not yet specified. Observed large scatter indicates that only a portion of SNe is a dominant r-process source.

2. Computation Method

We build a merger tree based on the extended Press-Schechter theory. We follow chemical evolution along the tree. Each mini-halo is assumed to be chemically homogeneous. We register all the individual stars in the computations. Masses of stars are assigned randomly following the high-mass initial mass function (IMF) derived by Komiya et al. (2007). We also follow the inhomogeneous metal enrichment process of intergalactic matter. Surface pollution of EMP stars by accretion of interstellar matter (ISM) is traced assuming Bondy-Hoyle accretion. Detailed model description is in Komiya et al. (2009, 2011).

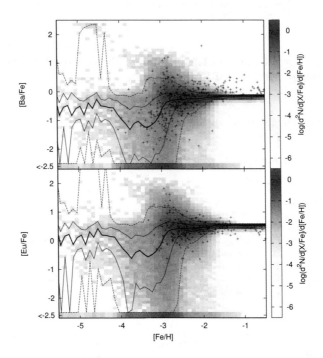

Figure 1.   (Color online) Abundance distributions of Ba and Eu against [Fe/H]. Predicted number density of stars per unit area of Δ[Fe/H] = Δ[r/Fe] = 0.1 is color coded. Blue lines are 5, 25, 50, 75, 95 percentile curves of predicted distributions. Crosses(+) denote abundances of observed stars registered in SAGA database.

3. Results

The model assuming that O-Ne-Mg SNe with $9 - 10M_\odot$ are the r-process source well reproduces observed trend and scatter of [Ba/Fe] and [Eu/Fe], as shown in Figure 1. Models with wider mass range for r-process site predict smaller abundance scatters. When high-mass SNe assumed to be the r-process sites, decreasing trend of [Ba/Fe] as decreasing metallicity for EMP stars is not reproduced. Predicted number and typical metallicity of r-II stars by our O-Ne-Mg SN model are consistent with observations.

References

Komiya, Y., Habe, A., Suda, T., & Fujimoto, Y. M. 2009, ApJ, 696L, 79
Komiya, Y., Suda, T., Minaguchi, H., Shigeyama, T., Aoki, W., & Fujimoto, Y. M. 2007, ApJ, 658, 367
Komiya, Y., Yamada, S., Suda, T., & Fujimoto, Y. M. 2011, in preparation.
McWilliam, A, Preston, G. W., Sneden, C., & Searle, Leonard, 1995, AJ, 109, 2757
Suda, T., Katsuta, Y., Yamada, S., Katsuta, Y., Komiya, Y., Ishizuka, C., Aoki, W., & Fujimoto, M. Y. 2011, MNRAS, 412, 843

Galactic Archaeology: Near-Field Cosmology and the Formation of the Milky Way
ASP Conference Series, Vol. 458
W. Aoki, M. Ishigaki, T. Suda, T. Tsujimoto, N. Arimoto, eds.
© 2012 Astronomical Society of the Pacific

Diagnosis of PAH Properties and ISM Conditions based on the Near-Infrared and Mid-Infrared UIR Bands

T. I. Mori,[1] I. Sakon,[1] T. Onaka,[1] H. Kaneda,[2] H. Umehata,[3] and R. Ohsawa[1]

[1] *Department of Astronomy, University of Tokyo, Tokyo 113-0033, Japan*

[2] *Graduate School of Science, Nagoya University, Nagoya 464-8602, Japan*

[3] *Institute of Astronomy, The University of Tokyo, Tokyo 181-0015, Japan*

Abstract. We report the results of near-infrared (NIR) to mid-infrared (MIR) slit spectroscopic observations of the diffuse emission from the Large Magellanic Cloud (LMC) with the Infrared Camera (IRC) on board AKARI. The present results suggest that the 3.3 μm Unidentified Infrared (UIR) band provides powerful information on the size distribution and/or the excitation conditions of PAHs. A combination of the MIR bands with the 3.3 μm band, such as the diagram of $I_{3.3}/I_{11.3}$ v.s. $I_{7.7}/I_{11.3}$, is shown to be a useful diagnostic tool for the radiation conditions of the PAH emitting regions.

The UIR bands refer to a series of the NIR to MIR prominent emission bands observed in various astronomical objects, whose main carriers are supposed to be polycyclic aromatic hydrocarbons (PAHs). The properties of the bands reflect the chemical and physical properties of PAHs, which may be altered according to the conditions of the host environments. Therefore, the UIR band ratios have a great potential as efficient diagnostic tools to prove physical conditions of the ISM (Tielens 2008).

We have carried out NIR and MIR slit spectroscopic observations by AKARI/IRC (Onaka et al. 2007; Murakami et al. 2007), toward 9 positions in the LMC (Mori et al. 2012). These positions are selected based on IRAS colors (Sakon et al. 2006) and CO mapping data (Mizuno et al. 2001), to cover a wide range of radiation field conditions. Since the IRC enables simultaneous spectroscopic observations for NIR and MIR for the same slit area (5" $\times$ 1') by means of the beam splitter, we can investigate the intensity ratios among the UIR bands from 2.5 to 13.4 μm correctly for the first time.

Among six positions whose spectra do not show apparent ionization signatures (classified into Group A), the ratio of $I_{3.3}/I_{11.3}$, which is sensitive to the temperature of PAHs, and the ratios of $I_{6.2}/I_{11.3}$, $I_{7.7}/I_{11.3}$ and $I_{8.6}/I_{11.3}$, which can be used to infer the ionization degree of PAHs, increase linearly with the IRAS and AKARI colors, which are sensitive to massive star-formation activities. Under such quiescent environments as those associated with Group A members, the size distribution of PAHs does not change considerably, and thus the observed trend indicates that PAHs are heated to higher excitation temperatures and their ionization fraction increases as the incident radiation field becomes harder and stronger. However, the ratios of the other three positions, which are associated with harsh environments (classified into Group B), do not follow the trend. It can be attributed to destruction of small-sized PAHs by electron collisions and enhanced recombination of electrons due to a sudden increase in the electron density inside HII regions.

Taking advantage of the relationship between PAHs and incident radiation conditions suggested by the results, we propose a combination of the MIR bands with the 3.3 μm band as an efficient diagnostic tool for the interstellar radiation conditions, which provide information on the ionization degree of PAHs and the size distribution and/or the excitation conditions of PAHs. Fig. 1 shows the observed band ratios plotted together with model calculations on the diagnostic diagram of $I_{3.3}/I_{11.3}$ versus $I_{7.7}/I_{11.3}$. These model results demonstrate that the ratio of $I_{3.3}/I_{11.3}$ is in particular sensitive to T_* or $n_{C,min}$, that is, the temperature of PAHs. We note that the present study is based on only nine data points and that the target positions are spatially separated from each other. Therefore, further investigation with ground-based large telescopes such as Subaru/IRCS+COMICS is useful, to establish it as a reliable diagnostic tool.

Acknowledgments. This work is based on observations with AKARI, a JAXA project with the participation of ESA.

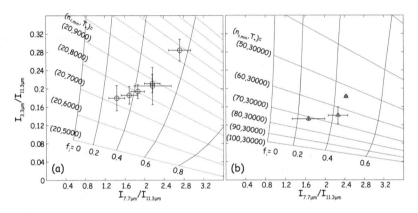

Figure 1. A diagnostic diagram of $I_{3.3}/I_{11.3}$ versus $I_{7.7}/I_{11.3}$. In the left panel (a), Group A members are plotted as open circles together with the model results. In the calculation, we assume a quiescent environment where the size distribution of PAHs does not change and the minimum-sized PAHs is set as those with the number of carbon atoms, n_C, = 20. The band ratios vary according to the ionization degree of PAHs, f_i, and the effective temperature of the heating source, T_*. In the right panel (b), Group B members are plotted as open triangles together with the model results, in which the minimum size is varied from n_C = 50 to 100 and T_* is fixed as 30000 K. We find that the results do not depend on T* for T*=20000–50000K because of the Lynman cut-off. See (Mori et al. 2012) for details of the model calculation.

References

Mizuno, N., et al. 2001, PASJ, 53, 971
Mori, T. I., et al. 2012, ApJ, 744, 68.
Murakami, H., et al. 2007, PASJ, 59, 369.
Onaka, T., et al. 2007, PASJ, 59, 401.
Sakon, I., et al. 2006, ApJ, 651, 174
Tielens, A. G. G. M. 2008, ARA&A, 46, 289

Galactic Archaeology: Near-Field Cosmology and the Formation of the Milky Way
ASP Conference Series, Vol. 458
W. Aoki, M. Ishigaki, T. Suda, T. Tsujimoto, N. Arimoto, eds.
© 2012 Astronomical Society of the Pacific

Formation and Evolution of Dust in Various Types of Supernovae

T. Nozawa,[1] T. Kozasa,[2] K. Maeda,[1] K. Nomoto,[1] H. Umeda,[3] N. Tominaga,[4] and A. Habe[2]

[1] *Institute for the Physics and Mathematics of the Universe, TODIAS, University of Tokyo, Kashiwa, Chiba 277-8583, Japan*

[2] *Department of Cosmosciences, Graduate School of Science, Hokkaido University, Sapporo 060-0810, Japan*

[3] *Department of Astronomy, School of Science, University of Tokyo, Bunkyo-ku, Tokyo 113-0033, Japan*

[4] *Department of Physics, Faculty of Science and Engineering, Konan University, Okamoto, Kobe 658-8501, Japan*

Abstract. We demonstrate how the formation and destruction processes of dust in supernovae (SNe) depend on the type of SNe classified through the mass of their outer envelopes. We show that, for Type II-P SNe with massive hydrogen envelopes, relatively large grains ($\gtrsim 0.01$ μm) can condense in the ejecta, and that ~ 0.1–1 $M_{\odot}$ of dust can be injected into the interstellar medium. On the other hand, for Type IIb/Ib/Ia SNe with no massive envelope, the radii of newly formed grains are considerably small, less than 0.01 μm, so the dust grains are almost completely destroyed in the shocked hot gas. These results suggest that envelope-retaining SNe can be major sources of dust, whereas envelope-deficient SNe are likely to be minor dust sources.

1. Introduction

Supernovae (SNe) are considered to be rapid and efficient producers of dust grains. In the ejecta of SNe, dust grains can form within the He core where the densities of condensible heavy elements are much higher than in the outer envelope. On the other hand, the newly formed dust can subsequently undergo the erosion due to sputtering in the hot gas swept up by the reverse and forward shocks. Thus, the size distribution and mass of dust finally ejected from SNe to the interstellar medium (ISM) are regulated by these two processes. However, both processes depend on the type of SNe through their envelope mass. In this proceedings, to show this dependence, we describe the results for a series of our works on the calculations of dust formation in the ejecta of various types of SNe and dust destruction in the shocked gas inside the SN remnants (SNRs).

2. Dust Formation and Evolution in Type II-P SNe

Type II-P SNe (SNe II-P) are core-collapse SNe (CCSNe) that retain massive H envelopes at the explosions. Nozawa et al. (2003) find that 0.1–1 $M_{\odot}$ of dust grains can

135

condense in the ejecta of SNe II-P and that the grain radii range from 0.0005 μm up to 1.0 μm, with the average radius larger than $\sim$0.01 μm. Meanwhile, the fates of the newly formed grains within SNRs depend on their initial radii a_{ini} (Nozawa et al. 2007); small grains of $a_{ini} \lesssim 0.01$–0.05 μm are trapped in the hot gas to be entirely destroyed, while larger grains are injected into the ISM without being eroded significantly. For interstellar hydrogen densities of $n_{H,0} = 1.0$–0.1 cm^{-3}, SNe II-P can supply 0.07–0.8 $M_\odot$ of dust to the ISM, so that SNe II-P can be primary sources of interstellar dust.

3. Dust Formation and Evolution in Type IIb/Ib SNe

Type IIb/Ib SNe (SNe IIb/Ib) are CCSNe that have lost almost all or all of their H envelopes before the explosions. Because of the less massive envelopes, SNe IIb/Ib have very high expansion velocities of the He core, resulting in much lower gas densities than in SNe II-P. The dust formation calculations in a SN Ib (Nozawa et al. 2008) and a SN IIb (Nozawa et al. 2010) show that the total masses of dust formed in SNe IIb/Ib are in the range of 0.1–1.5 $M_\odot$ and are comparable with the dust mass formed in SNe II-P. However, too low gas density in the He core of SNe IIb/Ib prevents dust grains from growing up to the radii larger than 0.01 μm. Nozawa et al. (2010) also investigate the evolution of dust in the Type IIb SNRs. They find that the newly formed grains are almost completely destroyed in the hot gas for the ISM densities of $n_{H,0} \geq 0.1$ cm^{-3}. This is because the grain radii are considerably small and because the early arrival of the reverse shock at the He core causes more efficient destruction of dust. Given that both of these result from the small-mass envelopes of SNe IIb/Ib, envelope-stripped CCSNe are not expected to furnish a significant amount of dust to the ISM.

4. Dust Formation and Evolution in Type Ia SNe

Type Ia SNe (SNe Ia) are considered to be thermonuclear explosions of C–O white dwarfs that have released the H and He envelopes during their evolutions. Nozawa et al. (2011) show that at most $\sim$0.1–0.2 $M_\odot$ of dust can condense in the ejecta of SNe Ia. On the other hand, as is the case of SNe IIb/Ib, the gas density in SNe Ia is much lower than SNe II-P, so the radii of newly formed grains are found to be below $\sim$0.01 μm. Therefore, these small grains cannot survive the destruction within the SNRs, which allows us to conclude that SNe Ia may not be important sources of interstellar dust.

Acknowledgments.   This research has been supported in part by World Premier International Research Center Initiative (WPI Initiative), MEXT, Japan, and by the Grant-in-Aid for Scientific Research of the Japan Society for the Promotion of Science (20340038, 22684004, 23224004).

References

Nozawa, T., et al. 2007, ApJ, 666, 955
Nozawa, T., et al. 2008, ApJ, 684, 1343
Nozawa, T., et al. 2010, ApJ, 713, 356
Nozawa, T., Kozasa, T., Umeda, H., Maeda, K., & Nomoto, K. 2003, ApJ, 598, 785
Nozawa, T., Maeda, K., Kozasa, T., Tanaka, M., Nomoto, K., & Umeda, H. 2011, ApJ, 736, 45

Galactic Archaeology: Near-Field Cosmology and the Formation of the Milky Way
ASP Conference Series, Vol. 458
W. Aoki, M. Ishigaki, T. Suda, T. Tsujimoto, N. Arimoto, eds.
© *2012 Astronomical Society of the Pacific*

Dust and Chemical Abundances of the Young Planetary Nebula M1-11; First Detection of Fullerenes C_{60}

M. Otsuka,[1,2] F. Kemper,[1] B. Sargent,[2] S. Hyung,[3] M. Meixner,[2] A. Tajitsu[4] and K. Yanagisawa[5]

[1] *Institute of Astronomy and Astrophysics, Academia Sinica P.O. Box 23-141, Taipei 10617, Taiwan, R.O.C.*

[2] *Space Telescope Science Institute, 3700 San Martin Drive, Baltimore, MD 21218, U.S.A.*

[3] *School of Science Education (Astronomy), Chungbuk National University, 12 Gaeshin-dong Heungduk-gu, CheongJu, Chungbuk 361-763, Korea*

[4] *Subaru Telescope, NAOJ, 650 North A'ohoku Place, Hilo, Hawaii 96720, U.S.A.*

[5] *Okayama Astrophysical Observatory, NAOJ, Kamogata, Okayama 719-0232, Japan*

Abstract. We investigated the dust and elemental abundances of the planetary nebula M1-11 based on the multiwavelength data. We calculated elemental abundances using recombination lines and collisionally excited lines. The C/O gas abundance ratio suggests that M1-11 is an O-rich PN, while C-rich dust features are seen in the *AKARI*/IRC and *Spitzer*/IRS spectra. The detection of the fullerenes C_{60} 17.3/18.9 μm is the first time for this PN. We constructed a spectral energy distribution model to derive properties of the central star and the ionized nebula and estimate the dust mass.

Planetary Nebulae (PNe) represent a final stage in the evolution of 1-8 $M_\odot$ stars. In the early asymptotic giant branch (AGB) stage, dust grains are formed outside the surface of the star. Dust grains receive radiation pressure from the central star and move radially outward. The grains drag the H-rich gas; as a result, dramatic gas loss begins. Dust controls the mass-loss history. In the ejected nebula, many elements synthesized in the PN progenitors have been observed. Therefore, to investigate both the dust and the elemental abundances of the nebula would provide us an insight to a history of the PN progenitors. In this paper, we discuss the evolution of the PN M1-11 from the viewpoint of dust and elemental abundances. In this study, we used the data taken by Subaru/HDS, OAO/ISLE, *AKARI*/IRC&FIS, and *Spitzer*/IRS.

We estimated the abundances of 11 elements using recombination lines (RLs) and collisionally excited lines. The C/O ratio derived from RLs (<-0.37 dex) suggests that the nebula is O-rich, while the mid-infrared spectra show C-rich dust features such as 3.3/11.3 μm polycyclic aromatic hydrocarbons (PAHs), 11 μm SiC, amorphous carbon, and $\sim$30 μm MgS. M1-11 might have silicate dust, too (Fig.1 *left*).

We have detected the candidate of the fullerenes C_{60} 17.3/18.9 μm lines (the inner box of Fig.1 *left*). These C_{60} lines were recently detected in 5 Galactic PNe including M1-11 (Cami *et al.* 2010; García-Hernández *et al.* 2010; this work). In Fig.1 *left*,

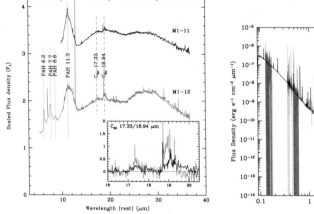

Figure 1.   (*left*) The *Spitzer* spectra of M1-11 (black line) and M1-12 (gray line). The line-profiles of C_{60} 17.33 and 18.94 μm with the local dust continuum subtracted are shown in the inner box. (*right*) The fitted SED from the CLOUDY modeling (dots) and the modified blackbody fitting (long dash) and the resultant SED (thick black line). The gray circles and lines are data from the observations. In the CLOUDY model, we considered PAHs, amorphous carbon, SiC, and astronomical silicate. The modified blackbody fitting is performed for MgS only. The close-up feature of the observed and fitted SEDs around 10-40 μm are presented in inner box.

we show the IRS spectrum of M1-12 (García-Hernández et al. 2010) as a reference to verify whether our detected C_{60} candidates are real. The positions of the intensity peak and the line widths of C_{60} lines in M1-11 are almost coincident with those in M1-12, assuring our confidence to the identification of these lines with C_{60}. The derived C_{60} temperature (376 K) is close to that of solid-state measured in laboratory experiments (300 K, see Cami *et al.* 2010).

Using the photo-ionization code CLOUDY and a modified blackbody fitting technique, we have built a $\sim$0.1-90 μm spectral energy distribution (SED) model (Fig.1 *right*) to estimate the dust mass (8.9×10^{-5} $M_{\odot}$, 112-284 K) and investigate the properties of the central star (T_{eff}=31960 K, 4450 $L_{\odot}$, log g = 3.5 dex). M1-11 is perhaps a descendant of a 1-1.5 $M_{\odot}$ star. The age is 1000-4000 yrs after leaving the AGB phase. Since M1-11 is a young PN, the C/O ratio of the ionized nebula might be >1 after the C-rich gas and dust were well mixed.

Further detailed analyses and interpretation will be found in a full paper by Otsuka et al. (submitted to the ApJ).

References

Cami, J. *et al.*, Science, 329, 1180
García-Hernández, D. A. *et al.* 2010, ApJ, 724, L39

Galactic Archaeology: Near-Field Cosmology and the Formation of the Milky Way
ASP Conference Series, Vol. 458
W. Aoki, M. Ishigaki, T. Suda, T. Tsujimoto, N. Arimoto, eds.
© 2012 Astronomical Society of the Pacific

Multi-Epoch Observations of Dust Formed around WR140

Itsuki Sakon,[1] Ryou Ohsawa,[1] Kentaro Asano,[1] Tamami I. Mori,[1]
Takashi Onaka,[1] Takaya Nozawa,[2] Takashi Kozasa[3] and Takuya Fujiyoshi[4]

[1]*Department of Astronomy, Graduate Schools of Science, University of Tokyo,
7-3-1 Hongo Bunkyo-ku, Tokyo 113-0033*

[2]*Institute for the Physics and Mathematics for the Universe, University of
Tokyo, 5-1-5 Kashiwanoha, Kashiwa, Chiba 277-8568, Japan*

[3]*Department of Cosmosciences, Graduate School of Science, Hokkaido
University, Sapporo 060-0810, Japan*

[4]*Subaru Telescope, National Astronomical Observatory of Japan, 650 North
A'ohoku Place, Hilo, HI96720, USA*

Abstract.   We present results of the mid-infrared multi-epoch observations of periodically dust-making Wolf-Rayet binary WR140 with Subaru/COMICS. Based on the N- and Q-bands photometric observations, the mass evolution of dust in the expanding concentric arc structures formed during the 2001 and 2009 periastron events is investigated. Our results show that at most $1.0 \times 10^{-8} M_\odot$ of dust survives per periastron later than an orbital phase, suggesting that such WR binary systems may not be the major dust budget in the early universe unless the grain growth later on should not take place.

WR140 is a long-period, colliding-wind binary (WC7 class Wolf-Rayet star+O4 type star, $P = 7.93$y, $e = 0.881$; see Williams 2011, for a review) located at the distance of 1.85kpc (Daugherty et al. 2005). When the companion passes through the periastron of the primary WR star, dust is supposed to be formed in the wind-wind collision zone, where the WR outflow is compressed and the shocked gas is cooled quickly to the dust condensation temperature. Actually, Marchenko et al. (2007) presented the high-quality 12.5μm image of WR140 taken with Michelle/Gemini-North in November/December 2003 and they detected two concentric dust arcs, which can be unequivocally linked with the dust formation episodes in 1993 and 2001 periastron events. Williams et al. (2009) have shown that the mass of amorphous carbon dust formed during the 2001 periastron event decreases after the orbital phase of $\phi=0.14$ based on successive mid-infrared observations from 2001 to 2005. Therefore, further observations to monitor the dust mass evolution in each arc structure and to elucidate the diversity in the dust production efficiency among different periastron events are important to examine whether or not the WR binary systems can contribute efficiently as the dust budget in the early universe. The last periastron event of WR140 was on May 2009. We have started the mid-infrared multi-epoch observations of WR140 with Cooled Mid-Infrared Camera and Spectrometer (COMICS Kataza et al. 2000) onboard Subaru since then. So far, our observations have been carried out on the orbital epochs at $\phi = 1.097(0.097)$, $1.170(0.170)$ and $1.30(0.30)$ from the 2001 (2009) periastron. The dust formed during the 2009 periastron has constituted in an extended core-like structure in the N- and Q-band images obtained at ϕ = 0.097 and 0.170 (Fig. 1a), but it has become detached from the central WR core and has constituted in an arc-like structure in those images obtained at ϕ = 0.30 (Fig. 1b) with the resolution of Subaru/COMICS. For a direct

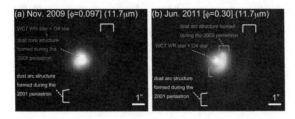

Figure 1.   11.7μm images of WR140 on (a) November 2009 and (b) June 2009.

comparison with the results of Williams et al. (2009), we employ a single component dust emission model, where amorphous carbon (ACAR) is assumed as the composition of dust and its optical properties are calculated from Colangeli et al. (1995). We find that the dust formed during the 2001 periastron has been cooled to 300 – 400K at ϕ = 1.097 and 1.170 based on the results of the photometry with N11.7 (11.7μm) and Q17.7 (17.7μm) bands. These temperatures are generally in good agreement with the expected relation of $T_d \propto r^{-2/5.2}$ (Williams et al. 2009), where the radiative equilibrium with the energy input from both the WR primary and O4 secondary is assumed and T_d and r are the dust temperature and the distance between the dust and the WR+O4 stars, respectively. Moreover, the dust mass in the arc structure formed during the 2001 periastron is estimated as ~1.0×10^{-8}M$_\odot$ at those epochs. This value is significantly smaller than the dust mass of 2.0×10^{-8}M$_\odot$ at ϕ = 0.55 (Williams et al. 2009), which may suggest the on-going process of dust destruction. The temperature and the mass of dust formed during the 2009 periastron, on the other hand, are obtained as 440 ± 20K and 3.2×10^{-8}M$_\odot$ based on our observations at ϕ = 0.30, indicating the similar-scale dust production activities between the 2001 and 2009 periastrons. Even if 1.0×10^{-8}M$_\odot$ of dust survives per periastron, a WR binary system produces much smaller amount of dust during the lifetime of its WC phase (e.g., 10^5 years for the initial mass 85M$_\odot$ and metallicity Z = 0.004; Maeder & Meynet 1994) than is requested for a massive star to contribute efficiently as the dust budget in the early universe as long as the grain growth should not take place later on. Observations with longer wavelengths are indispensable to examine the later-epoch mass evolution of dust produced by WR binary systems.

Acknowledgments.   This work is based on data collected at Subaru Telescope, which is operated by National Astronomical Observatory of Japan. I.S. thanks all the staffs of Subaru Telescope for their continuous support and help. This work is supported in part by a Grant-in-Aid for Scientific Research from the JSPS.

References

Collangeli, L; Mennella, V., Palumbo,P., Rotundi, A., Bussoletti,E., 1995, A&AS, 113, 561
Dougherty, S. M., et al., 2005, ApJ, 623, 447
Kataza,H., et al., 2000, SPIE, 4008, 1144
Maeder, A., & Meynet, G., 1994, A&A, 287, 803
Marchenko,S.V. et al., 2007, ASP Conf. Ser., 367, 213
Williams, P., 2011, BSRSL, 80, 595
Williams, P.M., et al., 2009, MNRAS, 395, 1749

Galactic Archaeology: Near-Field Cosmology and the Formation of the Milky Way
ASP Conference Series, Vol. 458
W. Aoki, M. Ishigaki, T. Suda, T. Tsujimoto, N. Arimoto, eds.
©*2012 Astronomical Society of the Pacific*

Chemical Abundances of Upper Red Giant Branch Halo Stars

Luis C. Vargas[1] and Wako Aoki[2]

[1]*Department of Astronomy, Yale University, New Haven, CT 06511, USA*

[2]*National Astronomical Observatory of Japan, Mitaka, Tokyo 181-8588, Japan*

Abstract. We present preliminary results from a spectroscopic program that targeted RGB halo stars of comparable luminosities to those of stars in dwarf spheroidal galaxies (dSphs) accessible to high-resolution spectroscopy. We have measured abundances for α, iron-peak, and other light elements in 39 stars. In this contribution, we compare some of the halo and classical dSph abundance patterns We report slight enhancements in α-elements in the halo relative to the classical dSphs, between $-2.5 \lesssim$ [Fe/H] $\lesssim$ -1.5. [Na/Fe] in the dSphs is likewise under-abundant by at least ~ 0.2 dex in the same metallicity range. We also detect a tentative a $T_{\rm eff}$ dependence in the Mg and Si abundance ratios of our RGB sample.

1. Abundance Patterns for α-elements, Na, Ni and Zn

We compare our halo abundances to those in three classical dSphs in Figure 1. Our mean halo α abundances have a constant value of ~0.4-0.5 between $-2.5 <$ [Fe/H] $<$ -1.5, with a level of scatter of the order of the measurement uncertainties or slightly larger. [Mg/Fe] and [Ca/Fe] in the dSphs are underabundant relative to our halo giants over most of our entire metallicity range, although [Mg/Fe] in UMi reaches halo values at [Fe/H] ~ -2.5. Similarly, [Si/Fe] in UMi reaches halo levels at [Fe/H] ~ -2.

We measure solar [Ni/Fe] abundances across our entire sample, whereas [Ni/Fe] in the dSphs is slightly subsolar at [Fe/H] ~ -1.5. The [Zn/Fe] halo abundance are also solar, except at [Fe/H] $\lesssim -2.5$, where the scatter increases. The dSphs are progressively underabundant in [Zn/Fe] relative to the halo towards higher metallicities. Our [Na/Fe] abundances, which did not rely on the NLTE-sensitive Na D lines, are higher than those in dSphs across our entire metallicity range by $\gtrsim 0.2$ dex. [Na/Fe] in the dSphs is determined from the D lines; hence, the negative NLTE corrections (e.g. Andrievsky et al. 2007) suggest that the differences in [Na/Fe] between the halo and the dSphs are substantial (at least 0.2 dex).

2. $T_{\rm eff}$ - Dependence of Abundance Ratios

In order to explore the origin of the differences between halo and dSph abundances, we plot the abundance ratios as a function of $T_{\rm eff}$ in Figure 2. We find significant $T_{\rm eff}$−dependent trends for [Mg/Fe] and [Si/Fe]. The [Mg/Fe]-$T_{\rm eff}$ in particular may explain the discrepant [Mg/Fe] values measured in the halo and the dSphs. If so, it highlights the need to account for these trends when comparing chemical abundance

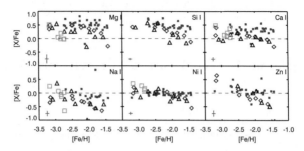

Figure 1.   Abundance trends for program stars (filled squares) and dSph stars (triangles: Draco; open squares: Sextans; diamonds: Ursa Minor). The dSph abundances were taken from Aoki et al. (2009), Cohen & Huang (2009, 2010), and Fulbright et al. (2004). All abundance ratios have been placed on the same abundance scale, assuming $\epsilon(Fe_\odot) = 7.52$. A representative error bar, corresponding to BD+1 2916, is shown as a brown cross.

patterns between different stellar populations. A full analysis for this RGB sample will be presented in a forthcoming publication (Vargas & Aoki, in prep).

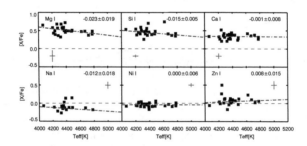

Figure 2.   Abundance trends as a function of T_{eff} for program stars. The slopes for the best linear-fits to the abundance patterns as a function of temperature are shown as red dot-dashed lines, and their values written on the upper-right corners. We restricted our sample to stars with [Fe/H] < -1.5 and $T_{eff} < 5000$ K.

Acknowledgments.   LCV acknowledges support from NSF Award OISE-1015518 (NSF East Asia and Pacific Fellowship) and the Japan Society for the Promotion of Science (JSPS).

References

Andrievsky, S. M., Spite, M., Korotin, S. A., Spite, F., Bonifacio, P., Cayrel, R., Hill, V., & François, P. 2007, A&A, 464, 1081
Aoki, W., Arimoto, N., Sadakane, K., Tolstoy, E., Battaglia, G., Jablonka, P., Shetrone, M., Letarte, B., Irwin, M., Hill, V., Francois, P., Venn, K., Primas, F., Helmi, A., Kaufer, A., Tafelmeyer, M., Szeifert, T., & Babusiaux, C. 2009, A&A, 502, 569
Cohen, J. G., & Huang, W. 2009, ApJ, 701, 1053
— 2010, ApJ, 719, 931
Fulbright, J. P., Rich, R. M., & Castro, S. 2004, ApJ, 612, 447

Galactic Archaeology: Near-Field Cosmology and the Formation of the Milky Way
ASP Conference Series, Vol. 458
W. Aoki, M. Ishigaki, T. Suda, T. Tsujimoto, N. Arimoto, eds.
© 2012 Astronomical Society of the Pacific

The AMBRE Project: Exploring Stellar Populations in the Milky Way Disk with FEROS Archived Spectra

C. C. Worley,[1] P. de Laverny,[1] A. Recio-Blanco,[1] V. Hill[1] and G. Kordopatis[1,2]

[1]*Laboratoire Lagrange, UMR7293, Université de Nice Sophia-Antipolis, CNRS, Observatoire de la Côte d'Azur, 06300 Nice, France*

[2]*Institute of Astronomy, University of Cambridge, Madingley Road, Cambridge, CB3 0HA, United Kingdom*

Abstract. The archived spectra of the FEROS spectrograph have been homogeneously analysed for their stellar parameters (T_{eff}, $\log g$, [M/H], [α/Fe]) in the first phase of the AMBRE Project. We have extracted samples of FEROS stellar spectra that correspond to the thin and thick disk populations, and open clusters in the Milky Way. The consequent exploration of these samples in terms of their chemical properties ([M/H], [α/Fe]) as determined in the AMBRE:FEROS analysis, and their distribution in the Milky Way is discussed and compared with previous studies.

1. The AMBRE Project

AMBRE is a joint project between the European Southern Observatory (ESO) and the Observatoire de la Côte d'Azur to determine the stellar parameters of effective temperature (T_{eff}), surface gravity ($\log g$), global metallicity ([M/H]), and a global α-element abundance ([α/Fe]) for the archived spectra of the FEROS, UVES, HARPS and FLAMES/GIRAFFE spectrographs. The combined sample of archived spectra total to at least 250,000 spectra. The FEROS analysis is now complete and the analyses of the remaining three datasets is underway. Worley et al. (2012) fully describes the automated spectral analysis pipeline that has been built around the stellar parameterisation algorithm MATISSE, and presents the analysis of the FEROS archived spectra. Here, the FEROS sample was explored for stellar populations in the Milky Way disk.

1.1. Pollution by Supernova in the Milky Way Disk

Using available photometry distance were determined for 3261 spectra (~1261 stars) in the FEROS archived sample using isochrones based on the method of Zwitter et al. (2010). Comparison was made with 21 thick disk and 45 thin disk dwarf stars analysed in Bensby et al. (2003) (B03). Dwarf stars ($\log g > 3.4$ dex) were extracted from the FEROS sample. Figure 1 compares the distribution of [α/Fe][1] with [M/H] ([Fe/H]). The FEROS sample is in good agreement with B03 thick and thin disk populations.

For the thick disk the high [α/Fe] at low [Fe/H] (< -0.5 dex) followed by a steep negative gradient to solar [α/Fe] at solar [Fe/H] reflects the transition from pollution

---

[1]$[\alpha/\text{Fe}]_{B03} = \langle [\text{Mg/Fe}]_{B03}, [\text{Si/Fe}]_{B03}, [\text{Ca/Fe}]_{B03}, [\text{Ti/Fe}]_{B03} \rangle$

by Type II Supernova (α-element production) to pollution by Type Ia Supernova (Fe production) in the star forming history of the thick disk evolution. The FEROS sample clearly traces this well-studied relation.

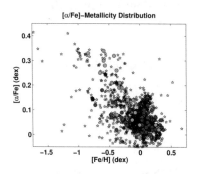

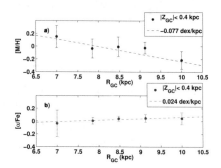

Figure 1. [α/Fe] vs [Fe/H] with $\log g > 3.4$ dex for FEROS spectra in the galactic disk. Cyan circles = B03 thick disk; Red circles = B03 thin disk.

Figure 2. Galactocentric distance distribution of open clusters for a) [M/H], and b) [α/Fe]. Cluster samples are binned in $\Delta R_{GC} = 0.85$ kpc.

1.2. Open Clusters within the FEROS archived sample

A sample of 147 spectra (~107 stars) in over 26 open clusters were extracted from the FEROS archived spectra using kinematic information. The distance and accepted metallicity for each cluster were taken from WEBDA (Mermilliod 1995).

Figure 2a shows the mean metallicity of the thin disk cluster samples (0.4 kpc above or below the galactic plane) binned by galactocentric distance (R_{GC}) against R_{GC}. The derived gradient of -0.077 ± 0.02 dex/kpc is in good agreement with previous work (Haywood 2008). Figure 2b shows the same analysis but for [α/Fe], but there is not as strong evidence of a gradient in [α/Fe].

2. Conclusion

These examples of the extraction and analysis of stellar populations in the Milky Way disk show how the FEROS (and other) archived spectra can be used in studies of galactic archaeology.

Acknowledgments. The authors would like to thank OCA, ESO and CNES for their funding support for this project.

References

Bensby, T., Feltzing, S., & Lundström, I. 2003, A&A, 410, 527
Haywood, M. 2008, MNRAS, 388, 1175. 0805.1822
Mermilliod, J.-C. 1995, in Information On-Line Data in Astronomy, edited by D. Egret & M. A. Albrecht, vol. 203 of Astrophysics and Space Science Library, 127
Worley, C. C., de Laverny, P., Recio-Blanco, A., Hill, V., Bijaoui, A., & Ordenovic, C. 2012, submitted
Zwitter, T., Matijevič, G., Breddels, M. A., & ... 2010, A&A, 522, A54. 1007.4411

Part IV

Milky Way Galaxy

Galactic Archaeology: Near-Field Cosmology and the Formation of the Milky Way
ASP Conference Series, Vol. 458
W. Aoki, M. Ishigaki, T. Suda, T. Tsujimoto, N. Arimoto, eds.
©2012 Astronomical Society of the Pacific

Evolution of the Milky Way: Some Open Issues for Gaia

Gerry Gilmore

Institute of Astronomy, University of Cambridge, Madingley Road, Cambridge, CB3 0HA, UK

Abstract. Chemical element distribution functions provide essential information to develop our understanding of galaxy formation and evolutionary processes. Current determination of the [Fe/H] and elemental abundance distribution functions of representative samples of the main stellar populations is surprisingly limited - most observational focus is on either the very local or the very extreme. One robust result is however the extremely small *scatter* in element ratios, especially [α/Fe], about what are also very small amplitude trends, over the whole observed range $-4 \leq$ [Fe/H] $\leq +0.3$. Another is that the thin disc really does lack a significant metal-poor tail: the *G-dwarf problem* is still providing us with information. Small elemental abundance scatter requires extremely efficient ISM mixing on large scales at all times. At face value this is not consistent with significant merger or accretion events being an important aspect of Galaxy evolution, contrary to expectation. Future progress in our understanding is expected to be rapid, with the launch of Gaia in 2013, and the beginning of large dedicated spectroscopic surveys, to complement Gaia, and to define the typical. Subaru, with an appropriate multi-object spectrograph, could become the northern hemisphere leader in this exciting scientific opportunity.

1. Forming a Milky Way

Understanding how galaxies actually form and evolve within our ΛCDM universe continues to be an enormous challenge. Extant simulations of the aggregation of cold dark matter suggest that galaxies grow through a sequence of merger and accretion events. Most events involve accreting an object that is so small that it barely perturbs the system, some events involve an object large enough to produce a mild perturbation, and a handful of events involve an object that causes a major convulsion. Exactly how these events impact on a galaxy cannot be predicted at this time because the extremely complex physics of baryons cannot be reliably simulated: at a minimum it involves interstellar chemistry, magnetic reconnection, radiative transfer in the presence of spectral lines and significant velocity gradients, thermonuclear fusion, neutron absorption, neutrino scattering, radioactive decay, cosmic ray acceleration and diffusion. Theoretical models of galaxy formation inevitably rely more heavily on phenomenological models than on physical theory. Thus, these models require calibration with well-studied (nearby) test cases. For example, star formation involves turbulence, magnetic reconnection, collisionless shocks, and radiative transfer through a turbulent medium. Similarly, the treatment of convection, mixing, equations of state at high density, opacities, rotation and magnetic fields can all significantly affect stellar luminosities, radii, and lifetimes

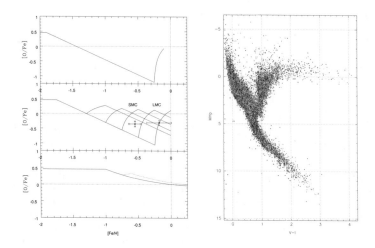

Figure 1.   LHS: A simple model of chemical evolution, with efficient mixing and variable star formation rates. The top panel is for a system with early and late bursts, quiescent in between. The middle panel is for a series of bursts, perhaps like the LMC/SMC. The bottom panel is for continuing steady star formation with a super-imposed burst. The essential deduction is that very wide ranges of element ratios are expected in most situations. This figure is from Gilmore & Wyse (1991). RHS: HR diagram of the re-reduced Hipparcos stars (van Leeuwen, pri commn). The stars are colour coded by proper motion, green being smaller proper motion, red larger. Given the small sample volume, proper motion corresponds to space motion, so the correlation betwen the stellar luminosity and the colour of the symbol instantly makes clear an age velocity-dispersion relation. This illustrates the remarkable gain in information as one adds extra dimensions to the data available for analysis.cf Fig 2 below.

at different evolutionary phases. We are far from being able to simulate the coupled evolution of CDM and baryons from ab-initio physics.

Observations are crucial to learning how galaxies and stars were formed and evolved, and what their structure now is. Observations of objects at high redshifts and long look-back times are important for this endeavour, as is detailed examination of our Galaxy, because such near-field cosmology gives insights into key processes that cannot be obtained by studying faint, poorly resolved objects with uncertain futures. Just as the history of life was deduced by examining rocks, we expect to deduce the history of our Galaxy by examining stars. Stars record the past in their ages, compositions, and in their kinematics.

For this article I focus on what I find most surprising - the unexpected narrowness of chemical elemental abundance distribution functions in the several Galactic stellar populations, and the very small overlap between the abundance distributions of Halo, Thick Disc, and Thin Disc populations.

2.   Chemical abundances in stellar populations - some puzzles

Unbiased samples determining metallicity distribution functions of the various Galactic stellar populations are remarkably sparse. Observers, being cool people, are attracted more by the exotic and the extreme than by the average. Thus, for example, heroic efforts are being invested in finding the very rare extreme metal-poor stars, especialy those with [Fe/H] ≤ -3. These rare stars are extremely important as probes of the earliest stars, and the reionisation epoch. They have much of importance to tell us. They however are not all of the interest in chemical abundances, and they tell us directly very little about the (later) assembly and growth of our Milky Way.

We know only in very general terms of the field halo metallicity distribution function. Fortunately the Solar neighbourhood is a convenient place to measure the distribution, since most halo stars are interior to the Sun, but local halo stars have sufficiently high velocity dispersion to probe a fair volume. [Of course, the very outer halo stars need not bear very much relation to most of the halo.] The local halo distribution has maximum near -1.5dex, and a gaussian width of perhaps 0.6dex. This means that 99% of the halo is in the currently under-fashionable regime, with [Fe/H] ≥ -3. That 99% is what we need to quantify and to explain to understand galaxy formation. Intruigingly, in so far as the distribution is known, the halo metallicity distribution function is adequately described by a simple model of *in situ* star formation with mass-loss proportional to the star formation rate. The need to determine the distribution sufficiently well to be able to test more detailed models is of course my point hcre.

A second well-established property of halo stars is that the [α/Fe] distribution is approximately constant, with very little scatter, across the whole range in [Fe/H]. This is a tight constraint on the duration of halo star formation. Halo star formation must have completed the formation of the field halo sufficiently rapidly that Ia SNe iron production was not an important contributor to chemical enrichment. Rapid star formation is the only model which is consistent with the well-observed lack of a trend in [α/Fe] with [Fe/H] across the entire halo abundance range. That well-known lack of a trend is in sharp contrast to observations of satellite dwarf galaxies, including the Magellanic Clouds and the Sagittarius dwarf, where element ratios range over one dex in amplitude, and values of [α/Fe] up to 1.5 dex below the halo plateau are routinely found. It may be more than a coincidence (but it may not!) that the mass-loss from such a halo star-forming system is consistent with providing the pre-enrichment necessary to explain the absence of many metal-poor stars in the Galactic discs and inner bulge. Though angular momentum issues remain to be understood (e.g. Wyse & Gilmore 1992).

This ridiculously simple description is the only class of model which is consistent with the observations of halo stars, yet is quite inconsistent with standard merger hierarchy and multiple building-block models. Perhaps our preconceptions are making us miss the significance of what we see? To recall the famous aphorism, looking is not the same as seeing. Certainly, spending effort on the typical continues to have the opportunity to teach us a lot we have not yet understood about galaxy evolution.

What then of the Galactic discs? - I leave discussion of the bulge, whatever it/they may be, to specialist papers in this volume. Most of our information on the chemical abundance, and element ratio distributions, of the thin and thick discs comes from local samples. Fortunately, some of these approach volume-completeness - or at least are unbiased. Excellent examples include Fuhrmann (1998), Reddy et al. (2003), Fuhrmann (2004), Reddy et al. (2006), Fuhrmann (2008), Reddy & Lambert (2008), and Fuhrmann (2011).

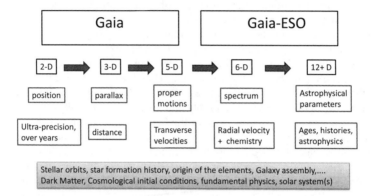

Figure 2.   A cartoon view of the complementarity between Gaia and ground-based spectroscopic surveys, such as Gaia-ESO, or a future major Subaru stellar populations survey.

The recent use of the RAVE survey to quantify the properties of the metal-poor thick (and thin) disks is also making impressive advances (Ruchti et al. 2011). The very sophisticated RAVE sample statistical analysis of Burnett et al. (2011) makes clear that indeed thick disc stars are older than are thin disc stars, that they have a larger vertical scale height, and they extend to lower metallicity. Figure 17 of Burnett et al. (2011) also reminds us that the thin disk metallicity distribution function has remained essentially unchanged over at least the last 8Gyr. The element ratio studies noted above establish that there is very little scatter in element ratios at any [Fe/H] value, even though evolution has proceeded over that very long time.

Is this observational result anticipated? Is this comprehensible? Standard models of chemical evolution (cf figure 1a) show that a large range/scatter in element ratios is a natural feature of varying star formation histories. That is the exact opposite of what we see in the Milky Way, but is exactly what we do see in the Galactic satellites and dIrr galaxies. Why is it so? The only way to generate systems of wide age range but narrow elemental abundance range is to maintain steady star formation rates, efficient gas mixing, and no substantial inflow of new material at faster than the star formation rate - ie, no significant merger events. Low scatter does require that mixing in the ISM has always been extremely efficient. Approximately steady star formation in an isolated disc, where star formation and SNe drive hot fountains, is one natural explanation. Fountain models are naturally capable of explaining small scatter, as the fountains ensure efficient ISM mixing over large scales, if the fountains operated very efficiently over the whole history of the disc (Marinacci et al. 2010; Binney et al. 2009).

Once again, however, such long-lasting (since redshits of two) gentle evolution is very far from the expectation of hierarchical merger/accretion models.

2.1.   The Future: Gaia and large spectroscopic surveys

Astrometry and spectroscopy together provide the key information to progress our understanding. The H-R diagram shown illustrates the information content even in the very local survey by Hipparcos. To understand the Galaxy, however, we need to survey the Galaxy. The Gaia mission, scheduled for launch in 2013, is key to answering many of these questions. It will provide photometry and astrometry of unprecedented precision for all stars brighter than G=20, and obtain low-resolution spectra for most stars brighter than G=17. The first astrometry data release is likely to be in 2016, with spectrophotometry and stellar parameters to follow later, and 2021 for the final catalogue. While Gaia is remarkable and will bring us into a new domain of research, it crucially has limited spectroscopic capabilities and, like all spacecraft, it leaves for large ground-based telescopes what those do best. That is the high quality spectroscopy: ground-based spectroscopy complements and completes Gaia astrometry, and vice versa. Each project is intrinsically exciting, and each benefits from synergy with the other.

A convenient way of picturing the Gaia ground complementarity is to look at the dimensionality of data which can be obtained on an astrophysical object. Larger amounts of information of higher quality are the goal, to allow increasing understanding. The figure shows a cartoon view of this information set. There are four basic thresholds which we must pass. The first is to know a source exists, its position, and basic photometric data. Photometric surveys, such as SDSS and VISTA, deliver this information. The second is to add the time domain motions, including parallax, providing distances and speeds. Here Gaia will be revolutionary. The third threshold is radial velocity, turning motions into orbits. While Gaia will provide some radial velocities, its magnitude limit is three magnitudes brighter than that of the astrometry and the precision is much below that of the proper motions. Large ground based surveys, such as the ESO VLT Gaia-ESO Survey starting in the south, are crucial to supplement Gaia spectroscopy. A new major northern survey, for which Subaru is the most suitable telescope, especially with a new wide-field multi-object spectrograph, is critically needed to deliver the Gaia science potential. The fourth threshold is chemistry, and astrophysical parameters. These latter two both require spectroscopy, which is the key information from large spectroscopic surveys.

3.   Conclusions

1) We lack a suitable definition of "Stellar Population"
2) Large disk galaxies remain a challenge for the models
3) Thin discs are old, Thick discs common, their angular momentum Distribution Functions are similar
4) Vertical separation between the discs seems established, element ratios are bimodal
5) The "G-dwarf" problem survives - the thin disc metallicity DF is narrow, limiting gradients
6) Chemical evolution over the last 8Gyr is minimal - does this imply efficient gas mixing?
7) There is apparent halo to thick disc chemical continuity
8) The stellar high-mass IMF, constrained by element ratios, is remarkably invariant
9) An open question is how much real chemical scatter exists at any radius - open clusters will answer this
10) There are chemical differences between field and globular cluster RGB stars - this

really needs to be understood

11) Those same cluster-field differences show globular clusters are not important tracers of building blocks

12) Secular disc evolution models are interesting but preliminary - can they be quantified without knowing the history of bar-spiral evolution?

13) Merger disc evolution models are also uncertain

14) Turbulent disc formation at high redshift is seen - but seems to build bulges

15) Why are there metal-rich globular clusters with thick disc-like angular momentum, if the thick disc formed from a thin disc?

17) Gaia will launch in 2013, and provide much information to progress our knowledge and (possibly) understanding

18) Gaia needs massive ground-based spectroscopic surveys, to complement the astrometry

19) Subaru and PFS have a unique opportunity to lead near-field cosmology in the North.

Discussion

Ferrara: I was struck by the very efficient mixing evident in the thin disc of the Milky Way. What is your interpretation?

Gilmore: The physical process we know happens, and which has this effect, is fountains. A plausible answer is that fountains are always efficient and effective at mixing.

Andersen: I'm glad you emphasised the importance of complete and unbiassed samples. As an observer I am appalled by the way data are interpreted with inadequate consideration of biasses. Just recall the history of determinations of the age-metallicity relation.

References

Binney, J., Nipoti, C., & Fraternali, F. 2009, MNRAS, 397, 1804
Burnett, B., Binney, J., Sharma, S., et al. 2011, A&A, 532, A113
Fuhrmann, K. 1998, A&A, 338, 161
Fuhrmann, K. 2004, Astronomische Nachrichten, 325, 3
Fuhrmann, K. 2008, MNRAS, 384, 173
Fuhrmann, K. 2011, MNRAS, 414, 2893
Gilmore, G., & Wyse, R. F. G. 1991, ApJ, 367, L55
Marinacci, F., Binney, J., Fraternali, F., et al. 2010, MNRAS, 404, 1464
Reddy, B. E., Tomkin, J., Lambert, D. L., & Allende Prieto, C. 2003, MNRAS, 340, 304
Reddy, B. E., Lambert, D. L., & Allende Prieto, C. 2006, MNRAS, 367, 1329
Reddy, B. E., & Lambert, D. L. 2008, MNRAS, 391, 95
Ruchti, G. R., Fulbright, J. P., Wyse, R. F. G., et al. 2011, ApJ, 737, 9
Wyse, R. F. G., & Gilmore, G. 1992, AJ, 104, 144

Galactic Archaeology: Near-Field Cosmology and the Formation of the Milky Way
ASP Conference Series, Vol. 458
W. Aoki, M. Ishigaki, T. Suda, T. Tsujimoto, N. Arimoto, eds.
© 2012 Astronomical Society of the Pacific

On the Nature of the Stellar Bridge Between Leo IV and Leo V

Shoko Jin,[1,2] Nicolas Martin,[2,3] Jelte de Jong,[4] Blair Conn,[2] Hans-Walter Rix[2] and Mike Irwin[5]

[1]*ARI/ZAH, Mönchhofstr. 12–14, D-69120 Heidelberg, Germany*

[2]*MPIA, Königstuhl 17, D-69117 Heidelberg, Germany*

[3]*Observatoire de Strasbourg, 11 rue de l'Université, 67000 Strasbourg, France*

[4]*Sterrewacht Leiden, P.O. Box 9513, NL-2300 RA Leiden, The Netherlands*

[5]*Institute of Astronomy, Madingley Road, Cambridge CB3 0HA, UK*

Abstract.   We present a revised analysis of a speculated stellar bridge between the Milky Way dwarf galaxies Leo IV and Leo V. Using data acquired with Subaru/Suprime-Cam over a $1° \times 4°$ field encompassing the two satellites and the region in between, we confirm our previous detection of a stellar overdensity between Leo IV and Leo V (de Jong et al. 2010). The larger area coverage and improved depth of our current dataset allow for an improved analysis of the stellar overdensity that had previously appeared to bridge the two galaxies. A main-sequence turn-off feature visible in the stacked colour-magnitude diagram of the contiguously observed Subaru fields reveals an extended stellar structure at a distance of approximately 20 kpc. Its angular proximity to the Virgo overdensity, as well as a good correspondence in distance and metallicity, suggests that the smaller structure we detect may be associated with the much larger Virgo stellar overdensity.

1. Introduction

The discovery of numerous dwarf galaxies through the Sloan Digital Sky Survey (SDSS) over the last decade has helped to advance our understanding of the Milky Way in a cosmological context, with our appreciation of the Galaxy as a micro-cosmos, together with our ever-growing understanding of the Andromeda galaxy, leading to the development of 'near-field cosmology'. The constellation that boasts the largest number of Milky Way satellites is the realm of Leo, and two of its five dwarf-galaxy inhabitants form the subject of our current study. Discovered by Belokurov et al. (2007b, 2008), Leo IV and Leo V are close neighbours not just in projection — separated on the sky by a mere $3°$ — but also spatially, sharing residence of the Galactic halo beyond 150 kpc. Targeted observations for studying these Milky Way satellites and their surrounding environment by de Jong et al. (2010) using the LAICA imager on the 3.5m telescope at the Calar Alto observatory led to the unexpected detection of an overdensity of stars, seemingly bridging the two galaxies. However, the loss of one of three planned fields due to bad weather unfortunately left us with only a tentative detection of the possible stellar bridge, whose true nature unfortunately could not be resolved from these data alone. Follow-up observations using Subaru/Suprime-Cam aimed at obtaining a

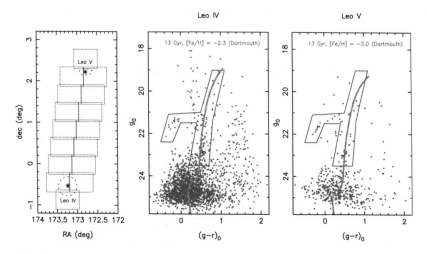

Figure 1.   Left panel: footprint of the observed Subaru fields. Locations of the individual Subaru/Suprime-Cam fields are shown, together with dotted ellipses marking 4 half-light radii of Leo IV and Leo V. Middle panel: colour-magnitude diagram of stars within 2 half-light radii of Leo IV, overlaid with a 13-Gyr Dartmouth isochrone with [Fe/H] = −2.3. The delineated section (same in both CMDs) is used as a selection box for avoiding Leo IV and Leo V members when exploring the question of a stream's presence within the Subaru fields. Right panel: as for middle panel but for Leo V; the isochrone has been altered to reflect the metallicity differences in the Leo IV and Leo V stellar populations.

wider and deeper dataset has enabled us to shed clearer light on the nature of this stellar overdensity, as well as allowing for an improved set of structural parameters to be derived for Leo IV and Leo V. These results are presented in summarised form in this contribution, with full details to be presented in a paper currently in preparation.

2.   Structural Parameters of Leo IV and Leo V

Altogether, 16 Subaru/Suprime-Cam fields were used to obtain a wide coverage of Leo IV, Leo V, and their surrounding environment. Figure 1 provides an overview of the location of the observed fields, as well as the colour-magnitude diagrams (CMDs) of the two Leo systems; the data have been photometrically calibrated field-by-field to the SDSS, and extinction-corrected following the Schlegel et al. (1998) dust maps. The updated structural parameters, derived using a maximum-likelihood procedure as described by Martin et al. (2008), are summarised in Table 1.

3.   Positioning the Stellar Stream: Near or Far?

Despite the improved depth and coverage of the Subaru data with respect to our earlier dataset, we identified no clear spatial overdensity indicative of a distant stellar stream in our new dataset. However, a CMD of the data from all 16 Suprime-Cam fields, with

Parameter	Leo IV	Leo V
R.A. (J2000)*	$11^h32^m58.1^s$	$11^h31^m08.3^s$
Dec. (J2000)*	$-00°32'11.2''$	$02°13'20.9''$
θ (deg)*	5^{+45}_{-45}	30^{+15}_{-22}
ϵ*	$0.03^{+0.18}_{-0.03}$	$0.15^{+0.34}_{-0.15}$
r_h (arcmin)*	$2.3^{+0.3}_{-0.4}$	1.8 ± 0.5
D (kpc)	154 ± 5	175 ± 9

Table 1.   Structural parameters of Leo IV and Leo V (*updated using the current dataset); from top to bottom: centroid position, position angle, ellipticity, half-light radius and heliocentric distance (Moretti et al. 2009; de Jong et al. 2010).

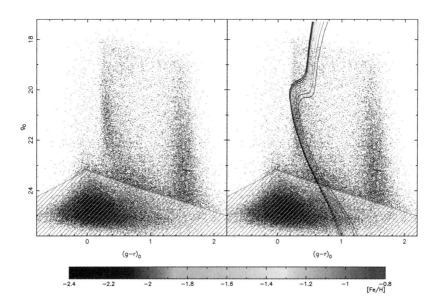

Figure 2.   (color online) Left panel: stacked CMD of all stars within the Subaru fields. Stellar contributions from Leo IV and Leo V have been removed by designating an elliptical exclusion region with a semi-major axis of 4 half-light radii for each galaxy, together with the selection box shown in Figure 1. The grey shaded region is expected to contain mainly galaxy contamination; only one in four data points have therefore been plotted. Right panel: as in left panel, but with 13-Gyr Dartmouth isochrones of different metallicities (Dotter et al. 2008) overlaid to roughly match the location of the main-sequence turn-off feature.

stars belonging to the dwarf galaxies removed, shows a feature resembling a main-sequence turn-off at $g_0 \sim 20$ mag (see Figure 2). Its location and profile are well matched by a 13-Gyr-old stellar population roughly 20 kpc away with [Fe/H] of approximately -1.6 dex when compared with Dartmouth isochrones (Dotter et al. 2008).

As can be seen from the Milky Way's 'field of streams' (Belokurov et al. 2007a), the stellar overdensity lying on top of Leo IV and V is found near a region of the sky occupied by several prominent streams and stellar overdensities. Given its currently understood properties and angular separation from the Sagittarius stream, an association of the newly detected structure with Sagittarius is unlikely. A connection with the nearby Virgo overdensity is in fact more probable, given a close agreement in distance and metallicity (e.g., Duffau et al. 2006; Jurić et al. 2008). Whatever its allegiance, the stars once thought to possibly be associated with the Leos are clearly not occupants of the distant halo, but more likely members of a structure enjoying inner-halo residency.

4. Summary

Using deep Subaru/Suprime-Cam data, we have obtained an improved set of structural parameters for the Milky Way dwarf galaxies Leo IV and Leo V. Additionally and more interestingly, we find that a tentative stream of stars previously detected between the two dwarfs is part of a more extended stellar overdensity, coincidentally overlapping the satellite galaxies. Previously taken as a hint of a feature related to the dwarf galaxies, the deeper and wider Suprime-Cam data reveal a main-sequence turn-off in the stacked CMD consistent with that of a 13-Gyr-old stellar population with [Fe/H] of -1.6 dex at a distance of approximately 20 kpc.

While being far enough away from the multiple wraps of the imposing Sagittarius stellar stream to avoid this affiliation, the on-sky proximity of the stellar overdensity enveloping Leo IV and Leo V to the Virgo stellar overdensity, along with a comparable distance and consistent metallicity, appears to imply an association with the latter structure. Indeed, our former Leo stellar-bridge hopeful appears to be suffering a constellation membership crisis. Instead of being trapped inside the lion's den, however, the stars of the newly detected stellar substructure manage to escape the Leos' jaws, only to be lured into the arms of Virgo.

Acknowledgments. SJ thanks the Alexander von Humboldt Foundation for a research fellowship held during the time this work was carried out. BC is an Alexander von Humboldt research fellow.

References

Belokurov, V., Evans, N. W., Irwin, M. J. et al. 2007a, ApJ, 658, 337
Belokurov, V., Zucker, D. B., Evans, N. W. et al. 2007b, ApJ, 654, 897
Belokurov, V., Walker, M. G., Evans, N. W. et al. 2008, ApJ, 686, L83
de Jong, J. T. A., Martin, N. F., Rix, H.-W. et al. 2010, ApJ, 710, 1664
Dotter, A., Chaboyer, B., Jevremović, D. et al. 2008, ApJS, 178, 89
Duffau, S., Zinn, R., Vivas, A. K. et al. 2006, ApJ, 636, L97
Jurić, M., Ivezić, Z., Brooks, A. et al. 2008, ApJ, 673, 864
Martin, N. F., de Jong, J. T. A., & Rix, H.-W. 2008, ApJ, 684, 1075
Moretti, M. I., Dall'Ora, M., Ripepi, V. et al. 2009, ApJ, 699, L125
Schlegel, D. J., Finkbeiner, D. P. & Davis, M. 1998, ApJ, 500, 525
York, D. G. & The SDSS Collaboration 2000, AJ, 120, 1579

Galactic Archaeology: Near-Field Cosmology and the Formation of the Milky Way
ASP Conference Series, Vol. 458
W. Aoki, M. Ishigaki, T. Suda, T. Tsujimoto, N. Arimoto, eds.
©*2012 Astronomical Society of the Pacific*

Chemical Abundances of the Kinematically Selected Thick Disk and Halo Stars

Miho Ishigaki,[1] Masashi Chiba,[2] and Wako Aoki[1]

[1]*National Astronomical Observatory of Japan, Osawa 2-21-1, Mitaka, Tokyo 181-8588, Japan*

[2]*Astronomical Institute, Tohoku University, Aoba-ku, Sendai 980-8578, Japan*

Abstract. We have estimated the abundances of Fe, Mg, Si, Ca and Ti for more than 90 nearby metal-poor ($-3.5 <$[Fe/H]< -0.5) stars, likely belonging to the Milky Way thick disk, inner and outer stellar halo. High-resolution (R~50000) spectra for the sample stars have been obtained with Subaru/HDS and analyzed using an LTE abundance analysis code in combination with Kurucz model atmosphere. We show that the thick disk sample stars show constantly high [Mg/Fe] and [Si/Fe] ratios with a small scatter, while the inner/outer halo stars show larger scatter as well as a mild decreasing trend with increasing metallicity at [Fe/H]> -2.0. Implications of these results for possible progenitors of the thick disk, inner/outer halo are discussed.

1. Introduction

Kinematics and chemical compositions of nearby stars have been used as one of the major constraint on the formation history of the Milky Way (MW) Galaxy, which provide us a test for the galaxy formation in the Universe and the underlying cosmology. Recent photometric and spectroscopic surveys including Sloan Digital Sky Survey (SDSS) have discovered a growing number of substructures in the MW, that are likely signatures of the MW formation involving accretions of smaller stellar systems. Further insights on properties of the progenitor stellar systems can be obtained from chemical abundances of individual constituent stars of the old MW components, since they reflect past star formation and subsequent chemical enrichment at the star's birth place.

In our previous studies (Zhang et al. 2009; Ishigaki et al. 2010) we have estimated abundances of α, iron-peak and neutron-capture elements for the sample stars likely belonging to the outer MW stellar halo and have reported lower [α/Fe] ratios for these stars than those of the inner halo stars from literature in $-2 <$[Fe/H]< -1. In order to examine this possible abundance difference between the inner and outer stellar halo, unaffected by systematic errors, we have performed a homogeneous chemical abundance analysis for stars spanning a wide range in orbital parameters, typical of the thick disk, inner and outer halo, to get insights on the origins of these old MW components.

2. The Sample

The sample metal-poor stars were selected from catalogues of Carney et al. (1994), Ryan & Norris (1991) and Beers et al. (2000), so that stars having a wide range in

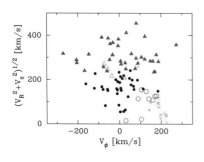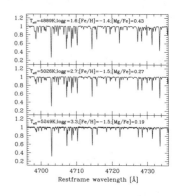

Figure 1.   Left: Toomre diagram for the sample stars. Crosses, filled circles and filled triangles show the sample stars with $P_{TD} > 0.9$, $P_{IH} > 0.9$ and $P_{OH} > 0.9$, respectively. Open circles show the stars whose kinematics are intermediate between the thick disk and the inner halo ($P_{TD}, P_{IH} \leq 0.9$ and $P_{TD}, P_{IH} \geq P_{OH}$), while open triangles show stars whose kinematics are intermediate between the inner and the outer halo ($P_{IH}, P_{OH} \leq 0.9$ and $P_{IH}, P_{OH} \geq P_{TD}$). Right: The spectra obtained with Subaru/HDS for three stars in our sample.

orbital parameters are included in the sample. Velocity components in a cylindrical coordinate (V_R, V_ϕ and V_Z), apo/peri-Galactic distances (R_{apo} and R_{peri}) and maximum distances above/below the Galactic plane (Z_{max}) have been calculated as in Chiba & Beers (2000), based on the updated proper motions, radial velocities and metallicity estimates. Using the calculated orbital parameters, probabilities that each of the sample stars belongs to either the thick disk, inner halo or outer halo component (P_{TD}, P_{IH} and P_{OH}, respectively) were calculated. In this calculation, velocity distributions of the thick disk, inner and outer halo are assumed to be Gaussian with mean velocities and dispersions, as well as a fractional contribution of each component at a given Z_{max} range taken from recent estimates from SDSS Data Release 7 by Carollo et al. (2010). Additionally, we impose that $P_{OH} = 1.0, P_{IH}, P_{OH} = 0.0$ for stars having $R_{apo} > 15$ kpc, so that a star having an orbit with a low Z_{max} but a large R_{apo} is classified as an outer halo candidate. Finally, P_{TD}, P_{IH} and P_{OH} are normalized so that they sum up to one. The toomre diagram for the sample stars with their classifications is shown in the left panel of Figure 1.

3.   Observation and Analysis

The high-resolution spectra of the sample stars have been obtained with Subaru/HDS (HDS; Noguchi et al. 2002) in several observing runs during 2003 - 2010. The wavelength range of about 4000-6800 Å is covered with a spectral resolution of $R \sim 50000$ for most of the sample stars. Examples of the reduced spectra are shown in the right panel of Figure 1. Equivalent widths (EWs) of Fe I, Fe II, Mg I, Si I, Ca I, Ti I and Ti II lines were measured by fitting Gaussian to each absorption feature.

The abundance analysis is performed using an LTE abundance analysis code as in Aoki et al. (2009). In the present work, effective temperatures (T_{eff}) based on $V - K$ colors are adopted, while surface gravities (log g) and micro-turbulence velocities

(ξ) were estimated spectroscopically. Abundances of Fe, Mg, Si, Ca, Ti have been estimated from the measured EWs ($\log EW/\lambda < -4.7$) with the revised $\log gf$ values. The derived abundances were normalized with the solar values (Asplund et al. 2009) and the [X/Fe] ratios were derived by normalizing with the [Fe I/H] of [Fe II/H] for the neutral and ionized species, respectively.

4. Results

4.1. [α/Fe] - [Fe/H]

Figure 2 shows the obtained Mg, Si, Ca, Ti to Fe abundance ratios plotted against [Fe/H]. In [Fe/H]> -2, the thick disk stars ($P_{TD} > 0.9$) show high [Mg/Fe] and [Si/Fe] ratios at a mean larger than 0.35 with small scatter. In contrast, the inner and outer halo stars in the present sample show the lower [Mg/Fe] and [Si/Fe] ratios on average at means ~ 0.2. Additionally, the inner and outer halo stars show modest decreasing trends in the [Mg/Fe] and [Si/Fe] with increasing [Fe/H]. Such decreasing trends are frequently observed for nearby dwarf spheroidal galaxies (dSphs) like Sculptor dSphs but the trends are generally much steeper than those seen in the present halo sample (Tolstoy et al. 2009). The [Ca/Fe], [Ti I/Fe] and [Ti II/Fe] ratios for the thick disk and inner/outer halo stars show largely overlapping distributions in the [X/Fe]-[Fe/H] plane, in contrast to those for the [Mg/Fe] and [Si/Fe] ratios. In [Fe/H]< -2.0, the [Mg/Fe], [Ca/Fe], [Ti I/Fe] and [Ti II/Fe] values of the inner and outer halo stars do not show significant trends with the [Fe/H] and similar to those reported in literature.

5. Discussion

The trends and dispersions in the [X/Fe] ratios with [Fe/H] characterise relative contributions of different nucleosynthesis mechanisms that have produced these elements. In particular, α-element like Mg or Si is thought to be synthesized in massive stars and ejected through Type II SNe within a short time scale, while Fe could be largely enriched through Type Ia SNe for an extended period of time. As a result, chemical evolution models predict that the metallicity at which the [Mg/Fe] or [Si/Fe] ratios start to decrease would vary according to the relative contribution of the Type II and Type Ia SNe, which may be determined by the star formation rate or galactic wind efficiency in the system.

Our results in Figure 2 show constantly high [Mg/Fe] ratios with small scatter for the thick disk stars. This result suggests that the thick disk stars have formed within a short time scale so that the chemical enrichment mainly proceeds via Type II SNe. In contrast, the inner and outer halo stars show lower [Mg/Fe] ratios on average and span a wider [Mg/Fe] range than the thick disk stars, probably containing both 'high-α' and 'low-α' stars as reported in Nissen & Schuster (2010). Comparison of this result with a simple chemical evolution model suggests that the halo stars could be originated from stellar systems having various properties, some of which may have higher star formation rates producing the high [Mg/Fe] or [Si/Fe] stars, while others may have lower star formation rates producing stars with lower values for these abundance ratios. The cosmological simulations of Zolotov et al. (2010) suggest that such a hybrid scenario for the halo formation, in which both accretions of dwarf galaxies and star formation *in situ* have played a role in forming the stellar halo, can be understood in the frame-

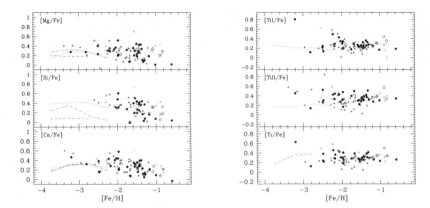

Figure 2. α-elements (Mg, Si, Ca: left, Ti I, Ti II, Ti=(Ti I+Ti II)/2: right) to Fe abundance ratios plotted against [Fe/H]. Symbols are the same as in the left panel of Figure 1. Mean values of the abundance ratios within a given metallicity interval obtained by Cayrel et al. (2004), Lai et al. (2008) and Bonifacio et al. (2009) are connected with *dotted*, *dash-dotted* and *dashed* lines, respectively.

work of galaxy formation under the currently standard cosmology, with an assumption on a prescription for star formation. More quantitative constraints on the fractional contributions from each scenario, it is essential to investigate kinematics and chemical abundances for a larger volume of the stellar halo. Accurate astrometry with *Gaia* in combination with wide and deep spectroscopic surveys beyond the solar neighborhood would give new insights on the nature and origin of the thick disk and stellar halo.

Acknowledgments.   Based on data collected at Subaru Telescope, which is operated by the National Astronomical Observatory of Japan. This work is supported in part from Grant-in-Aid for Scientific Research (23740162) of the Ministry of Education, Culture, Sports, Science and Technology in Japan.

References

Aoki, W., Barklem, P. S., Beers, T. C., et al. 2009, ApJ, 698, 1803
Asplund, M., Grevesse, N., Sauval, A. J., Scott, P., et al. 2009, ARA&A, 47, 481
Beers, T. C., Chiba, M., Yoshii, Y., et al. 2000, AJ, 119, 2866
Bonifacio, P., Spite, M., Cayrel, R., et al. 2009, A&A, 501, 519
Carney, B. W., Latham, D. W., Laird, J. B., & Aguilar, L. A. 1994, AJ, 107, 2240
Carollo, D., Beers, T. C., Chiba, M., et al. 2010, ApJ, 712, 692
Cayrel, R., Depagne, E., Spite, M., et al. 2004, A&A, 416, 1117
Chiba, M., & Beers, T. C. 2000, AJ, 119, 2843
Ishigaki, M., Aoki, W., & Chiba, M. 2010, PASJ, 62, 143
Lai, D. K., Bolte, M., Johnson, J. A., et al. 2008, ApJ, 738, 51
Nissen, P. E., & Schuster, W. J. 2010, A&A, 511, 10
Noguchi, K., Aoki, W., Kawanomoto, S., et al. 2002, PASJ, 54, 855
Ryan, S. G., & Norris, J. E. 1991, AJ, 101, 1835
Tolstoy, E., Hill, V., & Tosi, M. 2009, ARA&A, 47, 371
Zhang, L., Ishigaki, M., Aoki, W., Zhao, G., & Chiba, M. 2009, ApJ, 706, 1095
Zolotov, A., Willman, B., Brooks, A., et al. 2010, ApJ, 721, 738

Galactic Archaeology: Near-Field Cosmology and the Formation of the Milky Way
ASP Conference Series, Vol. 458
W. Aoki, M. Ishigaki, T. Suda, T. Tsujimoto, N. Arimoto, eds.
©2012 Astronomical Society of the Pacific

A Small Slice of the Milky Way Disk in SDSS

Martin C. Smith[1,2]

[1]*Kavli Institute for Astronomy and Astrophysics, Peking University, Beijing 100871, China; msmith@pku.edu.cn*

[2]*National Astronomical Observatories, Chinese Academy of Sciences, Beijing 100012, China*

Abstract. The present-day state of the Milky Way disk can tell us much about the history of our Galaxy and provide insights into its formation. We have constructed a high-precision catalogue of disk stars using data from the Sloan Digital Sky Survey (SDSS) and use these stars to probe the heating history as well as investigating the detailed phase-space distribution. We also show how this sample can be used to probe the global properties of the Milky Way disk, employing the Jeans equations to provide a simple model of the potential close to the disk. Our model is in excellent agreement with others in the literature and provides an indication that the disk, rather than the halo, dominates the circular speed at the solar neighborhood. The work presented in these proceedings has been published as "Slicing and dicing the Milky Way disc in SDSS" (Smith et al. 2012).

1. Introduction and sample construction

Large surveys such as SDSS are beginning to enable detailed studies to be made of the properties of the Milky Way. It is now possible to construct high-precision catalogues of stars with full 3D kinematics and from these analyse the structure and evolution of our Galaxy. In the following proceedings I summarise our study of the disk of the Milky Way (presented in full in Smith et al. 2012), highlighting two of the most important results.

We use data from the 7th public data release of the SDSS, concentrating on the 250 square degree Stripe 82 region for which it is possible to obtain high precision photometry and proper motions (Bramich et al. 2008). This catalogue has been exploited in a variety of works, covering white dwarfs (Vidrih et al. 2007), halo kinematics (Smith et al. 2009a,b) and RR Lyrae in the outer halo (Watkins et al. 2009).

We take all dwarf stars with good quality spectra (Lee et al. 2008), estimating distances using a slightly modified version of the Ivezić et al. (2008) photometric parallax relation. Our modification concerns the turn-off correction (equation A6 of Ivezić et al. 2008), which we argue is not applicable to disk stars (see the Appendix of Smith et al. 2012). We then calculate the three-dimensional velocities for our sample, propagating all uncertainties, and obtain final errors of around 20 to 30 $km\,s^{-1}$ for each component of the velocity.

As we are interested in the kinematics of the disk as a function of height from the plane, we restrict ourselves to $7 \leq R(kpc) \leq 9$. We also split the data into three ranges in metallicity ($-1.5 \leq$ [Fe/H] $\leq -0.8, -0.8 \leq$ [Fe/H] ≤ -0.5 and $-0.5 \leq$ [Fe/H]), and then for each metallicity bin we further divide the data into four ranges in z out to a maximum distance of 2 kpc. The stars are equally divided between the four distance bins, resulting in around 500 to 800 stars per bin from our full sample of 7280 stars. This binning is necessary in order to avoid having to model the SDSS spectroscopic selection function.

Once we have divided up our stars, we then proceed to fit the distribution of kinematics using maximum likelihood methods (incorporating the uncertainties on the individual velocities). Both v_R and v_z are fit using Gaussian distributions, but since it is well known that the distribution of v_ϕ for the disk is highly skewed and non-Gaussian we adopt an asymmetric functional form (equation (15) of Cuddeford & Binney 1994). When carrying out this analysis it is crucial to remove contamination from halo stars, particularly for the most metal-poor bins. We do this by including a non-rotating Gaussian component into the velocity fits, where the level of contamination (and hence amplitude of the Gaussian) is assumed to be twice the number of counter-rotating stars. The halo dispersions are fixed according to the values found in Smith et al. (2009a).

2. The rotation lag of the disk and the asymmetric drift

A comprehensive analysis of the results are presented in Smith et al. (2012). Here we concentrate on the most important properties, starting with rotation lag. We are able to trace the lag (Fig. 1) to a couple of kpc outside the plane and find that it follows the well-known asymmetric drift relation. The hotter (metal-poor) stars exhibit greater lag than the colder (metal-rich) populations, resulting in a clear correlation between lag and metallicity. The gradient of the lag with respect to |z| varies from around 15 to 40 $\mathrm{km\,s^{-1}kpc^{-1}}$, depending on metallicity. Fig. 1 also shows how the lag is correlated with σ_R^2. For the solar-neighbourhood it is known that this is a linear relation (Dehnen & Binney 1998a), but as we can see from our figure this is no longer true once we move beyond 0.5 kpc. However, it can be seen that there is still a relatively tight correlation with σ_R^2, which is independent of metallicity.

3. Constraining the gravitational potential of the disk

As has been shown by many authors, most notably in the seminal work of Kuijken & Gilmore (1991), the vertical velocity dispersion profile can be used to constrain the gravitational potential of the disk. We show the results derived from our data in Fig. 2, where we have included an additional solar-neighbourhood metal-rich data point derived from the Geneva-Copenhagen survey (Nordström et al. 2004). We take a simplified two-parameter model for the potential, consisting of an infinite razor-thin sheet embedded in a constant background. Our best-fit model estimates that the mass density of these two components are 32.5 $\mathrm{M_\odot pc^{-2}}$ and 0.015 $\mathrm{M_\odot pc^{-3}}$, respectively.

As can be seen from Fig. 2, our measurement of the potential is in good agreement with existing models, especially Model 1 of Dehnen & Binney (1998b). This is the least halo-dominated model of Dehnen & Binney (1998b), with the disk (which has a relatively short scale-length) dominating the circular speed at the solar neighborhood. Interested readers should consult section 2.7 of Binney & Tremaine (2008) for a detailed comparison of these models.

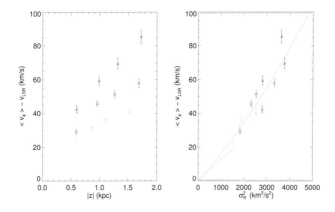

Figure 1. The rotational lag, plotted against z (left) and against the radial velocity dispersion (right). The triangles, squares and crosses correspond to metal-
poor, intermediate-metallicity and metal-rich populations, respectively. The dotted
line in the right panel corresponds to the solar-neighborhood relation from Dehnen
& Binney (1998a) and the solid line denotes an empirical fit with the lag equal to
$0.0149\sigma_R^2 + 1.21 \times 10^{-6}\sigma_R^4$. Figure taken from Smith et al. (2012).

Note that this background mass density is close to the $0.014\ M_\odot pc^{-3}$ predicted
using isothermal spherical halo models (equation 4.279 of Binney & Tremaine 2008). If
we assume our background mass represents the dark halo, it corresponds to a local dark
matter density of $0.57\ GeV\ cm^{-3}$, which is noticeably larger than the canonical value
of $0.30\ GeV\ cm^{-3}$ typically assumed (e.g. Jungman et al 1996). Our analysis adds still
more weight to the argument the local halo density may be substantially underestimated
by this generally accepted value. Perhaps more robust than the local mass density is the
surface mass density. By integrating our mass distribution we obtain a total surface
mass density of $\Sigma_{1.1kpc} = 66\ M_\odot pc^{-2}$, which agrees well with the classical value of
$71 \pm 6\ M_\odot pc^{-2}$ from Kuijken & Gilmore (1991). If we integrate beyond 1.1 kpc, we
find $\Sigma_{2kpc} = 94\ M_\odot pc^{-2}$ and $\Sigma_{4kpc} = 155\ M_\odot pc^{-2}$.

4. Conclusion

Our results (presented in full in Smith et al. 2012) can be used to address the global
properties of the disk and also the heating processes that have shaped its evolution. In
order to fully understand the nature of disk heating and to disentangle the contributions from various mechanisms, one needs to go beyond the work presented here. The
most crucial improvement will be the ability to make direct estimates for stellar ages,
rather than relying on correlations with metallicity. One aspect that will help us in this
effort is by folding in measurements of alpha-element abundances that are now being
determined routinely for vast numbers of stars (e.g. Lee et al. 2011).

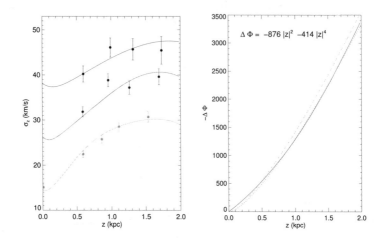

Figure 2.   The results of our modeling of the potential of the Galactic disk. The left panel shows the vertical velocity dispersion profiles (metal-poor - top; metal-rich - bottom), along with the corresponding profiles for the potential (solid lines). The right panel shows the potential resulting from this model. For the purposes of comparison we have included models for the potential taken from Dehnen & Binney (1998 – Model 1, dotted; Model 4, dashed). Figure adapted from Smith et al. (2012).

Discussion

Martin: Can you develop your model to test for the presence of a dark disk (e.g. Read et al. 2008)?

Smith: Due to the limitations of the data that we have used there are a number of uncertainties in our modelling. As a consequence of these limitations, I think it would be difficult to include extra parameters.

Acknowledgments.   MCS acknowledges financial support from the Peking University One Hundred Talent Fund (985) and NSFC grants 11043005 and 11010022. This work was also supported by the European Science Foundation (ESF) for the activity entitled 'Gaia Research for European Astronomy Training'.

References

Binney, J.J., & Tremaine, S. 2008, Galactic Dynamics. Princeton Univ. Press, Princeton, NJ
Bramich, D.M., Vidrih, S., Wyrzykowski, L., et al. 2008, MNRAS, 386, 887
Cuddeford, P., & Binney, J. 1994, MNRAS, 266, 273
Dehnen, W., & Binney, J.J. 1998a, MNRAS, 298, 387
Dehnen, W., & Binney, J.J. 1998b, MNRAS, 294, 429
Ivezić, Z., Sesar, B., Jurić, M., et al. 2008, ApJ, 684, 287
Jungman, G., Kamionkowski, M., Griest, K., 1996, Phys. Rep., 267, 195
Kuijken, K., & Gilmore, G. 1991, ApJ, 367, L9

Lee, Y.S., Beers, T.C., Sivarani, T., et al. 2008, AJ, 136, 2022
Lee, Y.S., Beers, T.C., A., D., et al. 2011, ApJ, 738, 187
Nordström, B., Mayor, M., Andersen, J., et al. 2004, A&A, 418, 989
Read, J.I., Lake, G., Agertz1, O., Debattista, V.P. 2008, MNRAS, 389, 1041
Smith, M.C., Evans, N.W., Belokurov, V., et al. 2009a, MNRAS, 399, 1223
Smith, M.C., Evans, N.W., An, J.H. 2009b, ApJ, 698, 1110
Smith, M.C., Whiteoak, S.H., Evans, N.W. 2012, ApJ, in press (arXiv:1111.6920)
Vidrih, S., et al. 2007, MNRAS, 382, 515
Watkins, L.L., et al. 2009, MNRAS, 398, 1757

Active discussions in sessions. M. Rich (raising a hand).

Galactic Archaeology: Near-Field Cosmology and the Formation of the Milky Way
ASP Conference Series, Vol. 458
W. Aoki, M. Ishigaki, T. Suda, T. Tsujimoto, N. Arimoto, eds.
© 2012 Astronomical Society of the Pacific

Milky Way Kinematics from RAVE Data

S. Pasetto,[1] E.K. Grebel,[2] and the RAVE Co.

[1] *University College London, Department of Space & Climate Physics, Mullard Space Science Laboratory, Holmbury St. Mary, Dorking Surrey RH5 6NT, United Kingdom*
[2]*Astronomisches Rechen-Institut, Zentrum für Astronomie der Universität Heidelberg, Mönchhofstr. 12-14, 69120 Heidelberg, Germany*

Abstract. We present a method to derive kinematic parameters for the Galactic thick and thin disks of the Milky Way (MW) based on the Radial Velocity Experiment (RAVE Steinmetz et al. 2006). We introduce selection criteria in order to clean the observed radial velocities from the Galactic large scale effects and to take into account the partial sky coverage of RAVE. The data are disentangled from a mixture of thin and thick disk stars as explained in a forthcoming paper (Pasetto et al. 2012) on the basis of pure kinematics arguments and supplied with photometric distances and proper motions. We deduce the components of the Solar motion relative to the Local Standard of Rest (LSR) in the radial and vertical directions as well as the components of the velocity dispersion tensors for the two MW component on the basis of pure kinematics arguments. The selected sample is a limited subsample from the RAVE catalogue roughly extending 500 pc above and below the Galactic plane. This sample tracks the velocity dispersion trend in radial direction to 1 kpc within and 500pc outside the Solar radius in the Galactic reference system.

1. Method and dataset

For a star at a given position $\mathbf{x}$ in the Milky Way's disk, the following general vector relation holds:

$$\bar{\mathbf{v}}_{LSR}(\mathbf{x}_\odot) + \mathbf{v}_\odot + \mathbf{v}_{hel} = \bar{\mathbf{v}}_c(\mathbf{x}) + \mathbf{v}_p, \qquad (1)$$

where $\bar{\mathbf{v}}_c(\mathbf{x})$ is the mean rotational velocity at the given position $\mathbf{x}$ in the Galactic disk reference system centred on the barycentre of the Milky Way (MW). $\bar{\mathbf{v}}_{LSR}(\mathbf{x}_\odot)$ is the Solar Local Standard of Rest which differs from the Local Standard of Rest (LSR) speed at any other location in the Galaxy. $\mathbf{v}_\odot$ is the Solar peculiar velocity relative to the Solar LSR and $\mathbf{v}_p$ is the peculiar velocity of the star relative to its own mean Galactic rotational speed. We consider all the stars in the RAVE catalogue (Zwitter et al. 2008) for which the Galactic contribution to the radial velocity component, $\delta v_r^{[G]}$, expected to be much small (Pasetto et al 2012, in preparation). For this sample (in Fig. 1) the Galactic effect in the radial velocity component, $\delta v_r^{[G]}$, can be approximated as:

$$\delta v_r^{[G]} = \delta v_r^{[G]}(r_{hel}, l, b, \|\mathbf{v}_m\|) \cong \delta v_r^{[G]}(l, b, \|\mathbf{v}_m\|) \qquad (2)$$

where r_{hel}, the unknown or photometrically determined heliocentric distance (Zwitter et al. 2010), (l, b) are the Galactic coordinates for the stars and $\|\mathbf{v}_m\|$ is an optimized thick disk mean stream velocity for the sample of data selected as explained in our forthcoming paper (Pasetto et al. 2012). From the sample of stars that survive the selection imposed by Eqn. 2 and shown in Figure 1, we further require the near-infrared colours of the RAVE stars taken from 2MASS observations to be in the range of $J - K \in$ [0.2, 1.1] in order to clean the dataset from extremely young stars, $v_r^{RAVE} < 300$ km s^{-1} to avoid stars dynamically not representative of the thick disk within 2 kpc from the Sun's position, $\Delta v_r^{RAVE} < 14$ km s^{-1} to reduce the propagation error while retaining a considerable amount of stars (see the velocity contour highlighted in black in Fig. 1), $|b| > 10°$, and $\log_{10} g > 3.5$ to avoid the influence of giant stars which may sample a much more distant part of the Galaxy and it represents one of the most severe cut on the total number of stars that we can use. Where possible a further cut [Fe/H] > -1 dex was applied adopting the metallicity determination described by Zwitter et al. (2008). Starting with an initial number of roughly 260,000 stars in the data release of Zwitter et al. (2010), the final, remaining number of stars for which we can perform the analysis is $N_{tot} \simeq 38,805$ that is is orders of magnitude larger than samples actually available in the literature. We then proceed by using the Singular Value Decomposition technique to solve for the mean velocity of the sample and then by computing the central moment (or the cumulants) of the distribution up to 4th order. The thick disk component is disentangled from the mixture of thin and thick disk stars with procedure similar to Cubarsi & Alcobé (2004) but implemented in Monte Carlo sense.

2.   Results

We obtained first and second moment of the mixture of thin and thick disk from pure radial velocities, then proceeded disentangling the thick disk kinematic components by determining its distributions first and second moments. Finally with photometrically determined distances and proper motions we determined the first and second-order kinematic moments of the thin disk component. One limitation of the method is its inability to disentangle first order moment along the azimuthal direction relative to an inertial reference frame.

2.1.   Solar motion relative to the Local Standard of Rest

With the approach outlined above, we obtained the solar motion relative to the Local Standard of Rest (LSR) along the radial and vertical direction twice, from thin disk component and from the thick disk component:

$$\{v_R, v_z\}_\odot = (9.87, 8.01) \pm (0.37, 0.29) \, \text{km} \cdot \text{s}^{-1} \tag{3}$$

and thin disk alone:

$$\{v_R, v_z\}_\odot = (10.9, 7.2) \pm (1.0, 1.3) \, \text{km} \cdot \text{s}^{-1} \tag{4}$$

This was obtained from a selected kinematically unbiased sample of stars where the directional vector to each star and the velocity vector are uncorrelated. The azimuthal value cannot be disentangled from the lag of the thick disk component with the present method. We tested this assumption with the help of the Padova Hertzsprung-Russel Diagram Galactic Software Telescope combined with a kinematic model and a potential-density model well tuned on the Galaxy (e.g., Vallenari et al. (2006), Pasetto, PhD thesis, 2005).

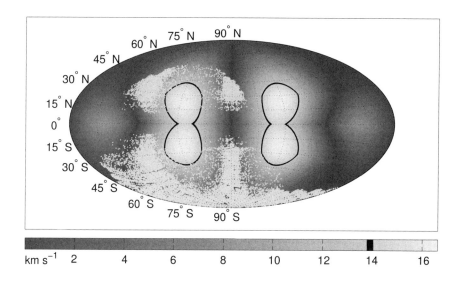

Figure 1.   (color online) Isocontour plot on an Aitoff projection of the contribution in radial velocity due to Galactic rotation. The gradients of the velocity dispersion tensor are treated as in Vallenari et al. (2006). The assumed values for the motion of the Sun relative to the LSR are from this paper. The points outside the black colour lines show the RAVE data selection.

2.2.   Thick disk velocity dispersion tensor

2.2.1.   Velocity dispersion tensor (without distances)

Our approach permits us to compute the velocity dispersion tensor without the use of distances. We find in the RAVE data a vertical tilt of 4.9 ± 1.2 deg in the thick disk data alone. We derive for the diagonal elements of the velocity dispersion tensor:

$$\left(\sigma_{RR}, \sigma_{\phi\phi}, \sigma_{zz}\right)_{\odot} = (59.2, 49.6, 35.5) \pm (4.2, 5.3, 3.8)\,\mathrm{km \cdot s^{-1}} \qquad (5)$$

2.2.2.   Velocity dispersion tensor (with distances)

Finally, we use a subsample of the RAVE dataset with photometrically determined distances (Zwitter et al. 2008) to check the validity of the method and to extend our analysis. We are able to disentangle the thick disk velocity dispersion tensor of stars within and outside the Sun's position in the Galactic plane:

$$\left(\sigma_{RR}, \sigma_{\phi\phi}, \sigma_{zz}\right)(R < R_{\odot}) = (61.1, 48.7, 37.2) \pm (16.1, 7.6, 12.7)\,\mathrm{km \cdot s^{-1}} \qquad (6)$$

$$\left(\sigma_{RR}, \sigma_{\phi\phi}, \sigma_{zz}\right)(R \geq R_{\odot}) = (57.1, 48.4, 35.3) \pm (3.2, 5.7, 3.9)\,\mathrm{km \cdot s^{-1}} \qquad (7)$$

RAVE is able for the first time to indicate the possibility of a small decreasing trend in the velocity ellipsoid from the inner to the outer part of the galaxy and may show the need to forgo the classical isothermal anisotropic thick disk picture.

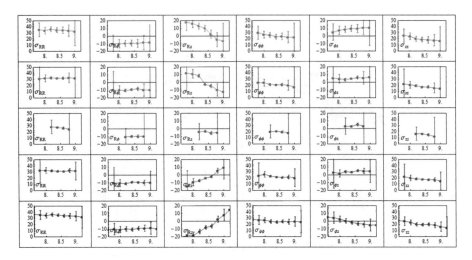

Figure 2.   Thin disk velocity dispersion tensor in the meridional plane. See text for a guide of how to read the figure panels.

2.3.   Thin disk velocity dispersion tensor

We determined the thin disk velocity ellipsoid as in Fig. 2 where a plot of all the velocity ellipsoid elements σ_{ij} in the plane (O, R, z) for the thin disk alone is shown. The axis labels are omitted in favour of a small indicator of the element we are considering in the lower right part of the plot. In order to visualize different z distance ranges, we use a gradation of increasing red for the plot lines from the upper row of the plot, $z \in \,]0.3, 0.5]$ kpc down to the redder row for the range $z \in \,]-0.5, 0.3]$ kpc: the first row of the upper 6 panels refers to $z \in \,]0.3, 0.5]$ kpc, the second to $z \in \,]0.1, 0.3]$ kpc, the central to the Galactic plane $z \in \,]-0.1, 0.1]$ kpc and it is more limited in the radial extension because of the selection of the RAVE survey directions as seen in Fig. 1. Finally the fourth row includes panels for $z \in \,]-0.1, -0.3]$ kpc and the lower one to $z \in \,]-0.3, -0.5]$ kpc.

Acknowledgments.   SP thanks the organizers for the enjoyable and stimulating conference. Funding for RAVE (www.rave-survey.org) has been provided by institutions of the RAVE participants and by their national funding agencies.

References

Cubarsi, R., & Alcobé, S. 2004, A&A, 427, 131
Pasetto, S., Grebel, E., & et al. 2012, A&A
Steinmetz, M., Zwitter, T., & Siebert 2006, AJ, 132, 1645
Vallenari, A., Pasetto, S., & Bertelli, G. 2006, A&A, 451, 125
Zwitter, T., Matijevič, G., & Breddels, M. A. 2010, A&A, 522, A54
Zwitter, T., Siebert, A., & Munari, U. 2008, AJ, 136, 421

Galactic Archaeology: Near-Field Cosmology and the Formation of the Milky Way
ASP Conference Series, Vol. 458
W. Aoki, M. Ishigaki, T. Suda, T. Tsujimoto, N. Arimoto, eds.
© 2012 Astronomical Society of the Pacific

Abundance Trends in the Inner and Outer Galactic Disk

T. Bensby,[1] A. Alves-Brito,[2,4] M.S. Oey,[3] D. Yong,[4] and J. Meléndez[5]

[1]*Lund Observatory, Box 43, SE-221 00 Lund, Sweden*
[2]*Dpto de Astronomía y Astrofísica, Pontificia Univ. Católica, Santiago, Chile*
[3]*Department of Astronomy, University of Michigan, Ann Arbor, MI, USA*
[4]*Research School of Astronomy and Astrophysics, ANU, Weston, Australia*
[5]*Dpto de Astronomia do IAG/USP, Univ. de São Paulo, São Paulo, Brasil*

Abstract. Based on high-resolution spectra obtained with the MIKE spectrograph on the Magellan telescopes we present detailed elemental abundances for 64 red giant stars in the inner and outer Galactic disk. For the inner disk sample (4-7 kpc from the Galactic centre) we find that stars with both thin and thick disk abundance patterns are present while for Galactocentric distances beyond 10 kpc, we only find chemical patterns associated with the local thin disk, even for stars far above the Galactic plane. Our results show that the relative densities of the thick and thin disks are dramatically different from the solar neighbourhood, and we therefore suggest that the radial scale length of the thick disk is much shorter than that of the thin disk. A thick disk scale-length of $L_{thick} = 2.0$ kpc, and $L_{thin} = 3.8$ kpc for the thin disk, better match the data.

1. Introduction

The inner and outer Galactic disks are the most poorly studied regions of the Milky Way. Especially the abundance structure of the inner disk is largely unknown due to the high interstellar extinction and contamination by background bulge stars. There are only a few studies of bright hot OB stars (e.g., Daflon & Cunha 2004) and Cepheids (e.g., Luck et al. 2006). The outer disk is somewhat better studied using red giants in open clusters (e.g., Yong et al. 2005; Carraro et al. 2007; Jacobson et al. 2011, and references therein). Also OB stars (e.g., Daflon & Cunha 2004; Daflon et al. 2004), and Cepheids (e.g., Andrievsky et al. 2004; Yong et al. 2006) have been observed in the outer disk, and Carney et al. (2005) observed three outer disk field red giants. Open clusters, OB stars, and Cepheids are all tracers of the young stellar population of the disk, and it is therefore unclear wether the inner and outer disk shows a similar abundance structure as seen in the solar neighbourhood, where it has been shown that the thin and thick disks have different abundance trends, metallicity distributions, and abundance distributions (e.g., Fuhrmann 1998; Bensby et al. 2003; Reddy et al. 2003; Bensby et al. 2005, 2007).

To investigate the abundance structure of these poorly studied regions of the Galaxy, we have obtained high-resolution and high signal-to-noise spectra of 44 red giants in the inner disk and 20 red giants in the outer disk with the MIKE spectrograph at the Magellan II telescope on Las Campanas in Chile. The inner disk giants are located at Galactoccentric distances 4-7 kpc and the outer disk giants at Galactocentric distances 9-12 kpc. In order to trace both the thin and the thick disks, if they are present, the

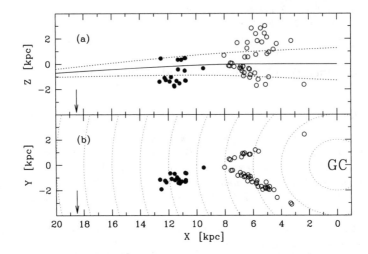

Figure 1.   Galactic X, Y, and Z coordinates. Dotted lines in (a) represent the distances above and below the plane where the thin and thick disk stellar densities are equal, given the scale-lengths, scale-heights, and normalisations for the thin and thick disks given by Jurić et al. (2008). The warp of the disk as given by Momany et al. (2006) has been included.

stars were observed at different Galactic longitudes. Figure 1 shows the positions of the stars in Galactic X, Y, and Z coordinates. The inner disk sample will be valuable for verification of the claimed similarities between the nearby thick disk and the Galactic bulge (Bensby et al. 2010b; Alves-Brito et al. 2010; Bensby et al. 2011a; Gonzalez et al. 2011). Our results so far have been presented in two letters (Bensby et al. 2010a, 2011b) and we will in the proceeding give a short summary.

2.   Analysis

Details of the analysis are given in Bensby et al. (2010a). We would like to stress that the analysis is identical to the K giant samples of the thin and thick disks in the solar neighbourhood and the bulge K giant sample presented by Alves-Brito et al. (2010). Hence, the analysis is strictly differential between the different stellar populations.

3.   Results and discussion

In the upper panel of Figure 2 we show the metallicity distributions of the inner and outer disk samples. A first thing to notice is that the metallicity distributions (MDF) for the inner and outer disk samples are very different. The inner disk MDF has a large spread ($\langle[Fe/H]\rangle_{inner} = -0.42 \pm 0.27$) and suggests a bi-modal distribution, while the outer disk MDF has a much smaller spread $\langle[Fe/H]\rangle_{outer} = -0.48 \pm 0.12$. Within the limited sample, the outer disk MDF is entirely consistent with a single value! The dispersion can be attributed solely to measurement uncertainties. Dividing the inner disk sample into two, one with stars that have $[Mg/Fe] \geq 0.2$ (thick disk) and one with

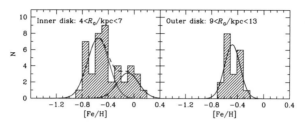

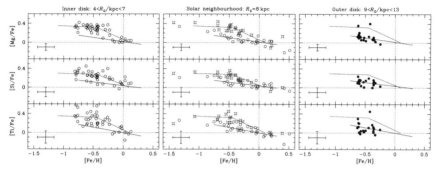

Figure 2.   *Upper:* Metallicity distributions for the inner and outer disk samples. Gaussian distributions, based on the mean metallicities and the metallicity dispersions, are overplotted. *Lower:* Abundance trends for the α-elements Mg, Si, and Ti. The left panel shows the 44 inner disk red giants, the middle panel the solar neighbourhood thin and thick disk stars (blue circles and red stars, respectively) by Alves-Brito et al. (2010), and the right panel the 20 outer disk red giants. Solid lines are fiducial lines based on the solar neighbourhood sample in the lower middle panel.

stars that have [Mg/Fe] < 0.2 (thin disk), results in two metallicity distributions with $\langle[\mathrm{Fe/H}]\rangle_{\mathrm{inner}} = -0.55 \pm 0.12$ and $\langle[\mathrm{Fe/H}]\rangle_{\mathrm{inner}} = -0.09 \pm 0.17$, respectively.

The abundance results for the inner and outer disk giants are shown in the lower panels of Figure 2, where they are compared to the Alves-Brito et al. (2010) sample of thin and thick disk red giants in the solar neighbourhood. Regarding the outer disk, almost all stars have abundance ratios similar to what is seen in the nearby thin disk. This result is surprising because, based on the kinematics and the distances from the plane, a majority of the 20 stars should be thick disk stars. But only one, or maybe two, of the outer disk giants show thick disk abundance patterns. The abundance trends of the inner disk sample appears to contain stars with abundance patterns consistent with the nearby thin and thick disks. An explanation for the apparent lack of stars with thick disk properties in the outer disk is that the thick disk has a significantly shorter scale-length than the thin disk. This would lead to the conclusion that the thick disk will be more dominant in the inner disk region, and the thin disk will be more dominant in the outer disk region. This is illustrated by the dashed line in Figure 3 where the thick disk scale-length has been changed so that a majority of the outer disk stars are within the limits where the thick disk stars start to dominate. The solid lines represent the case when the scale-height is allowed to vary with Galactocentric radius (see Bensby et al. 2011b). With the new scale-lengths there is a better match of chemistry vs. vertical distance from the Galactic plane, for both inner and outer disk samples.

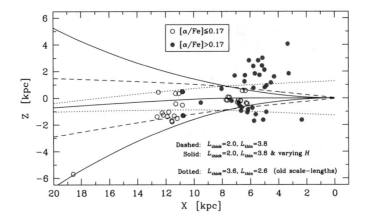

Figure 3.   The inner and outer disk samples in the Galactic $X - Z$ coordinate system. The curves show loci where the two populations have equal stellar density, for different assumed scale lengths L and scale heights H. Stars with $[\alpha/Fe] > 0.17$ are marked by filled red circles, while stars with $[\alpha/Fe] \le 0.17$ by open blue circles.

Further discussions and details can be found in Bensby et al. (2010a, 2011b).

Acknowledgments.   T.B. was funded by grant No. 621-2009-3911 from The Swedish Research Council. This work was also funded by the NSF grant AST-0448900 to M.S.O. A.A.-B. acknowledges grants from FONDECYT (process 3100013).

References

Alves-Brito, A., Meléndez, J., Asplund, M., Ramírez, I., & Yong, D. 2010, A&A, 513, A35
Andrievsky, S. M., Luck, R. E., Martin, P., & Lépine, J. R. D. 2004, A&A, 413, 159
Bensby, T., Adén, D., Meléndez, J., et al. 2011a, A&A, 533, A134
Bensby, T., Alves-Brito, A., Oey, M. S., Yong, D., & Meléndez, J. 2010a, A&A, 516, L13
— 2011b, ApJ, 735, L46
Bensby, T., Feltzing, S., Johnson, J. A., et al. 2010b, A&A, 512, A41
Bensby, T., Feltzing, S., & Lundström, I. 2003, A&A, 410, 527
Bensby, T., Feltzing, S., Lundström, I., & Ilyin, I. 2005, A&A, 433, 185
Bensby, T., Zenn, A. R., Oey, M. S., & Feltzing, S. 2007, ApJ, 663, L13
Carney, B. W., Yong, D., Teixera de Almeida, M. L., & Seitzer, P. 2005, AJ, 130, 1111
Carraro, G., Geisler, D., Villanova, S., et al. 2007, A&A, 476, 217
Daflon, S., & Cunha, K. 2004, ApJ, 617, 1115
Daflon, S., Cunha, K., & Butler, K. 2004, ApJ, 606, 514
Fuhrmann, K. 1998, A&A, 338, 161
Gonzalez, O. A., Rejkuba, M., Zoccali, M., et al. 2011, A&A, 530, A54
Jacobson, H. R., Friel, E. D., & Pilachowski, C. A. 2011, AJ, 141, 58
Jurić, M., Ivezić, Ž., Brooks, A., et al. 2008, ApJ, 673, 864. arXiv:astro-ph/0510520
Luck, R. E., Kovtyukh, V. V., & Andrievsky, S. M. 2006, AJ, 132, 902
Momany, Y., Zaggia, S., Gilmore, G., et al. 2006, A&A, 451, 515
Reddy, B. E., Tomkin, J., Lambert, D. L., & Allende Prieto, C. 2003, MNRAS, 340, 304
Yong, D., Carney, B. W., & Teixera de Almeida, M. L. 2005, AJ, 130, 597
Yong, D., Carney, B. W., Teixera de Almeida, M. L., & Pohl, B. L. 2006, AJ, 131, 2256

Galactic Archaeology: Near-Field Cosmology and the Formation of the Milky Way
ASP Conference Series, Vol. 458
W. Aoki, M. Ishigaki, T. Suda, T. Tsujimoto, N. Arimoto, eds.
© *2012 Astronomical Society of the Pacific*

Metallicity and Kinematics of Thick Disc Stars at Intermediate Galactic Latitudes

G. Kordopatis,[1,2] A. Recio-Blanco,[2] P. de Laverny,[2] G. Gilmore,[1] V. Hill,[2]
R.F.G Wyse,[3] A. Helmi,[4] A. Bijaoui,[2] M. Zoccali,[5] and O. Bienaymé[6]

[1]*Institute of Astronomy, University of Cambridge, Madingley Road, Cambridge CB3 0HA, UK*

[2]*Université de Nice Sophia Antipolis, CNRS, Observatoire de la Côte d'Azur, Cassiopée UMR 6202, BP 4229, 06304 Nice, France*

[3]*Johns Hopkins University, Baltimore, MD, USA*

[4]*Kapteyn Astronomical Institute, University of Groningen, PO Box 800, 9700 AV Groningen, The Netherlands*

[5]*Departamento de Astronomía y Astrofísica, Pontificia Universidad Católica de Chile, Av. Vicuña Mackenna 4860, Casilla 306, Santiago 22, Chile*

[6]*Université de Strasbourg, Observatoire Astronomique, Strasbourg, France*

Abstract. Using the pipeline presented in Kordopatis et al. (2011a), we analysed 700 stellar spectra of targets towards intermediate galactic latitudes, in order to test the formation scenarios of the thick disc of the Milky Way. We found that the properties of the thick disc far from the solar neighbourhood are similar to the ones that have been measured locally by previous studies and that the thick disc is characterised by only one stellar population of constant scalelength and scaleheight, in contradiction with a thick disc mainly formed by radial migration mechanisms.

1. Introduction

The creation of the Galactic thick disc remains a riddle in the paradigm of a cold dark matter dominated Universe. During the last decade there have been several theoretical works suggesting how this structure could have been created. One can cite, for example, Abadi et al. (2003) who proposed a thick disc formed by the accretion of a satellite deposing its stars in a coplanar orbit, or Villalobos & Helmi (2008) who rather proposed a dynamical heating of the thin disc after several minor mergers. Another commonly cited work is the one of Brook et al. (2004) who suggested a thick disc formed in situ, after a gas rich accretion. On the other hand, other scenarios do not need any external accretion events (e.g. Schönrich & Binney 2009; Loebman et al. 2011) and manage to explain the local thick disc observational properties through radial migration processes.

Typical F, G, K and M main-sequence stars are particularly useful to study Galactic evolution, since they are both numerous and long-lived, and their atmospheres reflect their initial chemical composition. However, a direct measurement of their spatial distribution requires accurate estimates of stellar distances, which is a delicate step involving (when the parallax is not available) the determination of precise stellar parameters (effective temperatures T_{eff}, surface gravities log g, and metal contents [M/H]).

In order constraint the thick disc properties, we explored spectroscopically towards ($l \sim 277°$, $b \sim 47°$) the stellar contents outside the Solar neighbourhood, that we complemented with the proper motions and U, B, V colours from Ojha (1994). Here we present the results concerning the vertical gradients that we measured for the stars at a distance above the galactic plane where the thick disc is supposed to be the dominant population.

2. The catalogue of stars

The targets were selected having $14 \leq m_v \leq 18.5$ mag in order to probe the Galactic thick disc and have acceptable signal-to-noise ratios (S/N > 20). According to Ojha (1994), the proper motions errors are estimated to be 2 mas/year.

Radial velocities have been derived by cross-correlating the spectra with a binary template of a K0 type star, reaching a mean estimated error of 4.7 km s^{-1}. The observations were obtained with VLT/FLAMES feeding the GIRAFFE spectrograph with the LR8 grating (8206-9400 Å, $R \sim 6500$). In that wavelength range, the IR CaII triplet is predominant for most of the spectral types and luminosity classes as well as for very metal poor stars. In addition, these strong features are still detectable even at a low S/N, allowing a good radial velocity derivation and an overall metallicity estimation. Paschen lines are visible for stars hotter than G3. Finally, the Mg I (8807 Å) line, which is a useful indicator of surface gravity, is also visible even for low S/N.

We used the pipeline presented in Kordopatis et al. (2011a) which consists in using simultaneously two different algorithms, MATISSE (Recio-Blanco et al. 2006) and DEGAS (Bijaoui et al. 2010), in order to iteratively renormalise the spectra and derive the atmospheric parameters of the observed targets. The method returns for an intermediate metallicity dwarf star, at S/N $\sim$ 50 (which is the mean S/N of our spectra), accuracies of $\sim$ 150 K, 0.3 dex and 0.2 dex for T_{eff}, log g and [M/H], respectively.

3. Chemical and dynamical properties of the thick disc stars

To obtain the line-of-sight distances of the stars, we projected the atmospheric values found from our pipeline on a set of isochrones generated from the Yonsei-Yale (Y^2) models (version 2, Yi et al. 2001). This procedure consists in finding the most likely values of the stellar parameters, given the measured atmospheric ones, and the time spent by a star on each region of the H–R diagram (see Kordopatis et al. 2011b).

We computed the metallicity and the velocity distributions of the stars for narrow height bins, between 1 and 4 kpc from the plane. The size of the bins has been chosen in order to include at least 20 stars. To fully take into account the uncertainties in the computed positions and metallicities of the observed stars, the linear fits have been obtained from 5.10^3 Monte-Carlo realisations on both parameters (*i.e.* D and [M/H]). For each realisation, we computed the new velocities, and measured the median metallicity and the median V_ϕ velocity of the stars inside each bin. Then, the mean value and their 1σ uncertainties rising from the Monte-Carlo realisations have been linearly fitted in order to obtain the vertical gradients.

For the stars associated to the thick disc, we found that the mean metallicity was $\overline{[M/H]}$ = -0.45 ± 0.02 dex with a mean lag V_{lag} = 53 km s^{-1}. In addition, a gradient $\partial[M/H]/\partial Z$ = -0.09 ± 0.04 dex kpc^{-1} has been measured, in agreement (within the errors) with the one found by Katz et al. (2011) and Ruchti et al. (2011). Nevertheless, let us note that this gradient might be under-estimated, since our sample might be lacking low metallicity stars at large distances due to selection effects (see Kordopatis et al. 2011b) . As far as the velocities are concerned, a gradient of $\partial V_\phi/\partial Z$ = 18 ± 7 km s^{-1} kpc^{-1} is observed, in relatively good agreement with the results found by Casetti-Dinescu et al. (2011) and Girard et al. (2006).

Also, it is worth mentioning that a clear correlation between V_ϕ and [M/H] is found for the stars between 0.8 and 2 kpc ($\partial V_\phi/\partial [M/H]$ = 43 ± 10 km s^{-1} dex^{-1}), in agreement with Spagna et al. (2010) and Lee et al. (2011), though in disagreement with the SDSS view of Ivezić et al. (2008), based on photometric metallicities. We recall that according to the radial migration scenarios (Schönrich & Binney 2009; Loebman et al. 2011), no or very small correlation is expected in the transition region, since the older stars, which compose the thick disc have been radially well mixed.

Supposing that the thick disc and the thin disc are in equilibrium, we used the Jeans equations and the velocity ellipsoids of the thin and thick discs to infer an estimation of their radial scale lengths (h_r) and scale heights (h_z). With the values derived for the thick disc of ($\sigma_{V_r}; \sigma_{V_\phi}; \overline{V_\phi}$) = $(75\pm3; 55\pm2; -164\pm3)$ km s^{-1}, we find h_r = 3.4 ± 0.5 kpc and h_Z = 842 ± 54 pc. This value is found in the upper end of the values cited in the literature (ranging from 2.2 kpc (Carollo et al. 2010) up to 3.6 kpc (Jurić et al. 2008), or even 4.5 kpc in the case of Chiba & Beers (2001)).

As far as the thin disc is concerned, using ($\sigma_{V_r}; \sigma_{V_\phi}; \overline{V_\phi}$) = $(43 \pm 1; 31 \pm 1; -204 \pm 2)$ km s^{-1}, we find that it has similar radial extent, within our uncertainties, as the thick disc, with h_r = 3.1 ± 0.2 kpc, and a scale height roughly three times smaller than the thick disc, with h_Z = 220 ± 11 pc. A radially smaller thin disc has been suggested by other recent observations (see Jurić et al. 2008), but once more, the value we derive is at the upper end of the previously reported values in the literature. Nevertheless, such an extended thin disc is plausible, since our data probe mainly the old thin disc, which is likely to be more extended than its young counterpart.

4.   Evidence of multiple accreted populations or stellar radial migration?

In order to investigate furthermore the metallicity gradients found for the rotational velocity of the thick disc, we computed the radial scalelengths and scaleheights for different metallicity bins. We found that both h_r and h_Z increased with decreasing metallicity, though this trend is not strong enough to stand out significantly from the errors. We conclude that, within the errors, the same scalelengths and scaleheights are found, which is the signature of only one population. Indeed, if an important amount of relics of a destroyed massive satellite should exist in our line-of-sight, as suggested by Gilmore et al. (2002), one would expect them to have a different spatial distribution compared to the canonical thick disc, which we do not observe. Unless, of course, if the satellite debris provide the dominant stellar population in the thick disc.

This result can also be discussed in the frame of a thick disc formed according to a radial migration scenario. In that case, the older stars being at the Solar radius have come from the inner parts of the Galaxy, and are expected to have a higher vertical velocity dispersion and a different metallicity, and hence, should exhibit scale heights dependent on metallicity. In particular, the model of Schönrich & Binney (2009) predicts a smaller scale height for the metal poor thick disc, compared to its metal rich counter part. Such a trend is not seen in our data (if it exists, it should be rather small), which challenges the migration scenario as being the most important process of creation of the Galactic thick disc.

Discussion

Renzini: High spatial resolution observations of high redshift ($z \sim 2$) galaxies have shown that discs are characterised by high velocity dispersion, thus suggesting a natural way of producing thick discs in the first place. How is this scenario compatible with your observations?

Kordopatis: One of the strongest predictions of such a scenario is that the scale length of the thick disc should be shorter than the one of the thin disc (e.g. Bournaud et al. 2009). Our observations don't show such evidence, suggesting that this scenario is unlikely to be the dominant mechanism which has formed the thick disc of our Galaxy.

Acknowledgments.	G.K. would like to thank the CNES and CNRS as well as the LOC for financial support.

References

Abadi, M. G., Navarro, J. F., Steinmetz, M., & Eke, V. R. 2003, ApJ, 591, 499
Bijaoui, A., Recio-Blanco, A., de Laverny, P., & Ordenovic, C. 2010, in ADA 6
Bournaud, F., Elmegreen, B. G., & Martig, M. 2009, ApJ, 707, L1
Brook, C. B., Kawata, D., Gibson, B. K., & Freeman, K. C. 2004, ApJ, 612, 894
Carollo, D., Beers, T. C., Chiba, M., & ... 2010, ApJ, 712, 692
Casetti-Dinescu, D. I., Girard, T. M., Korchagin, V. I., & van Altena, W. F. 2011, ApJ, 728, 7
Chiba, M., & Beers, T. C. 2001, ApJ, 549, 325
Gilmore, G., Wyse, R. F. G., & Norris, J. E. 2002, ApJ, 574, L39
Girard, T. M., Korchagin, V. I., Casetti-Dinescu, D. I., & ... 2006, AJ, 132, 1768
Ivezić, Ž., Sesar, B., Jurić, M., & ... 2008, ApJ, 684, 287
Jurić, M., Ivezić, Ž., Brooks, A., & ... 2008, ApJ, 673, 864
Katz, D., Soubiran, C., Cayrel, R., & ... 2011, A&A, 525, A90+
Kordopatis, G., Recio-Blanco, A., de Laverny, P., Bijaoui, A., Hill, V., Gilmore, G., Wyse, R. F. G., & Ordenovic, C. 2011a, A&A, 535, A106
Kordopatis, G., Recio-Blanco, A., de Laverny, P., Gilmore, G., Hill, V., Wyse, R. F. G., Helmi, A., Bijaoui, A., Zoccali, M., & Bienaymé, O. 2011b, A&A, 535, A107
Lee, Y. S., Beers, T. C., An, D., & ... 2011, ApJ, 738, 187
Loebman, S. R., Roškar, R., Debattista, V. P., & ... 2011, ApJ, 737, 8
Ojha, D. K. 1994, Ph.D. thesis, Universite de Strasbourg
Recio-Blanco, A., Bijaoui, A., & de Laverny, P. 2006, MNRAS, 370, 141
Ruchti, G. R., Fulbright, J. P., Wyse, R. F. G., & ... 2011, ApJ, 737, 9
Schönrich, R., & Binney, J. 2009, MNRAS, 399, 1145
Spagna, A., Lattanzi, M. G., Re Fiorentin, P., & Smart, R. L. 2010, A&A, 510, L4+
Villalobos, Á., & Helmi, A. 2008, MNRAS, 391, 1806
Yi, S., Demarque, P., Kim, Y., & ... 2001, ApJS, 136, 417

Galactic Archaeology: Near-Field Cosmology and the Formation of the Milky Way
ASP Conference Series, Vol. 458
W. Aoki, M. Ishigaki, T. Suda, T. Tsujimoto, N. Arimoto, eds.
© 2012 Astronomical Society of the Pacific

Metallicity Distribution of the Galactic Halo from SDSS Photometry

Deokkeun An,[1] Timothy C. Beers,[2,3] Jennifer A. Johnson,[4] Marc H. Pinsonneault,[4] Young Sun Lee,[3] Željko Ivezić,[5] and Matthew Newby[6]

[1]*Department of Science Education, Ewha Womans University, Seoul 120-750, Republic of Korea.*

[2]*National Optical Astronomy Observatory, Tucson, AZ 85719, USA.*

[3]*Department of Physics & Astronomy and Joint Institute for Nuclear Astrophysics, Michigan State University, E. Lansing, MI 48824, USA.*

[4]*Department of Astronomy, Ohio State University, Columbus, OH 43210, USA.*

[5]*Department of Astronomy, University of Washington, Seattle, WA 98195, USA.*

[6]*Department of Physics, Applied Physics and Astronomy, Rensselaer Polytechnic Institute, Troy, NY 12180, USA.*

Abstract.   We describe the methodology required for the estimation of photometric metallicity from the SDSS *ugriz* passbands and present a preliminary metallicity distribution of the Galactic halo system. Stellar isochrones have been empirically calibrated against observations of several star clusters over a wide range of metal abundance, and the accuracy of photometric T_{eff} and [Fe/H] from these models has been confirmed using the Infrared Flux Method (IRFM) temperature scale and [Fe/H] values from SDSS/SEGUE. Based on these models, we estimate distances and metallicities for individual main-sequence stars in the SDSS Stripe 82 region, and present a preliminary *in situ* metallicity distribution of the halo system. Correlations between kinematic and metallicity distributions are discussed.

1. Introduction

Knowledge of the nature of the stellar Galactic halo has advanced a great deal in the past few years. Previous results have been based primarily on spectroscopic surveys of likely halo stars selected from kinematically-(un)biased searches for metal-poor stars. These approaches have the advantage of efficiently identifying stars of the lowest metallicity, which are of great interest in their own right, but they suffer from selection biases that can be difficult to quantify. Biases are of particular importance if one seeks to understand the global properties of the stellar halo system, a necessary step in order to tell a coherent story of the assembly and evolution of large spiral galaxies such as the Milky Way. Fortunately, the opportunity to recover relatively unbiased information on the nature of the Galactic halo system has arrived, with the advent of large photometric surveys such as the Sloan Digital Sky Survey (SDSS; York et al. 2000).

Broadband photometry can provide reasonably accurate estimates of stellar metallicities, temperatures, and distances, at least for main-sequence stars. In the pioneering work to recover stellar metallicities from SDSS *ugriz* photometry, Ivezić et al. (2008) devised a method of using polynomial regressions based on spectroscopic calibrations of dereddened $u - g$ and $g - r$ colors. However, their photometric metallicities become insensitive at [Fe/H]$\lesssim -2$. To push the limit down to below [Fe/H]~ -2.5 or perhaps -3, we took an independent approach, which uses empirically-calibrated theoretical isochrones. In this proceedings, we present a preliminary result on the metallicity distribution function (MDF) of the Galactic halo, using an unbiased sample of stars over a wide range of metallicity.

2. Method

The key ingredient in the photometric estimation of stellar metallicities and distances is the well-established stellar color-magnitude relations over a wide range of stellar parameters. For this purpose, we adopted the strategy in An et al. (2009b), where we used an empirically calibrated set of stellar isochrones in the SDSS filter system (An et al. 2009a). The empirical corrections on color-T_{eff} relations were performed based on a set of the cluster photometry in the native SDSS filter system over $-2.4 \lesssim$ [Fe/H] $\lesssim 0.4$ (An et al. 2008). Our calibration is valid for main-sequence stars only, and we assume that most of the stars in the sample are on the main sequence.

We applied calibrated stellar isochrones to the observed *ugriz* magnitudes, and searched for the best fitting stellar parameters – T_{eff}, [Fe/H], and an absolute magnitude (distance) – by minimizing the χ^2 of the fit. As an initial exploration of the technique, we have previously used the SDSS *gri* data to constrain (median) photometric metallicities for a bulk stellar population in the halo (An et al. 2009b). However, it was necessary to include *u*-band measurements to tightly constrain photospheric metal abundances, and therefore to construct a precise MDF. This has a consequence of limiting the application of the photometric technique to more nearby stars, because of the relatively shallow survey limit in the SDSS *u* passband. We adopted the standard foreground dust estimates in SDSS by Schlegel et al. (1998), with theoretical extinction coefficients in *ugriz* in An et al. (2009a).

Because the metallicities and temperatures are correlated with each other, it is necessary to check the accuracy of the temperature scale. We verified the accuracy of our photometric estimation of T_{eff} using the most recent temperature scale from the Infrared Flux Method (IRFM) by Casagrande et al. (2010). The *Kepler* Input Catalog (Brown et al. 2011) provides a useful sample of stars for this comparison. We computed photometric temperatures from *ugriz* using our calibrated isochrones, and found good agreement overall with the IRFM temperatures in $J - K_s$. Detailed discussions on the comparison between these two fundamental temperature scales are found in Pinsonneault et al. (2012).

In addition, we compared our photometric temperatures with spectroscopic measurements from the medium-resolution SDSS/SEGUE spectra (Yanny et al. 2009). The left panel in Figure 1 shows the comparison between the two for 160,000 stars. The maximum deviation is less than 100 K at $5000 < T_{eff} < 6500$ K, and the random scatter is ~ 100 K for individual stars.

The right panel in Figure 1 shows the comparison between spectroscopic metallicities from SDSS/SEGUE and our photometric estimates for the same sample of stars.

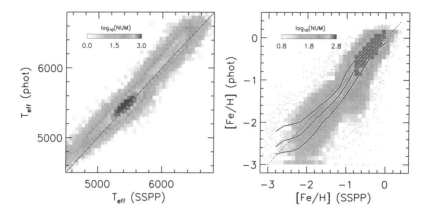

Figure 1.   Comparison between photometric and spectroscopic temperature and metallicity estimates from SDSS/SEGUE. Three curves in the right panel show a median and an interquartile range.

The maximum deviation is less than 0.2 dex down to below [Fe/H]~ −2.5 or perhaps ~ −3, and the random scatter is about 0.2–0.4 dex for individual stars. The [Fe/H] in SDSS/SEGUE is as accurate as ~ 0.2 dex for individual stars, so it is expected that photometric metallicities can be as precise as ~ 0.3 dex per star, when good photometry is available.

3. Results

Using the new metallicity estimator described in the previous section, we estimated distances and metal abundances for individual stars in Stripe 82, which is one of the imaging stripes in SDSS that has been repeatedly scanned along the celestial equator. Currently the best *ugriz* photometry (~ 1%) is available in this region.

There are two photometric catalogs available in Stripe 82: the *calibration* (Ivezić et al. 2007) and the *coadded* (Annis et al. 2011) catalogs. The calibration star catalog contains stellar magnitudes for approximately one million sources, where magnitudes were averaged in the catalog level. On the other hand, the coadded imaging catalog is based on the coadded image products, and is about 0.5 mag deeper than the calibration catalog. Both catalogs, which were in principle produced from the same observations using the main SDSS survey telescope facilities, provide the most precise photometry set in SDSS.

Although photometric samples are less susceptible to a sample bias than in the spectroscopic studies, there still exists a bias that needs to be taken into account. At fixed stellar mass, a star becomes brighter as the metal abundance decreases, and therefore can be used to explore a larger and deeper volume of the Galaxy. However, this luminosity-metallicity dependence naturally produces a bias in the sample, in the sense that more metal-poor stars are preferentially found at greater distances in a magnitude-limited sample.

The calibration catalog has a median photometric error in u of $\sigma \approx 0.03$ mag at $u \approx 20.6$ mag, while the coadded catalog has the same median error at $u \approx 21.0$ mag.

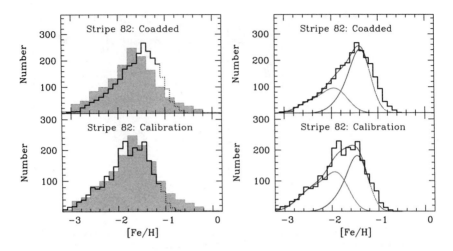

Figure 2.   Photometric MDFs from the coadded (*top*) and the calibration (*bottom*) catalogs are shown in black histograms. The MDFs above [Fe/H]= −1.2 are incomplete. *Left*: Comparisons with kinematically selected local halo stars in Ryan & Norris (1991, grey shaded). *Right*: Decompositions of the halo MDF using two simple metallicity profiles.

We computed the distance limit where each star can be observed at a given stellar mass and metal abundance. It is possible to have an unbiased sample of stars over the entire metallicity range in a nearby volume, but we begin to lose more metal-rich stars at greater distances because of the luminosity-metallicity limit. Since we generally expect to find halo stars at [Fe/H]$\lesssim$ −1, we imposed a mass-distance limit to insure that the sample is unbiased at [Fe/H] ≤ −1.2. We also imposed an upper limit on the stellar mass ($0.75 M_\odot$) because it corresponds to the main-sequence turn-off mass at [Fe/H]= −3; turn-off masses are greater than this at [Fe/H]> −3. Lastly, the lower limit on the heliocentric distance (5 kpc) is set to exclude possible thick disk interlopers in the sample, resulting in a narrow parameter space on the stellar mass versus distance plane ($5 \leq d_{\mathrm{helio}} \lesssim 8$ kpc).

    The black histograms in Figure 2 show our preliminary *in situ* MDFs constructed using the two photometric catalogs in Stripe 82, which are complete at $-3.0 <$ [Fe/H] $<$ −1.2. The left panels in Figure 2 also display the MDF from Ryan & Norris (1991, grey shaded), which is based on a kinematically selected sample of 372 *local* halo stars. We multiplied their sample by a factor of 8 to match our photometric MDF. Our *in situ* MDF matches that of the local MDF, although there is a systematic shift in the metallicity scale in the coadded catalog relative to both the Ryan & Norris (1991) and that from the calibration catalog, which is likely caused by the photometric zero-point error. Note that the Ryan & Norris (1991) sample is incomplete above [Fe/H]= −1.

    The right panels in Figure 2 show decomposition results for our MDFs using two simple [Fe/H] profiles. Each simulated profile includes effects of photometric errors ($\sigma_u = 0.03$) and a 50% unresolved binary fraction, assuming a delta functional form of the MDFs at a given [Fe/H], and has nothing to do with a chemical evolution model. Of course, this is not strictly true, but illustrates a limiting case, where the stellar halo was formed out of instantaneous bursts of a number of subhalos pre-enriched in metals.

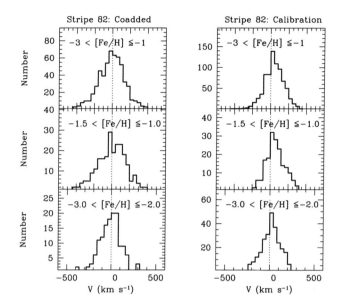

Figure 3.   Distribution of the *V* velocity component of the high galactic latitude samples for the coadded (*left*) and the calibration (*right*) star catalogs. The top to bottom panels show the sample in different metallicity bins.

We attempted to fit the observed MDF using one such [Fe/H] profile, but found that *at least* two sub-components are required to properly account for the shape of the metal-poor tail. Motivated by the recent argument by Carollo et al. (2007, 2010) that our Milky Way stellar halo is a superposition of two components, inner and outer halos, that are distinct in metallicity, kinematics, and spatial distributions, we tried to match the MDF using two simulated profiles at [Fe/H]~ −1.6 and ~ −2.0, respectively. We allowed changes in the centroid of the peak and the relative contributions of each component until we found satisfactory fits, but the centroids of these profiles did not change significantly from the initial values. Three curves in Figure 2 show individual contributions and the summed profile of these two subcomponents. If we take the difference from the two catalogs as an effective 2σ error, the metal-poor population consists of $44 \pm 8\%$ of the entire population in the halo at $5 \le d_{\text{helio}} \lesssim 8$ kpc.

The fact that the observed MDF is well described by the two metallicity peaks at [Fe/H]~ −1.6 and ~ −2.0 supports the duality of the Galactic halo (Carollo et al. 2007, 2010), and is further evidenced by the kinematic analysis, as described below. However, it does not preclude the possibility that the halo is made of multiple subcomponents. Ryan & Norris (1991) found that their MDF is well fit by the MDF from a simple chemical evolution model by Hartwick (1976); likewise, our *in situ* MDF is well fit by this model. However, we do not consider this as proof of a single halo population, because of the simplified assumptions, such as an instantaneous recycling or an effective yield, coded in the simple chemical evolution model.

Most stars in Stripe 82 do not have full velocity information, but proper motion measurements (Munn et al. 2008) at high Galactic latitudes ($|b| > 50$ deg) can provide useful constraints on *U* (towards the Galactic center) and *V* (in the direction of the

Galactic disk rotation) velocity components. Figure 3 shows the velocity distribution in *V* for the coadded and the calibration star catalogs, respectively. Top panels show the velocity distribution for all samples, while middle and bottom panels show those for the metal-rich ($-2.0 < $ [Fe/H] ≤ -1) and metal-poor ($-3.0 < $ [Fe/H] ≤ -2.0) stars. A Kolmogorov-Smirnov (K-S) test suggests that the null hypothesis that the two samples at two different metallicity bins are drawn from the same parent is rejected at levels of 96.4% for the coadded catalog and 98.1% for the calibration catalog, respectively. More metal-poor halo stars are found in retrograde rotation.

4. Summary

We used the empirically-calibrated set of stellar isochrones to derive distances, temperatures, and metallicities for individual stars in Stripe 82 using *ugriz* photometry. We checked our photometric temperature and metallicity estimates using the IRFM temperature scale and SDSS/SEGUE medium-resolution spectroscopic values. Using the unbiased photometric sample of stars, we were able to construct a preliminary *in situ* MDF of the Galactic halo. We found that dual components with metallicity peaks at [Fe/H]≈ -1.6 and -2.0 are sufficient to describe the shape of the observed MDF, although this does not preclude a possibility of more than two subcomponents in the halo. Additional analysis suggests that the two subcomponents have different kinematic signatures, which is consistent with the claim by Carollo et al. (2007, 2010) that the halo is composed of the two overlapping systems.

Acknowledgments. DA thanks Gerry Gilmore for helpful comments. DA acknowledges support from the Ewha Womans University Research Grant of 2010, as well as support by the National Research Foundation of Korea to the Center for Galaxy Evolution Research. TCB and YSL acknowledges partial support of this work from grants PHY 02-16783 and PHY 08-22648: Physics Frontiers Center/Joint Institute for Nuclear Astrophysics (JINA), awarded by the U.S. National Science Foundation.

References

An, D., et al. 2008, ApJS, 179, 326
An, D., et al. 2009a, ApJ, 700, 523
An, D., et al. 2009b, ApJ, 707, L64
Annis, J., et al. 2011, ApJ, submitted (arXiv:1111.6619)
Brown, T. M., Latham, D. W., Everett, M. E., & Esquerdo, G. A. 2011, AJ, 142, 112
Carollo, D., et al. 2007, Nature, 450, 1020
Carollo, D., et al. 2010, ApJ, 712, 692
Casagrande, L., Ramírez, I., Meléndez, J., Bessell, M., & Asplund, M. 2010, A&A, 512, A54
Hartwick, F. D. A. 1976, ApJ, 209, 418
Ivezić, Ž., et al. 2007, AJ, 134, 973
Ivezić, Ž., et al. 2008, ApJ, 684, 287
Munn, J. A., et al. 2008, AJ, 136, 895
Pinsonneault, M. H., et al. 2012, ApJS, submitted (arXiv:1110.4456)
Ryan, S. G., & Norris, J. E. 1991, AJ, 101, 1865
Schlegel, D. J., Finkbeiner, D. P., & Davis, M. 1998, ApJ, 500, 525
Yanny, B., et al. 2009, AJ, 137, 4377
York, D. G., et al. 2000, AJ, 120, 1579

Galactic Archaeology: Near-Field Cosmology and the Formation of the Milky Way
ASP Conference Series, Vol. 458
W. Aoki, M. Ishigaki, T. Suda, T. Tsujimoto, N. Arimoto, eds.
©*2012 Astronomical Society of the Pacific*

The Galactic Bulge Radial Velocity/Abundance Assay

R. Michael Rich

Department of Physics and Astronomy, UCLA, PAB 430 Portola Plaza, Box 951547, Los Angeles, CA 90095-1547

Abstract. The Bulge Radial Velocity Assay *(BRAVA)* measured radial velocities for ~ 9500 late-type giants in the Galactic bulge, predominantly from $-10° < l < +10°$ and $-2° < b < -10°$. The project has discovered that the bulge exhibits cylindrical rotation characteristic of bars, and two studies of dynamics (Shen et al. 2010; Wang et al. 2012 MNRAS sub.) find that bar models- either N-body formed from an instability in a preexisting disk, or a self-consistent model- can account for the observed kinematics. Studies of the Plaut field at $(l, b) = 0°, -8°$ show that alpha enhancement is found in bulge giants even 1 kpc from the nucleus. New infrared studies extending to within $0.25° = 35$ pc of the Galactic Center find no iron or alpha gradient from Baade's Window $(l, b) = 0.9°, -3.9°$ to our innermost field, in contrast to the marked gradient observed in the outer bulge. We consider the case of the remarkable globular cluster Terzan 5, which has a strongly bimodal iron and $[\alpha/Fe]$ within its members, and we consider evidence pro and con that the bulge was assembled from dissolved clusters. The Subaru telescope has the potential to contribute to study of the Galactic bulge, especially using the Hyper Superime-Cam and planned spectroscopic modes, as well as the high resolution spectrograph. The planned *Jasmine* satellite series may deliver a comprehensive survey of distances and proper motions of bulge stars, and insight into the origin and importance of the X-shaped bulge.

1. The Bulge Radial Velocity Assay

The central bulge of the Milky Way is globular cluster age (Clarkson et al. 2008) and exhibits the alpha enhancement signature of early, rapid, formation (McWilliam & Rich 1994, Fulbright et al. 2007). The precise formation timescale and sequence of events remains to be clarified. Taking advantage of the discovery of M giants in the bulge (Blanco et al. 1984), Mould (1983) used M giants as velocity probes to measure the first line of sight velocity dispersion of Baade's Window. With the advent of multi-object spectroscopy at the AAO, Sharples et al. (1990) used the autofib instrument to measure 239 radial velocities in Baade's Window $l, b = 0.9°, -4°$. While it would have been straightforward to identify candidates with simple CCD imaging, the advent of the 2MASS survey provided an enormous list of late-type giant candidates. It became apparent that it would now be possible to map the rotation field of the bulge over its entirety with sample sizes large enough to measure high order moments in the velocity distribution and search for rare objects like metal poor stars (Rich et al. 2007). It required 3 rounds of proposing - from 2003 to 2006 before successfully getting observing time. Although not formally an NOAO survey proposal, *BRAVA* data are in the public archive at IRSA http://irsa.ipac.caltech.edu/ and at UCLA http://brava.astro.ucla.edu/.

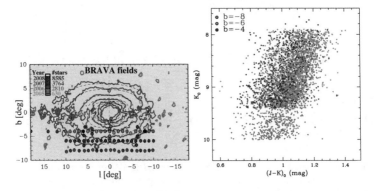

Figure 1.   (color online) **Left:** Fields observed in the course of the BRAVA survey; different symbols correspond to year of observation. The Southern bulge has lower extinction. **Right:** BRAVA giants with latitude noted populate the bright portion of the red giant branch, a disadvantage in terms of abundance measurement, but the bright red giants are easy to measure and give excellent radial velocities. Figures courtesy of Kunder et al. (2012)

The *BRAVA* survey employed hydra at the 4m, with $R \sim 3000$ spectra, to measure radial velocities late-type giants over a large volume of the Galactic bulge (Fig 1).

The principle results of *BRAVA* was the measurement of rotation curves at latitudes $-4°, -6°$ and $8°$; these rotation curves also clearly show "cylindrical rotation" that is, no dependence of rotation speed on latitude, a hallmark of rapidly rotating bars (Fig. 2). Further, the bulge kinematics are consistent with the bulge having formed via the disk experiencing secular evolution (e.g. Kennicutt & Kormendy 2004) leading to bar formation (Shen et al. 2010). We are now in the process of updating (Wang et al. 2012 in prep.) the self-consistent bulge model of Zhao (1996). We are finding a strong (> 80%) fraction of chaotic orbits in the self consistent models. It is difficult to imagine how such orbits support the X-shaped bulge (McWilliam & Zoccal 2010; Saito et al. 2011) which would appear to require more regular orbits to support the structure. The next generation of models will require large scale surveys of proper motion data.

2. Surveys of the Bulge's composition

Since McWilliam & Rich (1994), there has been substantial work on the detailed composition of the bulge (e.g. Fulbright et al. 2007, Lecureur et al. 2007, Hill et al. 2011). Our work on the Plaut Field $l, b = 0°, -8°$ extends the confirmation of enhanced alpha element abundances to 1 kpc from the nucleus (Figure 3), a very significant volume. We also find surprising alpha enhancement for red clump stars consistent with lying roughly halfway to the bulge (Fig. 3; Johnson et al. 2011). For the first time, detailed compositions are being measured for fields well off of the minor axis, like $(l, b) = -5°, = 7°$ (Johnson et al. 2012 in prep.). Some of these minor axis fields have iron abundance distributions more metal rich than that found in Baade's Window at $b = -4°$. As is noted in all other bulge fields, the alpha elements are enhanced relative to the thin and thick disk.

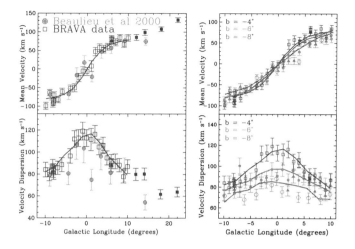

Figure 2. (color online) **Left:** Complete rotation curve and velocity dispersion profile from the BRAVA project (see Kunder et al. 2012). **Right:** The Shen et al. (2010) model is an excellent fit to the bulge data. The rotation curve is constant with Galactic latitude (cylindrical rotation). Plots from Kunder et al. 2012.

Studies of the heavy elements (McWilliam, Fulbright, & Rich 2010) find a generally r-process dominated composition for [Fe/H]< 0, while more metal rich stars show a distinct trend toward greater s-process enhancement. It will be of great importance to undertake more surveys of heavy elements in the bulge, as there is a growing tension between the younger ages derived from self-consistent analysis of microlensed bulge dwarfs (Bensby et al. 2011) versus globular cluster-aged turnoff ages inferred from color-magnitude diagrams (Zoccali et al. 2003; Clarkson et al. 2008).

The bulge globular cluster Terzan 5 was shown by Ferraro et al. (2009) to have a remarkable horizontal branch, bimodal in luminosity. Livia Origlia and I obtained high resolution infrared spectra of the red giants in this very heavily obscured cluster. Figure 5 shows the most remarkable abundance pattern known for any globular cluster: two groups of stars 0.5 dex apart in iron abundance, and separated by 0.3 dex in [α/Fe]. Ferraro et al. (2009) propose that Terzan 5 might have retained the gas for a second burst because the cluster we observe today is the remnant of a stellar system that was much more massive in the past, perhaps even, a building block of the bulge.

3. Exploring the Bulge with Subaru and Jasmine

With the advent of Hyper Suprime-Cam, Subaru will be in a privileged position to obtain a remarkable set of images of the bulge covering a wide range of filter bandpasses. Even at high airmass, Subaru might achieve better than 0.5″ imagery of the bulge, sufficient to resolve the main sequence turnoff even in Baade's Window, enabling exploring of large scale population gradients (age and abundances). Imagery in blue colors might help to isolate candidate metal poor stars that are believed to be present in the inner

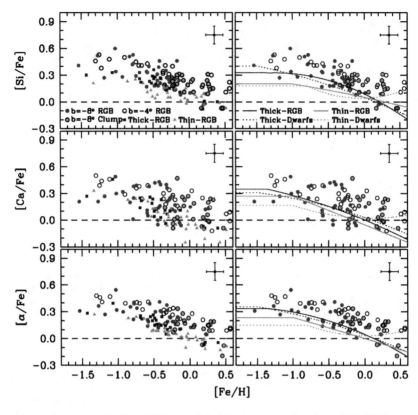

Figure 3. (color online) Different alpha elements as a function of [Fe/H] from Johnson et al. 2011; see electronic version for color. The red points are new giant measurements in the bulge at $(l, b) = 0, -8$. The cyan points are likely clump giants that lie about 2-4 kpc along the line of sight toward the bulge. Open points are from Fulbright, McWilliam, & Rich (2007). Notice that even 1 kpc from the nucleus, all alpha elements are elevated in the bulge, relative to the thick/thin disk. The clump giants are strikingly alpha rich (and metal rich). Johnson et al. 2012 in prep. finds that the elevated alpha abundances and high metallicities extend to off-axis bulge fields.

bulge (e.g. Scannapieco et al. 2006), as well as enable a better exploration of the extreme HB population in the bulge. Subaru has the potential to extend our knowledge of the bulge in other areas: composition studies of unusual stars using HDS, and kinematic surveys in the very crowded fields of the inner bulge, with FMOS. Perhaps the most exciting possibility comes from instrumentation planned for space. The Jasmine satellite program, commencing with nano-Jasmine, will obtain astrometry over the whole of the inner bulge. Illustrated in Figure 5 is the planned survey program of the Small Jasmine satellite, which has the potential to derive a proper motion and parallax for every star studied int he *BRAVA* survey, ultimately yielding over a million new proper motions. Extending precision astrometry to the infrared, the Jasmine satellites will push high

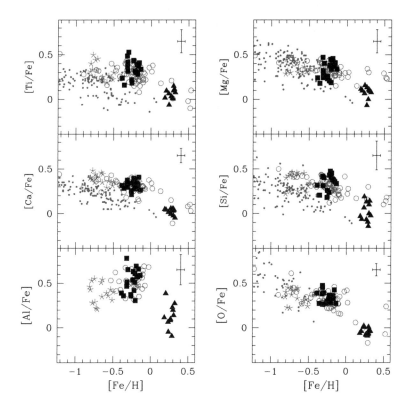

Figure 4.   Striking bimodality in [Fe/H] and [α/Fe] for the massive bulge globular cluster Terzan 5. Solid points are Terzan 5 members; triangles are metal rich sub-population. Open symbols are bulge giants. The metal rich population may be ∼ 6 Gyr younger than the metal poor stars.

precision astrometry to the bulge, nuclear region, and inner disk, where GAIA will be restricted by heavy extinction and image crowding.

Acknowledgments.   R.M.R. acknowledges funding from AST07-09479 from the National Science Foundation.

References

Blanco, V. M., McCarthy, M. F., & Blanco, B. M. 1984, AJ, 89, 636.
Clarkson, W. et al. 2008, ApJ, 684, 1110.
Ferraro, F. R. et al. 2009, Nat, 462, 483.
Fulbright, J. P., McWilliam, A., & Rich, R. M. 2007, ApJ, 661, 1152.
Hill, V. et al. 2011, A&A, 534, A80.
Johnson, C. I., Rich, R. M., Fulbright, J. P., Valenti, E., & McWilliam, A. 2011, ApJ, 732, 108.
Kormendy, J., & Kennicutt, R. C., Jr. 2004, ARA&A, 42, 603.

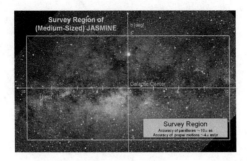

Figure 5.   (color online) The proposed Small Jasmine satellite (Gouda et al. 2011) will obtain precision astrometry over the entire Galactic bulge field considered by BRAVA

Kunder, A. et al. 2012, AJ, 143, 57.
Lecureur, A. et al. 2007, A&A, 465, 799.
McWilliam, A., & Rich, R. M. 1994, ApJS, 91, 749.
McWilliam, A., & Zoccali, M. 2010, ApJ, 724, 1491.
Mould, J. R. 1983, ApJ, 266, 255.
Rich, R. M., Origlia, L., & Valenti, E. 2012, ApJ, 746, 59.
Rich, R. M., Reitzel, D. B., Howard, C. D., & Zhao, H. 2007, ApJ, 658, L29.
Saito, R. K. et al. 2011, AJ, 142, 76.
Scannapieco, E. et al. 2006, ApJ, 653, 285.
Sharples, R., Walker, A., & Cropper, M. 1990, MNRAS, 246, 54.
Shen, J. et al. 2010, ApJ, 720, L72.
Tumlinson, J. 2010, ApJ, 708, 1398.
Zhao, H. 1996, MNRAS, 283, 149.

Galactic Archaeology: Near-Field Cosmology and the Formation of the Milky Way
ASP Conference Series, Vol. 458
W. Aoki, M. Ishigaki, T. Suda, T. Tsujimoto, N. Arimoto, eds.
© *2012 Astronomical Society of the Pacific*

Unfolding the Milky Way Bulge

O. A. Gonzalez,[1] M. Rejkuba,[1] M. Zoccali,[2] E. Valenti,[1] and D. Minniti[2]

[1]*European Southern Observatory, Karl-Schwarzschild-Strasse 2, D-85748 Garching, Germany*

[2]*Departamento Astronomía y Astrofísica, Pontificia Universidad Católica de Chile, Av. Vicuña Mackenna 4860, Stgo., Chile*

Abstract.   Recent studies attempting to characterize the stellar populations and morphology of the Milky Way bulge suggest that the Bulge structure and stellar population mixture could be more complicated than previously thought, with results which might even appear contradictory. A large scale mapping of the Bulge is necessary to make significant progress. We present here our results based on alpha elements abundances for a total of 650 RGB stars in 4 fields across the Bulge. Results point towards a spatial homogeneity of alpha element enhancement in the metal-poor regime and a population of alpha-poor metal-rich stars which disappears at high latitudes ($b = -12°$). Further constrains are being obtained from the VVV public survey from which we are deriving a high-resolution extinction map as well as the general picture of structure and metallicity gradients in the Bulge.

1. Introduction

The presence of the bar in the central parts of the Galaxy is well established from several studies (e.g. Stanek et al. 1997). The detailed mapping of a double red clump (RC) feature in the luminosity function of the outer bulge regions from McWilliam & Zoccali (2010), interpreted as two over-densities at different distances, led to the conclusion that the Bulge is actually an X-shaped bar. In addition, the kinematic Brava survey (Shen et al. 2010), found no evidence for the existence of an additional spheroidal component.

In contrast to the above structure and kinematics studies, the combination of chemical abundances and kinematics suggests that there might be mixed populations in the Bulge. Hill et al. (2011) showed that, when looking at the metallicities derived from high resolution spectroscopy of RC giants in Baade's Window, and after producing an error deconvolution, the metallicity distribution appears to be bimodal, with a metal-poor and a metal-rich component. The known minor axis metallicity gradient (Zoccali et al. 2008; Johnson et al. 2011) would be then a result of the different contribution of these two populations at different latitudes. Babusiaux et al. (2010) showed that these two components have actually also distinct kinematics. In particular, based on accurate proper-motions and radial velocities, they concluded that the vertex deviation of the velocity ellipsoid is consistent with a metal-poor component showing spheroid kinematics and a metal-rich with bar-like kinematics.

To investigate further this results, in Gonzalez et al. (2011a) we have used a large sample of 650 FLAMES-GIRAFFE spectra to measure the alpha element abundances

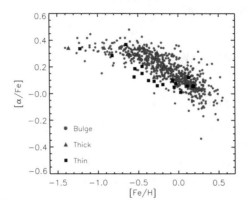

Figure 1.   (color online) [α/Fe] abundances calculated as the average between Ca,
Mg, Ti and Si abundances for 650 bulge giant stars shown as red filled circles. Abundances for the thick disk stars are shown as blue filled triangles and as filled black
squares for the thin disk stars.

of the Bulge and to place them in the context of the above described results. This
provides important constrains for the formation timescale of the Bulge. Furthermore,
an extension of such studies to other regions of the Bulge is now required. We are now
using the VISTA Variables in the Via Lactea (VVV), a public survey of the Bulge, to
derive detailed extinctions and the general view of structure and photometric metallicity
distributions.

2.   The Bulge Alpha-Element Enhancement

Important constrains for the formation scenario of the Bulge can be obtained from the
observed alpha-element abundances in the Bulge. In particular the [α/Fe] ratio can be
used as indicator of its timescale of formation. We analyzed the α-element abundances
for a large number of red giants in the Bulge across different regions as well as for
thin and thick disk giants, thus comparing in a homogeneous way distinct Galactic
components. Figure 1 shows that the metal-poor part of the distribution of Bulge giants
(red circles), has a high [α/Fe] ratio, which is indistinguishable from the thick disk (blue
triangles), and therefore interpreted as a fast formation scenario for both components.
On the other hand the metal-rich stars have a low [α/Fe] ratio, as low as those of the
thin disk, and are consistent with a more extended timescale of formation.

When looking at the same figure but this time across our three different fields along
the minor axis (Fig. 2), we can see two clear properties: i) The metal-poor stars at different latitudes show no variation neither in the level of α-element enhancement nor in
the location of the down-trend knee. This hints for a homogeneously α-enhanced metal-
poor component which, as previously shown in Babusiaux et al. (2010), has spheroid-
like kinematics. The metal-rich component on the other hand, which shows a low
[α/Fe] abundance ratio and bar-like kinematics, disappears at larger latitudes producing
the observed minor axis metallicity gradient.

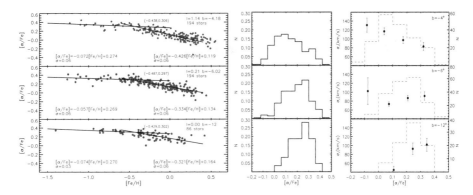

Figure 2. *Left panel:* [α/Fe] trends as a function of [Fe/H] in 3 bulge fields located along the minor axis, $b = -4°, -6°$ and $-12°$. Best fit trends are shown for both [Fe/H] ranges, a metal-poor between -1.2 and -0.5 dex and a metal-rich between -0.3 and 0.2 dex, as well as the location of the knee in all fields. *Center panels:* [α/Fe] distribution for each field. *Right panel:* Dispersion of radial velocity as a function of [α/Fe], in bins of 0.15 dex, for the three fields along the minor axis (filled circles and left axis scale). Overploted as a dashed line is the [α/Fe] distribution for each field, which scale is given on the right.

3. Extinction, Structure and Metallicities from The VVV Survey

Clearly there is a need to extend these studies to a larger coverage of the Bulge. On-going and future large spectroscopic and photometric surveys across the Bulge aim to address this issue. In this context, the VVV public survey is already providing important results. VVV is an almost complete Bulge photometric survey in 5 near-infrared bands, with a significantly improved resolution and a depth that allows to trace the RC in all regions, including the most highly reddened ones.

In Gonzalez et al. (2011b) we have used the *J*, *H*, and K_s photometry of VVV to work on a method to obtain extinction, structure and metallicities of the Bulge. In the case of extinction, we select RC stars to study their color distribution and, by means of a Gaussian fit, to relate the mean RC color to a $E(J - K_s)$ reddening value. We repeat this procedure in the complete Bulge region covered by the survey, dividing the area in 2'×2' subfields, a size small enough to avoid differential extinction. Figure 3 shows the derived extinction map for the inner Bulge region ($-2° < b < +2°$). The small scale extinction variations are clearly seen, given the strong dust features traced in our map. The extinction values for this map and for the outer regions will be presented in a dedicated article (Gonzalez et al. 2012). A web based tool (BEAM calculator) allows any user to obtain the corresponding extinction values for a given region of interest. This is an important tool for field selection and later analysis of large coverage samples from either spectroscopic or photometric surveys.

In Gonzalez et al. (2011b) we also show how the dereddened magnitudes can be used to build the luminosity function and then using a gaussian fit to the red clump to obtain a mean distance for each Bulge line of sight. This provides a full view of the Bulge structure such as the inclination angle of the bar and the X-shape in the outer regions. We later used this distance determination to study the Color-Magnitude dia-

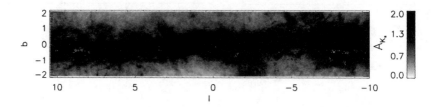

Figure 3.   (color online) Our reddening map (A_K) for the inner regions of the bulge ($-2 < b < 2$) using the method described in Gonzalez et al. (2011b). The resolution of the map is (2') and the color bar is saturated at $A_K = 2.0$ for visualization.

grams now in the absolute plane to interpolate the colors of bright RGB stars, between templates of globular clusters with known metallicities (Valenti et al. 2007). From this procedure we derived individual metallicities and built the corresponding photometric MDF, which resembled very well that of HR spectroscopy and traced the observed metallicity gradient. The complete procedure allows us to build maps of extinction and metallicity that, when extended to the complete bulge, will provide a first look to the general properties of the Milky Way bulge.

Acknowledgments.   We gratefully acknowledge use of data from the ESO Public Survey program ID 179.B-2002 taken with the VISTA telescope, data products from the Cambridge Astronomical Survey Unit. We acknowledge funding from the FONDAP Center for Astrophysics 15010003, the BASAL CATA Center for Astrophysics and Associated Technologies PFB-06, the MILENIO Milky Way Millennium Nucleus from the Ministry of Economycs ICM grant P07-021-F and Proyectos FONDECYT Regular 1087258, 1110393 and 1090213. MZ is also partially supported by Proyecto Anillo ACT-86.

References

Babusiaux, C., Gómez, A., Hill, V., Royer, F., Zoccali, M., Arenou, F., Fux, R., Lecureur, A., Schultheis, M., Barbuy, B., Minniti, D., & Ortolani, S. 2010, A&A, 519, A77
Gonzalez, O. A., Rejkuba, M., Zoccali, M., Hill, V., Battaglia, G., Babusiaux, C., Minniti, D., Barbuy, B., Alves-Brito, A., Renzini, A., Gomez, A., & Ortolani, S. 2011a, A&A, 530, A54
Gonzalez, O. A., Rejkuba, M., Zoccali, M., Valenti, E., & Minniti, D. 2011b, A&A, 534, A3
Hill, V., Lecureur, A., Gómez, A., Zoccali, M., Schultheis, M., Babusiaux, C., Royer, F., Barbuy, B., Arenou, F., Minniti, D., & Ortolani, S. 2011, A&A, 534, A80
Johnson, C. I., Rich, R. M., Fulbright, J. P., Valenti, E., & McWilliam, A. 2011, ApJ, 732, 108
McWilliam, A., & Zoccali, M. 2010, ApJ, 724, 1491
Shen, J., Rich, R. M., Kormendy, J., Howard, C. D., De Propris, R., & Kunder, A. 2010, ApJ, 720, L72
Stanek, K. Z., Udalski, A., Szymanski, M., Kaluzny, J., Kubiak, M., Mateo, M., & Krzeminski, W. 1997, ApJ, 477, 163
Valenti, E., Ferraro, F. R., & Origlia, L. 2007, AJ, 133, 1287
Zoccali, M., Hill, V., Lecureur, A., Barbuy, B., Renzini, A., Minniti, D., Gómez, A., & Ortolani, S. 2008, A&A, 486, 177

Galactic Archaeology: Near-Field Cosmology and the Formation of the Milky Way
ASP Conference Series, Vol. 458
W. Aoki, M. Ishigaki, T. Suda, T. Tsujimoto, N. Arimoto, eds.
©*2012 Astronomical Society of the Pacific*

Signatures of Formation: The Galactic Bulge of the Milky Way

Melissa Ness,[1] Ken Freeman,[1] and Evangelia Athanassoula [2]

[1]*RSAA Australian National University, Mount Stromlo Observatory, Cotter Road, Weston Creek, Canberra, ACT 2611, Australia*
[2] *LAM, UAM & CNRS, UMR7326, 38 rue F. Joliot-Curie, Marseille 13, France*

Abstract. The bulge of the Milky Way is an important signature of formation of our Galaxy. From our observational survey we report on the kinematics and metallicity of about 28,000 stars across the bulge and out into the thick disk. Our results demonstrate that the likely origin of formation of the Galactic Bulge is internal dynamical processes, rather than mergers. We present our preliminary results for chemodynamical N-body simulations which test some of our key observational findings.

1. Introduction

Galactic Bulges are believed to be formed via different mechanisms; mergers which are a ubiquitous part of Cold Dark Matter (CDM) formation (Abadi et al. 2003) or by an internal instability of the rotating galactic disk (Athanassoula 2005). Mergers typically generate large, spheroidal bulges with a higher-n Sersic light profile, a metallicity gradient and an alpha enhanced stellar population, the proxies of rapid star formation. Instability bulges are characterised by a boxy-triaxial morphology and exponential light profile and common chemical properties of bulge stars and thin and thick disk stars, as the bulge is believed to have formed out of the disk (Kormendy & Kennicutt 2004). Our observational survey measures the kinematics and the metallicity and alpha enhancement of 28,000 stars distributed along the bulge and into the thin and thick disk, which can differentiate the formation scenarios. Our 28 fields, each of diameter two degrees, cover the Southern bulge and the nearby thin and thick disks. Our fields span in longitude from $l = -31°$ to $+26°$, at latitudes of $b = -5°, -7.5°$ and $-10°$.

2. Methods

We have observed our stars at the Australian Anglo Telescope at Siding Spring in Australia, using the 2dF AAOmega fiber-fed spectrograph. The survey was completed in four years, using 42 nights observing time. Our primary region of spectra for analysis covers 8400 - 8850 Å, at resolution $R \sim 11,000$, S/N = 80 per resolution element. We have reduced our data using the stellar pipeline provided by the Australian Anglo Observatory: 2dfdr. Radial velocities were determined using the IRAF routine fxcor, employing a number of different stellar templates to find the best correlation for each observation. We have obtained the stellar parameters (T_{eff}, $\log g$, [Fe/H], [α/Fe]) with a χ^2 pipeline written for this dataset. Our aim is to compare our observational data with

N-body models of the dynamical instability process, as well as predictions of CDM Cosmology, to determine the formation history of the Galactic Bulge of the Milky Way.

3.   Results

3.1.   Kinematics

The rotation curve for the bulge is cylindrical and blends smoothly out into the disk (to $|l| \leq 20°$). Our measured rotation velocities and dispersion (Figure 1) agree well with the nearby latitudes modelled by Shen (across $|l| \leq 10°$) for the Brava data (Shen et al. 2010).

3.2.   Metallicity and Alpha Enhancement

The generalised Metallicity Distribution Functions (MDFs) for the bulge at $b = -5°$, $-7.5°$ and $-10°$, across $|l| \leq 15°$ demonstrate that the bulge is a composite population, which can be described by up to 5 gaussians, labeled A-E (Figure 2). We attribute these gaussian components to already known stellar populations of the Milky Way. We make the simple assumption that these gaussians conserve their standard deviation across latitude. The amplitude changes to determine the best fit, determined via a Pearson χ^2 minimisation. We find the most metal rich population A attenuates with latitude; it is 35% of the total MDF at the lowest latitude and 9% at the highest latitude, which is in inverse behaviour to the more metal poor component C. Our intermediate metallicity gaussian component B remains in about the same contribution fraction across latitude. We find a radial metallicity gradient for the most metal rich component A only, of about -0.03 dex/kpc (±0.01). We find a small gradient with latitude, per component, of about -0.07dex/kpc (±0.02), for components A-D.

We associate the most metal rich component A with the inner thin disk, which is continuing to undergo star formation and is more metal rich in the central regions. We believe component B ([Fe/H] $\sim$ −0.24) is the true bulge bar, formed from the early disk. The metallicity of C is consistent with the thick disk; an older more metal poor population with a larger scale height than the thin disk. Components D and E we believe to be metal weak thick disk and inner halo stars in the central regions in our survey.

We find a very small fraction ($\sim$ 0.15%) of very metal poor ([Fe/H]< −2.0) stars within R_{gal} < 3.5 kpc. These may be halo stars on highly eccentric orbits, or they may be a first stars population predicted to be concentrated to the central regions under CDM cosmology (Tumlinson 2010). We propose follow up high resolution observations to test the detailed s- and r-process abundance information of these stars.

4.   Tests of Signatures of Formation: N-body Models

N-body models are a key test of our observational signatures and of our assertion that the most metal rich fraction of stars we observe, component A, is the metal rich thin disk, in the inner regions. Athanassoula has completed preliminary chemodynamical N-body simulations of Milky Way type galaxies and we have investigated the distribution of the most metal rich fraction of stars at 10 Gyr. From these preliminary simulations, we find that the metal rich stars in the simulation are concentrated to the plane and in higher fractions in the inner galaxy. The majority, ($\sim$ 75%) of the metal rich 10% of stars are located at scale heights $|z| \leq 0.5$ kpc, so very close to the plane. These stars span ages of 1 to 10 Gyr; 70% are ≥ 9 Gyr old and 15% have an age of < 8 Gyr.

According to the N-body models (Athanassoula 2008), the instability event occured 1-2 Gyr after the bar was created, which was formed from the disk. We would expect the bulge itself is younger than the stars in it and so a chemical imprint of the instability event. The majority of the metal rich population in the simulation are 1-2 Gyr younger than the more metal poor stars we associate observationally with the bar/bulge, and they appear in larger fractions in the inner regions. Furthermore, the metal rich stars span a wide range of ages, as is seen observationally (Bensby et al. 2010). The simulations are qualitatively consistent with our interpretation of the most metal rich component observed being the thin disk, formed after the bulge buckling instability and located preferentially toward the plane.

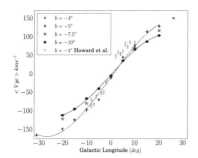 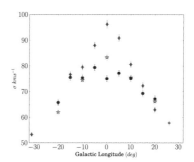

Figure 1.   Rotation curve (*left*) and dispersion (*right*) for our 17,000 stars within 3.5 kpc of the Galactic centre.

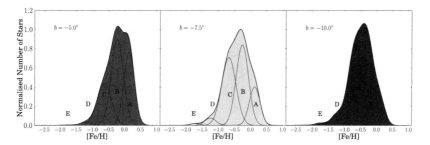

Figure 2.   Generalised histograms and best fit gaussian components A-E across the bulge at latitudes: $b = -5°$ (far left), $b = -7.5°$ (centre), $b = -10°$ (far right).

Discussion

Q.: What is the proportion of the metal-rich disk population in the N-body simulations and could that be large enough to match your A population at $b = -5°$)?

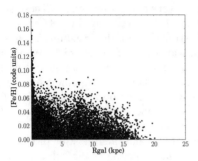 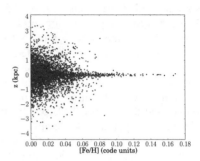

Figure 3.   The radial distribution of stars in [Fe/H] (*left*) and the height from the plane (z) versus [Fe/H] for stars (*right*) within $R_{gal} \leq 5$ kpc.

Ness: The simulation work is still ongoing, so we can not make quantitative comparisons yet. For the one run we have fully reduced so far, the metal rich fraction of stars is located nearer to the plane than observed.

Q.: Prior results (i.e. Ortolani et al. 1995) do not permit a substantial young population. Also, how is it that there is a metal rich population in the central regions?

Ness: 85% of the stars in the simulation are old (> 8 Gyr). Only a very small fraction (3%) are 5 Gyr or younger. The star forming gas is preferentially located in the plane and in the central regions.

Q.: If you have 5 MDF components, some of them being (thin and thick) disk, how do the [α/Fe] trends end up looking so well defined in HR studies?

Ness: We find alpha enhancement to be a proxy for the [Fe/H] and increases with decreasing [Fe/H]. The [Fe/H] and [α/Fe] distributions are overlapping in our decomposed MDFs: we are not sampling discrete populations and comparing them, but what we believe we are seeing is the mixture of stellar populations which we propose comprises the inner regions of the galaxy: the thin and thick disks and the bar/bulge.

Acknowledgments.   The survey is an ARGOS team effort and the authors would like to thank the Subaru organising committee for the opportunity to present this work.

References

Abadi, M. G., Navarro, J. F., Steinmetz, M., & Eke, V. R. 2003, ApJ, 597, 21. arXiv: astro-ph/0212282
Athanassoula, E. 2005, MNRAS, 358, 1477. arXiv:astro-ph/0502316
— 2008, in IAU Symposium, edited by M. Bureau, E. Athanassoula, & B. Barbuy, vol. 245 of IAU Symposium, 93
Bensby, T., Feltzing, S., Johnson, J. A., Gould, A., Adén, D., Asplund, M., Meléndez, J., Gal-Yam, A., Lucatello, S., Sana, H., Sumi, T., Miyake, N., Suzuki, D., Han, C., Bond, I., & Udalski, A. 2010, A&A, 512, A41. 0911.5076
Howard, C. D., Rich, R. M., Reitzel, D. B., Koch, A., De Propris, R., & Zhao, H. 2008, ApJ, 688, 1060. 0807.3967
Kormendy, J., & Kennicutt, R. C., Jr. 2004, ARA&A, 42, 603. arXiv:astro-ph/0407343
Shen, J., Rich, R. M., Kormendy, J., Howard, C. D., De Propris, R., & Kunder, A. 2010, ApJ, 720, L72. 1005.0385

Tumlinson, J. 2010, in American Institute of Physics Conference Series, edited by D. J. Whalen, V. Bromm, & N. Yoshida, vol. 1294 of American Institute of Physics Conference Series, 84

Excursion to the Jogasaki coast on November 3rd.

Galactic Archaeology: Near-Field Cosmology and the Formation of the Milky Way
ASP Conference Series, Vol. 458
W. Aoki, M. Ishigaki, T. Suda, T. Tsujimoto, N. Arimoto, eds.
© 2012 Astronomical Society of the Pacific

Chemical Evolution of the Galactic Disk(s)

Thomas Bensby and Sofia Feltzing

Lund Observatory, Box 43, SE-221 00 Lund, Sweden

Abstract. We highlight some results from our high-resolution spectroscopic elemental abundance survey of F and G dwarf stars in the solar neighbourhood.

1. Introduction

To investigate the chemical and kinematical properties of the Galactic disk, and the thick disk in particular, we have undertaken a spectroscopic survey of 703 kinematically selected F and G dwarf stars in the Solar neighbourhood. Based on high resolution ($R = 45\,000$ to $110\,000$) and high signal-to-noise ($S/N \approx 150$ to 300) spectra for all stars we determined detailed elemental abundances for O, Na, Mg, Al, Si, Ca, Ti, Cr, Fe, Ni, Zn, Y, Ba, and stellar ages from isochrones. Including the results for the first 102 stars of the sample presented in Bensby et al. (2003, 2005), our main findings include: (i) at a given metallicity, the thick disk abundance trends are more α-enhanced than those of the thin disk; (ii) the metal-rich limit of the thick disk reaches at least solar metallicities (Bensby et al. 2007a); (iii) the metal-poor limit of the thin disk is around [Fe/H] ≈ -0.8; (iv) the thick disk shows an age-metallicity gradient; (v) the thin disk does *not* show an age-metallicity gradient; (vi) the most metal-rich thick disk stars at [Fe/H] ≈ 0 are significantly older than the most metal-poor thin disk stars at [Fe/H] ≈ -0.7; (vii) based on our elemental abundances we find that kinematical criteria produce thin and thick disk stellar samples that are biased in the sense that stars from the low-velocity tail of the thick disk are classified as thin disk stars, and stars from the high-velocity tail of the thin disk are classified as thick disk stars; (viii) age criteria appears to produce thin and thick disk stellar samples with less contamination. These points were recently discussed in Bensby & Feltzing (2011). Based on the current sample we have also found that the Hercules stream is likely to be of dynamical origin and that its stars just is a mix of thin and thick disk stars (Bensby et al. 2007b). In this proceeding we will discuss new findings about the variation of the elemental abundance ratios in the Galactic disk with Galactocentric distance.

2. Variation with Galactocentric radius

Fig. 1 shows the [Fe/Ti]-[Ti/H] abundance plot for the full sample. The stars have been colour-coded based on their orbits mean distance from the Galactic centre (R_{mean}), as well as size-coded based on their estimated ages. A majority of the stars with $R_{\mathrm{mean}} <$ 7 kpc are α-enhanced and have high ages (i.e. red and big circles). The opposite is

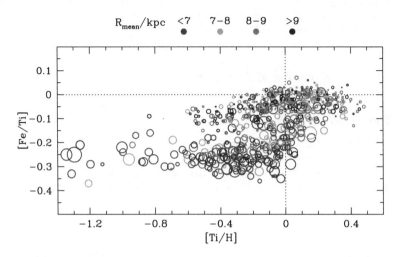

Figure 1.   [Fe/Ti] - [Ti/H] abundance plot. The color-coding refers to the mean Galactocentric radius of the orbits of the stars and is defined at the top of the figure. The sizes of the circles have been scaled by the ages of the stars (larger = older).

observed for the stars with $R_{mean} > 9$ kpc which tend to be less α-enhanced and have lower ages (i.e. blue and small circles).

If R_{mean} can be associated with the approximate birthplace of a star, and if a main characteristic of the Galactic thick disk is that its stars mainly are old and α-enhanced, the above finding indicates that the thick disk stars in the solar neighbourhood, should mainly originate from the inner disk region. Younger and less α-enhanced (thin disk) stars on the other hand are more prone to originate from the outer disk region. This result agrees well with the study of red giants located in the inner and outer disk by Bensby et al. (2010, 2011) where it was found that the stars with thick disk abundance patterns appears extremely sparse in the outer disk, even at large distances from the Galactic plane. In the inner disk region on the other hand, both thin and thick disk abundance patterns were found. A possible explanation is that the scale-length for the thick disk is significantly shorter than for the thin disk (Bensby et al. 2011). What this means for the existence of an outer thick disk, and the dichotomy of the Galactic disk as seen in the solar neighbourhood, will be further investigated in an upcoming paper.

Acknowledgments.   T.B. was funded by grant No. 621-2009-3911 from The Swedish Research Council. S.F. was partly funded by the Swedish Royal Academy of Sciences and partly by grant No. 2008-4095 from The Swedish Research Council.

References

Bensby, T., Alves-Brito, A., Oey, M. S., Yong, D., & Meléndez, J. 2010, A&A, 516, L13
— 2011, ApJ, 735, L46
Bensby, T., & Feltzing, S. 2011, arXiv:1110.0905v1 [astro.ph.GA]
Bensby, T., Feltzing, S., & Lundström, I. 2003, A&A, 410, 527
Bensby, T., Feltzing, S., Lundström, I., & Ilyin, I. 2005, A&A, 433, 185
Bensby, T., Zenn, A. R., Oey, M. S., & Feltzing, S. 2007a, ApJ, 663, L13
Bensby, T., Oey, M. S., Feltzing, S., & Gustafsson, B. 2007b, ApJ, 655, L89

Galactic Archaeology: Near-Field Cosmology and the Formation of the Milky Way
ASP Conference Series, Vol. 458
W. Aoki, M. Ishigaki, T. Suda, T. Tsujimoto, N. Arimoto, eds.
© *2012 Astronomical Society of the Pacific*

Signatures of an Intermediate-Age Metal-Rich Bulge Population

T. Bensby,[1] S. Feltzing,[1] A. Gould,[2] J.A. Johnson,[2] M. Asplund,[3] D. Adén,[1] J. Meléndez,[4] J.G. Cohen,[5] I. Thompson,[6] S. Lucatello,[7] and A. Gal-Yam[8]

[1] *Lund Observatory, Box 43, SE-221 00 Lund, Sweden*
[2] *Department of Astronomy, Ohio State University, Columbus, OH, USA*
[3] *Research School of Astronomy and Astrophysics, ANU, Weston, Australia*
[4] *Dpto de Astronomia do IAG/USP, Univ. de São Paulo, São Paulo, Brasil*
[5] *Palomar Observatory, California Inst. of Technology, Pasadena, CA, USA*
[6] *Carnegie Observatories, 813 Santa Barbara St., Pasadena, CA, USA*
[7] *INAF-Astronomical Observatory of Padova, Padova, Italy*
[8] *Benoziyo Center for Astrophysics, Weizmann Inst. of Science, Rehovot, Israel*

Abstract. We have determined detailed elemental abundances and stellar ages for a sample of now 38 microlensed dwarf and subgiant stars in the Galactic bulge. Stars with sub-solar metallicities are all old and have enhanced α-element abundances – very similar to what is seen for local thick disk stars. The metal-rich stars on the other hand show a wide variety of stellar ages, ranging from 3-4 Gyr to 12 Gyr, and an average around 7-8 Gyr. The existence of young and metal-rich stars are in conflict with recent photometric studies of the bulge which claim that the bulge only contains old stars.

1. Signatures on an intemediate-age metal-rich bulge population

The first 26 microlensed dwarf and subgiant stars in the bulge from Bensby et al. (2010, 2011) showed that the metallicity distribution of the Galactic bulge is likely bimodal with a paucity of stars around solar metallicities. Adding another 12 microlensed bulge dwarfs from the 2011 observing campaign the metallicity distribution of the current sample of 38 microlensed dwarfs is still bi-modal with two distinct peaks: one metal-poor peak with 16 stars and an average metallicity of [Fe/H] $\approx$ −0.6 and one metal-rich peak with 22 stars and an average metallicity of [Fe/H] $\approx$ +0.3. A two-sided KS-test with the red giant sample in Baades window from Zoccali et al. (2008), re-analysed by Hill et al. (2011), gives a p-value of 0.47. This means that we can not reject the null hypothesis that the microlensed sample and the red giant sample are drawn from the same underlying metallicity distribution.

Figure 1 (left-hand plot) shows the age-metallicity diagram for the microlensed bulge dwarfs. At sub-solar metallicities the stars are pre-dominantly old with ages between 9 and 13 Gyr. The average age is 10.6 Gyr with a spread of 3.3 Gyr. The 22 stars at super-solar metallicities on the other hand show a wide range of ages from only a few billion years old to as old as the Universe, i.e. spanning the full range of ages from the Galactic disk to the halo. The average age is 6.9 Gyr with a spread of 3.6 Gyr for the stars at super-solar [Fe/H].

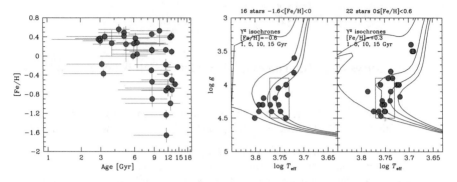

Figure 1. *Left:* Age-metallicity diagram. *Right:* The metal-poor and metal-rich bulge dwarfs plotted on isochrones representative of their respective average metallicity. The (red) rectangle occupy the same region in each plot.

Photometric studies toward the Galactic bulge appear to indicate that the bulge population is all old and that there are no signs of a young or intermediate age population in the HR diagrams (e.g., Zoccali et al. 2003; Clarkson et al. 2008). However, the metallicity distribution of the bulge spans a large range of metallicities (e.g., Fulbright et al. 2007). In the right-hand plot of Fig. 1 we show the microlensed sample, divided into the metal-poor and metal-rich sub-samples, on top are shown isochrones with different metallicities. The rectangle outlines the same $T_{\rm eff}$ − $\log g$ region in each of the two plots. It is clear that, if a metal-poor isochrone would be plotted on top of the metal-rich stars, they would all appear old. This demonstrates the importance of taking isochrones with a suitable range of metallicities into account when estimating the age of the bulge from HR diagrams.

In summary, the sample of microlensed dwarf stars in the bulge shows evidence for a bi-modal bulge population and that the metal-rich population has a significant fraction of intermediate-age stars (but see Nataf & Gould 2011). This will be further investigated in an upcoming paper.

Acknowledgments. T.B. was funded by grant No. 621-2009-3911 from The Swedish Research Council. Work by A.G. was supported by NSF Grant AST 0757888.

References

Bensby, T., Adén, D., Meléndez, J., Gould, A., Feltzing, S., Asplund, M., Johnson, J. A., Lucatello, S., Yee, J. C., Ramírez, I., Cohen, J. G., Thompson, I., Bond, I. A., Gal-Yam, A., Han, C., Sumi, T., Suzuki, D., Wada, K., Miyake, N., Furusawa, K., Ohmori, K., Saito, T., Tristram, P., & Bennett, D. 2011, A&A, 533, A134
Bensby, T., Feltzing, S., Johnson, J. A., Gould, A., Adén, D., M., A., Meléndez, J., Gal-Yam, A., Lucatello, S., Sana, H., Sumi, T., Miyake, N., Suzuki, D., Han, C., Bond, I., & Udalski, A. 2010, A&A, 512, A41
Clarkson, W., Sahu, K., Anderson, J., et al. 2008, ApJ, 684, 1110
Fulbright, J. P., McWilliam, A., & Rich, R. M. 2007, ApJ, 661, 1152
Hill, V., Lecureur, A., Gómez, A., et al. 2011, A&A, 534, A80
Nataf, D. M., & Gould, A. P. 2011, arXiv:1112.1072 [astro-ph.GA]
Zoccali, M., Hill, V., Lecureur, A., et al. 2008, A&A, 486, 177
Zoccali, M., Renzini, A., Ortolani, S., et al. 2003, A&A, 399, 931

Galactic Archaeology: Near-Field Cosmology and the Formation of the Milky Way
ASP Conference Series, Vol. 458
W. Aoki, M. Ishigaki, T. Suda, T. Tsujimoto, N. Arimoto, eds.
©2012 Astronomical Society of the Pacific

The Case of the Missing Cyanogen-rich AGB Stars in Galactic Globular Clusters

S. W. Campbell,[1] D. Yong,[2] E. C. Wylie-de Boer,[2] R. J. Stancliffe,[2] J. C. Lattanzio,[1] G. C. Angelou,[1] F. Grundahl,[3] and C. Sneden[4]

[1] *Monash Centre for Astrophysics, Monash University, VIC 3800, Australia*

[2] *Research School of Astronomy and Astrophysics, Australian National University, Weston, ACT 2611, Australia*

[3] *Department of Physics and Astronomy, Aarhus University, Denmark*

[4] *Department of Astronomy and McDonald Observatory, The University of Texas, Austin, TX 78712, USA*

Abstract. The handful of available observations of AGB stars in Galactic Globular Clusters suggest that the GC AGB populations are dominated by cyanogen-weak stars (eg. Norris et al. 1981; Sneden et al. 2000). This contrasts strongly with the distributions on the RGB (and other) populations, which generally show a 50:50 bimodality in CN band strength. If this is a real difference then it presents a serious problem for low metallicity stellar evolution theory – since such a surface abundance change going from the RGB to AGB is not predicted by stellar models. However this is only a tentative conclusion, since it is based on very small AGB sample sizes. To test whether this problem really exists we have carried out an observational campaign targeting AGB stars in GCs. Our preliminary results indicate there is indeed a lack of CN-strong AGB stars.

1. Introduction

One of the first chemical inhomogeneities discovered in GCs was in cyanogen (CN, often used as a proxy for nitrogen abundance). A picture of 'CN-bimodality' emerged in the early 1980s whereby there appears to be two distinct chemical populations of stars in most, if not all, GCs. The populations are referred to as 'CN-strong' and 'CN-weak' (see Fig. 3 of Norris et al. 1981). The CN bimodality has been observed in stars on the red (first) giant branch (RGB) and more recently on the main sequence (MS; Cannon et al. 1998).

Asymptotic (second) giant branch stars (AGBs) have not been well studied in GCs. This is due to their scarcity (a function of their short lifetimes) and the difficulty in separating them from the RGB stars in colour magnitude diagrams. With recent advances in observational astronomy it is now possible to get significant samples of AGB stars (eg. see Fig. 4 of Sandquist & Bolte 2004, in which they identify 105 AGBs).

The few spectral observations in the literature that do include GC AGB stars suggest that there is a dearth of of CN-strong stars on the asymptotic giant branches of globular clusters (Campbell et al. 2006). Some clusters appear to have no CN-strong stars on the AGB *at all*. The number of AGB stars studied in each GC is small, so no concrete conclusions can be drawn. However, if it is true that there is a difference in CN distribution between the AGB and earlier populations, then this presents a problem for stellar evolution theory – since a surface abundance change such as this is not predicted by the models.

2. Preliminary Results and Future Work

We now have observational data for many AGB stars across 9 globular clusters. The data were collected over 5 nights on the AAT using the 2dF/AAOmega multi-object spectrograph, yielding spectra for ~ 250 AGB stars as well as hundreds of horizontal branch and RGB stars. The spectral resolution is R ~ 3000. In Figure 1 we show our results for NGC 6752. We confirm that, even with a larger sample of AGB stars, there are *zero* CN-strong stars on the AGB in this cluster! This is in stark contrast to the RGB where CN-strong stars dominate with a ratio of 80:20. We find the same result for NGC 288. However for some GCs the situation is less clear since we find that some have a small population of CN-strong stars on the AGB, such as in M10 and NGC 1851.

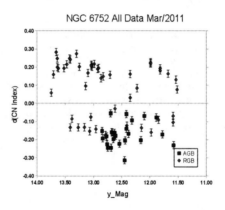

Figure 1.   Results for NGC 6752. The vertical axis is the same as the delta CN index (S) defined in Norris et al. (1981) except we have taken the zero line to bisect the two CN populations. Thus stars with d(CN Index) > 0 are CN-strong.

We plan to calculate stellar models to investigate this phenomenon. We also have upcoming high-resolution spectral observations (with VLT-FLAMES) in which we will check if the CN correlates with the other light element anomalies such as Na-O and Mg-Al in the AGBs.

References

Campbell, S. W., Lattanzio, J. C., & Elliott, L. M. 2006, MmSAI, 77, 864
Cannon, R. D., Croke, B. F. W., Bell, R. A., Hesser, J. E., & Stathakis, R. A. 1998, MNRAS, 298, 601
Norris, J., Cottrell, P. L., Freeman, K. C., & Da Costa, G. S. 1981, ApJ, 244, 205
Sandquist, E. L., & Bolte, M. 2004, ApJ, 611, 323
Sneden, C., Ivans, I. I., & Kraft, R. P. 2000, MmSAI, 71, 657

Galactic Archaeology: Near-Field Cosmology and the Formation of the Milky Way
ASP Conference Series, Vol. 458
W. Aoki, M. Ishigaki, T. Suda, T. Tsujimoto, N. Arimoto, eds.
©*2012 Astronomical Society of the Pacific*

Kinematics of Stars Along the Sagittarius Trailing Tidal Tail and Constraints on the Milky Way Mass Distribution

Jeffrey L. Carlin

Department of Physics, Applied Physics, and Astronomy, Rensselaer Polytechnic Institute, 110 8th Street, Troy, NY 12180, USA (carlij@rpi.edu)

Abstract. To date, models of the Sagittarius (Sgr) tidal debris streams have been constrained by positions, distances, and radial velocities of detected debris, but no systematic survey has addressed the tangential velocities (derived from proper motions) of Sgr detritus. We present three-dimensional kinematics of Sgr trailing tidal debris in six fields located $70 - 130°$ along the stream from the Sgr dwarf galaxy core. The data are from our proper-motion (PM) survey of Kapteyn's Selected Areas, in which we have measured accurate PMs to faint magnitudes in $40' \times 40'$ fields evenly spaced across the sky. The radial velocity (RV) signature of Sgr has been identified among our follow-up spectroscopic data in four of the six fields and combined with mean PMs of spectroscopically-confirmed members to derive space motions of Sgr debris based on 15-64 confirmed stream members per field. These kinematics are compared to predictions of the Law & Majewski (2010) model of Sgr disruption; we find reasonable agreement with model predictions in RVs and PMs along Galactic latitude. However, an upward adjustment of the Local Standard of Rest velocity (Θ_{LSR}) from its standard 220 km s^{-1} to at least 232 ± 14 km s^{-1} (and possibly as high as 264 ± 23 km s^{-1}) is necessary to bring 3-D model debris kinematics and our measurements into agreement. Satisfactory model fits that simultaneously reproduce known position, distance, and radial velocity trends of the Sgr tidal streams, while significantly increasing Θ_{LSR} could only be achieved by increasing the Galactic bulge and disk mass while leaving the dark matter halo fixed to the best-fit values from Law & Majewski (2010).

1. The Data

We combine deep, precise proper motions (1-2 mas yr^{-1} per star) to V (or g)> 21 from our photographic survey in Kapteyn's Selected Areas (Casetti-Dinescu et al. 2006) with follow-up spectroscopy from the Hydra (WIYN) and Hectospec (MMT) multifiber spectrographs. Spectra were obtained at $R \sim 1000 - 1500$ of ~ 1300 stars in 6 fields; four fields show a clear signature of Sagittarius debris among their radial velocities. Roughly 12% of the stars in SAs 117, 93, 94, and 71 have RVs well outside the broad peak made up of Milky Way populations. These RV peaks are at the positions expected for Sgr debris. The radial velocities are used in conjunction with proper motion and color-magnitude criteria to isolate Sgr stream members in each field.

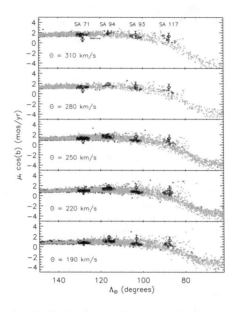

Figure 1.   Mean longitudinal proper motions, $\mu_l \cos(b)$ (large open diamonds with error bars), in (from left to right) SAs 71, 94, 93, and 117 as a function of $\Lambda_\odot$. Model debris from the Sgr simulations are shown as the colored points; from top to bottom, these represent models with $\Theta_{LSR} = 310, 280, 250, 220,$ and 190 km s^{-1}. The sudden drop in $\mu_l \cos(b)$ for $\Lambda_\odot < 90°$ is due to the inversion in sign that occurs as the debris sweeps past the South Galactic pole. Small open black squares denote model debris corresponding (within $\pm 3°$ in RA, Dec, and $\Lambda_\odot$) to each SA field. Higher values of Θ_{LSR} provide a better match of the small open squares to the observed $\mu_l \cos(b)$ values in the SAs (diamonds).

2. Results

We have measured 3-D kinematics of Sagittarius trailing tail stars in four fields between $70 < \Lambda_\odot < 130°$. The kinematics agree with the Law & Majewski (2010) model in V_{GSR} and μ_b, but there is systematic disagreement in $\mu_l \cos(b)$. Because of the orientation of the Sgr debris stream, we can use $\mu_l \cos(b)$ to constrain Θ_{LSR}, the rotation velocity at the Solar circle. We find $\Theta_{LSR} = 232 \pm 14$ km s^{-1} using all 3 dimensions of the motions. When we exclude the questionable field SA 71, we derive $\Theta_{LSR} = 244 \pm 17$ km s^{-1}. Finally, using only the $\mu_l \cos(b)$ motions, we find 264 ± 23 km s^{-1} for Θ_{LSR}. We argue that the additional mass required to increase Θ_{LSR} must reside in the disk and bulge components of the Milky Way, *not* the halo. More details about the results of this work can be found in Carlin et al. (2012).

References

Carlin, J. L., Majewski, S. R., Casetti-Dinescu, D. I., et al. 2012, ApJ, 744, 25
Casetti-Dinescu, D. I., Majewski, S. R., Girard, T. M., et al. 2006, AJ, 132, 2082
Law, D. R., & Majewski, S. R. 2010a, ApJ, 714, 229

Galactic Archaeology: Near-Field Cosmology and the Formation of the Milky Way
ASP Conference Series, Vol. 458
W. Aoki, M. Ishigaki, T. Suda, T. Tsujimoto, N. Arimoto, eds.
© *2012 Astronomical Society of the Pacific*

Chemical Fingerprinting of Stellar Populations in the Milky Way Halo

Mei-Yin Chou,[1,2] Steven R. Majewski,[2] Katia Cunha,[3] Verne V. Smith,[3] Richard J. Patterson,[2] and David Martínez-Delgado[4]

[1]*Institute of Astronomy and Astrophysics, Academia Sinica, Taiwan*

[2]*Department of Astronomy, University of Virginia, USA*

[3]*National Optical Astronomy Observatories, USA*

[4]*Max-Planck-Institut fur Astronomie, Germany*

Abstract. The idea of "chemically fingerprinting" stars to their birth systems has been discussed over the last decade. Here we present an investigation of the chemical abundance patterns of halo substructures using high-resolution spectra. In particular, we study the abundances of the α-like element titanium (Ti) and the s-process elements yttrium (Y) and lanthanum (La) for M giant candidates of the Galactic Anticenter Stellar Structure (GASS, also known as the Monoceros Ring) and the Triangulum-Andromeda (TriAnd) Star Cloud. We apply "chemical fingerprinting" to the GASS/Monoceros Ring and TriAnd Star Cloud, to explore the origins of the two systems and the hypothesized connections between them. GASS has been debated either to originate from a part (e.g., warp) of the Galactic disk or tidal debris of a disrupted Milky Way (MW) satellite galaxy. Our exploration shows that GASS is indeed made of stars from a dwarf spheroidal (dSph) galaxy, although we still can not rule out the possibility that GASS was dynamically created out of a previously formed outer MW disk. And whereas the TriAnd Star Cloud has been assumed to come from the tidal disruption of the same accreted MW satellite as the GASS/Monoceros Ring, our comparison of the abundance patterns in GASS and TriAnd M giants suggests that the TriAnd Star Cloud is likely an independent halo substructure unrelated to GASS/Monoceros Ring. Furthermore, our findings also suggest that the MW may have accreted other satellites in addition to the on-going, well-known Sagittarius (Sgr) dwarf galaxy.

1. Data and Results

Targets were 2MASS-selected giants and their relative spatial positions has been illustrated in the left panel of Figure 1. Data were obtained from echelle spectrographs mounted on the Apache Point Observatory 3.5-m telescope (with resolution R∼ 32, 000), Kitt Peak National Observatory 4-m telescope (with R∼ 35, 000) and Telescopio Nazionale Galileo 3.5-m telescope (with R∼ 46, 000). The right panel of Figure 1 compares derived distributions of [Ti/Fe], [Y/Fe], and [La/Fe] as a function of [Fe/H] for our TriAnd, GASS/Monoceros Ring and Sgr stars (from Chou et al. 2007 and 2010a) . We found similar chemical patterns between Sgr and GASS (except in [La/Fe]), and therefore GASS probably enriched in a dSph-like environment (Chou et al. 2010b). TriAnd has lower [Ti/Fe] compared with the MW, and different chemical patterns than GASS,

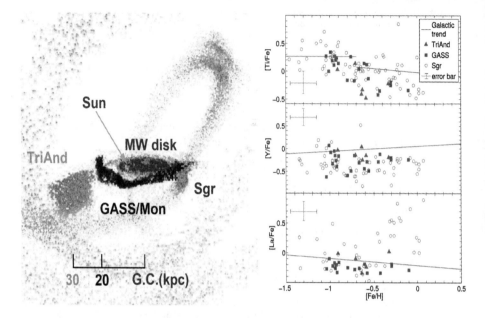

Figure 1.   (color online) **Left:** Sgr tidal debris model by Law et al. (2005) superposed with the MW halo substructure TriAnd and GASS/Monoceros Ring. Stars from these three stellar populations we present here are selected from the colored points: TriAnd overdensity (green), GASS/Monoceros Ring (magenta) and Sgr core+stream (yellow). The MW disk is color-coded in blue, the Galactic center (G.C.) is shown with a bright red circle, and the sun is marked with a white dot. The surrounding red points are older Sgr debris from the simulation which can be ignored here. The estimated distance from the Galactic center is also shown at the bottom of the figure. **Right:** Distribution as a function of [Fe/H] of (a) [Ti/Fe], (b) [Y/Fe] and (c) [La/Fe] for TriAnd (blue triangles), GASS (green squares) and Sgr (red open circles) stars. The solid line is a fit to the Galactic trend for halo and disk field stars. Typical error bars are shown in each panel in blue.

so TriAnd is possibly from a dSph but not related to GASS (Chou et al. 2011). GASS and TriAnd may be accreted from different satellites, which suggests minor mergers may play an important role in the MW formation history.

References

Law, D. R., Johnston, K. V., & Majewski, S. R. 2005, *ApJ*, 619, 807

Chou, M.-Y., Majewski,S. R., Cunha, K., Smith, V. V., Patterson, R. J., Martínez-Delgado, D., Law, D. R., Crane, J. D., Muñoz, R. R., López, R. G., Geisler, D., & Skrutskie, M. F. 2007, *ApJ*, 670, 346

Chou, M.-Y., Cunha, K., Majewski, S. R., Smith, V. V., Patterson, R. J., Martínez-Delgado, D., & Geisler, D. 2010a, *ApJ*, 708, 1290

Chou, M.-Y., Majewski, S. R., Cunha, K., Smith, V. V., Patterson, R. J., & Martínez-Delgado, D. 2010b, *ApJ*, 720, L5

Chou, M.-Y., Majewski, S. R., Cunha, K., Smith, V. V., Patterson, R. J., & Martínez-Delgado, D. 2011, *ApJ*, 731, L30

Galactic Archaeology: Near-Field Cosmology and the Formation of the Milky Way
ASP Conference Series, Vol. 458
W. Aoki, M. Ishigaki, T. Suda, T. Tsujimoto, N. Arimoto, eds.
©2012 Astronomical Society of the Pacific

Slicing the Monoceros Overdensity

Blair Conn,[1] Noelia Noël,[1] Hans-Walter Rix, [1] Nicolas Martin, [1]
Richard Lane,[2] Geraint Lewis,[3] Mike Irwin,[4] Rodrigo Ibata,[5] Andy Dolphin[6]
and Scott Chapman[4]

[1]*Max Planck Institut für Astronomie, Königstuhl 17, 69117, Heidelberg, Germany*

[2]*Departamento de Astronomía, Universidad de Concepción, Casilla 160-C, Concepción, Chile*

[3]*Sydney Institute for Astronomy, School of Physics, The University of Sydney, A28, Sydney, 2006, Australia*

[4]*Institute of Astronomy, Madingley Road, Cambridge, CB3 0HA, U.K.*

[5]*Observatoire de Strasbourg, 11, rue de l'Université, F-67000, Strasbourg, France*

[6]*Raytheon Company, PO Box 11337, Tucson, AZ, 85734-1337*

Abstract.   We have surveyed the Monoceros Overdensity (MO) using SUPRIME-CAM and obtained deep Colour-Magnitude diagrams in three longitudinal stripes at l = 130°, 150° and 170°. The data in g and r bands are 100% complete to 24th magnitude and as such extends over three magnitudes beyond the MO main sequence turn-off. The data quality ensures a clean detection of the MO providing distance, density and metallicity information. We find that the MO appears as a wall of stars protruding out of the disk, across 40° of our survey, with a metallicity that is more metal rich than the surrounding stars. We test three formation scenarios for the MO finding that neither the galactic flare or the perturbed disc model can match the observations while the tidal stream scenario is viable but needs significantly more numerical modeling to refine a solution.

1.   Surveying the Monoceros Overdensity

The MO is an extended stellar structure found in the outskirts of the Milky Way at galactocentric distances of 16 -18 kpc (Newberg et al. 2002; Momany et al. 2004; Conn et al. 2008). It is detected in locations spanning over 200° of Galactic longitude and on both sides of the Galactic plane. There are three competing theories to explain it origins: a tidal stream scenario from a disrupting dwarf galaxy (Martin et al. 2004; Peñarrubia et al. 2005), an extension of the galactic flare above the plane (Hammersley & López-Corredoira 2011) and a ring of stars induced by a close passage of a massive dwarf satellite (Purcell et al. 2011).

The analysis has used MATCH (Dolphin 2002) which applies isochrone fitting techniques to a subset of the Colour-Magnitude space. This generates profiles with

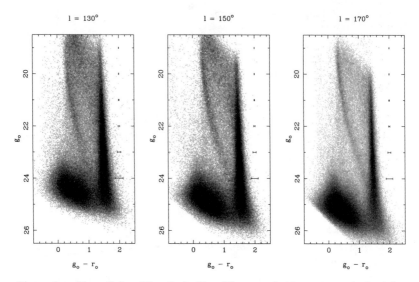

l = 130°   l = 150°   l = 170°

Figure 1.   Deep Colour-Magnitude Hess Diagram of point sources obtained for each of the three stripes.   The data has been extinction corrected according to Schlegel et al. (1998). The cloud of sources in the bottom-left of each panel stems from unresolved galaxies. Main sequence turn-off (MSTO) stars, which we associated with the MO, are found at $g_o - r_o \sim 0.4, g_o \sim 19.5$. The strong overdensity of stars at $g_o - r_o \sim 1.5$ are the local low mass dwarf stars.

stellar density and metallicity abundance as a function of heliocentric distance and from this the MO signature is clearly visible.

The MO is found at constant heliocentric distance across the survey and at all galactic latitudes. We have compared the flare model of Hammersley & López-Corredoira (2011), to our data and by searching extensively through a large parameter space of flare models, the MO is most closely related to a flare with a short scale length and a smaller onset radius than that of more typical flare models. This suggests the MO is a very localized structure. The MO is more metal-rich than nearby stars at the same distance and latitude and therefore is difficult to reconcile with a flaring disk. For the perturbed disk model also predicts that the metallicity of the induced rings should be an average of the galactic disk as stars are migrated in and out of the ring from different starting radii. The metallicity of the MO is still too metal-poor, in general, to have been drawn from the much more metal-rich disk population. Finally, the density profile of the MO shows an excess on top of a smooth Milky Way component. The perturbed disk models of Purcell et al. 2011 predict that an MO-like feature should be accompanied by a dramatic drop in stellar density adjacent to the overdensity which is not observed. Combined with the metallicity findings, the perturbed disc scenario is unlikely.

The tidal stream scenario remains as a possible formation mechanism but the large parameter space of such an encounter excludes an easy conclusion to finding the MO's origins. Extensive modeling is needed to determine the possible progenitors for the MO. Complete tracing of the MO around the Galactic plane is required to completely break the degeneracy between scenarios.

References

Conn, B. C. et al. 2008, MNRAS, 390, 1388
Dolphin, A. E. 2002, MNRAS, 332, 91. arXiv:astro-ph/0112331
Hammersley, P. L., & López-Corredoira, M. 2011, A&A, 527, A6. 1011.2405
Martin, N. F. et al. 2004, MNRAS, 355, L33. arXiv:astro-ph/0407391
Momany, Y. et al. 2004, A&A, 421, L29. arXiv:astro-ph/0405526
Newberg, H. J. et al. 2002, ApJ, 569, 245. arXiv:astro-ph/0111095
Peñarrubia, J. et al. 2005, ApJ, 626, 128. arXiv:astro-ph/0410448
Schlegel, D. J., Finkbeiner, D. P., & Davis, M. 1998, ApJ, 500, 525. arXiv:astro-ph/9710327

Breakfast at the conference site. A. Ferrara (left) and J. Bland-Hawthorn.

Galactic Archaeology: Near-Field Cosmology and the Formation of the Milky Way
ASP Conference Series, Vol. 458
W. Aoki, M. Ishigaki, T. Suda, T. Tsujimoto, N. Arimoto, eds.
© 2012 Astronomical Society of the Pacific

Chemically Tagging Disk Fossils: the Case of the Hyades Supercluster

G.M. De Silva,[1] K.C. Freeman,[2] J. Bland-Hawthorn,[3] and M. Asplund[3]

[1]*Australian Astronomical Observatory*

[2]*Australian National University*

[3]*University of Sydney*

Abstract. The Hyades supercluster is a kinematically defined group of stars, which are located across the Galactic disk. Advocated by Eggen in the 1970's as part of the Hyades open cluster, recent simulations suggest the Hyades supercluster is a dynamical stream caused by spiral density waves. We present high resolution elemental abundances of probable supercluster members. We recover supercluster stars that share a similar chemical signature as the Hyades open cluster. Our results support the Hyades supercluster being at least partly the debris of an originally large star-forming event.

1. Introduction

Chemical tagging is the use of detailed chemical abundance patterns of individual stars to tag them to common star-forming events (Freeman & Bland-Hawthorn 2002). The aim is to recover fossil stellar substructures which are otherwise unidentifiable, in order to disentangle a physical sequence of events that led to the present Galactic disk (De Silva et al. 2009). Moving groups and superclusters form such stellar substructure (E.g. De Silva et al. 2007).

2. Hyades Supercluster

The Hyades supercluster is a kinematically defined group so stars, which are located across the Galactic disk. It is a prominent over-density in the velocity space, located at $U, V = -40, -23$ km s^{-1}. Eggen (1969) identified it as part of the Hyades open cluster, however recent simulations suggest the Hyades supercluster is a dynamical stream caused by spiral density waves.

High resolution elemental abundances of 20 probable Hyades supercluster members were presented by De Silva et al. (2011) based on VLT/UVES spectra (Program IDs: 080.D-0094(A) and 381.B-0045(A), PI: De Silva). Of this sample 7 stars have Hyades open cluster metallicity, while the remaining have solar level metallicity. Examining the individual elemental abundances, 4 of these 7 metal-rich stars match the Hyades open cluster abundance pattern as observed for Hyades cluster dwarfs by De Silva et al. (2006). In particular the abundance pattern of the s-process elements among the cluster dwarfs, where [Ba/Fe] is enhanced, but [La/Fe] and [Ce/Fe] are of solar proportions,

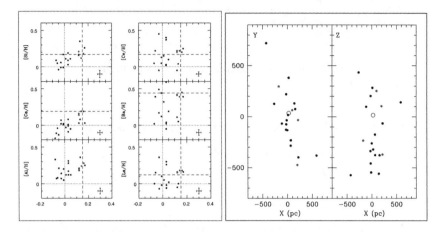

Figure 1.   Left (a): Abundances of the sample stars. The dotted lines mark the solar level and the dashed lines mark the Hyades open cluster level. The red stars are those with Hyades-like abundances. Right (b): The location of the sample stars in X-Y and X-Z plane. The open circle represents the Hyades open cluster.

is shared by the 4 supercluster stars as well (see Figure 1a).

These four supercluster stars also meet the Hyades cluster velocity criteria, confirming their kinematical membership. Figure 1b. shows their location in the X-Y-Z plane relative to the Hyades cluster. Clearly these four stars are spatially well separated from the cluster despite the common kinematics and chemical signature.

3.   Conclusion

Enforcing both kinematical and chemical tagging criteria, 4 supercluster stars were identified as former members of the Hyades open cluster from a sample of 20 probable members. Pompeia et al. (2011) also find such stars out of 21 in an independent sample. These results support the Hyades supercluster being at least partly the debris of an originally large star-forming event associated with the Hyades open cluster.

References

De Silva, G., Freeman, K., Bland-Hawthorn, J., Asplund, M., & Bland-Hawthorn, J. 2009, PASA, 26, 11
De Silva, G., Freeman, K., Bland-Hawthorn, J., Asplund, M., Bland-Hawthorn, J., & Bessell, M. 2007, AJ, 133, 694
De Silva, G., Freeman, K., Bland-Hawthorn, J., Asplund, M., Bland-Hawthorn, J., Williams, M., & Holmberg, J. 2011, MNRAS, 415, 563
De Silva, G., Sneden, C., Paulson, D., Asplund, M., Bland-Hawthorn, J., Bessell, M., & Freeman, K. 2006, AJ, 131, 455
Eggen, O. 1969, PASP, 430, 165
Freeman, K., & Bland-Hawthorn, J. 2002, ARAA, 40, 487
Pompeia, L., Masseron, T., Famaey, B., van Eck, S., Jorissen, A., Minchev, I., Siebert, A., Sneden, C., Lepine, J., & Siopis, C. 2011, MNRAS, 415, 563

Galactic Archaeology: Near-Field Cosmology and the Formation of the Milky Way
ASP Conference Series, Vol. 458
W. Aoki, M. Ishigaki, T. Suda, T. Tsujimoto, N. Arimoto, eds.
©2012 Astronomical Society of the Pacific

Chemical Enrichment Mechanisms in Omega Centauri: Clues from Neutron-Capture Elements

V. D'Orazi,[1,2] R. Gratton,[1] E. Pancino,[3] A. Bragaglia,[3] E. Carretta,[3] S. Lucatello,[1] and C. Sneden[4]

[1]INAF Osservatorio Astronomico di Padova, vicolo dell'Osservatorio 5, Padova, 35122, Italy

[2]Department of Physics and Astronomy, Macquarie University, Balaclava Rd, North Ryde, Sydney, NSW, 2109, Australia

[3]INAF Osservatorio Astronomico di Bologna, via Ranzani 1, Bologna, 40127, Italy

[4]Department of Astronomy and McDonald Observatory, The University of Texas, Austin, TX, 78712, USA

Abstract. In the complex picture of multiple stellar populations in globular clusters (GCs), a special role is played by NGC 5139 (ω Centauri). At variance with the majority of GCs, ω Cen exhibits significant star-to-star variations in metallicity and in relative neutron-capture element abundance ratios with respect to Fe, along with split evolutionary sequences as revealed from colour-magnitude diagrams. Combining information from photometry and spectroscopy, several studies suggested that an age spread of several Gyr has to be invoked to explain (at least partially) some of the observed features. However, a comprehensive understanding of the formation, evolution and chemical enrichment processes is still not at hand. Relatively metal-rich ω Cen stars display neutron-capture abundance distributions dominated by contributions from the s-process, but it is not clear what roles have been played by the so-called main and weak s-process components in generating these abundances. To gain better insight into this question we derived lead (Pb) abundances for several ω Cen cluster members, because this element can only be produced by the mains-process. We analysed high-resolution UVES@VLT spectra of a sample of twelve red-giant branch stars, deriving abundances of Pb and also of Y, Zr, La, Ce, Eu, and the C+N+O sum. Spectral synthesis was applied to all features, taking into account isotopic shifts and/or hyperfine structure as needed. We measured for the first time the Pb content in ω Cen, discovering a clear hint for a Pb production occurring at [Fe/H]> -1.7 dex. Our data suggest that the role of the weak component in the production of s-process elements is negligible. Moreover, evidence gathered from the abundances of other elements indicates that the main component occurring in this GC is peculiar and shifted towards higher mass polluters than the standard one.

These results are now published in D'Orazi et al. (2011).

References

D'Orazi, V., Gratton, R. G., Pancino, E., Bragaglia, A., Carretta, E., Lucatello, S., & Sneden, C. 2011, A&A, 534, A29

BBQ lunch on November 2nd.

Galactic Archaeology: Near-Field Cosmology and the Formation of the Milky Way
ASP Conference Series, Vol. 458
W. Aoki, M. Ishigaki, T. Suda, T. Tsujimoto, N. Arimoto, eds.
© 2012 Astronomical Society of the Pacific

A Matched Filter Analysis of SDSS DR8 Photometry in the Vicinity of the Cetus Polar Stream

Carl J. Grillmair

Spitzer Science Center, 1200 E. California Blvd., Pasadena, CA 91125, U.S.A.

Abstract. We examine the region of sky in the vicinity of the Cetus Polar Stream and find indications of at least three narrow and metal poor streams at distances ranging from from 28 to 37 kpc and extending over 60 degrees of sky. We suggest that we may have resolved the substructure in this region into a number of relatively cold streams, and that the original Cetus Polar Stream detection may have sampled two or more of these streams. Similarities in distance and orientation suggest that these streams may be dynamically related and/or share a common origin.

1. Introduction

The number of stellar debris streams that we can trace over an appreciable portion of their orbits currently stands at 14 (Grillmair 2010). Since we can measure all six phase space coordinates for the stars in these streams, they have the potential to significantly improve our understanding of the mass distribution in the Galaxy, particularly in regions where we have no comparable tracers (Law & Majewski 2010; Newberg et al. 2010; Koposov et al. 2010). The coldest streams are particularly interesting as they may provide a sensitive means of detecting dark matter subhalos (Carlberg 2009; Yoon et al. 2011). Here we examine the region around the recently detected Cetus Polar Stream (Newberg et al. 2009) in the hopes of further refining its position, orientation, and extent, and to select targets for spectroscopic follow-up.

2. Analysis

Photometric data in g, r, and i were extracted from the Sloan Digital Sky Survey (SDSS) Data Release 8. We used theoretical isochrones to construct color-magnitude filters and generate the filtered surface density map shown in Figure 1. The new streams appear as long, narrow enhancements extending across the southern SDSS footprint. Using the "T" statistic of Grillmair (2009), we find that the northern half of stream 'a' is detected at a signal-to-noise ratio of 7. The stream has a FWHM of 30 arcmin, or about 150 pc at a distance of 37 kpc. This is similar to the widths measured for presumed globular cluster streams (Grillmair & Dionatos 2006a,b; Grillmair 2011). On the other hand, there are indications of either a broader, 1.2 kpc wide stream characteristic of presumed dwarf galaxy streams (Grillmair 2006a, 2009) or possibly multiple stream components (Grillmair 2006b)). The stream candidates labeled 'b' and 'c' are only marginally detected. The similarities in distance and orientation suggest that these streams may share a common progenitor or infall event.

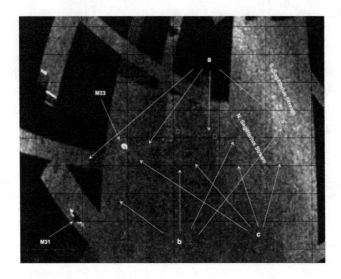

Figure 1.   A filtered surface density map of a portion of the SDSS DR8, using a matched filter based on a theoretical isochrone with Z = 0.0001 and an age of 12 Gyr, optimized for a distance of 36 kpc. The image has been smoothed with a Gaussian kernel with a width of 20 arcmin. The new streams are labeled 'a', 'b', and 'c'. The Cetus Polar Stream detections (Newberg et al. 2009) are shown as boxes. Coordinates are in offset RA and dec, with north to the left and east upwards.

References

Carlberg, R. G. 2009, ApJ, 705, L223. 0908.4345
Grillmair, C. J. 2006a, ApJ, 645, L37. arXiv:astro-ph/0605396
— 2006b, ApJ, 651, L29. arXiv:astro-ph/0609449
— 2009, ApJ, 693, 1118. 0811.3965
— 2010, in Galaxies and their Masks, edited by D. L. Block, K. C. Freeman, & I. Puerari, 247
— 2011, ApJ, 738, 98. 1107.5044
Grillmair, C. J., & Dionatos, O. 2006a, ApJ, 641, L37. arXiv:astro-ph/0603062
— 2006b, ApJ, 643, L17. arXiv:astro-ph/0604332
Koposov, S. E., Rix, H.-W., & Hogg, D. W. 2010, ApJ, 712, 260. 0907.1085
Law, D. R., & Majewski, S. R. 2010, ApJ, 714, 229. 1003.1132
Newberg, H. J., Willett, B. A., Yanny, B., & Xu, Y. 2010, ApJ, 711, 32. 1001.0576
Newberg, H. J., Yanny, B., & Willett, B. A. 2009, ApJ, 700, L61. 0906.3291
Yoon, J. H., Johnston, K. V., & Hogg, D. W. 2011, ApJ, 731, 58. 1012.2884

Galactic Archaeology: Near-Field Cosmology and the Formation of the Milky Way
ASP Conference Series, Vol. 458
W. Aoki, M. Ishigaki, T. Suda, T. Tsujimoto, N. Arimoto, eds.
©2012 Astronomical Society of the Pacific

The AMANOGAWA-2SB Surevey and the Gas Density Histogram of Milky Way Galaxy to Address the Origin of the Density Structure of ISM

T. Handa,[1] T. Yoda,[2] K. Kohno,[2] J.-i. Morino,[3] T. Nakajima,[3] N. Kuno,[3] H. Ogawa,[4] and K. Kimura[4]

[1] *Kagoshima University*

[2] *University of Tokyo*

[3] *National Astronomical Observatory of Japan*

[4] *Osaka Prefectual University*

Abstract. We made a Galactic plane survey in both ^{12}CO(2-1) and ^{13}CO(2-1) with 9 arcmin resolution. It covers the largest area on the sky in these lines with denser sampling than the beam size. Using the survey data we derived the gas density histogram of the galactic disk in the 20-pc scale, which corresponds to the probability distribution function of a stochastic process. The derived histogram is log-normal. It suggests the current gas density structure is a result of many density modulations which happens randomly without any characteristic scale.

1. Introduction

It is a big quation how the density structure of the interstellar matter (ISM) is made. A gas density histgram (GDH) is an approach to address it. It corresponds to the probability density function (PDF) of the gas density discussed in theoretical works. For example, the PDF is log-normal in the case that many density modulations make the density structure Vazquez-Semadeni (1994). We made an extenstion of AMANOGAWA-2SB Galactic plane survey Yoda et al. (2010). Using the data which has a large spatial dynamic range, we can estimate the GDH.

2. Observations & Data Analysis

We use the data in the ^{12}CO (2-1) and ^{13}CO (2-1) lines from an extension of the AMANOGAWA-2SB survey on the galactic equator. The beamsize is about 9′ Nakajima et al. (2007) and the observation grid is 7.5′. The sky coverage we used is the range of $5° \leq l \leq 90°$ and $|b| \leq 3°$. The rms noise level with 1.3 km s^{-1} resolution, σ_{rms}, is about 0.05 K for both lines.

We also use the data in the ^{12}CO (1-0) line from the CfA 1.2m survey Dame et al. (2001). The HPBW is 8.7′ and the observation grid is 7.5′. The velocity resolution is 1.3 km s^{-1} and σ_{rms} is about 0.12 K. We use the data in the same sky coverage as ours to minimize the bias due to molecular clouds near the Sun.

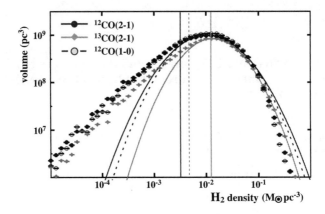

Figure 1.　The gas density histograms from three CO lines. The statistical ambiguity of the ordinates is smaller than the size of the symobls. The effective noise limits are shown by the vertical lines in corresponding colors.

To derive the volume of the voxel in the $l - b - v$ domain we used the kinematic distance based on the flat-circular rotation with $R_0 = 8.5$ kpc and $v_0 = 220$ km s^{-1}. The gas mass in a voxel is derived from the CO line intensity with the conversion factor X. We used $X = 1.8 \times 10^{20}$ cm^{-2} (K km s^{-1})$^{-1}$ for the ^{12}CO (1-0) line Dame et al. (2001). For other lines we modify X using the averaged line intensity ratio over the AMANOGAWA-2SB survey on the Galactic equator. We assume that all molecular gas is confined within 100 pc from the galactic plane. The final shape of the GDH is less affected by the kinematic model of the Galaxy, radial variation of X, or the disk thickness.

3.　Results & Discussion

The resultant GDH is shown in the fig.1. This is the first molecular GDH over the galactic disk. All GDHs shown here can be fitted by log-normal functions, although they have deviations at the denser end. Using optical depth estimation shown by Paper I, the ^{13}CO (2-1) GDH can be corrected and it is consistent to the log-normal fitting of the other GDHs. Our result suggests that the gas density structure in 20-pc scale is made by many density modulations and the ISM should be well mixed in the galactic disk.

References

Dame, T. M., Hartmann, D., & Thaddeus, P. 2001, ApJ, 547, 792
Nakajima, T., et al. 2007, PASJ, 59, 1005
Vazquez-Semadeni E., 1994, ApJ, 423, 681
Yoda T., et al., 2010, PASJ, 62, 1277 (Paper I)

Galactic Archaeology: Near-Field Cosmology and the Formation of the Milky Way
ASP Conference Series, Vol. 458
W. Aoki, M. Ishigaki, T. Suda, T. Tsujimoto, N. Arimoto, eds.
©2012 Astronomical Society of the Pacific

Slowly Orbiting Old Open Clusters in the Galactic Outerdisk

Takashi Hasegawa[1] and Tsuyoshi Sakamoto[2]

[1] *Gunma Astronomical Observatory, Agatsuma, 377-0702 Gunma, Japan*

[2] *Japan Spaceguard Association, Bisei, Ibara, 714-1411 Okayama, Japan*

Abstract. Slowly orbiting old open clusters are reported in the outerdisk of the Galaxy by means of radial velocity measurements. Clusters in question are estimated to be $2 \sim 5$ Gyr old around the putative Canis Major dwarf galaxy (the Galactocentric distances are $10 \sim 15$ kpc). Not a small fraction of old clusters in this field are orbiting $30 \sim 50$ km s^{-1} slower than the rotation of the Galactic disk. Though the sample is incomplete, there seems some mechanism that make these clusters rotate slowly, such as the warp of the Galactic disk and/or merging process of the Canis Major dwarf galaxy. The former possibility is less favored when compared with dynamics of young clusters.

1. Old Open Clusters as a Tracer

Old open clusters are one of the important tracer of the state of the Milky Way (hereafter MW) several Gyrs ago. By referring to *in situ* clusters, we could learn the star (cluster) formation history during a large fraction of the history of the MW, and the metallicity gradient across the MW disk, and dynamical evolution of the Galactic disk. From clusters of extragalactic origin, we could learn the accretion and merging event of the MW. Advantages in referring to the clusters over individual stars include relatively accurate estimates on the distance and age from simple photometric work and on the velocity and metallicity from the low to intermediate resolution spectroscopy.

Photometric work was made for long (e.g. Ann et al. 2002, Hasegawa et al. 2004, 2008) and compiled (e.g. Dias et al. 2002), providing us with insights on the star cluster formation history. Subsequent spectroscopic work for measurements on metallicity and radial velocity would improve the understanding of the MW disk, however, progress is still on the way (Carraro et al. 2007). Anyway it is apparent that this is the most detailed case-study of the Galactic archaeology because of the proximity of the sample.

2. Radial Velocities

Our sample of clusters consists of Berkeley 36, Berkeley 78, and with less significance due to the background contamination, Biurakan 12 and Auner 1. Stars for spectroscopy were red giants or red clump stars retrieved from our photometric work, and spectroscopic observations were made with KOOLS attached with the 188-cm telescope at Okayama Astrophysical Observatory. The resolution of ~ 1200 and a moderate SN ratio of $20 \sim 50$ provided us with the velocities of 5 km s^{-1} accuracy for several stars in each clusters.

Resultant systemic velocities of the clusters are shown as the offset from the Galactic rotation of 220 km s^{-1} in Fig. 1. Clusters of our interest are shown with error bars within $\cos\Psi = -0.2 \sim -0.5$. Among them, while Berkeley 36 is squarely on the rotation, Berkeley 78, and possibly Auner 1, are ragging from the rotation (slow orbiters) along with several clusters in this location that have radial velocities in the literature.

Similar diagram is shown for the younger open clusters in the literature. Slow orbiters could be indeed expected from the warp of the disk, however, in this case we expect not only the old clusters but also young clusters (and other populations) should share such motion. In contrast to this expectation, it seems that slow orbiters other than old clusters are very limited. On the contrary, slow orbiters are consistent with the merging picture only if merging of the Canis Major dwarf galaxy occurred in the way that Peñarrubia et al. (2005) have presented.

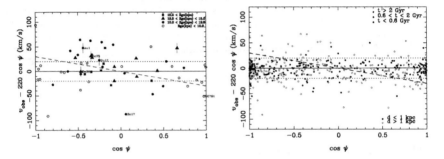

Figure 1.   Line of sight velocities of open clusters (*left*: old ones, *right*: young ones) versus location of the cluster in the disk. The location is shown by means of Ψ defined by Frenk and White (1980). The dotted lines indicate the typical velocity dispersion of old open clusters (20 km s^{-1}). Long dashed lines stand for the slower rotation (190 km s^{-1}).

Acknowledgments.   The authors express special thanks to the observatory staffs for runs of spectroscopic observation with OAO/KOOLS.

References

Ann, H. B., Lee, S. H., Sung, H., Lee, M. G. et al. 2002, AJ, 123, 905
Carraro, G., Geisler, D., Villanova, S., Frinchaboy, P. M., et al. 2007, A&A, 476, 217
Dias, W. S., Alessi, B. S., Moitinho, A., Lpine, J. R. D 2002, A&A, 389, 871
Frenk, C. S., White, S. D. M., 1980, MNRAS, 193, 295
Hasegawa, T., Malasan, H. L., Kawakita, H., Obayashi, H., et al. 2004, PASJ, 56, 295
Hasegawa, T., Sakamoto, T., Malasan, H. L. 2008, PASJ, 60, 1267
Peñarrubia, J., Martnez-Delgado, D., Rix, H., Gmez-Flechoso, M. A., et al. 2005, ApJ, 626, 128

Galactic Archaeology: Near-Field Cosmology and the Formation of the Milky Way
ASP Conference Series, Vol. 458
W. Aoki, M. Ishigaki, T. Suda, T. Tsujimoto, N. Arimoto, eds.
© *2012 Astronomical Society of the Pacific*

Distribution Function of the Milky Way Inner Halo

Kohei Hattori,[1] Yuzuru Yoshii,[1] Timothy C. Beers,[2,3] and Daniela Carollo[4,5]

[1]*Institute of Astronomy, School of Science, University of Tokyo, 2-21-1, Osawa, Mitaka, Tokyo 181-0015, Japan*

[2]*National Optical Astronomy Observatories, Tucson, AZ 85719, USA*

[3]*Department of Physics and Astronomy and JINA: Joint Institute for Nuclear Astrophysics, Michigan State University, E. Lansing, MI 48824, USA*

[4]*Macquarie University - Dept. Physics & Astronomy, Sydney, 2109 NSW, Australia*

[5]*INAF - Osservatorio Astronomico di Torino, 10025 Pino Torinese, Torino - Italy*

Abstract.   Rich information on the formation process of the Milky Way is contained in the distribution function (DF) of the stellar halo. Here, we show how solar-neighbour observations of halo stars can constrain the DF of stellar halo. We model the inner halo of the Milky Way with a new family of DF models. We find that DF models that satisfy *local* constraints such as the observed density slope and velocity dispersions at the solar neighbourhood would exhibit distinct marginal energy and eccentricity distributions, depending on the *global* nature of the DF. Comparison of our results with recent observation by SDSS suggests that the velocity dispersion of the inner halo is isotropic at the center of the Milky Way and it becomes highly radially-biased at large Galactocentric distance.

1. Generalized Anisotropic Polytropes with Central Anisotropy

The distribution function (DF) of a static, spherically-symmetric stellar system embedded in a spherical potential $V(r)$ can be always put in the form $f(E, L)$, where $E = v^2/2 + V(r)$ and $L = |r \times v|$ are the specific energy and angular momentum, respectively. In this presentation, we propose a new family of such distribution function models of the form

$$f(E, L) = K \mathcal{E}^{\nu - 3/2} \kappa^{-\beta_0} (1 + \kappa)^{\mu + \beta_0} \quad (\mathcal{E} > 0), \qquad (1)$$

where $\mathcal{E}$ is the specific binding energy; $\kappa \equiv L^2/(2r_a^2 \mathcal{E})$ is a dimensionless, auxiliary variable which measures the angular momentum; and K, ν, β_0, μ and r_a are constants.

In this model, the density and velocity moments can be expressed analytically, as can the velocity anisotropy parameter $\beta(r) = 1 - \sigma_\theta^2/\sigma_r^2$. We note that $\beta(r)$ varies monotonically from $\max\{\beta_0, -\nu + 1/2\}$ at $r \ll r_a$ to $\min\{1, -\mu\}$ at $r \gg r_a$.

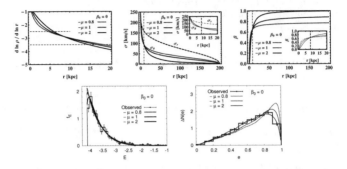

Figure 1.   *Upper panels*: Density slope ($d \ln \rho / d \ln r$), velocity dispersions (σ_r, σ_θ), and velocity anisotropy parameter (β) of our model distribution functions. With $(\nu, \beta_0, \beta_\odot) = (5, 0, 0.65)$ fixed, representative results for $-\mu = 0.8, 1$, and 2 are shown. *Lower panels*: Marginal distribution of energy (left) and eccentricity distribution (right) for these models. Also shown are re-derived observational data from SDSS.

2.   The Inner Halo Model: Comparison with Observation

We model the Milky Way potential by a singular isothermal potential with a flat rotation curve, and regard the inner halo of the Milky Way as an ensemble of test particles moving within this potential. For the inner halo DF, we use our model (1), adopting $\nu = 5$ to match the nearby observation of $\sigma_r \simeq 160$ km s^{-1} (Carollo et al. 2010, hereafter C10). Other *local* constraints such as $\beta_\odot \simeq 0.65$ and $d \ln \rho / d \ln r \simeq -3$ (C10) are also taken into account and we calculate the marginal energy distribution and eccentricity distribution for representative parameter sets of (β_0, μ, r_a).

We then compare our results with the recent observation by SDSS (C10). We select nearby stars (within 4 kpc from the sun) with $-2.0 <$[Fe/H]< -1.5 and 2 kpc $<$ $|z| < 4$ kpc, which is adequate for selecting likely inner halo stars (C10). Since the position and velocity of the sample stars in C10 are available, we determine E and L by assuming the above-mentioned model potential and *re-derive* the orbital eccentricity e.

We find that the marginal energy distribution and eccentricity distribution can discriminate several models that satisfy the same *local* constraints. For demonstration, we show some results for our models with $\beta_0 = 0$ in Figure 1. The best-fit model is that with $(\beta_0, -\mu) = (0, 2)$, and in this case β increases from zero (isotropic velocity distribution) at $r = 0$ to ~ 1 (radially-biased) at large r. This behaviour of velocity anisotropy matches well with numerical simulations in which the stellar halo experiences cold collapse and violent relaxation (e.g., Figure 3 of Voglis 1994), and therefore may indicate that the inner halo of the Milky Way have experienced such physical processes.

Acknowledgments.   KH is supported by JSPS Research Fellowship for Young Scientists (DC1 23·954). TCB acknowledges partial support for this work from PHY 02-16783 and PHY 08-22648: Physics Frontiers Center / JINA, awarded by the US NSF.

References

Carollo, D., Beers, T. C., Chiba, M., et al. 2010, ApJ, 712, 692 (C10)
Voglis, N. 1994, MNRAS, 267, 379

Galactic Archaeology: Near-Field Cosmology and the Formation of the Milky Way
ASP Conference Series, Vol. 458
W. Aoki, M. Ishigaki, T. Suda, T. Tsujimoto, N. Arimoto, eds.
©2012 Astronomical Society of the Pacific

Natures of Clump-Origin Bulges: Similarities to the Milky Way Bulge

Shigeki Inoue

Mullard Space Science Laboratory, University College London, Holmbury St. Mary, Dorking, Surrey, RH5 6NT, United Kingdom

Abstract. Bulges in spiral galaxies have been supposed to be classified into two types: classical bulges or pseudobulges. Classical bulges are thought to form by galactic merger with bursty star formation, whereas pseudobulges are suggested to form by secular evolution. Noguchi (1998, 1999) suggested another bulge formation scenario, 'clump-origin bulge'. He demonstrated using a numerical simulation that a galactic disc forms clumpy structures in the early stage of disc formation, then the clumps merge into a single bulge at the centre. I perform a high-resolution N-body/SPH simulation for the formation of the clump-origin bulge in an isolated galaxy model. I find that the clump-origin bulge resembles pseudobulges in dynamical properties, but this bulge consists of old and metal-rich stars. These natures, old metal-rich population but pseudobulge-like structures, mean that the clump-origin bulge can not be simply classified into classical bulges nor pseudobulges. From these results, I discuss similarities of the clump-origin bulge to the Milky Way (MW) bulge.

1. Introduction

Kormendy & Kennicutt (2004) has suggested that bulges in spiral galaxies can be classified into *classical bulges* or *pseudobulges*. Classical bulges are thought to form through galactic merger. Pseudobulges are discussed to form through secular evolution caused by non-axisymmetric structures in a galactic disc. Noguchi (1998, 1999) demonstrated that clumpy structures form due to gas instability, which could also explain some clumpy galaxies observed in the high-redshift Universe. These galaxies are referred to as clump clusters (chain galaxies). Noguchi (1998, 1999) suggested that these clumpy stellar structures fall into the galactic centre by dynamical friction and merge into a single bulge at the galactic centre, a clump-origin bulge. Clump-origin bulges form through '*mergers of the clumps*' in a galactic disc, neither the galactic merger nor the secular evolution. Therefore, properties of clump-origin bulges could be different from those of the conventional ones, classical bulges nor pseudobulges. I perform a similar numerical simulation to Noguchi (1998, 1999) using an isolated halo model by a N-body/SPH code and study the naive natures of clump-origin bulges in details.

2. Results

Our initial condition follows the spherical model that was used to study the formation of disc galaxies in an isolated environment. I assume an equilibrium system with the

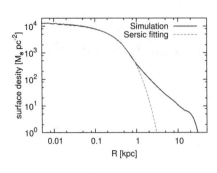

Figure 1.   Stellar surface density profile and a fitting by the Sérsic profile (left).
Stellar surface density maps in central 3×3 kpc region from the edge-on view (right).

NFW profile with a virial mass $M_{vir} = 5.0 \times 10^{11}$ $M_\odot$. Baryon mass fraction of the system is set to 0.06. The details of my simulation settings are given in Inoue & Saitoh (2011a,b).

In Fig. 1, I plot the azimathally averaged surface density and density map from the edge-on view. The fitting is given by the Sérsic index, $n = 1.18$ indicating a nearly exponential density profile. As seen from the central panel, it clearly appears that this bulge is a boxy bulge from the edge-on view. Furthermore, I find that this bulge shows a significant rotation with a value of $V_{max}/\sigma_0 \simeq 0.9$, the rotation (spin) is *not* negligible in kinematics. These are indicating pseudobulge signatures Kormendy & Kennicutt (2004).

However, I find that the clump-origin bulge consists of stars with an over-solar metallicity Inoue & Saitoh (2011b). Additionally, this bulge formation scenario, the clump cluster phase, is expected to happen only at the high-redshift. Therefore, the clump-origin bulge consists of old stars. Such old and metal-rich natures are better similar to classical bulges rather than pseudobugles Kormendy & Kennicutt (2004).

The MW bulge is also known to be an ambiguous bulge. The MW bulge shows a nearly exponential profile, an oblate peanut shape (X-shape) and a significant rotation, which are similar to pseudobulges. At the same time, the MW bulge is made of old and metal-rich stars, which are classical bulge signatures Kormendy & Kennicutt (2004). These properties of the MW bulge are consistent with the clump-origin bulge obtained in this study. Such unclassifiable bulges (old pseudobulge) are also observed in some other disc galaxies Bica & Alloin (1987). My simulation results imply that such old pseudobulges like the MW bulge may be a clump-origin bulge and the MW might use to be a clump cluster.

References

Bica, E., & Alloin, D. 1987, A&AS, 70, 281
Inoue, S., & Saitoh, T. R. 2011a, MNRAS, 418, 2527
— 2011b, preprint (astro-ph/1109.2898). 1109.2898
Kormendy, J., & Kennicutt, R. C., Jr. 2004, ARA&A, 42, 603
Noguchi, M. 1998, Nat, 392, 253
— 1999, ApJ, 514, 77

Galactic Archaeology: Near-Field Cosmology and the Formation of the Milky Way
ASP Conference Series, Vol. 458
W. Aoki, M. Ishigaki, T. Suda, T. Tsujimoto, N. Arimoto, eds.
© *2012 Astronomical Society of the Pacific*

Observational Properties of the Chemically Divided Galactic Disks

Young Sun Lee,[1] Timothy C. Beers,[2,3] Deokkeun An[4], and the SEGUE
Collaboration

[1]*Department of Physics & Astronomy and Joint Institute for Nuclear Astrophysics, Michigan State University, East Lansing, MI 48824, USA*

[2]*National Optical Astronomy Observatory, 950 North Cherry Avenue, Tucson, AZ 85719, USA*

[3]*Joint Institute for Nuclear Astrophysics, Michigan State University, East Lansing, MI 48824, USA*

[4]*Department of Science Education, Ewha Womans University, Seoul 120-750, Republic of Korea*

Abstract. We make use of $[\alpha/\mathrm{Fe}]$ ratios derived from the spectra of 17,277 SEGUE G dwarfs to separate them into likely thin- and thick-disk subsamples, and investigate the rotational velocity and eccentricity gradients with metallicity, $[\mathrm{Fe/H}]$, distance from the plane, $|Z|$, and Galactocentric distance, R, in order to provide observational constraints on contemporary models of the formation of the Milky Way's thick disk.

1. Introduction

The Milky Way's thick disk differs in its structure, kinematics, and chemical abundances from the thin disk. These discrepancies imply that the thick disk has experienced different formation and evolution history from the thin disk. The currently discussed mechanisms for thick-disk formation include the dynamical heating of a pre-exising thin disk by satellite mergers (e.g., Kazantzidis et al. 2008), accretion of satellite galaxies (e.g., Abadi et al. 2003), chaotic mergers of gas-rich systems (e.g., Brook e al. 2004), and the radial migration of stars (Sellwood & Binney 2002).

In this study, using $[\alpha/\mathrm{Fe}]$ ratios obtained for a large sample of low-resolution ($R \sim 2000$) spectra of G-type dwarf stars from the Sloan Extension for Galactic Understanding and Exploration (SEGUE; Yanny et al. 2009), we divide the sample into likely thin- and thick-disk populations, and explore the observed correlations of rotational velocity and orbital eccentricity with metallicity, Galactocentric distance, and distance from the Galactic plane, as well as the orbital eccentricity distributions for the individual populations in order to provide observational constraints on the formation models of the thick disk.

2. The SEGUE G-dwarf Sample

The SEGUE G-dwarf sample covers the color and magnitude range $0.48 < (g - r)_0 < 0.55$ and $r_0 < 20.2$. With information on the distances, radial velocities, and proper motions for the sample in hand, we derive the U, V, W space velocity components, rotational velocity, V_ϕ, Galactocentric distance projected onto the Galactic plane, R, and the vertical distance from the Galactic plane, $|Z|$. In addition, by adoption of an analytic Stäckel-type gravitational potential we compute r_{apo} (r_{peri}), the maximum (minimum) distance from the Galactic center that a star reaches during its orbit, as well as the orbital eccentricity, e. We next apply cuts of $d < 3$ kpc, $\log g \geq 4.2$, S/N ≥ 30 Å^{-1}, $V_\phi > +50$ km s^{-1}, [Fe/H] > -1.2, and $7 < R < 10$ kpc in order to select only dwarf stars with a greater probability of belonging to the disk system than to the halo. The surviving sample from the above conditions numbers $\sim$17,300 stars. This sample is further split into likely thin-disk stars with [α/Fe] $\lesssim 0.2$, and thick-disk stars with [α/Fe] $\gtrsim 0.3$.

3. Results

The thin-disk population exhibits a negative rotational velocity gradient with increasing [Fe/H] (-22.6 ± 1.6 km s^{-1} dex^{-1}), while the thick-disk population exhibits a positive slope ($+45.8 \pm 2.9$ km s^{-1} dex^{-1}). The distribution of V_ϕ appears independent of R for our thin-disk subsample, while there exists a very small correlation (-5.6 ± 1.1 km s^{-1} kpc^{-1}) between V_ϕ and R for the thick-disk subsample. We have found that the observed lag of V_ϕ for the high-[α/Fe] stars relative to the low-[α/Fe] population is quite constant at a given $|Z|$ distance (30 km s^{-1}). The vertical gradient of V_ϕ with $|Z|$ for our thick-disk subsample is -9.4 ± 1.3 km s^{-1} kpc^{-1}, while without application of our proposed separation of the thin- and thick-disk subsamples, we find a vertical gradient of -19.4 ± 1.8 km s^{-1} kpc^{-1} for the stars with $|Z| > 1.0$ kpc.

There is no correlation between orbital eccentricity and metallicity for the thin-disk subsample, while the trend of e for the thick-disk subsample steeply increases as the metallicity decreases. The e distribution for the low-[α/Fe] stars appears to be independent of R, whereas the high-[α/Fe] stars exhibit an increasing trend with distance from the Galactic center. As our approach of separating the thin-disk and thick-disk components by chemical tagging on their [α/Fe] abundance ratios yields well-defined, and distinct, kinematic trends for these populations, we emphasize that models of thick-disk formation can be strongly constrained by observations such as those presented here.

Acknowledgments. This work was supported in part by grants PHY 02-16783 and PHY 08-22648: Physics Frontiers Center/Joint Institute for Nuclear Astrophysics (JINA), awarded by the U.S. National Science Foundation.

References

Abadi, M. G., Navarro, J. F., Steinmetz, M. & Eke, V. R. 2003, ApJ, 597, 21
Brook, C. B., Kawata, D., Gibson, B. K., & Freeman, K. C. 2004, ApJ, 612, 894
Kazantzidis, S., Bullock, J. S., Zentner, A. R., Kravtsov, A. V., & Moustakas, L. A. 2008, ApJ, 688, 254
Sellwood, J. A., & Binney, J. J. 2002, MNRAS, 336, 785
Yanny, B., et al. 2009, AJ, 137, 4377

Galactic Archaeology: Near-Field Cosmology and the Formation of the Milky Way
ASP Conference Series, Vol. 458
W. Aoki, M. Ishigaki, T. Suda, T. Tsujimoto, N. Arimoto, eds.
© 2012 Astronomical Society of the Pacific

Cepheids as Tracers of the Galactic Structure and Evolution

Noriyuki Matsunaga

Kiso Observatory, The University of Tokyo, 10762-30 Mitake, Kiso, Nagano 397-0101, Japan

Abstract. In this contribution, first, we review how useful Cepheids are as tracers to study the structure and evolution of the Galaxy. Then, we discuss results of our survey towards the Galactic Centre, where we discovered three Cepheids for the first time.

1. Roles of Cepheids

Classical Cepheid variable stars are pulsating supergiants with periods in the range 1–100 days. They can play important roles in the Galactic archaeology as tracers:

- to study the Galactic structure,

- to study the kinematics of the Galaxy,

- to study the star formation history,

- to study the chemical evolution.

First of all, Cepheids follow the period-luminosity relation with which their distances can be accurately determined (Sandage & Tammann 2006). This allows us to trace the distribution of stars in the Galaxy. Then, their positions can be combined with the kinematic information, radial velocities and proper motions, to reproduce the kinematic structure of the Galaxy. For example, Feast et al. (1997) used the proper motions of the Cepheids in the solar neighbourhood, to investigate the Galactic rotation, whereas Nardetto et al. (2008) carefully derived the radial velocities of the nearby Cepheids to show that their velocities are consistent with the axisymmetric rotation model of the Galaxy. In addition, Cepheids follow the period-age relation (Bono et al. 2005), so that we can estimate ages of individual Cepheids based on their period. A period distribution of Cepheids may be transformed to star formation history of a stellar system (Alcock et al. 1999; Meschin et al. 2009). Finally, with their locations and ages derived, they are useful to investigate the chemical properties of stellar populations across the Galaxy (Pedicelli et al. 2009).

The above properties of the Cepheids make them very useful tracers of the Galactic structure and evolution. However, search for the Cepheids in our Galaxy is far from complete. Previously known Cepheids are limited to within a few kpc of the Sun, and the current samples are not enough to investigate the global structure of the Galaxy (for example, see Figure 7 in Majaess, Turner, & Lane, 2009). The main reason of this incompleteness is the interstellar extinction towards the Galactic disk, and infrared surveys can extend the frontier.

2. Cepheids in the Galactic nuclear bulge

We are conducting near-infrared monitoring surveys of Cepheids and other pulsating stars in a few regions towards the Galactic plane using the IRSF telescope and the SIR-IUS camera (Nagayama et al. 2003) located in South Africa (SAAO). These equipments can take images in three wavelengths, J (1.25 μm), H (1.63 μm), and K_s (2.14 μm), simultaneously, with a field of view of 7.7 arc-minute square. In the following, we present results of our survey of Cepheids towards the Galactic Centre.

Between 2001 and 2008, using the IRSF and SIRIUS, we observed $20'\times30'$ around the Galactic Centre for approximately 90 times. In 2009, we reported more than 1000 long-period variable stars including 143 Miras for which we determined the distances (Matsunaga et al. 2009). They are concentrated to the Galactic bulge, and their average distance, 8.24±0.42 kpc, agrees well with other estimates of the distance to the Galactic Centre (e.g. Gillessen et al. 2009). Recently, using the same dataset, we discovered three classical Cepheids as well as dozens of other short-period variables (Matsunaga et al. 2011). Their estimated distances agree with the distance to the Galactic Centre within the uncertainty, and they probably belong to the nuclear bulge, stellar population with a radius of ~ 200 pc around the Galactic Centre (Launhardt et al. 2002)).

All of the three Cepheids have periods ~ 20 days. According to the period-age relation (Bono et al. 2005), the Cepheids we discovered are 25 ± 5 Myr old. They give the first clear evidence of the star formation in the Galactic Centre a few tens of Myr ago. Furthermore, the absence of the shorter-period Cepheids indicates the change in star formation. Such a time variation may be related to stochastic gas infall into the central part of a galaxy. A change in such a time scale is in fact suggested by Stark et al. (2004).

Our results regarding the Cepheids in the nuclear bulge demonstrated the impacts of Cepheids on the study of the stellar population and evolution of the Galaxy. Future infrared surveys of variable stars like the VVV project with the VISTA telescope (Minniti et al. 2010) would certainly reveal richer populations of Cepheids and other variable stars in wider regions of the Galaxy. In addition, follow-up observations like spectroscopic and astrometric measurements, should provide us with useful information of the Galactic structure and evolution.

References

Alcock, C., et al. 1999, AJ, 117, 920
Bono, G., et al. 2005, ApJ, 621, 966
Feast, M. W., Whietlock, P. A., 1997, MNRAS, 291, 683
Gillessen, S., et al. 2009, ApJ, 692, 1075
Launhardt, R., Zylka, R., & Mezger, P. G., 2002, A&A, 384, 112
Majaess, D. J., Turner D. G., & Lane, D. J., 2009, MNRAS, 398, 263
Matsunaga, N., et al. 2009, MNRAS, 399, 1709
Matsunaga, N., et al. 2011, Nature, 477, 188
Meschin, L., et al. 2009, AJ, 137, 3619
Minniti, D., et al. 2010, New Astronomy, 15, 433
Nardetto, N., et al. 2008, A&A, 489, 1255
Nagayama, T., et al. 2003, Proc. SPIE, 4841, 459
Pedicelli S., et al. 2009, A&A, 504, 81
Sandage, A., Tammann G. A., 2006, ARA&A, 44, 93
Stark, A. A., et al. 2004, ApJ, 614, L41

Galactic Archaeology: Near-Field Cosmology and the Formation of the Milky Way
ASP Conference Series, Vol. 458
W. Aoki, M. Ishigaki, T. Suda, T. Tsujimoto, N. Arimoto, eds.
©*2012 Astronomical Society of the Pacific*

Near-Infrared Study of the X-ray Point Sources Constituting the Galactic Ridge X-ray Emission

Kumiko Morihana,[1,2] Masahiro Tsujimoto,[1] and Ken Ebisawa[1,2]

[1]*Japan Aerospace Exploration Agency, Institute of Space and Astronautical Science, 3-1-1 Yoshinodai, Chuo-ku, Sagamihara, Kanagawa, 252-5210, Japan*

[2]*Department of Astronomy, Graduate School of Science, The University of Tokyo, 7-3-1 Hongo, Bunkyo-ku, Tokyo, 113-0033, Japan*

Abstract. The Galactic Ridge X-ray Emission (GRXE) is an apparently extended emission along the Galactic Plane. Its origin has been a mystery for a long time. However, recent study revealed that about 80% of the GRXE is consist of dim X-ray point sources. It raises a new question, what are the populations of them? In this study, we identified X-ray point sources constituting the GRXE with near-infrared (NIR) and obtained NIR spectra. The spectra suggest that almost the sources are late-type stars.

1. Introduction

The Galactic Ridge X-ray Emission (GRXE: Worrall et al. 1982) is an apparently extended emission of low surface brightness along the inner part of the Galactic Plane (GP: $|l| < 45°$, $|b| < 1°$). The spectrum is described by a thermal plasma with the Fe $K\alpha$ lines. A long-standing debate for its origin has been whether it is a truly diffuse plasma (Ebisawa et al. 2005) or the sum of dim X-ray point sources (Revnivtsev et al. 2006). The *Chandra* satellite brought a revolution with its unprecedented spatial resolution of 0.6″ at the on-axis. The deepest X-ray observation (~900 ks) was performed at $l = 0.0°$, $b = -1.4°$ (hereafter, we call the Revnivtsev field: Revnivtsev et al. 2009). The authors revealed that ~80% of the GRXE around the Fe $K\alpha$ lines was resolved into point sources. This result raises a new question; what are the populations of these point sources? We study the populations by X-ray and near-infrared (NIR) observations.

2. Observations

We extracted 2,002 X-ray sources in the *Chandra* archive data (~900 ks) of the Revnivtsev field (Figure 1 left) and made an X-ray source list. To identify them in NIR, we performed NIR observations in the same field using the Simultaneous three-color InfraRed Imager for Unbiased Surveys (SIRIUS; Nagayama et al. 2003) at the Infrared Survey Facility telescope. We obtained J, H, and K_s images in photometric nights with a typical seeing of 1.2″. We made a list of NIR identified X-ray sources (details in later). Then, we performed NIR spectroscopic observations with Subaru/MOIRCS K_s band for the NIR identified sources.

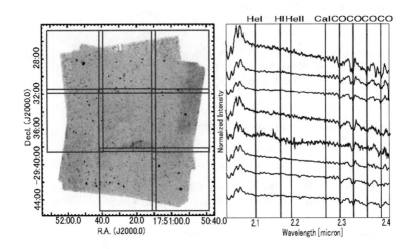

Figure 1.   (Left) Smoothed X-ray image of the Revnivtsev field (0.5–8 keV). The field of views of the SIRIUS observations are in red squares. (Right) Sample NIR K_s band spectra of NIR identified X-ray sources. The top label shows identifications of features.

3. Analysis and Results

We extracted 52,312 (J), 61,188 (H), and 65,061 (K_s) NIR sources down to $K_s \sim 16$ mag (3σ level) on the SIRIUS images. After that, we made a NIR source list including positions and J-, H-, and K_s-colors. For the astrometry and the photometry calibrations, we used 2MASS sources in the same fields. We searched for NIR counterparts for X-ray point sources within 1.2″ of each X-ray source. We recognized 222 X-ray sources (2MASS; 6 sources, SIRIUS; 216 sources) to have NIR counterpart within 1 σ circle ($\sim$12% of all X-ray sources). We obtained 33 NIR spectra of them (Figure 1 Right). There are two types of spectra: (1) HI and CO absorption, (2) CO absorption. The formers are considered to be G- or K-type stars and the latter are considered to be M-type stars. The number of type (1) and (2) sources are almost equal.

References

Ebisawa, K., Tsujimoto, M., Paizis, A., Hamaguchi, K., Bamba, A., Cutri, R., Kaneda, H., Maeda, Y., Sato, G., Senda, A., Ueno, M., Yamauchi, S., Beckmann, V., Courvoisier, T. J.-L., Dubath, P., & Nishihara, E. 2005, ApJ, 635, 214

Nagayama, T., Nagashima, C., Nakajima, Y., Nagata, T., Sato, S., Nakaya, H., Yamamuro, T., Sugitani, K., & Tamura, M. 2003, in Society of Photo-Optical Instrumentation Engineers (SPIE) Conference Series

Revnivtsev, M., Churazov, E., Postnov, K., & Tsygankov, S. 2009, A&A, 507, 1211

Revnivtsev, M., Sazonov, S., Gilfanov, M., Churazov, E., & Sunyaev, R. 2006, A&A, 452, 169

Worrall, D. M., Marshall, F. E., Boldt, E. A., & Swank, J. H. 1982, ApJ, 255, 111

Galactic Archaeology: Near-Field Cosmology and the Formation of the Milky Way
ASP Conference Series, Vol. 458
W. Aoki, M. Ishigaki, T. Suda, T. Tsujimoto, N. Arimoto, eds.
©2012 Astronomical Society of the Pacific

Chemical Tagging of Kinematic Stellar Groups in the Milky Way Disk

B. Nordström,[1] E. Stonkutė,[2] G. Tautvaišienė,[2] and R. Ženovienė[2]

[1]*Niels Bohr Institute, Juliane Maries Vej 30, DK-2100 Copenhagen, Denmark*

[2]*Institute of Theoretical Physics and Astronomy (ITPA), Vilnius University, A. Goštauto 12, LT-01108 Vilnius, Lithuania*

Abstract. We present a progress report on a chemical abundance analysis of two kinematic stellar groups in the Galactic disk, suspected to be relics of disrupted satellites. Their origin remains an open question, but chemical tagging is providing new clues.

Summary of Results

Helmi et al. (2006) searched for evidence of past accretion events in the large, homogeneous sample of F- and G-type dwarfs of the Geneva-Copenhagen Survey of the Solar Neighbourhood (Nordström et al. 2004, GCS). Numerical simulations were used to identify possible concentrations of debris from disrupted satellites in a variety of diagnostic diagrams.

Stars from a common origin should show distinct correlations between their orbital parameters, in particular between their vertical angular momentum vector (L_z) and the apo- and peri-galactoentric distances (A, P). In APL space, such stars are expected to cluster in regions of roughly constant eccentricity. Thus, the kinematic selection criterion used in this work is very different from the standard technique for selecting thick disk stars directly from their velocities.

Several kinematic groups of stars were identified in the GCS with this method. In order to look for signatures of a common origin in their chemical properties, we have selected stars in two such groups and observed them with the Nordic Optical Telescope (NOT) and its high resolution spectrograph FIES.

We find that the elements O, Ca, Mg, Ti, Si and Eu are overabundant in both groups as compared to normal dwarf stars, and briefly discuss the similarities in chemical composition between our stars and typical thick disk stars. The origin of these kinematically selected groups of stars remains an open question.

A more detailed paper has been submitted for publication in A&A.

Acknowledgments. This work is based on observations made with the Nordic Optical Telescope, operated on the island of La Palma jointly by Denmark, Finland, Iceland, Norway, and Sweden, in the Spanish Observatorio del Roque de los Muchachos of the Instituto de Astrofisica de Canarias. BN acknowledges financial support from the Danish Natural Science Foundation. This research has made use of the Simbad, VALD and NASA ADS databases.

References

Helmi et al. 2006, MNRAS 365, 1309
Nordström et al., 2004, A&A 418, 989

Galactic Archaeology: Near-Field Cosmology and the Formation of the Milky Way
ASP Conference Series, Vol. 458
W. Aoki, M. Ishigaki, T. Suda, T. Tsujimoto, N. Arimoto, eds.
©*2012 Astronomical Society of the Pacific*

UV Bright Stars in Globular Clusters

M. Parthasarathy,[1] G. Jasniewicz,[2] W. Aoki[1] and Y. Takeda[1]

[1]*National Astronomical Observatory of Japan 2-21-1 Osawa, Mitaka, Tokyo 181-8588 Japan*

[2]*LUPM UMR 5299 CNRS/UM2, Universite Montpellier II, CC 72, 34095 Montpellier Cedex 05, France*

Abstract.   Some aspects of UV bright stars in globular clusters and their chemical composition is discussed.

1.   Introduction

The term "UV-bright stars" was introduced by Zinn et al. (1972) (ZNG) for stars in globular clusters that lie above the horizontal branch (HB) and are bluer than red giants. The name resulted from the fact that, in the U band, these stars were brighter than all other cluster stars. Further studies showed that this group of stars consist of blue horizontal branch (BHB) stars, supra horizontal branch stars (SHB), EHB stars, post-HB stars, post asymptotic giant branch stars (post-AGB), post-early AGB (P-EAGB) stars and AGB-manque stars (Moehler 2010, and references therein). A list of UV-bright stars in globular clusters can be found in Zinn et al. (1972) and Harris et al. (1983). UIT satellite, HST and GALEX survey of globular clusters in the far UV has revealed many new hot UV bright stars. Earlier to 2003 only four UV-bright stars had detailed chemical composition study based on high resolution spectra : Barnard 29 in M 13 (Conlon et al. 1994; Moehler et al. 1998a), ROA 24 in ω Cen (Gonzalez and Wallerstein 1992), ROA 5701 in ω Cen (Moehler et al. 1998a) and ZNG 1 in M 10 (Mooney et al. 2001). To this list we can add the planetary nebulae K 648 in M 15 and IRAS 18333-2357 in M 22. These studies indicate that some UV bright stars show evidence for third dredge-up and overabundance of carbon and s-process elements, while others show severe carbon deficiency, indicating that they left the AGB before the third dredge-up occured.

2.   Observations

There seems to be significant variations in the abundance patterns, luminosities and evolutionary stages of UV bright stars in globular clusters. In order to further understand the chemical composition patterns and evolutionary stages of UV bright stars we obtained high resolution (45,000 and 40,000) spectra of several UV bright stars. Spectra of UV bright stars in northern globular clusters were obtained with Subaru/HDS and VLT/UVES for UV bright stars in southern globular clusters. We selected the UV bright stars from the lists of Zinn et al. (1972) and Harris et al. (1983).

3. Results and discussion

Ambika et al. (2004) made a detailed model-atmosphere analysis of UV bright star ZNG 4 in M 13. Except for Mg, Cr and Sr, all other even Z elements are enhanced with Ti and Ca being overabundant by a factor of 0.8 dex. Na is enhanced by a factor of 0.2 dex. The luminosity of ZNG 4 and its position in the color-magnitude diagram of M 13 indicate that it is a SHB (post-HB) star. The underabundance of He and overabundance of Ca, Ti, Sc, and Ba in the photosphere of ZNG 4 indicate that diffusion and radiative levitation of elements may be in operation in M 13 post-HB stars even at effective temperature of 8500 K. Detailed abundance analysis of post-HB stars in several globular clusters is needed to further understand their abundance anomalies.

Jasniewicz et al. (2004) derived the chemical composition of nine UV bright stars belonging to five southern globular clusters with [Fe/H] ranging from −1.0 to −2.4 dex. The UV bright star ID 7 in NGC 5986 (Alves et al. 2001) is found to be a post-AGB star, whereas ID 6 has left the AGB before the third dredge-up. ZNG 1 in NGC 6712 shows overabudance of Na, O and Si similar to that found in ID 6 in NGC 5986. V-4 and ZNG 5 in NGC 6656 are in post-HB phase of evolution, with V-4 in NGC 6656 being significantly overabundant in heavy elements (Sr, Zr, Ba). The three UV bright stars K 260, K 996 and K 1082 in NGC 7078 are post-HB stars. The abundance pattern of K 1082 in NGC 7078 seems to indicate the presence of mild diffusion and radiative levitation process similar to that found in ZNG 4 in M 13 (Ambika et al. 2004) and in blue HB stars of M13 and NGC 6752 (Moehler et al. 1999).

Thompson et al. (2006) made a non-LTE abundance analysis of the post-AGB star ROA 5701 in ω Cen. From the observed abundance pattern they conclude that ROA 5701 has evolved off the AGB prior to the onset of third dredge-up. Mooney et al. (2004) analysed high resolution spectra of three UV bright stars ZNG 1 in M 10, ZNG 1 in M 15 and ZNG 1 in NGC 6712. The derived atmospheric parameters and chemical composition confirm that all the three stars are in post-AGB phase of evolution. They find that ZNG 1 in M 10 and ZNG 1 in M 15 may have evolved off the AGB before the third dredge-up occurred similar to ZNG 1 in NGC 6712 (Jasniewicz et al. 2004). Dixon et al. (2004) find ZNG 1 in M 5 to be hydrogen-poor hot post-AGB star which may have undergone late shell flash. The rapid rotation of the star may be the result of interaction with a binary companion and or merger. Moehler et al. (1998b) find that among the seven UIT-selected UV bright stars in four globular clusters, three are post-early AGB stars and four are post-EHB stars, but no genuine post-AGB stars.

In the context of UV bright stars it is worth mentioning that there are only four planetary nebulae (PNe) in more than 100 and odd globular clusters of our Galaxy K 648 in M 15, IRAS 18333-2357 in M 22, JaFu1 in Pal 6 and JaFu2 in NGC 6441 (Jacoby et al. 1997). The PNe K 648 in M 15 and IRAS 18333-2357 in M 22 are relatively well studied. PNe in globular clusters are not expected from the single star evolution of low mass metal-poor population II stars which are 12 to 14 billion years old. Clearly the four PNe in globular clusters are the result of merger events of close binary stars. The carbon and s-process element rich post-AGB star ROA 24 in ω Cen also may be the result of close-binary merger event. ROA 24 may evolve into a PN.

Some of the UV bright stars which are in post-AGB evolutionary stage may also be the result of merger events and subsequent evolution.

Another class of hot UV bright stars are the "blue hook" stars. Moehler et al. (2004, 2007) made spectroscopic analyses of blue hook stars in NGC 2808 and ω Cen. The UV observations of NGC 2808 by Brown et al. (2001) revealed the presence of large population of blue hook stars in NGC 2808. Such stars are being found in the UV surveys of several other globular clusters. The evolutionary stage of blue hook stars cannot be explained by normal stellar evolutionary models of low mass stars. Moehler et al. (2007) conclude that there is a strong support for the late hot flasher scenario as the explanation for the blue hook stars based on their study of these stars in NGC 2808 and ω Cen. However, this does not rule out the helium enhancement scenario on the basis of helium and carbon abundances of very hot blue hook stars. The evolutionary processes that lead to the formation of these UV bright blue hook stars is far from clear.

From the GALEX data for 44 globular clusters Schiavon et al. (2012) find many new AGB-manque stars and post early-AGB stars. Detailed chemical composition analysis of these stars is needed in order to understand their abundance patterns , peculiarities and evolutionary stage.

Note : - In Tables 4 and 5 in Jasniewicz et al. (2004) the corrections are : in Table 4 the correct values of L/L$\odot$ for NGC 6656 V-4 is 275 and for NGC 6656 ZNG 5 it is 210 and, in Table 5 the He I abundance given for NGC 5986 ID 6 and ID 7 is a typing mistake. He I abundance was not derived for these two stars.

Acknowledgments. MP is thankful to Prof. Shoken Miyama for his kind support, encouragement and hospitality.

References

Alves, D.R., Bond, H.E., & Onken, C., 2001, AJ, 121, 318
Ambika, S., Parthasarathy, M., Aoki, W. et al. 2004, A&A, 417, 293
Brown, T.M., Sweigart, A.V., Lanz, T., et al. 2001, ApJ, 562, 368
Conlon, E.S., Dufton, P.L., & Keenan, F.P., 1994, A&A, 290, 897
Dixon, W.V., Brown, T.M., & Landsman, W.B., 2004, ApJ, 600, L43
Gonzalez, G., & Wallerstein, G., 1992, MNRAS, 254, 343
Harris, H.C., Nemec, J.M., & Hesser, J.E., 1983, PASP, 95, 256
Jacoby, G.H., et al. 1997, AJ, 114, 2611
Jasniewicz, G., de Laverny, P., Parthasarathy, M., et al. 2004, A&A, 423, 353
Moehler, S., et al. 1998a, A&A, 339, 537
Moehler, S., Landsman, W., & Napiwotzki, R., 1998b, A&A, 335, 510
Moehler, S., Sweigart, A.V., Landsman, W.B.,et al. 1999, A&A, 346, L1
Moehler, S., Sweigart, A.V., Landsman, W.B., et al. 2004, A&A, 415, 313
Moehler, S., Dreizler, S., Lanz, T., et al., 2007, A&A, 475, L5
Moehler, S., 2010, Mem. S. A. It. 81, 838
Mooney, C.J., et al. 2001, MNRAS, 326, 1101
Mooney, C.J., et al., 2004, A&A, 419, 1123
Schiavon, R., et al. 2012, arXiv 1201.5377
Thompson, H.M.A., et al. 2006, MNRAS, 368, 1749
Zinn, R.J., Newell, E.B., & Gibson, J.B., 1972, A&A, 18, 390

Excursion to the Shuzenji temple in the evening of November 3rd.

Galactic Archaeology: Near-Field Cosmology and the Formation of the Milky Way
ASP Conference Series, Vol. 458
W. Aoki, M. Ishigaki, T. Suda, T. Tsujimoto, N. Arimoto, eds.
©2012 Astronomical Society of the Pacific

Metallicity Gradients in Simulated Disk Galaxies

Kate Pilkington[1,2,3] and Brad K. Gibson[1,2,3]

[1]*Jeremiah Horrocks Institute, UCLan, Preston, PR1 2HE, UK*

[2]*Monash Centre for Astrophysics, Monash Univ, Clayton, 3800, Australia*

[3]*Dept of Physics & Astronomy, Saint Mary's Univ, Halifax, B3H 3C3, Canada*

Abstract. The stellar metallicity and abundance ratio gradients from the fiducial late-type galaxy simulation of Stinson et al. (2010) are presented. Over ~ 1–3 scalelengths, gradients are shown to flatten with time, consistent with empirical evidence at high- and low-redshifts. Kinematic effects, including radial migration, though, flatten these intrinsicly steep gradients such that by redshift z=0, the measured gradients of these (now) old stars are flatter than their young counterparts, in contradiction to what is observed locally. Conversely, the stellar [O/Fe] gradient is (to first order) robust against migration, remaining fairly flat for both young and old populations today.

1. Radial Gradients

We examine the abundance gradients for 25 cosmological simulations and 2 Milky Way chemical evolution models, to quantify the impact of hydrodynamic algorithms (e.g. SPH vs AMR), star formation thresholds, and energy feedback, in establishing gradients within the inside-out paradigm of galaxy formation (Pilkington et al. 2012).

We extend our work, using the fiducial disk (g15784) from Stinson et al. (2010), to determine its abundance *ratio* gradient. Disk stars are identified by applying the Abadi et al. (2003) kinematic decomposition; the disk scalelength is ~ 3 kpc. Its star formation history, inferred from the kinematically-defined component, is shown in Fig 1. The late-time behaviour can be characterised by an exponential declining with an ~ 7 Gyr timescale to a present-day rate of ~ 1–2 M$_\odot$/yr, consistent with the Milky Way.

In the middle and right panels of Fig 1, the radial [O/Fe] and [Fe/H] gradients are shown for young stars at three redshifts (z=0.0 (plus), 0.5 (diamonds), and 1.0 (triangles)), where, by 'young', we mean those corresponding to OB-stars at these redshifts. At early epochs, the recently-formed stars show steeper [O/Fe] and (especially) [Fe/H] gradients; for the latter, young stars at high-z show an [Fe/H] gradient of -0.08 dex/kpc, compared with the young stars at z=0 (which show -0.04 dex/kpc). As shown by (Pilkington et al. 2012), this is consistent with the *direct* measure of steeper gas-phase gradients high-z by Yuan et al. (2011), as well as the *indirect* measure of steeper gradients at early times *inferred* from the steeper gradients of older planetary nebulae (Maciel et al. 2003) and open cluster and field star giants (Yong et al. 2006), relative to younger tracers.

This latter conclusion merits further discussion; specifically, when the same star particles are viewed today (mimicing in a *direct* sense the manner in which Maciel et al. (2003) and Yong et al. (2006) inferred the above conclusions regarding early-time gradients from present-day data) - i.e., via the classification of 'old' vs 'young' star at

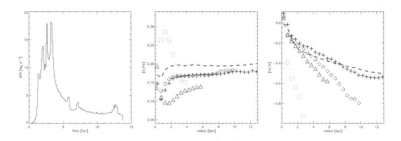

Figure 1.   *Left*: Star formation history of the kinematically-defined disk of
g15784; *Middle*: Radial [O/Fe] gradients for the young (born in the most recent
0.1 Gyr) disk stars at three redshifts: $z=0.0$ (plus symbols); $z=0.5$ (diamonds); $z=1.0$
(triangles). Right: Radial [Fe/H] gradients for the same 'young' stars at the same
three redshifts (symbols as for the middle panel). The dashed curve in the latter
panels is the mass-weighted gradient using all stars born since $z=2$.

$z=0$, one finds the apparent opposite conclusion (that old tracers today possess shallower abundance gradients than young tracers, similar to what was found by Sánchez-
Blázquez et al. (2009)). This apparent discrepancy is a reflection of the fact that the
older (steeper [Fe/H] gradient) star particles have preferentially migrated/scattered to
larger galactocentric distances, relative to the younger star particles (shallower [Fe/H]
gradients). Binned to match Maciel et al. (2003), we find that 6–9 Gyr old stars show
a flattening in their gradient by $z=0$ of ~0.05 dex/kpc, inverting the situation shown in
Fig 1 such that old stars in the simulations have shallower gradients than the younger
stars. Importantly, this does not impact on gas-phase abundance gradient analyses.

Interpreting the stellar [O/Fe] gradients is less complicated by these migrations;
since $z\sim1.0$, stars are born with mildly inverted (but essentially flat) [O/Fe] gradients
(with gradients <+0.005 dex/kpc). At $z\sim2$, the compact disk is apparent (middle panel
of Fig 1); the α-enhanced disk stars in the inner ~2.5 kpc, *by redshift $z\sim0$*, are radially
distributed (via migration/kinematic heating) throughout the disk, yielding (again) very
flat [O/Fe] gradients over ~1–3 disk scalelengths. Over the same radial range, these flat
gradients are consistent with those observed in nearby disk galaxies (Sánchez-Blázquez
et al. 2011) and in the Milky Way (Yong et al. 2006).

Acknowledgments.   We acknowledge the support of the UK's STFC and the financial assictance of Monash and Saint Mary's University, and the Organizing Committee
of the 3rd Subaru International Conference on Galactic Archaeology.

References

Abadi, M. G., Navarro, J. F., Steinmetz, M., & Eke, V. R. 2003, ApJ, 591, 499
Maciel, W. J., Costa, R. D. D., & Uchida, M. M. M. 2003, A&A, 397, 667
Pilkington, K., Gibson, B., et al. 2012, A&A, submitted
Sánchez-Blázquez, P., Courty, S., Gibson, B. K., & Brook, C. B. 2009, MNRAS, 398, 591
Sánchez-Blázquez, P., Ocvirk, P., Gibson, B. K., et al. 2011, MNRAS, 415, 709
Stinson, G. S., Bailin, J., et al. 2010, MNRAS, 408, 812
Yong, D., Carney, B. W., Teixera de Almeida, M. L., & Pohl, B. L. 2006, AJ, 131, 2256
Yuan, T.-T., Kewley, L. J., Swinbank, A. M., Richard, J., & Livermore, R. C. 2011, ApJ, 732,
      L14

Galactic Archaeology: Near-Field Cosmology and the Formation of the Milky Way
ASP Conference Series, Vol. 458
W. Aoki, M. Ishigaki, T. Suda, T. Tsujimoto, N. Arimoto, eds.
© 2012 Astronomical Society of the Pacific

Measurement of a Rotation Velocity of the Outer Galaxy with VERA: Mass Distribution of the Galaxy

Nobuyuki Sakai,[1] Mareki Honma,[1,2] Hiroyuki Nakanishi,[3] Hirofumi Sakanoue,[3] Tomoharu Kurayama,[3] and VERA project member

[1] *The Graduate University for Advanced Studies (Sokendai), Mitaka, Tokyo, 181-8588, Japan*

[2] *Mizusawa VLBI Observatory, NAOJ, Mitaka, Tokyo 181-8588*

[3] *Faculty of Science, Kagoshima University, 1-21-35 Korimoto, Kagoshima, Kagoshima 890-0065*

Abstract. We report measurement of trigonometric parallax of IRAS 05168+3634 with VERA. The parallax is 0.532 ± 0.053 mas, corresponding to a distance of $1.88^{+0.21}_{-0.17}$ kpc. This result is significantly smaller than the previous distance estimate based on kinematic distance, being 6 kpc. This drastic change in the source distance revises location of the source, placing it in the Perseus arm rather than the Outer arm. We also measure the proper motions of the source. Combination of the distance and the proper motions with the systemic velocity yields rotation velocity (Θ) of 227^{+9}_{-11} km s^{-1} at the source ($\Theta_0 = 240$ km s^{-1} assumed). This indicates that a part of the outer rotation at Galacto-centric distance of ~ 10 kpc is smaller than the galactic rotation at the LSR, which is consistent with previous VERA and VLBA results. The lower rotation velocity may be caused in inner edge of the Perseus arm where shock front predicted by the density-wave theory occurs.

1. Introduction

Rotation curve (RC) can be used to estimate mass for spiral galaxies. It revealed that many of external spiral galaxies have a flat rotation curve beyond optical disk, indicating existence of large amount of the dark matter for the galaxies. In contrast, the RC of the Milky Way (MW) has been unclear due to difficulty of distance measurement since we are in the MW. Today, well developed interferometer technique in radio wave length can be used to conduct galactic astrometry over kilo-parsec scale (e.g. VERA, VLBA). In order to construct the RC of the MW at outer region with high accuracy, we have been observing galactic objects emitting H_2O maser radiation with VERA. In this paper, we report one of our observation results with VERA for IRAS 05168+3634.

2. Results & Discussion

Eleven VLBI observations with VERA between 2009 October and 2011 May led parallax of 0.532 ± 0.053 mas, corresponding to a distance of $1.88^{+0.21}_{-0.17}$ kpc for IRAS 05168+3634.

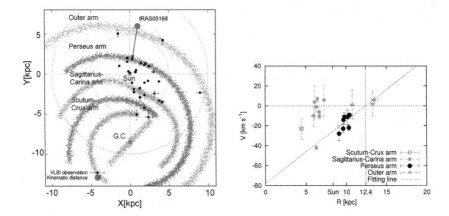

Figure 1.   (Left) Positions of IRAS 05168+3634 in discrete two methods. Big circle represents kinematic distance, while small ones show VLBI previous results including our result. These results are superposed on the galactic face-on image (Georgelin & Georgelin 1976). (Right) The peculiar motion toward the galactic rotation (V) is shown as function of the galacto-centric distance (R). Open square (the Scutum-Crux arm), filled square (the Sagittarius-Carina arm), filled circle (the Perseus arm), and open triangle (the Outer arm) represent V values obtained with VLBI, respectively. Dotted line was fitted to both the Perseus arm and the Outer arm sources. The intersection between zero value of V and the fitted line represents R of 12.4 kpc.

This is significantly smaller than the kinematic distance of ~6kpc (Molinari et al. 1996). By adapting our distance measurement, the source is placed in the Perseus arm rather than the Outer arm (see fig. 1). We also measured the proper motions of $(\mu_\alpha \cos\delta, \mu_\delta)$=(0.23± 1.07, −3.14± 0.28) mas yr^{-1} for the source. Combination of the distance and the proper motions with the systemic velocity yields rotation velocity (Θ) of $227\pm^9_{11}$ km s^{-1} at the source (Θ_0=240 km s^{-1} and R_0=8.33 kpc were assumed). The right panel of figure 1 shows the peculiar motion toward the galactic rotation (V) as a function of the galacto-centric distance for 20 sources with accurate VLBI astrometry observations. Note that the rotation model was assumed to be flat. Russeil et al. 2007 showed negative V values in the Perseus arm and positive V values in the Outer arm from optical observations, which is consistent with the VLBI observations. These peculiar motions may be explained by the density-wave theory if the co-rotation is existed between the Perseus arm and the Outer arm (e.g. Mel'Nik et al. 1999). However, the peculiar motion toward the galactic center (U) observed with VLBI so far can not be explained by placing the co-rotation between the two arms. More observations are necessary to confirm whether the density-wave theory can explain the peculiar motions of both U and V simultaneously or not.

References

Georgelin, Y. M. & Georgelin, Y. P. 1976, A&A, 49, 57
Mel'Nik, A. M., Dambis, A. K., & Rastorguev, A. S. 1999, Astron. Lett., 25, 518
Molinari, S., Brand, J., & Cesaroni, R., & Palla, F. 1996, A&A, 308, 573
Russeil, D., Adami, C., & Georgelin, Y. M. 2007, A&A, 470, 161

Galactic Archaeology: Near-Field Cosmology and the Formation of the Milky Way
ASP Conference Series, Vol. 458
W. Aoki, M. Ishigaki, T. Suda, T. Tsujimoto, N. Arimoto, eds.
© *2012 Astronomical Society of the Pacific*

Stellar Streams Traced by the Mira Variable Stars in the Galactic Halo

T. Sakamoto,[1] N. Matsunaga,[2] T. Hasegawa,[3] and Y. Nakada[2]

[1] *Japan Spaceguard Association, 1716-3, Ookura, Bisei, Ibara, Okayama 714-1411, Japan*

[2] *Kiso Observatory, Institute of Astronomy, School of Science, University of Tokyo, 10762-30, Mitake, Kiso-machi, Kiso-gun, Nagano 397-0101, Japan*

[3] *Gunma Astronomical Obseratory, 6860-86, Nakayama, Takayama, Agatsuma, Gunma 377-0702, Japan*

Abstract. We present the spatial distribution of the Mira variable stars (Miras) in the Galactic halo up to 100 kpc. We make a sample of 196 red stars in the Galactic latitudes $b > 30°$, and perform repeated observations over 3 years by 105-cm telescope at Kiso Observatory. We discover 16 Mira variable stars. We find that many of these Miras are located near the Sagittarius (Sgr) stream, as opposed to the spatially unbiased sample. We also detect one or two Miras toward the metal-poor Sextans dSph.

1. Introduction

Old stellar populations ($\sim$ 13 Gyr) are dominant in the Galactic halo, and they elucidate that the halo have many large-scale stellar streams like the Sgr streams (e.g., Yanny et al. 2000). In contrast, the intermediate-age (1-10 Gyr) stars are minor population in the halo, and their spatial distribution still remains unclear. Mira variable stars are one of luminous intermediate-age populations, and their period-luminosity relation provides relatively accurate distance estimate (e.g., Ita & Matsunaga 2011). Thus, we explore the Miras in the halo, and determine the 3-D spatial distribution of the intermediate-age population.

2. Our targets

The first targets are selected using $J - H > 0.7$, $H - K_s > 0.3$ on the 2MASS catalog and $g - r > 0.8$, $r - i > 0.3$ on the SDSS catalog in the Galactic latitudes $b > 30°$. The second target was one of the stars that show large photometric variation in the QUEST1 (QUasar Equatorial Survey Team, Phase 1) variability survey (Rengstorf et al. 2009). We perform repeated observations of 223 targets over 3 years in I_c -band by 105-cm telescope at Kiso Observatory.

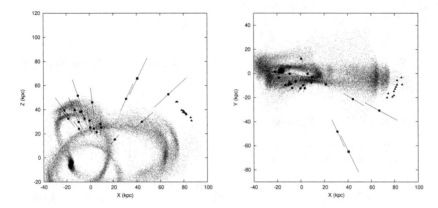

Figure 1.   Spatial distribution for our Miras. Filled circles denote Miras that have the amplitude $\Delta I_c > 1.0$ whereas a filled square show a long-period and relatively small amplitude ($\Delta I_c = 0.8$) star. Filled triangles and small dots show the Sgr stream at 90 kpc and that predicted by Law et al. (2005).

3. Results

We detect 16 Miras with periods longer than 100 days and the I_c amplitude, $\Delta I_c > 1.0$. Fig.1 shows the spatial distiribution of the Miras. We find that although the monitoring targets are unbiased to the regions of the known stellar streams, many of them are located near the known Sgr stream in $X < 20$ kpc. We also detect one Mira and a long-period, relatively small amplitude ($\Delta I_c = 0.8$) star toward the metal-poor Sextans dSph ([Fe/H] ~ -2.0). The distances and radial velocities support that they are associated with the Sextans dSph. In addition, one Mira is detected near the Sgr stream discovered at 90 kpc (Newberg et al. 2003).

References

Ita, Y. & Matsunaga, N. 2011, MNRAS, 412, 2345
Law, D. R., Johnston, K. V., & Majewski, S. R. 2005, ApJ, 619, 807
Newberg, H. J., et al. 2003, ApJ, 596, L191
Rengstorf, A. W., et al. 2009, ApJS, 181, 129
Yanny, B, et al. 2000, ApJ, 540, 825

Galactic Archaeology: Near-Field Cosmology and the Formation of the Milky Way
ASP Conference Series, Vol. 458
W. Aoki, M. Ishigaki, T. Suda, T. Tsujimoto, N. Arimoto, eds.
©*2012 Astronomical Society of the Pacific*

Detailed Chemical Abundances of Four Stars in the Unusual Globular Cluster, Palomar 1

Charli M. Sakari,[1] Kim A. Venn,[1] Mike Irwin,[2] Wako Aoki,[3,4]
Nobuo Arimoto,[3,4] and Aaron Dotter[5]

[1]*Department of Physics and Astronomy, University of Victoria, Victoria, BC V8W 3P2, Canada*

[2]*Institute of Astronomy, University of Cambridge, Madingley Road, Cambridge CB3 0HA, UK*

[3]*National Astronomical Observatory of Japan, Mitaka, Tokyo 181-8588, Japan*

[4]*Department of Astronomical Science, The Graduate University for Advanced Studies, Mitaka, Tokyo 181-8588, Japan*

[5]*Space Telescope Science Institute, Baltimore, MD 21218, USA*

Abstract. Chemical abundances for twenty one elements are presented for four red giants in the anomalous outer halo globular cluster Palomar 1. The mean metallicity, [Fe/H] = -0.60 ± 0.01, is high for a globular cluster so far from the Galactic center. In addition, its [α/Fe] and neutron capture abundances seem to indicate an origin in a dwarf galaxy, although it is not definitively associated with any known streams.

1. Introduction

Palomar 1 is typically classified as a globular cluster (GC). It is located in the Milky Way's outer halo (R_{GC} = 17.2 kpc, Z = 3.6 kpc; Harris 1996), which implies that it is a GC. However, it is an unusual GC, primarily because it is sparse and poorly populated. Still, it is more concentrated than a typical open cluster (c = 2.57; Harris 1996), it is young for a GC (5 ± 1 Gyr; Sarajedini et al. 2007), and its calcium-triplet measurements imply a high metallicity for an outer-halo GC ([Fe/H] = -0.6; Rosenberg et al. 1998). We investigate two possibilities for why Pal 1 could be unusual. Pal 1 could be an open cluster rather than a GC. Alternatively, Pal 1 could be an extragalactic cluster that was accreted by the Milky Way. To investigate Pal 1's origin, high resolution spectra (R = 36,000) of four stars were taken at the Subaru Telescope.

2. Results

Figure 1 shows Pal 1's abundances compared to stars in other galaxies. The left panel shows α-elements; Pal 1's low [α/Fe] values imply that it formed in a galaxy where SNe Ia began to contribute at a lower [Fe/H] than in the Milky Way. The right panel shows

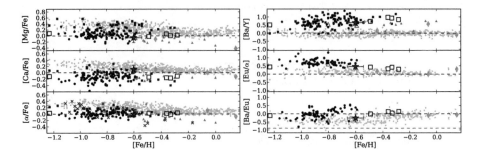

Figure 1.   Average Pal 1 abundances (red stars) compared to Galactic field stars (grey points, Venn et al. 2004, Reddy et al. 2006) and stars (solid) and clusters (open) in other galaxies (Fornax: black points, Letarte et al. 2010; Sgr: cyan triangles, Sbordone et al. 2007, Monaco et al. 2007, Chou et al. 2010a, Cohen 2004, and Sbordone et al. 2005a; LMC: blue squares, Pompéia et al. 2008, Johnson et al. 2006, and Mucciarelli et al. 2008; Canis Major: orange diamonds, Sbordone et al. 2005b; and the Monoceros Stream: green crosses, Chou et al. 2010b).

the neutron capture elements. The [Ba/Y] ratio provides a comparison of second- to first-peak s-process elements; the high value implies Pal 1 has been enriched by metal-poor AGB stars. The [Eu/α] ratio compares elements that should both be produced in massive stars; the high value in Pal 1 implies it had an additional r-process source, as was proposed for Fornax (Letarte et al. 2010). Finally, the [Ba/Eu] ratio indicates the contributions of s- and r-process elements. Since Pal 1 has high s-process abundances, the normal [Ba/Eu] also indicates that Pal 1 had an extra r-process source.

Altogether, Pal 1's [X/Fe] ratios imply that it likely originated in a galaxy with a similar chemical evolution history as dwarf galaxies. Ultimately, Pal 1's classification as a *globular* cluster remains uncertain, although it shares characteristics with open clusters and the intermediate-age LMC clusters. Pal 1 is therefore likely associated with a *recent* accretion event.

References

Chou, M.-Y., Cunha, K., Majewski, S. R., et al. 2010a, ApJ, 708, 1290
Chou, M.-Y., Majewski, S. R., Cunha, K., et al. 2010b, ApJ, 720, L5
Cohen, J. G. 2004, AJ, 127, 1545
Harris, W. E. 1996, AJ, 112, 1487
Johnson, J. A., Ivans, I. I., & Stetson, P. B. 2006, ApJ, 640, 801
Letarte, B., Hill, V., Tolstoy, E., et al. 2010, A&A, 523, A17
Monaco, L., Bellazzini, M., Bonifacio, P., et al. 2007, A&A, 464, 201
Mucciarelli, A., Carretta, E., Origlia, L., & Ferraro, F. R. 2008, AJ, 136, 375
Pompéia, L., Hill, V., Spite, M., et al. 2008, A&A, 480, 379
Reddy, B. E., Lambert, D. L., & Allende Prieto, C. 2006, MNRAS, 367, 1329
Rosenberg, A., Piotto, G., Saviane, I., et al. 1998, AJ, 115, 658
Sarajedini, A., Bedin, L., Chaboyer, B., et al. 2007, AJ, 133, 1658
Sbordone, L., Bonifacio, P., Buonanno, R., et al. 2007, A&A, 465, 815
Sbordone, L., Bonifacio, P., Marconi, G., et al. 2005a, A&A, 437, 905
— 2005b, A&A, 430, L13
Venn, K. A., Irwin, M., Shetrone, M. D., et al. 2004, AJ, 128, 1177

Part V

Local Group and Nearby Galaxies

Galactic Archaeology: Near-Field Cosmology and the Formation of the Milky Way
ASP Conference Series, Vol. 458
W. Aoki, M. Ishigaki, T. Suda, T. Tsujimoto, N. Arimoto, eds.
© *2012 Astronomical Society of the Pacific*

The Local Group in Cosmological Context

Rosemary F.G. Wyse

Department of Physics & Astronomy, Johns Hopkins University, Baltimore, MD 21218, USA

Abstract. Understanding the physics of the baryonic component of galaxies is clearly critical to understanding the nature of dark matter, particularly on galaxy scales. Resolved stellar populations play a unique role in constraining important aspects such as the merger history of galaxies in the Local Group, and in tracing the dark matter density profile, as briefly reviewed here.

1. Tracing Back Galaxy Formation

The Local Group of galaxies contains two large, apparently normal, disk galaxies, plus numerous less-luminous satellite galaxies. Most galaxies in the low-redshift Universe are found in groups, and the Local Group should be a typical environment. The galaxies of the Local Group are atypical from an observational stance in that individual stars can be studied. Several important properties of stars, such as their surface chemical abundances and orbital angular momentum, are conserved over long timescales and these distribution functions for old stars reveal much about conditions at early times, when those old stars formed. There are copious numbers of stars in the Milky Way and nearby galaxies that have ages $\gtrsim 10$ Gyr; standard cosmological parameters translate this look-back time to a redshift of formation of $z \gtrsim 2$ (12 Gyr corresponds to $z \sim 4$, 13 Gyr corresponds to $z \sim 10$).

These are exciting times to study local galaxies. Currently, observational and theoretical/computational capabilities are converging to providing both the stellar datasets and the simulations of galaxy formation that are required to test robustly our current paradigm. Very large observational surveys of stars in Local Group galaxies are now feasible using ground-based wide-field imagers and multi-object spectrographs, augmented by narrower but deeper space-based imaging and spectroscopy. The impending launch of the Gaia satellite will provide full 6-dimensional phase-space information on an unprecedented scale (see Gilmore's contribution). The wide field-of-view provided by the Subaru telescope and exploited by state-of-the-art cameras and spectrographs ensure that it will play an important role.

These surveys of local stars are complemented by studies of galaxies at high-redshift that are now starting to quantify the stellar content and morphologies of galaxies at similarly high look-back times. Further, large, high-resolution simulations of structure formation are allowing predictions of the formation of a Milky Way-like galaxy, plus its retinue of satellites, in a cosmological context. The vast majority of high-resolution simulations adopt the power spectrum and parameter values appropriate to ΛCDM, but there is increasing interest in – and, arguably, need for – simulations that assume Warm Dark Matter.

2. The Fossil Record

Comparing the properties of stars as a function of age (or an age proxy) within any one galaxy provides the evolution of that system, in comparison to direct study of galaxies at high redshift where one obtains snapshots of different galaxies at different epochs and must infer which are descendants of which ancestors. Further, the combination of spectroscopy and photometry can provide the metallicity and elemental abundance distributions, and age distributions, separately. This allows us to break degeneracies that are inherent in the analysis of the integrated light from a stellar population, such as that between star-formation rate and stellar Initial Mass Function (IMF) and age and metallicity (see Figure 1 for an example of the low-mass IMF). The kinematics of individual stars as a function of age allows inferences about the merger history, and hence the nature of dark matter, while the kinematics also enable dynamical analyses, more directly probing the dark matter content.

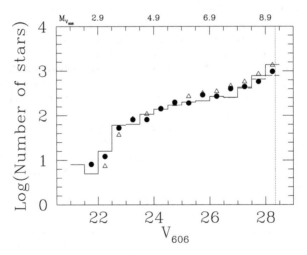

Figure 1.   Taken from Wyse et al. (2002). Comparison between the luminosity function of faint, low-mass stars in the Ursa Minor dwarf spheroidal galaxy (histogram; based on HST imaging) and those of two globular clusters (M15 and M92, points, shifted to a common distance modulus) of very similar old age and low metallicity (the Ursa Minor dwarf is unusual in being well-approximated by a simple stellar population, with a narrow range of age, 10 – 12 Gyr, and metallicity, ∼ −2 dex). The globular clusters show no evidence of dark matter, in contrast to the UMi dSph, but their luminosity functions are indistinguishable. This argues against the dark matter being associated with very low-mass objects, i.e. being baryonic. The high-mass IMF in the UMi dSph is constrained by the elemental abundances in these old stars and it is consistent with being 'normal'. There is therefore little room for variation in the stellar IMF over a wide range of time and physical conditions.

Stars retain memory of conditions when formed, with those memories being retained over different timescales. The most shortlived signature is a structure in coordinate space, such as high surface-density tidal streams. These will survive longer as structure in kinematic space, as will 'moving groups' formed by interactions with resonances associated with perturbations to a smooth gravitational field. Phase space structure is persistent, and is particularly useful if integrals of the motion can be identified. The surface chemical abundances of stars are essentially conserved and reflect those of the gas out of which the star formed, *modulo* mass transfer from a possible (close) binary companion, or episodes of deep mixing in evolved giant stages of stellar evolution. Different elements are produced in stars of different masses on different timescales, and the pattern of elemental abundances reflects the star formation history and stellar IMF (and binary population) of a given self-enriching system (see also Gilmore's contribution).

3. Testing the ΛCDM Paradigm

It is well-established that the ΛCDM cosmogony is extremely successful in explaining structure on large scales, such as the microwave background and galaxy clusters (Komatsu et al. 2011). However, as illustrated succinctly by Ostriker & Steinhardt (2003), galaxies and below are the scales on which the nature of dark matter is most strongly manifest. The first high-resolution (N-body) simulations of the formation of a Milky Way analog galaxy in ΛCDM immediately demonstrated that there are orders of magnitude more subhaloes surviving to the present day than there are satellite galaxies (Moore et al. 1999; Klypin et al. 1999), an issue that only worsened as the resolution improved (e.g. Stadel et al. 2009).

Simulations had also very quickly established that CDM dark matter haloes had a fairly steeply rising density profile towards the central parts (Navarro et al. 1996), also basicaly confirmed by later, higher-resolution simulations, albeit finding a slightly less 'cusped' fit (e.g. Stadel et al. 2009). Again, this is best tested on small scales, and again both gas-rich (Oh et al. 2011) and gas-poor dwarf galaxies (Gilmore et al. 2007; Walker & Peñarrubia 2011) appear to favor a cored density profile rather than the 'cusp' predicted by CDM (albeit that a cusped profile can also be fit to the data).

The ΛCDM power spectrum has more power on small scales and structure is formed through hierarchical clustering. Merging of smaller systems is very important in the evolution of galaxies of mass similar to that of the Milky Way, with active merging to late times (e.g. Stewart et al. 2008). The orbital energy and angular momentum must either be lost or be absorbed into the composite system. Gas can of course radiate energy and dissipate and angular momentum can be taken away by escaping material. The merging process increases the random motions within stellar systems, disrupting cold satellites and heating/thickening thin disks, and the associated torques cause angular momentum redistribution. Stars and gas are driven into the central regions to build-up the bulge. Generically ΛCDM simulations form disk galaxies with too many satellite galaxies, too prominent a bulge, thick disks that are too hot and too young, and thin disks whose stars have too narrow a range of ages (e.g. Scannapieco et al. 2011; House et al. 2011). Some of these trends may be exacerbated by limitations of the treatments of the gas physics, but the result that merging plays too dominant a role, leading to an inability to form late-type disk galaxies frequently enough, is robust.

3.1.   ΛCDM: How to Form a Disk Galaxy Like the Milky Way?

As noted above, the generic disk galaxy in ΛCDM has a large bulge-disk ratio and active merging history, with significant accretion events later than redshifts $z \sim 1$. The formation and evolution of a Milky-Way analog must therefore be simulated in a manner similar to that of Guedes et al. (2011), by carefully selecting, from low-resolution simulations, a – very atypical – Galaxy-mass halo that has had no significant (defined by a 1:10 mass ratio) merging since a redshift of three and then re-simulating this system at high resolution. Early star formation in the nascent thin disk must be suppressed to allow for a significant gas fraction at zero redshift, and this is achieved by adopting a sufficiently high enough threshold value for the gas density above which star formation can occur. This in turn creates tension with the fact that there are old stars in the local disk. The formation of a significant bulge is prevented by appealing to strong feedback in the central regions, to remove low angular momentum gas that otherwise would collect there and form stars. However, given that the dark halo has been pre-selected to have little addition of mass since a redshift of three, the central potential well is already in place, maximizing the required efficacy of the feedback.

The properties of the stellar halo and of the surviving satellite galaxies have been studied through semi-analytic modelling ('tagging' dark matter particles as 'stars', with properties based on prescriptions for star formation and chemical evolution) applied to substructure in several different high-resolution N-body simulations of the formation and evolution of a Milky Way analog (Cooper et al. 2010). These find complex and varied populations in the stellar haloes, created from the stellar content of totally disrupted subhaloes plus a non-negligible contribution from surviving satellites. Hydrodynamic simulations (e.g. Font et al. 2011) suggest an additional significant contribution from *in situ* star formation, perhaps dominating within ~ 30 kpc. It will be extremely interesting to see predictions for the detailed elemental abundance ratios in these heterogeneous haloes – the observations, as discussed at this conference by Judy Cohen, show very little scatter with only a few outliers while one would expect much larger scatter from the complex mix of star formation histories in the progenitors of the model haloes. The detailed age distribution is also an important constraint, since again most of the stellar mass of the field halo appears to be uniformly old (e.g. Unavane et al. 1996).

Thus most of the stellar halo, bulge, thick disk and even some part of (old?) thin stellar disk are all predicted to be created through mergers. We should see signatures of the merging process in the resultant stellar populations. I will briefly discuss the thick disk in the Milky Way.

3.2.   The Thick Disk

The thick disk in the Milky Way was first identified through star counts at high Galactic latitude (Gilmore & Reid 1983), similarly to the detection of thick disks in external disk galaxies through surface brightness profiles (e.g. van der Kruit & Searle 1981) – two exponentials fit and one does not. Whether or not the thick disk is distinct from the thin disk was the subject of much early debate (e.g. Norris 1999) with several lines of evidence favoring a discrete thick disk, such as a lack of metallicity and age gradients within the thick disk and little overlap with the thin disk, and the dichotomy in elemental abundances of local thin and thick disk stars (defined kinematically). The relevance for ΛCDM is that thick disks – kinematically hot disks – are robustly predicted to result from merging.

The vertical velocity dispersion of the local thick disk is generally accepted to be too high to be generated by local heating mechanisms within the disk. The stars in the local thick disk are typically around $10 - 12$ Gyr old, implying a formation redshift $z \sim 2$. Given that stars of all ages exist in the thin disk, a significant merger that occurred more recently than ~ 10 Gyr ago would have caused younger stars to be moved from thin to thick disk. The lack of younger stars in the thick disk thus requires an unusually quiet merger history for the Milky Way, far from typical in ΛCDM where 95% of dark haloes of mass 10^{12} M$_\odot$ experience a merger with a system of mass 5×10^{10}M$_\odot$ (which equals the mass of the disk) in the last 10 Gyr (Stewart et al. 2008). Of course, should the thick disk *not* be formed in a merger, but by some other process, then mergers have even less of a role to play.

The properties of the thick disk far from the solar radius are still not that well defined (see Kordopatis' contribution) and indeed how best to select a sample of thick disk stars far from the Sun is not clear without understanding the structure, kinematics and metallicity distribution of the thick disk, somewhat of a chicken and egg situation. Of course, as long as observation biases are understood one could hope to combine samples with different selection functions to get further insight. The dichotomy between the ratios of α-elements to iron, derived from high-resolution spectra, for local thin and thick disk stars (Bensby et al. 2003; Reddy et al. 2006; Fuhrmann 2008) might suggest that elemental abundances can be used to define the thick disk, in the sense that enhanced values of [α/Fe] imply thick disk and lower values imply thin disk membership. I would just caution that the pattern of elemental abundances is very sensitive to the past star formation history, and most models of disk formation predict variations in star formation history across the disk. It could therefore be dangerous to identify samples of distant thick disk stars through elemental-abundance criteria based on local samples.

3.2.1. If Not Mergers, How?

The observations of clumpy, turbulent 'thick' disks at redshifts $z \sim 2$ (Genzel 2009; Elmegreen & Elmegreen 2006) led naturally to the suggestion that these may be the progenitors of thick stellar disks at zero redshift. However it is not straightforward to translate the observed properties to those that would be observed for counterparts/descendants in local galaxies. Early thick disks will be compressed and heated by accretion/re-formation of a thin disk; for the simplest case of adiabatic growth of the thin disk by accretion of cold gas (Ostriker 1990; Elmegreen & Elmegreen 2006) the scale-height of the thick disk will decrease and its vertical velocity dispersion increase as $\Delta H/H \sim -\Delta M_{gas}/M_{disk}$, $\Delta \sigma^2/\sigma^2 \sim -2\Delta H/H$. Further, clumpy turbulent disks at redshift ~ 2 may instead form bulges (Elmegreen et al. 2008).

Radial migration is a process whereby stars and gas in circular orbits can be moved significant distances within the thin disk while maintaining circular orbits, i.e. with no associated heating. This can occur for stars and gas at the corotation resonance of transient gravitational perturbations such as spiral arms (Sellwood & Binney 2002). Radial migration can also result from the interaction between two perturbations with different pattern speeds, such as a bar and a spiral (Minchev & Famaey 2010). Migration of 'star particles' (mass $\sim 2 \times 10^4$M$_\odot$) from their birthplace has also been seen in hydrodynamical simulations of disk galaxy evolution (Roškar et al. 2008).

Radial migration has been proposed as a mechanism to form thick disk without any mergers, by bring stars outwards from the inner disk, where velocity dispersions are higher (Schönrich & Binney 2009). However, the efficiency of radial migration for stars that are on non-circular orbits has yet to be established and this is an active area of research.

4. Concluding remarks

At present many aspects of Local Group galaxies pose challenges for the current paradigm of ΛCDM. While 'more data are needed' is an obvious and much-used phrase, high-quality data for carefully selected, large, stellar samples really are lacking. The Subaru Telescope, with wide-field imaging and multi-object spectroscopy capabilities is extremely well-matched to the challenge.

Acknowledgments.   I acknowledge support from the National Science Foundation through grants AST-0908326 and OIA-1124403.

References

Bensby, T., Feltzing, S., & Lundström, I. 2003, A&A, 410, 527
Cooper, A. P. et al. 2010, MNRAS, 406, 744
Elmegreen, B. G., Bournaud, F., & Elmegreen, D. M. 2008, ApJ, 688, 67
Elmegreen, B. G., & Elmegreen, D. M. 2006, ApJ, 650, 644
Font, A. S. et al. 2011, MNRAS, 416, 2802
Fuhrmann, K. 2008, MNRAS, 384, 173
Genzel, R. 2009, in The Galaxy Disk in Cosmological Context, edited by J. Andersen, J. Bland-Hawthorn, & B. Nordström, vol. 254 of IAU Symposium, 33
Gilmore, G., & Reid, N. 1983, MNRAS, 202, 1025
Gilmore, G. et al. 2007, ApJ, 663, 948
Guedes, J., Callegari, S., Madau, P., & Mayer, L. 2011, ApJ, 742, 76
House, E. L. 2011, MNRAS, 415, 2652
Klypin, A., Kravtsov, A. V., Valenzuela, O., & Prada, F. 1999, ApJ, 522, 82
Komatsu, E. et al. 2011, ApJS, 192, 18
Minchev, I., & Famaey, B. 2010, ApJ, 722, 112
Moore, B. et al. 1999, ApJ, 524, L19
Navarro, J. F., Frenk, C. S., & White, S. D. M. 1996, ApJ, 462, 563
Norris, J. E. 1999, Ap&SS, 265, 213
Oh, S.-H. et al. 2011, AJ, 141, 193
Ostriker, J. P. 1990, in Evolution of the Universe of Galaxies, edited by R. G. Kron, vol. 10 of ASP Conference Series, 25
Ostriker, J. P., & Steinhardt, P. 2003, Science, 300, 1909
Reddy, B. E., Lambert, D. L., & Allende Prieto, C. 2006, MNRAS, 367, 1329
Roškar, R. et al. 2008, ApJ, 684, L79
Scannapieco, C., White, S. D. M., Springel, V., & Tissera, P. B. 2011, MNRAS, 417, 154
Schönrich, R., & Binney, J. 2009, MNRAS, 399, 1145
Sellwood, J. A., & Binney, J. J. 2002, MNRAS, 336, 785
Stadel, J. et al. 2009, MNRAS, 398, L21
Stewart, K. R. et al. 2008, ApJ, 683, 597
Unavane, M., Wyse, R. F. G., & Gilmore, G. 1996, MNRAS, 278, 727
van der Kruit, P. C., & Searle, L. 1981, A&A, 95, 116
Walker, M. G., & Peñarrubia, J. 2011, ApJ, 742, 20
Wyse, R. F. G. et al. 2002, New Astron, 7, 395

Galactic Archaeology: Near-Field Cosmology and the Formation of the Milky Way
ASP Conference Series, Vol. 458
W. Aoki, M. Ishigaki, T. Suda, T. Tsujimoto, N. Arimoto, eds.
©*2012 Astronomical Society of the Pacific*

A Relic Star Cluster in the Sextans Dwarf Spheroidal Galaxy – Implications for Early Star and Galaxy Formation

Torgny Karlsson[1,2] and Joss Bland-Hawthorn[2]

[1]*Department of Physics and Astronomy, Uppsala University, Box 516, 751 20 Uppsala, Sweden*

[2]*Sydney Institute for Astronomy, School of Physics, University of Sydney, NSW 2006, Australia*

Abstract. We present tentative evidence for the existence of a dissolved star cluster in the Sextans dwarf spheroidal galaxy. In a sample of six stars, we identify three (possibly four) stars around [Fe/H] = −2.7 that are highly clustered in a multi-dimensional chemical abundance space. The estimated initial stellar mass of the cluster is $M_{*,\mathrm{init}} = 1.9^{+1.5}_{-0.9}$ ($1.6^{+1.2}_{-0.8}$) $\times 10^5 \, M_\odot$ assuming a Salpeter (Kroupa) initial mass function (IMF). If corroborated by follow-up spectroscopy, this ancient star cluster at [Fe/H] = −2.7 is the most metal-poor system identified to date. Inspired by this finding, we also present a new way to interpret the cumulative metallicity functions of dwarf galaxies. From available observational data, we speculate that the ultra-faint dwarf galaxy population, or a significant fraction thereof, and the more luminous, classical dwarf spheroidal population were formed in different environments and would thus be distinct in origin.

1. Introduction

Little is known about the star formation process at the earliest cosmic times. Recent hydrodynamics simulations suggest that primordial stars might have been formed in binary or small multiple systems (Stacy, Greif, & Bromm 2010). Assuming turbulent initial conditions, Clark et al. (2011) showed that primordial stars could even have been formed in small, dense clusters. In their simulations, Wise et al. (2012) found that most Pop II clusters below [Z/H] = −2 were formed with masses in the range $5 \times 10^2 \lesssim M_*/M_\odot \lesssim 10^4$, with a relative frequency resembling that of what is found today in the Galactic Disk (see their Fig. 6).

The most metal-poor star clusters known to date have an iron abundance just below [Fe/H] = −2. One of the globular clusters (Cluster 1) in the Fornax dwarf spheroidal (dSph) currently holds the record with a metallicity [Fe/H] = −2.5 (Letarte et al. 2006). However, not all clusters have survived as gravitationally bound objects to the present epoch. Much like the Galactic Halo, dwarf galaxies have stars with metallicities well below [Fe/H] = −3 (Kirby et al. 2008; Starkenburg et al. 2010). The relatively simple environments of the low mass dwarf galaxies raises the prospect of identifying disrupted star clusters at much lower metallicity than has been possible before through the technique of chemical tagging (Bland-Hawthorn et al. 2010a,b). In the extension, this also gives us a unique tool to probe the formation and early evolution of the present dwarf galaxy population.

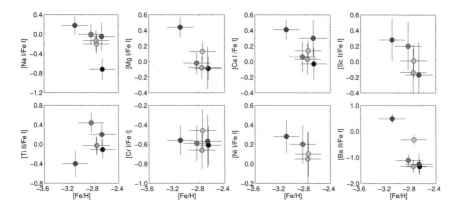

Figure 1.   (color online) Chemical abundance ratios of six very metal-poor stars
in the Sextans dSph. Abundance data are taken from Aoki et al. (2009). Stars are
color coded according to their location in the [Mg/Fe] – [Fe/H] diagram. The three
stars with nearly identical [Mg/Fe] (colored in different shades of blue) also have
very similar [Fe/H]. These stars all clump together in Ti, Cr, and Ba, as well.

In the following sections, we will demonstrate the possible existence, estimate the
initial mass, and discuss the likely nature of a disrupted stellar cluster at [Fe/H] = −2.7
in the Sextans dSph. We end by briefly explore the implications for near-field cosmology and the possibility that the population of ultra-faint dwarfs and the more luminous,
classical dSphs have a different origin.

2.   Observational evidences

Based on high-resolution ($\mathcal{R} \simeq 40,000$) spectroscopy, Aoki et al. (2009) recently determined the chemical abundances of six very metal-poor stars ([Fe/H] < −2.5) in the
Sextans dSph. Their excellent analysis revealed a group of four stars that display a sub-
zero [Mg/Fe] ratio with a small scatter around the weighted mean ⟨[Mg/Fe]⟩ = −0.06
(see Fig. 1). This is in contrast to the Mg-to-Fe enhancements commonly observed in
Galactic Halo stars of similar metallicity (Cayrel et al. 2004). A closer inspection of
Fig. 1 shows that three (colored in shades of blue) of the four stars more or less tightly
clump together in Ti, Cr and Ba as well. Two out of three "blue" stars also have similar
Na, Ca and Sc abundances (Sc was not measured in the dark blue star S 10 − 14). As
Aoki et al. (2009) points out, the higher [Ca/Fe] ratio in S 14 − 98 (medium blue) could
simply be due to a larger observational uncertainty in Ca for this star. In terms of the
chemistry, the star S 11 − 37 (color coded green in Fig. 1) may be regarded as a border-
line case. However, since it is slightly off ($1 - 2\sigma$) in Sc, Ti, and Ba we will not regard
this star as a member of the "blue" group. We will return to the low Na abundance of
S 10 − 14 in Sect. 3.

Starkenburg et al. (2010) determined re-calibrated metallicities for metal-poor
stars in four classical dSphs, including Sextans. The new data reveal an excess of stars
in the metallicity distribution function (MDF) of Sextans around [Fe/H] ≃ −2.9. Assuming a typical enhancement of ⟨[Ca/Fe]⟩ = +0.25 in metal-poor stars (Starkenburg
et al. 2010), this "bump" should be found at [Ca/H] ≃ −2.65 (see Fig. 2). Interestingly,

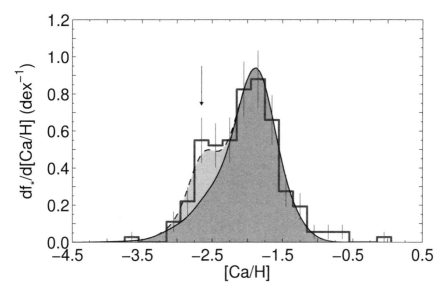

Figure 2. (color online) MDF of Sextans, as given by $df_*/d[Ca/H]$. The quantity f_* is the fraction of stars that fall below each [Ca/H] bin (1 dex). The black, solid line denotes the fiducial distribution of [Ca/H], predicted from our stochastic chemical evolution model while the black, dashed line denotes the corresponding distribution, including an $M_\star = 2.0 \times 10^5 \, M_\odot$ star cluster at [Ca/H] $= -2.65$ (arrow). Both MDFs are convolved with a $\sigma = 0.2$ dex gaussian. The light-grey shaded area contains 12.3% of the total stellar mass. The red step function (with Poissonian noise) shows the observed distribution of [Ca/H] (Starkenburg et al. 2010).

this is close to the weighted mean abundance of Ca for the three "blue" stars identified in the data of Aoki et al. (2009).

If real, the "bump" could be due to the presence of a relic cluster. In conjunction with our finding above, we will argue that the "blue" stars in Fig. 1 once were members of a chemically homogeneous star cluster that is now, at least partly, dissolved. This conclusion is also in accord with the detection of a kinematically cold substructure in the central region of Sextans, possibly originating from a remnant star cluster (Battaglia et al. 2011). The substructure has an observed mean metallicity of [Fe/H] $\simeq -2.6$ (Battaglia et al. 2011), which is very close to that of the "blue" group of stars.

3. Stellar mass and nature of relic cluster

We first estimate the initial mass of the potential star cluster by measuring the size of the "bump" in the MDF of Sextans (Fig. 2). By comparing the observed MDF with the MDF predicted from our stochastic chemical evolution model (for details, see Karlsson et al. 2012), we determine the initial mass to $M_{*,\text{init}} = 2.0 \, (1.6) \times 10^5 \, M_\odot$ for a Salpeter (Kroupa, Kroupa 2001) initial mass function (IMF). At face value, the identification of the three "blue" stars in Fig. 1, if they do belong to a dispersed cluster, point towards a cluster mass in the range $2.2 \times 10^5 \leq M_{*,\text{init}}/M_\odot \leq 3.6 \times 10^5$. Given this conditional constraint, the combined estimate of the most probable mass of the dissolved cluster (with asymmetric uncertainties) is determined to $M_{*,\mathrm{init}} = 1.9^{+1.5}_{-0.9} (1.6^{+1.2}_{-0.8}) \times 10^5 \, M_\odot$, for a Salpeter (Kroupa) IMF (Karlsson et al. 2012).

Globular clusters show specific elemental abundance correlations, such as the Na-O and the Al-Mg anti-correlations. These are not present in open clusters and could therefore be used as discriminators between the two types of clusters. Interestingly, the star S 10 − 14 (dark blue) has a significantly lower Na abundance than the other two potential cluster stars (see Fig. 1). This may be suggestive of an Na-O anti-correlation present in the data. The fact that one out of three stars show a low [Na/Fe] is also consistent with the fraction of globular cluster stars exhibiting primordial abundances (Carretta et al. 2009). Along with the inferred initial mass, we conclude that the relic cluster might have been a globular cluster. Further observations, including O and Al abundances are, however, required in order to readily determine the nature of the cluster.

4. On the origin of ultra-faint dwarfs and dSphs

A comparison between models and available metallicity data for dSphs and ultra-faints suggests that the formation of clusters in the ultra-faints differed from that of the dSphs (Karlsson et al. 2012). Together with a detected offset between the mean cumulative metallicity functions of the ultra-faints and the dSphs, and a putative offset in the $\langle[\mathrm{Mg/Fe}]\rangle$ ratio, we speculate that these two types of galaxies probably were formed in different environments and would therefore be distinct in origin. A possible explanation to the apparent absence of clumping in the ultra-faints below $[\mathrm{Fe/H}] = -2.5$ is that these galaxies were formed predominantly before the local Universe was reionized, while the dSphs formed mostly after reionization. However, whether there is a dichotomy, as suggested by the current observational data, or a continuous distribution of galaxies exhibiting a mix of properties should be investigated further.

References

Aoki, W., Arimoto, N., Sadakane, K., Tolstoy, E., Battaglia, G., Jablonka, P., Shetrone, M., Letarte, B., Irwin, M., Hill, V., et al. 2009, A&A, 502, 569.
Battaglia, G., Tolstoy, E., Helmi, A., Irwin, M., Parisi, P., Hill, V., & Jablonka, P. 2011, MN-RAS, 411, 1013.
Bland-Hawthorn, J., Karlsson, T., Sharma, S., Krumholz, M., & Silk, J. 2010a, ApJ, 721, 582
Bland-Hawthorn, J., Krumholz, M., & Freeman, K. 2010b, ApJ, 713, 166
Carretta, E., Bragaglia, A., Gratton, R. G., Lucatello, S., Catanzaro, G., Leone, F., Bellazzini, M., Claudi, R., D'Orazi, V., Momany, Y., et al. 2009, A&A, 505, 117.
Cayrel, R., Depagne, E., Spite, M., Hill, V., Spite, F., François, P., Plez, B., Beers, T., Primas, F., Andersen, J., et al. 2004, A&A, 416, 1117.
Clark, P. C., Glover, S. C. O., Klessen, R. S., & Bromm, V. 2011, ApJ, 727, 110.
Karlsson, T., Bland-Hawthorn, J., Freeman, K., & Silk, J. 2012, ApJ, (submitted), arXiv: 1201.5376[astro-ph.CO].
Kirby, E. N., Simon, J. D., Geha, M., Guhathakurta, P., & Frebel, A. 2008, ApJ, 685, L43.
Kroupa, P. 2001, MNRAS, 322, 231.
Letarte, B., Hill, V., Jablonka, P., Tolstoy, E., François, P., & Meylan, G. 2006, A&A, 453, 547.
Stacy, A., Greif, T. H., & Bromm, V. 2010, MNRAS, 403, 45.
Starkenburg, E., Hill, V., Tolstoy, E., González Hernández, J. I., Irwin, M., Helmi, A., Battaglia, G., Jablonka, P., Tafelmeyer, M., Shetrone, M., et al. 2010, A&A, 513, A34.
Wise, J. H., Turk, M. J., Norman, M. L., & Abel, T. 2012, ApJ, 745, 50.

Galactic Archaeology: Near-Field Cosmology and the Formation of the Milky Way
ASP Conference Series, Vol. 458
W. Aoki, M. Ishigaki, T. Suda, T. Tsujimoto, N. Arimoto, eds.
©*2012 Astronomical Society of the Pacific*

Origin and Evolution of Structure and Nucleosynthesis for Galaxies in the Local Group

G.J. Mathews,[1] X. Zhao,[1,2,3] and N. Q. Lan[1,2,4]

[1]*Center for Astrophysics, Department of Physics, University of Notre Dame, Notre Dame, IN 46556*

[2]*The Joint Institute for Nuclear Astrophysics, University of Notre Dame, Notre Dame, Indiana 46556, USA*

[3]*Department of Astronomy & Astrophysics, Penn State University, University Park, PA 16802*

[4]*Hanoi National University of Education, 136 Xuan Thuy, Hanoi, Vietnam*

Abstract. The Milky Way is the product of a complex evolution of generations of merges, collapse, star formation, supernova and collisional heating, radiative and collisional cooling, and ejected nucleosynthesis. Moreover, all of this occurs in the context of the cosmic expansion, the formation of cosmic filaments, dark-matter halos, spiral density waves, and emerging dark energy. In this paper we discuss recent calculations of the formation and evolution of galaxies and Local-Group like systems derived from simulations of large scale structure. Specifically, we describe simulations of poor clusters like our Local group that contain two large spirals presently separated by ∼ 800 kpc. In these systems there is a tendency for galactic halos to form within the dark matter filaments that define a super-galactic plane. Gravitational interaction along this structure leads to streaming flows toward the two dominant galaxies in the cluster. These simulations also suggest that a significant fraction of the Galactic halo formed as at large distances and then arrived later along these streaming flows.

1. Introduction

It has been clear for some time (cf. White & Rees 1978) that the Milky-Way Galaxy did not form in isolation as the collapse of a single cloud, but rather is the product of the development of a much more extended structure. This structure begins within the initial dark-matter potentials formed during the radiation-dominated epoch and then evolves into the filament/void morphology characteristic of the standard ΛCDM cosmology. Within this structure there has been a complex sequence of heating by mergers, star formation and supernovae, along with collisional and radiative cooling and the formation of star-forming cold molecular clouds. One must analyze all of these processes within the entire extended early Local Group (LG) in order to understand the properties of the Milky Way and its satellite systems.

The fact that galaxies in the Local Group exhibit puzzling alignments has been known since the pioneering work of Kunkel & Demers (1976) and Lynden-Bell (1982), where it was noted that the galaxies of the Local Group are aligned in a great circle. Moreover, the more recently discovered satellite galaxies (Koposov et al. 2008, and references therein) in the Sloan Digital Sky Survey (*SDSS*) appear also to be aligned upon the great circle (Metz, Kroupa & Jerjen 2009).

In other work (Godlowski & Flin 2010) it has been noted that on scales of ≤ 10 Mpc there is a tendency for galaxies to align in a direction toward the local super-cluster. A number of works (e.g. Libeskind et al. 2005; 2010; Zentner et al. 2005; Kang et al. 2005) have performed numerical simulations in a an attempt to explain this. In the present work we extend these investigations to analyze numerically the generic tendency for LG-type poor clusters to exhibit an alignment and streaming motion to-ward the dominant galaxies of the cluster. Our simulations imply that the Local Group should contain 1 to 3 aligned systems currently inflowing. We also argue that there is marginal evidence in observed dwarf galaxies for such streaming flows arriving from in the general direction of the Moffie and Sculptor systems (though the Sculptor galaxy itself is probably not a part of this motion). However more data on dwarf galaxies at large distances is required.

2. Numerical Simulations

It is rather straightforward (Zhao & Mathews 2011) to do large scale structure simu-lations with random initial conditions in a standard ΛCDM cosmology. One begins by specifying the content, i.e. $\Omega_\Lambda = 0.77$ and $\Omega_M = 0.23$ and a baryon content of $\Omega_B = 0.022$ as deduced from the Wilkinson Microwave Anisotropy Probe (*WMAP*) (Dunkley et al 2009; Komatsu et al. 2011; Larson et al. 2011) seven year analysis.

The code that we and others have adopted for numerical simulations of large scale structure and galaxy formation is the N-body Smoothed-particle hydrodynamics (SPH) code GADGET, originally developed by Springel & Hernquist (2003). The most cur-rent public version Gadget-2 (Springel 2005) is used for all of the simulations described in this paper. We have modified the public version of the Gadget-2 code to incorporate our own cooling and star formation routines. However, up to now we are only interested in the location and velocity distribution of dark matter halos and baryons and associated inflowing dwarf spheroidal galaxies. Hence, it is sufficient to ignore feed back from star formation. We do, however, include the collisional and radiative heating and cooling of baryonic matter in the simulation.

We use the usual cooling-function approach to compute the heating and cool-ing time scale using the *MAPPINGS III* software as described in Sutherland & Do-pita (1993) to construct a cooling rate table. The simulation then uses this table when needed to update the internal energy of a particular gas particle. These rates incorporate collisional and Compton ionization, two photon, continuum, and free-free scattering in the heating and cooling functions. In numerical simulations for primordial gas with-out heavy elements, the dominant cooling processes (Katz, Weinberg & L. Hernquist 1996) are two-body processes involving collisional excitation, collisional ionization, standard recombination, and dielectric recombination of H and He along with free-free emission. In our simulations, we first use the MAPPINGS III software (Sutherland and Dopita 1993) In simulations without nucleosynthesis feedback we adopt a metallicity of $Z/Z_{solar} = 0.25$ as roughly appropriate for dwarf galaxies in the Galactic halo. The deduced temperature vs, density relation for gas particles in our simulation of a Local-Group-like system is similar to those from other simulations (e.g. Katz, Weinberg & Hernquist 1996; Springel & Hernquist 2003). That is, we reproduce the expected broad temperature distribution for gas densities comparable to the background density and a population of gas up to high density with temperatures near 10^4 K due to the Lyman α edge.

Since the Gaussian fluctuations responsible for galaxy formation can be easily described by a power spectrum $P(k)$, calculating the matter power spectrum of a specific cosmological model is the first step to generate a proper initial condition. Numerous simulations were performed with different random initial conditions on scales up to 400 Mpc^3. For each large scale simulation, an initial linear matter power spectrum was generated using the standard CMB code CMBFAST (Seljak & Zaldarriaga 1996). This power spectrum was then used to generate random Gaussian fields using the Zel'dovich approximation (Zel'dovich 1970). For this purpose we utilized the Grafic (Bertschinger 2001) or the IC (Sirko 2005) package.

Subsequently, the initial-condition file was converted to the Gadget-2 format to start the simulation within various comoving boxes. We have run a number of large-scale simulations with box sizes varying from 200-800 Mpc^3. These simulations were generated with different random seed fluctuations. The results of the large-scale simulations were then post processed to identify volumes containing Local-Group-like poor clusters dominated by two large galaxies of ~ 800 kpc present separation. When suitable poor clusters were identified, these regions were then used to generate initial conditions for higher resolution simulations on a scale of 800 to 1200 kpc^3. For these systems, the boundary conditions were deduced directly from the LSS simulation, while the interior of the computational domain was allowed to contain Gaussian random fluctuations to higher resolution than that utilized in the LSS simulations.

3. Simulations of Local-Group Like Systems

Of interest to the present work is the formation of a large number of infalling dark matter halos neatly aligned along the filamentary structure of the simulation. Indeed, it is clear from the simulations that the halos of the dominant galaxies are the result of a number of infalling dwarf galaxies forming very early, but arriving up to much later times from distances up to hundreds of kpc away.

When the baryons are included, the two dominant galaxies clearly show spiral structure and also the presence of Magellanic-cloud or M32-like systems and impending *SagA*- like mergers occurring near the Galactic center. Figure 1 shows the positions and comoving flow of the baryonic galaxies and halos. One can see that the halos line up along filamentary structures. This alignment causes an enhanced gravity along the filament leading to a streaming flow of cosmic fluid toward the dominant galaxies. In this simulation the mass ratio of the two dominant galaxies is approximately 3 : 1, similar to the ~ 4 : 1 mass ratio for the M31 and the Milky way.

From this work we deduce that the first stars were likely formed far from the Milky Way and later arrived via streaming flows. We have begun work (Lan, Giang & Mathews 2010) to analyze the elemental abundances produced in these protogalactic structures.

Acknowledgments. Work at the University of Notre Dame supported in part by the U.S. Department of Energy under Nuclear Theory Grant DE-FG02-95-ER40934 and by the Joint Institute of Nuclear Astrophysics (JINA) through NSF-PFC grant PHY08-22648. Work in Vietnam supported in part by the National Foundation for Science and Technology Development (NAFOSTED) grant No: 103.02.112.09.

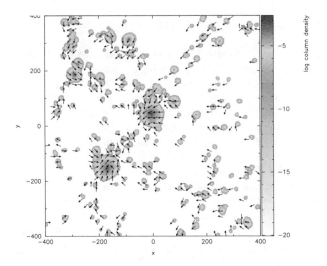

Figure 1.   Distribution of infalling halo galaxies in one of the simulations. Arrows show the directions of comoving flow. Note the appearance of two streaming flows; one from the lower right and one from the upper right.

References

Bertschinger, E. 2001 ApJS. 137, 1.
Dunkley, J. et al. 2009 [WMAP Collaboration], ApJS, 180, 306.
Godłowski, W., & Flin, P. 2010, ApJ, 708, 920
Kang X., Mao S., Gao L., Jing Y. P., 2005, A&A, 437, 383
Katz, N., Weinberg, D. H. & Hernquist, L. 1996, ApJS, 105, 19.
Komatsu, E. et al. 2011, ApJS, 192, 18,.
Koposov, S. et al. 2008, ApJ, 686, 279.
Kunkel, W. E., Demers S., 1976, RGO Bull., 182, 241
Lan, N. Q. , Giang, N. T. , Mathews, G. J. , & Saleh, L. 2010, Comm. Phys., 20, 23-29.
Larson, D. et al. 2011, ApJS, 192, 16.
Libeskind, N. I., Frenk C. S., Cole S., Helly J. C., Jenkins A., Navarro J. F. & Power C. 2005, MNRAS, 363, 146.
Libeskind, N. I., Knebe, A., Hoffman, Y., Gottlöber, S. Yepes, G., and Steinmetz, M. 2010, MNRAS, 411, 1525.
Lynden-Bell D. 1982, The Observatory, 102, 202
Metz M., Kroupa P., Jerjen H. 2009, MNRAS, 394, 2223
Seljak, U. & Zaldarriaga, M. 1996, ApJ, 469, 437.
Sirko, E. 2005, Astrophys. J. 634, 728.
Springel, V. 2005, MNRAS, 364, 1105.
Springel, V. & Hernquist L. 2003, MNRAS, 339, 289.
Sutherland, R. S & Dopita, M. A. 1993, ApJS, 88, 545.
White, S. D. M. & Rees, M. J. 1978, MNRAS, 183, 341.
Zentner A. R., Kravtsov A. V., Gnedin O. Y., Klypin A. A., 2005, ApJ, 629, 219
Zhao, X. & Mathews, G. J. 2011, PRD 83, 203524

Galactic Archaeology: Near-Field Cosmology and the Formation of the Milky Way
ASP Conference Series, Vol. 458
W. Aoki, M. Ishigaki, T. Suda, T. Tsujimoto, N. Arimoto, eds.
©2012 Astronomical Society of the Pacific

Wide-Field Views of Nearby Galaxies

Annette M. N. Ferguson

Institute for Astronomy, University of Edinburgh, Edinburgh UK EH9 3HJ

Abstract. I review the evidence for complex low surface brightness structures in the outer regions of large galaxies. While the most spectacular examples are provided by systems hosting coherent debris streams, the most common examples may be extremely diffuse smooth stellar envelopes. Wide-field imagers on large telescopes are allowing us to explore these components in quantitative detail well beyond the Local Group and I highlight some recent results obtained with Subaru/Suprime-Cam. Finally, I stress the importance of wide-field imagery for interpreting deep HST studies of nearby galaxies, and touch upon some new results on the star formation and chemical evolutionary history of the M31 outer disc.

1. Introduction

Complex stellar structures are frequently seen in the outer regions of both spiral and elliptical galaxies (e.g. Ferguson et al. 2002; Malin & Carter 1983). While the most spectacular examples are often discrete, consisting of tidal streams or other debris features (e.g. McConnachie et al. 2009; Martínez-Delgado et al. 2010), many systems exhibit relatively smooth extended stellar envelopes (e.g. Barker et al. 2009; Tanaka et al. 2011; Barker et al. 2012). It may be that the dominant morphology of the outer structure varies as a function of galaxy type, hinting at differences in recent accretion histories. Indeed, estimates suggest that 70% of bright ellipticals show evidence for discrete tidal features while only 15-20% of all local galaxies do (Tal et al. 2009; Miskolczi et al. 2011). The mere existence of low surface brightness structures provides support for the hierarchical picture of galaxy assembly in which interactions, accretions and mergers play a driving role in the evolution of galaxies (e.g. White & Frenk 1991). However, confirming this picture at the most basic level is only the first step in developing a robust model of galaxy formation. Further progress requires understanding the detailed structure – radial profile, shape, extent – and stellar content – age, metallicity, kinematics – of galaxy outskirts as these properties reflect the fossil record of their evolution and can help distinguish between accretion and in situ formation models.

2. Resolving Stellar Populations Beyond the Local Group

The peripheral regions of galaxies are very faint, generally lying $\gtrsim 7 - 8$ magnitudes below the sky level. The optimal approach to studying these parts is via resolved red giant branch (RGB) star photometry, a technique which can typically reach far fainter surface brightness levels than diffuse light analyses. While ground-based surveys have used this method to map the stellar outskirts of Local Group galaxies in unprecedented detail (e.g. Ferguson et al. 2002; McConnachie et al. 2009), extending this work to other galaxies is necessary in order to understand global trends. The stochastic nature

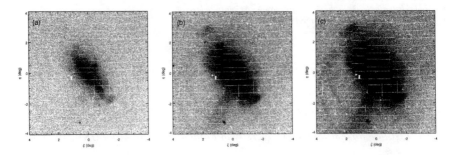

Figure 1.   Star count data from the Pan-Andromeda Archaeological Survey showing the inner halo of M31 at depths of (a) 1, (b) 2 and (c) 3.5 mags below the TRGB.

of the hierarchical assembly process means that the properties of accreted components
are largely determined by the few most massive progenitors (e.g. Cooper et al. 2010)
and hence system-to-system variance is not only possible but highly likely.

Surveying RGB populations in galaxies beyond the Local Group presents a variety of observational challenges. Wide-field imagers are essential in order to capture
significant portions of galaxy outskirts and avoid biases due to contaminating small-
scale substructures. It is also necessary to obtain sufficient photometric depth to detect
low surface brightness emission. Figure 1 (a)-(c) shows the inner halo of M31 with star
count data that reach a range of depths. While evidence for tidal structures is present
in all cases, the appearance of the halo changes drastically as the depth is increased.
Reaching to ~ 1.5 − 2 magnitudes below the tip of the red giant branch (TRGB) would
appear to be a minimum requirement for fully tracing even the brightest substructures.
As the TRGB is I_0 = 21.9, 23.7 and 24.5 at distances of 1.5, 3.5 and 5 Mpc respectively,
an 8m-class telescope is clearly warranted for this type of work.

The other main challenge concerns contaminants in the stellar catalogues (see Figure 2). Accurate star-galaxy separation becomes crucial as the photometric depth increases since the target RGB stars overlap in magnitude (and to a lesser extent in colour)
with the background galaxy population. Milky Way foreground stars also contaminate
the bluest and reddest giant populations. While excellent seeing and image quality can
weed out marginally-resolved galaxies, a sufficiently wide field-of-view is mandatory
to measure the unresolved contaminant level in areas free of galaxy emission.

3.   Case Studies: M81 and NGC 2403

We are conducting a program to explore the low surface brightness outer regions in
a sample of large galaxies lying within 5 Mpc using wide-field imagers on 8-m class
telescopes. I highlight here some results from our Subaru/Suprime-Cam studies of
NGC 2403 (Sc, D= 3.1 Mpc) and M81 (Sb, D= 3.6 Mpc). Both systems were observed
under good seeing conditions (0.7-1.1") with total exposure times per filter ranging
from 2500-6300s. Full details are provided in Barker et al. (2009, 2012).

The depth of our Subaru/Suprime-Cam photometry enables us to examine RGB
stars (1 − 10 Gyr), asymptotic giant branch (AGB) stars (0.5 − 8 Gyr), red supergiant
(RSG) stars (20−180 Myr), and main sequence plus blue helium-burning (MS+BHeB)
stars (10 − 150 Myr). Figure 3 shows the two-dimensional spatial distribution of these
sources in NGC 2403. In all cases, the populations define a flattened disc-like distribu-

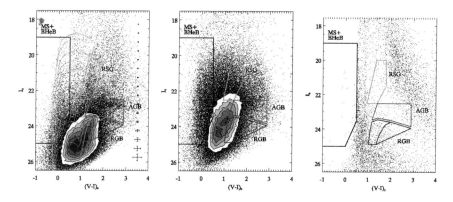

Figure 2.   (color online) Colour-magnitude diagrams (CMDs) of NGC 2403 showing (left) the stellar sources, (middle) the extended sources (i.e. galaxies) and (right)
the Besancon model predictions of the Galactic foreground along this sightline. Population boxes and Padova isochrones are overlaid.

tion with a similar inclination and position angle. The RGB populations are somewhat
more extended than the younger stars which, assuming all stars have formed in situ,
suggests outside-in growth of the disc. In contrast to our findings for M81, no obvious
substructures are apparent in the distribution of stars beyond the optical disc. The relatively smooth RGB and AGB stellar distributions indicate that NGC 2403 has evolved
quiescently with no recent significant accretions. However, our Subaru photometry
does not go as deep as the INT and CFHT surveys of M31 and M33 (e.g. Ferguson
et al. 2002; McConnachie et al. 2009), so the very faint structures seen around those
galaxies would lie below our detection limit.

Figure 4 shows surface brightness profiles for M81 and NGC 2403 constructed
from the combination of diffuse light surface photometry (inner regions) and star count
data (outer regions). Corrections for extinction, sky brightness and contaminant levels
have been made. The outer regions of M81 remain fairly bright to the extent of our imagery however NGC 2403's outskirts are far fainter ($\mu_V \sim 32$ mag/sq. arcsec). Beyond
the Local Group, such low level emission has generally only been detected through
stacking of thousands of galaxies (e.g. Zibetti et al. 2004; Tal & van Dokkum 2011).

Both galaxies show compelling evidence for extended structural components which
dominate over the main stellar discs beyond ~ 18 kpc. Overlaid on Figure 4 are different possible decompositions of the composite profiles. In the case of M81, two
different spherically-symmetric Hernquist halo models (scale radii of 14 and 53 kpc)
are combined with a bulge+disc model. For the bulgeless NGC 2403, an exponential
disc model is combined with Hernquist halos of scale radii 14 and 1.3 kpc. In all cases,
the models provide adequate descriptions of the data points, but are virtually indistinguishable over the observed radial range. A similar situation exists when considering
plausible disc+disc models. Depending on the adopted profile, the fractional luminosity contained in the extended components ranges from 1–5% in NGC 2403 to 10–15%
in M81, suggestive of a correlation with overall galaxy luminosity. The metallicities of
the extended stellar components, inferred from comparing RGB colours to the Padova
isochrones, are [M/H]= -1.0 ± 0.3 and -1.1 ± 0.3 for NGC 2403 and M81 respectively
and hence lie in between that of the Milky Way's stellar halo and thick disc.

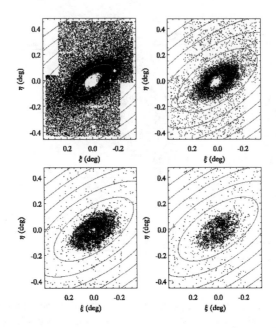

Figure 3.   Clockwise from top left, the tangent plane projection of RGB, AGB, RSG and MS+BHeB stars. Ellipses denote deprojected radii of 10 – 60 kpc in steps of 10 kpc. The hole in the nucleus is due to severe stellar crowding. No correction has been made for contaminants.

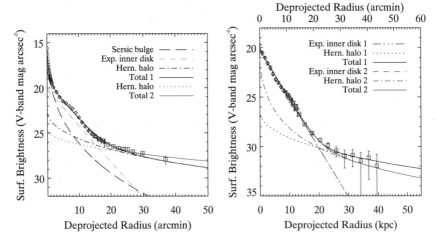

Figure 4.   (color online) Composite surface brightness profiles for M81 (left) and NGC 2403 (right) with possible structural decompositions overlaid. Solid lines show the total model profiles and broken lines show individual components. Note that 1 kpc ≈ 1.0′ for both systems.

Further insight into the nature of these enigmatic outer components requires star count data at more extreme radii, in order to distinguish between different radial profile forms, as well as kinematical information. Since individual RGB stars beyond the Local Group are too faint for even 8m-class telescopes, tracers such as globular clusters, planetary nebulae and AGB stars will have to be used. Finally, photometric analysis of our full sample of galaxies will establish how the presence and properties of these extended components vary with galaxy type, luminosity and environment and will enable constraints to be placed on models of galaxy formation and evolution.

4. The Necessity of Wide-Field Imaging for Interpreting HST Studies

The structural complexity of galaxy outskirts means that caution is required when interpreting small field-of-view studies of these parts. While it was once assumed that observing a field projected at $\gtrsim 10 - 20$ kpc from the centre of a nearby galaxy would be sufficient to capture its spheroid populations, it is now clear that such a field could in fact sample any number of stellar components in addition to or even instead of the halo – for e.g. the thick disc, the extended thin disc and/or tidal debris streams. This problem is particularly acute in the case of HST studies where the field-of-view ($\approx 3'$ on a side) is tiny compared to the $\gtrsim 20 - 30'$ typical extent of local galaxies. Thus, while deep HST CMDs allow exquisite star formation history (SFH) reconstructions for these remote parts, it is often unclear what component(s) they truly represent. The global structural analyses discussed above are therefore essential for the interpretation of small field-of-view datasets.

Taking advantage of our early wide-field imaging work, we used HST/ACS to target a field lying in the warped outer disc of M31. The resultant CMD reaches old main sequence turn-offs (~ 12.5 Gyr) with high precision and can be used to trace the outer disc SFH back to early epochs (see Figure 5). After undergoing roughly constant star formation until about 4.5 Gyr ago, there was a lull in activity for ~1.5 Gyr followed by a strong recent burst. This latter event appears to be accompanied by a decline in global metallicity which could be a signature of the inflow of metal-poor gas. The onset of the burst (~3 Gyr ago) corresponds to the last close passage of M31 and M33 predicted by N-body models (McConnachie et al. 2009), and may have been triggered by this event. The complex behaviour of the SFH and the smoothly-varying age-metallicity relation (AMR) suggest that the stellar populations observed in this field mostly formed in situ instead of having migrated from smaller galactocentric radii. Furthermore, the moderate metallicity of the oldest stars in this field suggests the outer disc formed from pre-enriched material. Full details of this analysis are presented in Bernard et al. (2012) (also see Bernard's contribution in this volume).

Discussion

Freeman: Do the halo stars seen at larger radii in M31 have abundances extending below −1.5 dex?

Ferguson: That remains controversial. Most studies have found that [Fe/H]= −1.5 dex is about the minimum level reached in the outer halo, however the reanalysis of one of these datasets has claimed metallicities as low as [Fe/H]= −2.5.

Kobayashi: Can you comment on the importance of gas flows in the M31 outer disc based on your derived SFH and AMR?

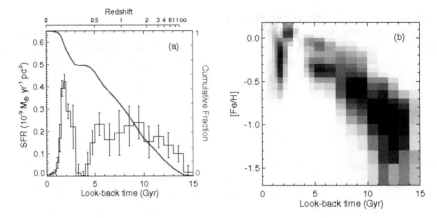

Figure 5.   The best-fit SFH solution for the M31 warp: (a) the SFR as a function of time, normalised to the deprojected area of the ACS field and (b) the age-metallicity relation. The cumulative mass fraction is shown by the red solid line in panel (a).

Ferguson: The decline in metallicity at recent epochs suggests inflow of metal-poor gas, but we have not modelled the shape of the AMR in detail.

Rich: Have you compared your SFH with that derived by Tom Brown in other M31 fields?

Ferguson: It's difficult to do a rigorous comparison but none of the Brown fields appear to show the bursty behaviour we see in our field. However, that might not be surprising. As discussed by Richardson et al. (2008), the Brown fields could be contaminated by stars from various stellar components, including substructures.

Acknowledgments.   Mike Barker and Edouard Bernard conducted much of the analysis presented here and their collaboration is gratefully acknowledged. The organizers are thanked for financial assistance and a very stimulating meeting.

References

Barker, M. K., Ferguson, A. M. N., Irwin, M., Arimoto, N., & Jablonka, P. 2009, AJ, 138, 1469
Barker, M. K., Ferguson, A. M. N., Irwin, M. J. et al. 2012, MNRAS, 419, 1489
Bernard, E. J., Ferguson, A. M. N., & Barker, M. K. et al. 2012, MNRAS, 2269
Cooper, A. P., Cole, S., & Frenk, C. S. et al. 2010, MNRAS, 406, 744
Ferguson, A. M. N., Irwin, M. J., Ibata, R. A. et al. 2002, AJ, 124, 1452
Malin, D. F., & Carter, D. 1983, ApJ, 274, 534
Martínez-Delgado, D., Gabany, R. J., & Crawford, K. et al. 2010, AJ, 140, 962
McConnachie, A. W., Irwin, M. J., & Ibata, R. A. et al. 2009, Nat, 461, 66
Miskolczi, A., Bomans, D. J., & Dettmar, R.-J. 2011, A&A, 536, A66
Richardson, J. C., Ferguson, A. M. N., Johnson, R. A. et al. 2008, AJ, 135, 1998
Tal, T., & van Dokkum, P. G. 2011, ApJ, 731, 89
Tal, T., van Dokkum, P. G., Nelan, J., & Bezanson, R. 2009, AJ, 138, 1417
Tanaka, M., Chiba, M., Komiyama, Y., Guhathakurta, P., & Kalirai, J. S. 2011, ApJ, 738, 150
White, S. D. M., & Frenk, C. S. 1991, ApJ, 379, 52
Zibetti, S., White, S. D. M., & Brinkmann, J. 2004, MNRAS, 347, 556.

Galactic Archaeology: Near-Field Cosmology and the Formation of the Milky Way
ASP Conference Series, Vol. 458
W. Aoki, M. Ishigaki, T. Suda, T. Tsujimoto, N. Arimoto, eds.
©2012 Astronomical Society of the Pacific

Near Field Cosmology with the Pan-Andromeda Archaeological Survey

Alan W. McConnachie[1] and the PAndAS collaboration

[1]*NRC Herzberg Institute of Astrophysics, 5071 West Saanich Road, Victoria, British Columbia, Canada, V9E 2E7*

Abstract. I describe the Pan-Andromeda Archaeological Survey (PAndAS), and discuss several recent science highlights, including studies of its dwarf satellite systems, its stellar halo, and correlations with the HI content. I also discuss the need for a large scale, wide field, multi-object spectroscopic survey, such as the type made possible with the proposed Next Generation Canada-France-Hawaii Telescope (NG-CFHT).

1. Introduction: The PAndAS Survey

PAndAS is a Large Program using the 3.6m CFHT/MegaCam 1 degree FOV wide field camera to contiguously survey the M31 and M33 galaxies over ~ 400 sq.degrees. Data was taken between 2008-2010, and built upon earlier surveys of this galaxy using the Isaac Newton Telescope Wide Field Camera (Ferguson et al. 2002) and CFHT/MegaCam (Ibata et al. 2007; McConnachie et al. 2008). Observations are sufficiently deep to obtain $S/N = 10$ for point sources at $g, i = 25.5$, approximately > 4 magnitudes down the red giant branch of M31 (nearly to the horizontal branch level). The top panel of Figure 1 shows the complete survey area, where each square corresponds to a 1 degree MegaCam field. Results from PAndAS are published in McConnachie et al. (2009); Martin et al. (2009); McConnachie et al. (2010); Cockcroft et al. (2011); Richardson et al. (2011); Carlberg et al. (2011); Conn et al. (2011).

2. Science Highlights

The bottom panel of Figure 1 is a reproduction of Figure 1 from Richardson et al. (2011). Here, we show the spatial density distribution of candidate metal-poor RGB stars in the environs of M31 and M33, selected using a color-cut in color-magnitude space.

2.1. The stellar halo

The bottom panel of Figure 1 shows a vast array of substructure in the area surrounding M31 and M33, down to equivalent surface brightnesses of $32 - 33$ mags arcsec^{-2}. Several of the streams visible are > 50kpc in extent, and the stars extend to vast radii (to beyond the edge of the survey). For comparison to the MW, the SDSS currently maps the MW halo out to radii of around 40kpc over approximately one-quarter of the sky.

271

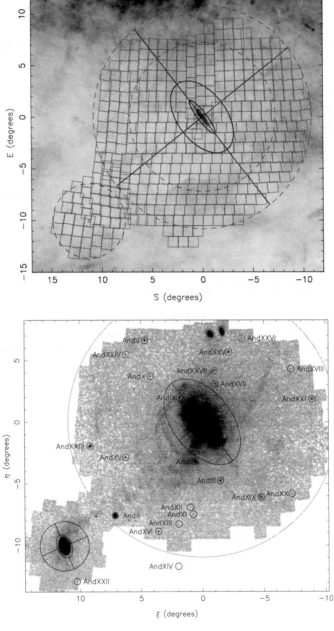

Figure 1.   Top panel: the PAndAS area, where each square represents a single
pointing of CFHT/MegaCam.   Dashed circles correspond to maximum projected
radii of 100 and 150kpc from M31, and 50kpc from M33. Grey-scale corresponds to
the extinction maps of Schlegel et al. (1998). Bottom panel: spatial density distribution of candidate red giant branch stars in the environs of M31 within the PAndAS
footprint. See Richardson et al. (2011).

Ongoing study of the global properties of the stellar halo include an analysis of the overall two-dimension shape of the "smooth" (i.e., lacking substructures at the limiting surface brightness level of the data) stellar halo (Ibata et al. in prep), building upon earlier studies of its radial profiles, most recently by Irwin et al. (2005); Guhathakurta et al. (2005); Ibata et al. (2007). Using the "smooth" halo as reference will enable a quantitative study of the statistical properties of substructures out to the limiting radius of the data (McConnachie et al., in prep).

2.2. The Dwarf Satellite System

A large number of dwarf galaxies are visible in the bottom panel of Figure 1 as concentrated overdensities of red giant branch stars. Many of these systems are new discoveries from the survey (e.g., Martin et al. 2009; Richardson et al. 2011). Current ongoing work in this area consists of a few related studies. Martin et al (a, in prep) develop a quantitative algorithm that identifies all such features - bona-fide dwarfs and also a prioritized list of candidates. Martin et al. (b, in prep) explore the completeness of the dwarf satellite population by quantifying the selection effects of the algorithm using "fake" satellites with a range of magnitude, scale size, distance, etc.. Finally, Irwin et al. (in prep) study in detail the environment, structure and dynamics of the binary dwarf elliptical satellites NGC147 and NGC185, the former of which is clearly undergoing tidal disruption in its orbit around M31.

2.3. Stars and Gas

Lewis et al. (in prep) are examining the spatial and velocity correlations (or lack thereof) between the (sub-)structures traced by the stars and those traced by HI, in particular from the wide-field surveys of Braun & Thilker (2004). How many, if any, of the stellar streams and other features come from systems with a significant gaseous content?

3. The Future

Numerous studies are currently underway that use PAndAS to help determine the structure of M31, its disks, halo, streams, dwarf galaxies, globular clusters, interaction history, etc.. While PAndAS presents an extremely comprehensive view of an $L\star$ galaxy, obtaining complimentary stellar spectra to understand the associated chemistry and dynamics is fundamentally challenging because of the huge area that must be surveyed. A large number of reasonably bright (red giant branch) stellar targets are within reach of 10-m spectroscopy (e.g., using Keck/DEIMOS or Gemini/GMOS) but the FOV of these instruments (arc-minutes) is not well suited to the hundreds of square degrees subtended by M31.

The Next Generation CFHT is a proposed upgrade to the existing CFHT, and would replace the current 3.6m telescope with a 10m-class, wide field (1.5 square degree), highly multiplexed spectrograph (3200 fibres), capable of working at $R = 2000, 6000$ and 20000 from ~ 380nm to 1.3μm. It would operate as a *dedicated* spectroscopic facility and would provide the essential compliment to the large number of photometric and astrometric surveys planned for the next decade and beyond. Driving science for this facility include cosmology, galaxy evolution (typically lower resolutions) and near field cosmology (typically higher resolutions). Ideally, it will see first light in the early 2020s, and requires the development of a new and extended partnership to realize this exciting and necessary capability. NGCFHT will provide the missing science capability for the next era of ground based OIR astronomy.

Acknowledgments. Based on observations obtained with MegaPrime/MegaCam, a joint project of CFHT and CEA/DAPNIA, at the Canada-France-Hawaii Telescope (CFHT) which is operated by the National Research Council (NRC) of Canada, the Institute National des Sciences de l'Univers of the Centre National de la Recherche Scientifique of France, and the University of Hawaii. We would like to thank the entire staff at CFHT for their great efforts and continuing support throughout this project. AM would like to thank the conference organiser for putting together such an enjoyable and interesting meeting.

References

Braun, R., & Thilker, D. A. 2004, A&A, 417, 421
Carlberg, R. G., et al. 2011, ApJ, 731, 124
Cockcroft, R., et al. 2011, ApJ, 730, 112
Conn, A. R., et al. 2011, ApJ, 740, 69
Ferguson, A. M. N., Irwin, M. J., Ibata, R. A., Lewis, G. F., & Tanvir, N. R. 2002, AJ, 124, 1452
Guhathakurta, P., et al. 2005, ArXiv Astrophysics e-prints
Ibata, R., Martin, N. F., Irwin, M., Chapman, S., Ferguson, A. M. N., Lewis, G. F., & McConnachie, A. W. 2007, ApJ, 671, 1591
Irwin, M. J., Ferguson, A. M. N., Ibata, R. A., Lewis, G. F., & Tanvir, N. R. 2005, ApJ, 628, L105
Martin, N. F., et al. 2009, ApJ, 705, 758
McConnachie, A. W., et al. 2010, ApJ, 723, 1038
McConnachie, A. W., et al. 2008, ApJ, 688, 1009
McConnachie, A. W., et al. 2009, Nat, 461, 66
Richardson, J. C., et al. 2011, ApJ, 732, 76
Schlegel, D. J., Finkbeiner, D. P., & Davis, M. 1998, ApJ, 500, 525

Galactic Archaeology: Near-Field Cosmology and the Formation of the Milky Way
ASP Conference Series, Vol. 458
W. Aoki, M. Ishigaki, T. Suda, T. Tsujimoto, N. Arimoto, eds.
©*2012 Astronomical Society of the Pacific*

The Newly-Discovered Outer Halo Globular Cluster System of M31

Dougal Mackey,[1] Avon Huxor,[2] and Annette Ferguson[3]

[1]*RSAA, The Australian National University, Mount Stromlo Observatory, Cotter Road, Weston Creek, ACT 2611, Australia*

[2]*Astronomisches Rechen-Institut, Universität Heidelberg, Mönchhofstraße 12-14, 69120 Heidelberg, Germany*

[3]*Institute for Astronomy, University of Edinburgh, Royal Observatory, Blackford Hill, Edinburgh, EH9 3HJ, UK*

Abstract. In this contribution we describe the discovery of a large number of globular clusters in the outer halo of M31 from the *Pan-Andromeda Archaeological Survey* (PAndAS). New globular clusters have also been found in the outskirts of M33, and NGC 147 and 185. Many of the remote M31 clusters are observed to preferentially project onto tidal debris streams in the stellar halo, suggesting that much of the outer M31 globular cluster system has been assembled via the accretion of satellite galaxies. We briefly discuss the global properties of the M31 halo globular cluster system.

1. Introduction

Observations of Andromeda (M31) are critically important to studies of globular clusters and the role these objects play in the formation and evolution of galaxies and galaxy haloes. M31 possesses the most numerous globular cluster population in the Local Group. It is also the nearest large spiral system to the Milky Way, and the only other large galaxy where globular clusters may be resolved into stars using presently-available technology. Our group has pioneered the resolved study of the M31 stellar halo via several wide-field imaging surveys (Ferguson et al. 2002; Ibata et al. 2007), most recently the *Pan-Andromeda Archaeological Survey* (PAndAS), which is dedicated to obtaining a contiguous deep panorama of M31 to a projected radius $R_p \approx 150$ kpc. PAndAS has revealed a copious amount of substructure – tidal debris streams and density enhancements – in the M31 stellar halo (McConnachie et al. 2009), as well as a large number of previously unknown satellite dwarf galaxies (e.g. Martin et al. 2006, 2009; McConnachie et al. 2008; Richardson et al. 2011).

2. Newly-Discovered Globular Clusters

PAndAS is facilitating the first detailed study of the remote globular cluster system of M31. The survey is notable for its excellent image quality, typically better than $\approx 0.7''$. This means that the majority of M31 globular clusters are identifiable by eye with almost no ambiguity (see Figure 1). A careful search of the survey imaging outside

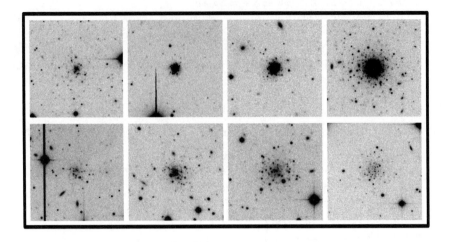

Figure 1.   Example PAndAS images of our newly-discovered M31 clusters.

the main disk of M31 (where the crowding and variable background are problematic) has revealed nearly 100 previously-uncatalogued globular clusters. Of these, 79 lie at projected radii beyond 30 kpc with the most distant at $R_p \approx 145$ kpc (Huxor et al. 2008, 2012 – in prep.). To place the significance of these discoveries into context, prior to our work just three M31 globular clusters were known outside 30 kpc.

PAndAS also covers several other important galaxies in the M31 sub-group – in particular M33, and NGC 147 and 185. We have discovered remote globular clusters in each of these three systems. Clusters found in M33 from a previous survey by Huxor et al. (2009) have been confirmed with PAndAS and one additional object added in a search out to $R_p \approx 50$ kpc (Cockcroft et al. 2011). There are three new outer clusters in NGC 147, extending to $R_p \approx 6.5$ kpc from this galaxy, and one new cluster (again the outermost, at $R_p \approx 1.2$ kpc) in NGC 185 (Veljanoski et al. 2012).

3.   Results and Discussion

The M31 halo globular cluster system contains a number of notable objects and sub-groups. One which has attracted particular attention in recent years is the set of so-called "extended clusters" identified by Huxor et al. (2005). The first few of these objects to be discovered possessed particularly large characteristic radii for their luminosities, leading to speculation that they were an unusual class of cluster peculiar to M31. However, as our sample has increased it appears more likely that these objects are not dissimilar to the diffuse Palomar-type clusters found in the outer Milky Way and in smaller Local Group members such as the Magellanic Clouds and NGC 6822. Certainly *Hubble Space Telescope* imaging has revealed that extended clusters in M31 are ancient, metal-poor systems possessing colour-magnitude diagrams typical of normal compact globular clusters (Mackey et al. 2006, 2007).

Another interesting object is the exceptionally remote cluster MGC1, which has been studied in detail by Mackey et al. (2010a). MGC1 lies ~ 160 kpc in front of M31;

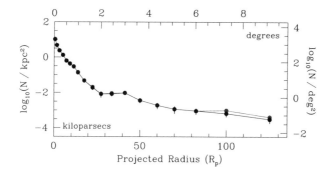

Figure 2. Radial density profile for globular clusters in M31. Two profiles are calculated, with our candidate objects included and excluded. Clusters within ≈ 25 kpc are taken from the Revised Bologna Catalogue (Galleti et al. 2004) V4.0.

combined with its large projected radius this implies a total galactocentric distance of ≈ 200 kpc, rendering it by far the most isolated known globular cluster in the Local Group. Remarkably, its radial density profile shows no evidence for a tidal limit to at least 450 pc, and possibly as far as ~ 900 pc, indicating that MGC1 has spent many Gyr in isolation. Conroy et al. (2011) have used the observed radial structure of MGC1 to demonstrate that it cannot be embedded in a substantial dark matter halo.

Our remote M31 cluster sample spans luminosities from M_V ≈ −9.5 to fainter than −5.0 where detection incompleteness becomes important. There are proportionally many more bright globular clusters observed at large radii in M31 than in the Milky Way (Mackey et al. 2007; Huxor et al. 2011). The luminosity function of remote clusters shows the usual peak near M_V = −7.5 as well as an unexpected secondary peak at −5.5. This second peak is, intriguingly, almost solely due to the contribution from faint extended clusters. The integrated colours of our M31 clusters, as well as those in the outskirts of M33, and NGC 147 and 185, occupy a narrow band near $(V − I)_0$ ≈ 0.9. This is very similar to the mean value for remote Milky Way globulars. There is no evident colour gradient with galactocentric radius for our M31 clusters, indicating that there is unlikely to be a significant radial metallicity gradient present outside ≈ 30 kpc.

Huxor et al. (2011) showed that the radial density profile for M31 globular clusters exhibits a flattening beyond R_p ≈ 30 kpc, very similar to that observed for the metal-poor field halo by Ibata et al. (2007). In Figure 2 we show the radial density profile constructed using our full PAndAS sample – the flattening is clearly evident and extends to beyond 100 kpc. We interpret this as evidence that accretion processes have played an important role in building up the outer M31 system. Compelling support for this is seen when the positions of our clusters are plotted on a density map of the stellar halo. Mackey et al. (2010b) have demonstrated, using around half of the PAndAS area, that globular clusters outside R_p ≈ 30 kpc are preferentially associated with underlying tidal debris features. This correlation appears to remain strong when the full map is considered[1]. These observations imply that the majority of the outer globular cluster system of M31 has been built up via the accretion of satellite host galaxies.

---

[1] We do not reproduce the full map here due to space constraints and issues of clarity.

Discussion

Majewski: Do you see any gross differences in the general properties of clusters lying on obvious substructure versus those not clearly associated with any substructure?

Mackey: We're still working on this. It does seem that the diffuse extended clusters are more likely to lie on substructure than normal compact clusters. It's not clear yet whether there is a systematic difference between the luminosities of clusters lying on and away from substructures. To delve any deeper into this (to look at, say, horizontal branch morphology, for example) you need resolved observations of the clusters – we have a Cycle 19 HST program in progress so keep an eye out for these results in future.

Freeman: The clusters now in the substructures will soon mix into the smooth population of clusters. Do you have any idea of how much the substructure clusters would contribute to the overall population, over time?

Mackey: Beyond about 30 kpc we think the contribution could be quite large, maybe up to 70 – 80% (see e.g., Mackey et al. 2010b). Further in than this it's difficult to say because there is so much substructure that it's very hard to isolate which clusters are associated with various features, and which constitute the smooth population.

Acknowledgments. DM is grateful for financial support from the Australian Research Council (DP1093431) and for contributions to this work by various members of the PAndAS collaboration – in particular Nial Tanvir, Alan McConnachie, Mike Irwin, Rodrigo Ibata, Geraint Lewis, Nicolas Martin, Cherie Fishlock, and Jovan Veljanoski.

References

Cockcroft, R., et al. 2011, ApJ, 730, 112
Conroy, C., Loeb, A., & Spergel, D. N. 2011, ApJ, 741, 72
Ferguson, A. M. N., Irwin, M., Ibata, R., Lewis, G., & Tanvir, N. 2002, AJ, 124, 1452
Galleti, S., Federici, L., Bellazzini, M., Fusi Pecci, F., & Macrina, S. 2004, A&A, 416, 917
Huxor, A. P., et al. 2005, MNRAS, 360, 1007
— 2008, MNRAS, 385, 1989
— 2009, ApJ, 698, L77
— 2011, MNRAS, 414, 770
Ibata, R. et al. 2007, ApJ, 671, 1591
Mackey, A. D., et al. 2006, ApJ, 653, L105
— 2007, ApJ, 655, L85
— 2010a, MNRAS, 401, 533
— 2010b, ApJ, 717, L11
Martin, N. F., et al. 2006, MNRAS, 371, 1983
— 2009, ApJ, 705, 758
McConnachie, A. W., et al. 2008, ApJ, 688, 1009
— 2009, Nature, 461, 66
Richardson, J. C., et al. 2011, ApJ, 732, 76
Veljanoski, J., et al. 2012, MNRAS, submitted

Galactic Archaeology: Near-Field Cosmology and the Formation of the Milky Way
ASP Conference Series, Vol. 458
W. Aoki, M. Ishigaki, T. Suda, T. Tsujimoto, N. Arimoto, eds.
© 2012 Astronomical Society of the Pacific

Structure and Population of the NGC 55 Stellar Halo from a Subaru/Suprime-Cam Survey

Mikito Tanaka,[1] Masashi Chiba,[1] Yutaka Komiyama,[2] Puragra Guhathakurta,[3] and Jason S. Kalirai[4]

[1]*Astronomical Institute, Tohoku University, Aoba-ku, Sendai 980-8578, Japan*

[2]*National Astronomical Observatory of Japan, 2-21-1 Osawa, Mitaka, Tokyo 181-8588, Japan*

[3]*University of California Observatories/Lick Observatory, University of California Santa Cruz, 1156 High Street, Santa Cruz, CA 95064, USA*

[4]*Space Telescope Science Institute, Baltimore, MD 21218, USA*

Abstract.   As part of our survey of galactic stellar halos, we investigate the structure and stellar populations of the north part of the stellar halo in NGC 55, using deep and wide-field V- and I-band images taken with Subaru/Suprime-Cam. From the stellar density maps, we detect the asymmetric disturbed disk structure and the two metal-poor overdense substructures in the north region of NGC 55, which may correspond to remnants of the hierarchical formation process of NGC 55's halo. In addition, we identify a diffuse metal-poor halo extended out to at least $z \sim 16$ kpc. We derive the metallicity distributions (MDs) of these structures on the basis of the photometric comparison of RGB stars with the theoretical stellar evolutionary model. The MDs of the thick disk structures show the peak metallicity of $[Fe/H]_{peak} \sim -1.4$ and the mean metallicity of $[Fe/H]_{mean} \sim -1.7$, while the outer substructures show more metal-poor features than the thick disk structures. Finally, we discuss the differences of the stellar population and the formation scenario along the Hubble sequence, by comparing with our previous studies of M31's halo[1].

1.   Introduction

Recently, most astronomers believe large galaxies like the Milky Way and the Andromeda galaxy formed through a lot of hierarchical merging events of small galactic fragments. The scenario is verified by both theoretical models and observational facts. Such a scenario may be the general view even beyond the Local group, because some groups identified the evidence of the hierarchical formation as many tidal streams. For example, Peng et al. (2002) found a lot of streams around NGC 5128 which is the nearest elliptical galaxy in Centaurus group. Furthermore, Mouhcine et al. (2010) discovered some streams around NGC 891, which is the edge-on spiral galaxy at about 10 Mpc from us and similar to our Galaxy.

---

[1]For analyses for the distance and the surface brightness of NGC 55, please refer to Tanaka et al. (2011).

However, because substructures of such galaxies beyond the Local group have not really been investigated statistically, we cannot yet discuss about a view of galaxy formation by comparing galaxies with different morphological types. Therefore, in this study, in addition to searching substructures of galaxies beyond the Local group, we quantitatively determined the fundamental physical properties of the substructures, such as surface brightness and metallicity. Furthermore, we discuss about galaxy formation between galaxies with different morphological types.

2.   Observation

We have observed a north part of a stellar halo in NGC 55 reaching out to about 15 kpc from the center, as shown in the left panel of Fig. 1, using Suprime-Cam on the Subaru telescope in 2009 December. NGC 55 is an edge-on spiral (Sc) galaxy, belonging to the Sculptor group. In addition, it has about the same mass as M33 in the Local group. Exposure times of our targeted fields are 960 sec and 1800 sec in V and I-band, respectively. The weather condition was photometric but slightly poor, with seeing of around $1\rlap{.}{''}0$.

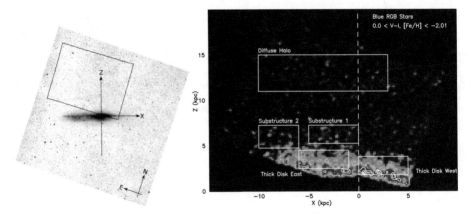

Figure 1.   (color online) **Left:** The locations and field of view of our Subaru/Suprime-Cam field, overlaid on a red Digitized Sky Survey image of NGC 55 covering about $60' \times 60'$. **Right:** Log-scaled matched filter maps. It presents the distributions of blue RGB stars within $0.0 < (V - I)$ and [Fe/H]< -2.01.

3.   Result

3.1.   Stellar Density Map

The right panel of Fig. 1 shows a density map of Red RGB stars, which is made by accounting resolved and metal-rich RGB stars where [Fe/H] is more than -2. Red shows higher stellar density, blue shows lower stellar density. We nominally refer the eastern structure to as "Thick Disk East (TDE)" and western one to as "Thick Disk West (TDW)", respectively hereafter. TDE seems to be related to the disturbed eastern disk which is in the shape of a tadpole tail. This fact might suggest that an accreted satellite galaxy gave an influence on the eastern part of the whole disk structure. Furthermore, from significant excess beyond the stellar density distribution of the diffuse halo, we have identified two metal-poor overdense substructures (referred to as Sub 1 and 2) in the north-east field of NGC 55.

3.2.   Color-Magnitude Diagrams (CMDs)

Fig. 2 shows CMDs of each structure with stellar evolutionary tracks of VandenBerg et al. (2006). The dotted lines show 80% and 50% completeness limits, respectively. The CMDs of TDE and TDW have a clear RGB. The RGBs in low metallicity range where [Fe/H] is less than −1. Furthermore, there are AGB stars at a brighter magnitude than $I \simeq 22.5$, suggesting that there is a somewhat young population in the inner field of NGC 55. On the other hand, the CMDs of Sub 1 and 2 have a fainter and more metal-poor RGB than those of the thick disk structures.

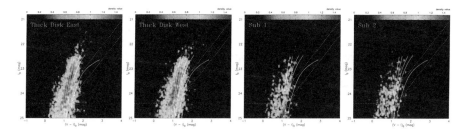

Figure 2.   CMDs for the four structures of NGC 55's outer region.

3.3.   Metallicity Distributions

Left panel of Fig. 3 shows contaminations-subtracted metallicity distributions of the four structures, made them by comparing each star on the CMD with theoretical stellar evolutionary models of VandenBerg et al. (2006). We have subtracted contaminations by using the control field data. Each mean [Fe/H] is −1.68 in TDE, −1.76 in TDW, −1.99 in Sub 1 and −1.84 in Sub 2. The MDs of TDE and TDW have a more metal-rich peak than the other MDs, where [Fe/H] is around −1.4. Furthermore, all the MDs show a somewhat broad distribution ranging from [Fe/H]= −3 to −1.

Based on these fundamental physical properties, we quantitatively discuss about the structural difference between the two galaxies with different morphological types. The right panel of Fig. 3 is the relation between metallicity and surface brightness of substructures of M31 (gray) and NGC 55 (black), suggesting that tidal debris with higher surface brightness probably tend to be more metal-rich. However, the trend of NGC 55 is systematically shifted toward more metal-poor than the one of M31. Therefore, NGC 55's halo may have formed through merging of relatively metal-poor dwarf galaxies compared to M31's halo. Provided that the mass-metallicity relation of dwarf galaxies in the Sculptor Group is the same as that observed in the Local Group, the NGC 55's halo may have originated from less massive dwarf galaxies than those for the formation of M31's halo.

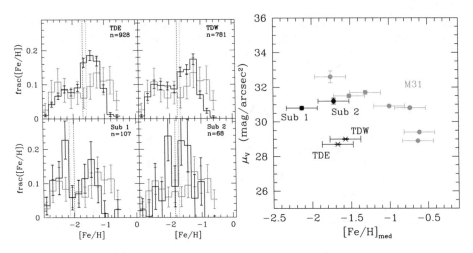

Figure 3.   **Left:** Black histograms show MDs for the four structures of NGC 55's outer region. The vertical dotted lines show the mean metallicity (black) and the median metallicity (grey) of the fields. Gray histograms correspond to the MD of the control field consisting of 69 stars. **Right:** The median metallicity against surface brightness for the substructures of NGC 55 (filled black circles) and M31 (filled grey circles, Tanaka et al. 2010).

4.   Conclusion

In this study, we have conducted Subaru/Suprime-Cam observations for NGC 55's outer region in order to estimate fundamental properties of the halo and quantitatively understand how different galaxy formation is between galaxies with different morphological types. We found some inhomogeneity structures around the galaxy. These structures are clearly metal-poor compared to M31's halo structures. By statistically comparing the relation between surface brightness and metallicity of substructures, we found the trend of NGC 55 is systematically shifted toward more metal-poor. Therefore, NGC 55's halo may have formed through merging of relatively metal-poor dwarf galaxies compared to M31's halo. It means NGC 55's halo may have originated from less massive dwarf galaxies than those for the formation of M31's halo. To more understand how different the galaxy formation is depending on morphology, we need to systematically and statistically compare a variety of galaxies in Local Volume much more.

Acknowledgments.   This work has been supported in part by a Grant-in-Aid for Scientific Research (20340039) of the Ministry of Education, Culture, Sports, Science and Technology in Japan.

References

Mouhcine, M., Ibata, R. & Rejkuba, M. 2010, ApJ, 714, L12
Peng, E. W., et al. 2002, AJ, 124, 3144
Tanaka, M., et al. 2010, ApJ, 708, 1168
Tanaka, M., et al. 2011, ApJ, 738, 150
VandenBerg, D. A., et al. 2006, ApJS, 162, 375

Galactic Archaeology: Near-Field Cosmology and the Formation of the Milky Way
ASP Conference Series, Vol. 458
W. Aoki, M. Ishigaki, T. Suda, T. Tsujimoto, N. Arimoto, eds.
© *2012 Astronomical Society of the Pacific*

The Stellar Populations of Ultra Faint Dwarf Galaxies

Sakurako Okamoto[1] and Nobuo Arimoto[2]

[1]*Kavli Institute for Astronomy & Astrophysics, Peking University, Yi He Yuan Lu 5, Hai Dian Qu, Beijing 100871, P. R. China*

[2]*National Astronomical Observatory of Japan, 2-21-1 Osawa, Mitaka, Tokyo 181-8588 JAPAN*

Abstract. We present the deep colour-magnitude diagrams (CMDs) of Galactic dwarf spheroidal (dSph) galaxies, including six ultra faint dwarf (UFD) galaxies, based on the images taken by Subaru/Suprime-Cam. The resulting CMDs show that the brighter galaxies have relatively younger populations than those of fainter ones. In the brighter dSphs, the younger populations are more spatially concentrated to the galaxy center than the old stars, indicating that the star formation in the central region continued for at least a few Gyrs, consistent with the different spatial distributions of red and blue HB stars. On the other hand, the CMDs of the faintest satellites show a single epoch of star formation as a metal-poor Galactic globular cluster. This result indicates that the gases in the progenitors of UFDs were removed more effectively than those of brighter dSphs at an occurrence of their initial star formation. This is reasonable if the UFD progenitors were likely to belong to the less massive halos than those of brighter dSphs.

1. Introduction

Dwarf galaxies around the Milky Way provide us a unique opportunity to investigate galaxy formation and evolution through their resolved stars. Most of them are considered to be both dynamically and chemically simple, with the high M/L ratio, and their number is doubled in recent years thanks to systematic surveys in the SDSS data archive (e.g. Willman et al. 2005; Belokurov et al. 2007). These newly discovered ultra faint dwarf (UFD) galaxies are roughly 10 to 100 times fainter than the well-known "classical" dSphs, having amorphous morphology and too low surface brightness to be found by the photographic plate. Because of their faint luminosities and apparently large sizes in the sky, the general natures of UFDs, such as star formation history (SFH) and detailed structural properties are still unclear.

In this contribution, we present the deep CMDs of six UFD galaxies, Canes Venatici I (CVn I), Boötes I (Boö I), Hercules, Canes Venatici II (CVn II), Leo IV and Leo T, with two classical dSphs, Draco and Ursa Minor (UMi). The images are taken with Subaru/Suprime-Cam, which is sensitive enough to derive the stellar ages based on the main sequence turn-off (MSTO), and wide enough to study the spatial distribution of stars in each galaxy. A more detail about four of these UFDs is shown in Okamoto et al. (2012).

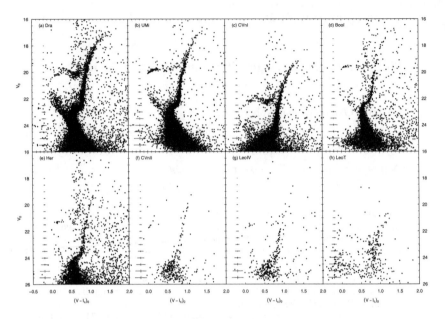

Figure 1.   The CMDs of the star-like objects within the half-light radius of Draco, Ursa Minor, Canes Venatici I, Boötes I, Hercules, Canes Venatici II, Leo IV, and Leo T. The magnitude errors are estimated by the artificial star test.

2.   Data Reduction

The observations were carried out with Subaru/Suprime-Cam. The combination of short and long exposures with Johnson V- and Cousins I-filters allowed us to construct the CMDs from the bright red giant branch (RGB) to below the old MSTO. The raw data were processed using a pipeline software SDFRED dedicated to the Suprime-Cam (Yagi et al. 2002; Ouchi et al. 2004) in usual manner. For the processed images, the DAOPHOT in IRAF package was used to obtain the PSF photometry of the resolved stars (Stetson 1987). The instrumental magnitudes of sources in the images were calibrated to the standard Johnson-Cousins photometric system using the photometric standard stars of Landolt (Landolt 1992). The average extinction in the direction of each field was taken from Schlegel, Finkbeiner & Davis (1998). To separate stars from the extended sources and noise-like objects, we used the image sharpness statistic *sharpness* and the goodness of fit statistic *chi* parameters of DAOPHOT, both were efficient to select point sources by the artificial star test. The result of artificial test was also used to estimate the accuracy and incompleteness of the photometric catalogues.

3.   Results and Discussion

The resulting CMDs of stellar objects within the half-light radii of target galaxies are shown in Figure 1, which are well extended below the MSTO except the Leo T dwarf. In Figure 1a and 1c, both red and blue HB of Draco and CVn I dSphs appear with the

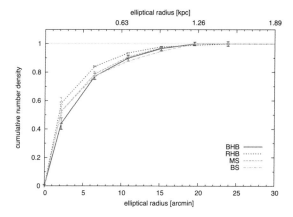

Figure 2. The cumulative radial profiles of each evolutionary phase, BHB, RHB, MS and BS stars in CVn I dSph derived by calculating the average number density within elliptical annuli, are shown in blue solid, red dashed, green long dashed, dotted, and cyan dotted-dashed lines, respectively.

well defined RGB and the blue straggler (BS) candidates, while red HB is not found in the CMD of UMi dSph (Figure 1b). The blue HB, the tight MS, and the BS candidates of Boö I and Her dSphs are seen in Figure 1d and 1e, which implies no age spread of stars in these galaxies. The CMD of CVn II dSph (Figures 1f) has similar distribution to that of the Leo IV dSph (Figures 1g), but the BS candidates are only seen in Leo IV. The distant UFD, Leo T shows broad RGB and blue loop stars, which indicate that Leo T dwarf has very different stellar population from other UFD galaxies.

By overlaying theoretical isochrones, the average age of stellar population was estimated. Padova isochrones (Marigo et al. 2008) are used by shifting to the distance of each galaxy. The fiducial sequence from MSTO to RGB of CVn I dSph is best reproduced by the isochrone of 12.6 Gyr, while the rest of UFDs are estimated as 13.7 Gyr old, with the spectroscopic confirmed metallicity (Kirby et al. 2008; Norris et al. 2008). In the case of Boö I, even the oldest isochrone shows slightly bluer colour at MSTO than that of Boö I dSph. This difference would be reduced if we adopt the more metal-rich isochrone, but it is not likely that the spectroscopically confirmed metallicity is underestimated significantly (Norris et al. 2008). The colour distributions of MSTO stars in Boö I dSph are all well represented by the photometric errors alone through the whole region, which strongly suggests that Boö I dSph has no intrinsic age spread, at least in the limit of Suprime-Cam photometry. A Kolmogorov-Smirnov test is applied to confirm that the MSTO colour distribution of four regions are the same as the distribution produced by the photometric errors alone. From this result, we conclude that Boö I dSph has a single old stellar population.

On the other hand, CVn I dSph shows the different spatial distribution in each stellar components. Figure 2 presents the cumulative radial distributions of BHB, RHB, MS and BS stars of CVn I dSph. In Figure 2, the BHBs are clearly more extended than other components, and the RHBs are more concentrated toward the galaxy centre. The colour of HB star reflects the age and metallicity; the metal-rich or younger HB stars become redder than the metal-poor or older HB stars. Therefore, this radial difference of HB morphology suggests the population gradient in CVn I dSph. The spatial distributions of the HBs are consistent with the result of Ibata et al. (2006) and Martin et al. (2007), who revealed the presence of two kinematically distinct populations in CVn I dSph. From these results, we conclude that CVn I dSph has the ancient (> 10 Gyr) but at least two populations of different metallicity, spatial distribution, and kinematics.

4. Summary

From the deep and wide images taken with Subaru/ Suprime-Cam, we demonstrate the single old stellar population of faint UFDs, Boö I, CVn II, and Leo IV dSphs as well as the population complexity of the relatively bright UFD, CVn I dSph. We confirm that Boö I dSph has no intrinsic colour spread in the width of MSTO, and no spatial difference in the CMD morphology. CVn I dSph, on the other hand, shows the relatively younger age (~ 12.6 Gyr), and different spatial distributions of BHB and RHB stars, implying the population gradient. These results indicate that the gases in the UFD progenitors were removed more effectively than those of the brighter dSphs when the initial star formation occurred. This is reasonable if the progenitors of UFDs belong to less massive halos than those of brighter dSphs at that moment.

Discussion

Bland-Hawthorn: Would you have detected tidal tails in the flattened UFD if they exist?

Okamoto: For Boö I and CVn I dSphs, the observed regions cover only the area within the half light radius, so it is still unclear whether they have the tidal tails. We are planning to investigate the outer region in future.

Wyse: Is there any evidence from the isochrone fitting for a younger torn-off age in the central regions where the RHB dominates in CVn I?

Okamoto: We could not detect any spatial difference of MSTO colour distribution in CVn I, which may be due to the relatively high photometric error at the magnitude.

References

Belokurov V., et al., 2007b, ApJ, 654, 897
Ibata R., Chapman S., Irwin M., Lewis G., Martin N., 2006, MNRAS, 373, L70
Kirby E. N., Simon J. D., Geha M., Guhathakurta P., Frebel A., 2008, ApJ, 685, L43
Landolt A. U., 1992, AJ, 104, 340
Marigo P. et al. 2008, A&A, 482, 883
Martin N. F., Ibata R. A., Chapman S. C., Irwin M., Lewis G. F., 2007, MNRAS, 380, 281
Norris J. E. et al. 2008, ApJ, 689, L113
Okamoto, S., Arimoto, N., Yamada, Y., & Onodera, M. 2012, ApJ, 744, 96
Ouchi M., et al., 2004, ApJ, 611, 660
Schlegel D. J., Finkbeiner D. P., Davis M., 1998, ApJ, 500, 525
Stetson P. B., 1987, PASP, 99, 191
Willman B., et al., 2005, ApJ, 626, L85
Yagi M. et al. 2002, AJ, 123, 66

Galactic Archaeology: Near-Field Cosmology and the Formation of the Milky Way
ASP Conference Series, Vol. 458
W. Aoki, M. Ishigaki, T. Suda, T. Tsujimoto, N. Arimoto, eds.
© 2012 Astronomical Society of the Pacific

Stellar Populations Gradients in Isolated Dwarf Galaxies

Sebastian L. Hidalgo[1] and the LCID group

[1] *Instituto de Astrofísica de Canarias. Vía Láctea s/n. E38200 - La Laguna, Tenerife, Canary Islands, Spain*

Abstract. We present the star formation history (SFH) as a function of galactocentric radius for a sample of isolated dwarf galaxies from the Local Cosmology from the Isolated Dwarfs (LCID) project. The results show a decrease of the star formation with radius for stars with ages $\lesssim 9$ Gyr. Star formation for ages $\gtrsim 10$ Gyr is present regardless of distance to the center. The maximum metallicity of Cetus and Tucana is reached earlier than in LGS-3 and Phoenix although this effect tends to disappear at larger distances from the center. The age-metallicity realtion of LGS-3 and Phoenix is more flat at old ages, increasing at younger ages. The results suggest that, regardless the morphological type, the properties of theses galaxies tend to be the same at larger distances from the center.

1. Introduction

Most of the dwarf galaxies observed in the Local Group show evidences of a complex star formation history (SFH) which last for a Hubble time (Tolstoy et al. 2009). Throughout this time, various mechanisms may have affected most notably the formation and evolution of dwarf galaxies. Among these mechanisms, the interplay between the UV-background and the self-shielding, and the effects of the supernova (SN) feedback, SN heating, and gas bulk motions on the star formation may depend on the density of the gas (Carraro et al. 2001; Mashchenko et al. 2008; Valcke et al. 2008) and hence, may show a dependency with radius affecting the spatial distribution of the star formation. The study of the radial stellar population distribution may shed light on the true extent of the role played by these mechanisms in the formation of small galaxies. This type of analysis has proven useful results in the study of the structure of dwarf galaxies and their evolution over time (Gallart et al. 2008; Hidalgo et al. 2009).

The results presented in this paper are based on the observations of the Local Cosmology from the Isolated Dwarfs (LCID) project. The aim of this project is to recover the full SFHs of six isolated dwarf galaxies of the Local Group: Phoenix, LGS-3, Cetus, Tucana, IC1613, and Leo-A. The global SFHs of these galaxies has been already described in Hidalgo et al. (2009), Hidalgo et al. (2011), Monelli et al. (2010b), Monelli et al. (2010a), Skillman et al. (2012), and Cole et al. (2007), respectively. Except in the case of Phoenix, the results presented in these papers describe the full SFHs of the observed fields of the galaxies but lack a detailed study of the SFHs as a function of the galactocentric radius. Here we present the star formation history as a function of the galactocentric radius of LGS-3, Phoenix, Cetus, and Tucana dwarf galaxies.

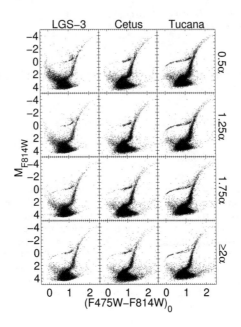

Figure 1.   Color-magnitude diagrams for LGS-3 (left), Cetus (center), and Tucana (right) for the stars located in four regions. Each row correspond to a region located at a distance marked on the right axis, which is shown in units of the scale length of each galaxy. The distance to the center increases from the top to the bottom.

2.   The Star formation History as a Function of Galactocentric Radius

The observed fields of the galaxies were divided into four elliptical regions. The regions were obtained by fitting ellipses to the isophotes determined in a Gaussian filtered image of the galaxies. The regions were selected according to the scale length (α) of each galaxy and are located at distance of 0.5α, 1.25α, 1.75α, and $r \geq 2\alpha$ from the center. In the case of Phoenix, we have not calculated the SFH for $r \geq 2\alpha$ due to the low number of stars.

Figure 1 shows the CMDs of LGS-3, Cetus, and Tucana as a function of galactocentric radius. The CMD of LGS-3 shows a gradual decrease in the number of stars located in the blue-plume with increasing distances from the center. For example, in the center there are some stars in the blue-plume above the horizontal branch (HB) which disappear completely in the outer regions. For Cetus and Tucana, the morphology of the blue-plume shows no change with radius. Monelli et al. (2010b,a) have identified these stars as a population of blue-stragglers (BSSs) with a flat radial distribution. Bernard et al. (2009) have also pointed to a change in the morphology of the HB and red giant branch (RGB) with radius. It is interesting to note that the CMD of LGS-3 at $r \geq 2\alpha$ is remarkably similar to those of Cetus and Tucana. These changes in the morphology of the CMDs suggest a gradient of the young and intermediate-age stellar populations which is more evident in LGS-3.

Using the CMDs shown in Fig. 2 we have obtained the SFHs of LGS-3, Cetus, and Tucana as a function of radius. We have used IAC-pop/MinnIAC to obtain the SFHs

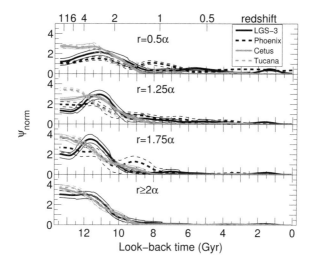

Figure 2.   Normalized SFRs obtained using the CMDs shown in Figure 1. The SFR of Phoenix has been obtained using the data presented in Hidalgo et al. (2009) but recalculated at the radius shown here. The SFR of Phoenix has not been obtained for $r \geq 2\alpha$ due to the poor statistics number of stars.

as described in Aparicio & Hidalgo (2009) and Hidalgo et al. (2011). In short, the technique uses IAC-star (Aparicio & Gallart 2004) to create a model synthetic CMD to compare its stellar population distribution with the star distribution in the observed CMD. This comparison is carried out using IAC-star/MinnIAC algorithms which finally give the SFH: mass of the stellar populations ever formed in the galaxy as a function of the age and metallicity. This technique does not assume any age-metallicity relation (AMR) for the stars and is able to explore a large range of physical parameters and functions (as stellar evolution libraries, binary fraction of stars, and initial mass function) along with variations in the values of the photometric zero points, distance modulus, and reddening. This procedure minimizes the impact of the uncertainties of these functions and parameters on the final SFH. The reader is referred to Aparicio & Hidalgo (2009) and Hidalgo et al. (2011) for a full description of the technique used here to obtain the SFHs.

Figure 2 shows the SFR of LGS-3, Phoenix, Cetus, Tucana obtained using the CMDs shown in Fig. 1 and, in the case of Phoenix, the results from Hidalgo et al. (2009). The SFR has been normalized to its integral at each radius. The results show for all galaxies a decrease of the SFR with radius for stars with ages $\lesssim 9$ Gyr. Star formation for ages $\gtrsim 10$ Gyr is present regardless of distance to the center. At a distance of $r \geq 2\alpha$ the normalized SFR is, within the error bars, indistinguishable. Although at $r \geq 2\alpha$ the star formation has virtually disappeared for stars with ages $\lesssim 10$ Gyr, can still be observed some star formation at ~ 3.5 Gyr for Cetus and Tucana and at ~ 1.5 Gyr for LGS-3. This star formation has been identified in Cetus and Tucana as a BSSs by Monelli et al. (2012). It is clear that the SFRs tend to be very similar as the distance to the center increases.

Figure 3 shows the AMR as a function of radius for all the galaxies. The maximum metallicity of Cetus and Tucana is reached earlier than in LGS-3 and Phoenix although

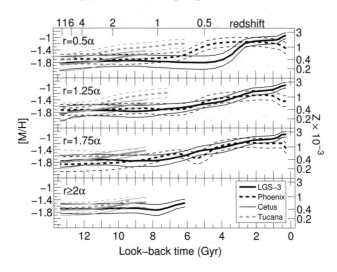

Figure 3.　　Age-metallcity relations obtained for the CMDs shown in Figure 1.

this effect tends to disappear at larger distances from the center. The AMR of LGS-3 and Phoenix is more flat at old ages, increasing at younger ages. In this case, as was the case for the SFR, the AMRs tend to be the same at larger radius.

References

Aparicio, A., & Gallart, C. 2004, AJ, 128, 1465

Aparicio, A., & Hidalgo, S. L. 2009, AJ, 138, 558

Bernard, E. J., Monelli, M., Gallart, C., Drozdovsky, I., Stetson, P. B., Aparicio, A., Cassisi, S., Mayer, L., Cole, A. A., Hidalgo, S. L., Skillman, E. D., & Tolstoy, E. 2009, ApJ, 699, 1742

Carraro, G., Chiosi, C., Girardi, L., & Lia, C. 2001, MNRAS, 327, 69

Cole, A. A., Skillman, E. D., Tolstoy, E., Gallagher, J. S., III, Aparicio, A., Dolphin, A. E., Gallart, C., Hidalgo, S. L., Saha, A., Stetson, P. B., & Weisz, D. R. 2007, ApJ, 659, L17

Gallart, C., Stetson, P. B., Meschin, I. P., Pont, F., & Hardy, E. 2008, ApJ, 682, L89

Hidalgo, S. L., Aparicio, A., Martínez-Delgado, D., & Gallart, C. 2009, ApJ, 705, 704

Hidalgo, S. L., Aparicio, A., Skillman, E., Monelli, M., Gallart, C., Cole, A., Dolphin, A., Weisz, D., Bernard, E. J., Cassisi, S., Mayer, L., Stetson, P., Tolstoy, E., & Ferguson, H. 2011, ApJ, 730, 14

Mashchenko, S., Wadsley, J., & Couchman, H. M. P. 2008, Science, 319, 174

Monelli, M., Bernard, E. J., Gallart, C., Fiorentino, G., Drozdovsky, I., Aparicio, A., Bono, G., Cassisi, S., Skillman, E. D., & Stetson, P. B. 2012, ArXiv e-prints. 1201.2821

Monelli, M., Gallart, C., Hidalgo, S. L., Aparicio, A., Skillman, E. D., Cole, A. A., Weisz, D. R., Mayer, L., Bernard, E. J., Cassisi, S., Dolphin, A. E., Drozdovsky, I., & Stetson, P. B. 2010a, ApJ, 722, 1864

Monelli, M., Hidalgo, S. L., Stetson, P. B., Aparicio, A., Gallart, C., Dolphin, A. E., Cole, A. A., Weisz, D. R., Skillman, E. D., Bernard, E. J., Mayer, L., Navarro, J. F., Cassisi, S., Drozdovsky, I., & Tolstoy, E. 2010b, ApJ, 720, 1225

Skillman et al. 2012, in prep.

Tolstoy, E., Hill, V., & Tosi, M. 2009, ARA&A, 47, 371

Valcke, S., de Rijcke, S., & Dejonghe, H. 2008, MNRAS, 389, 1111

Galactic Archaeology: Near-Field Cosmology and the Formation of the Milky Way
ASP Conference Series, Vol. 458
W. Aoki, M. Ishigaki, T. Suda, T. Tsujimoto, N. Arimoto, eds.
© 2012 Astronomical Society of the Pacific

Galactic Archaeology Using Star Clusters in Nearby Galaxies

Myung Gyoon Lee

Astronomy Program, Dept of Physics and Astronomy, Seoul National University, Seoul, 151-742, Korea

Abstract. Star clusters are an excellent tool for archaeology of nearby galaxies. Recently the paradigm for star clusters is changing from simplicity to variety. With the advent of the Hubble Space Telescope and wide field imagers in large telescopes new types of star clusters and cluster-like objects have been discovered in the nearby universe. These objects must include significant clues for understanding the formation of their host galaxies and galaxy groups. However, their nature and origin is still too intriguing to explain. I review the current status of our understanding of globular clusters in nearby galaxies in terms of galactic archaeology. There are cumulating evidence that every galaxy has a different star formation history, although some of them look similar in their morphology. Galaxies are formed via several mechanisms rather than any single one.

1. Prologue: Archaeology and Astronomy

In 1907 Harlow Shapley, the pioneer in galaxy archaelogy, entered Missouri University, majoring in journalism. He opened the curriculum book to choose courses to take. "The first course was a-r-c-h-a-e-o-l-g-y. I couldn't pronounce it. The second course was a-s-t-r-o-n-m-y. I could pronounce it – and here I am." (in 'Through rugged ways to the stars' by Shapley 1969).

Here we get together to discuss galaxy archaeology in astronomy. While archaelogy traces the history of humans using ancient fossils or clues, galactic archaeology reveals the history of galaxies using astronomical clues. Star clusters are an excellent archaeological tool, because they are mostly made of simple populations allowing us to measure their age and metallicity.

I present an overview of recent findings on early history of galaxies based on the study of globular clusters in the nearby universe. These will be critical clues to answer big questions such as the formation of globular clusters and dwarf galaxies, the formation of halos, bulges, bars, and disks in disk galaxies, and the formation of giant elliptical galaxies.

2. Globular Clusters in the Milky Way Galaxy

There are about 160 globular clusters in the Milky Way Galaxy (MWG) (Harris 1996). They serve as the reference objects for understanding the nature of globular clusters in other galaxies. The MW globular clusters can be divided into three groups: the bulge/thick disk group, the inner halo group, and the outer halo group. Fig. 1 displays their age, [Fe/H], and half-light radii (r_h) versus galactocentric distance (R_{GC}). Reliable ages based on the main-sequence fitting are available for many of these (Marín-Franch et al. 2009; Carretta et al. 2010; Dotter et al. 2011). Most globular clusters are older than 10 Gyrs with a scatter of about 1 Gyr, and only a few at 10 kpc $< R_{GC} <$ 20 kpc (Pal 1, Pal 12, and Ter 7) are 7 to 9 Gyrs old, much younger than the others. Their mean age is slightly decreasing from 13 Gyr to 11 Gyr as R_{GC} increases from 1 kpc to 20 kpc and outward. Most globular clusters are located at $R_{GC} <$ 40 kpc, but several are found far out at 70 kpc $< R_{GC} <$ 130 kpc. These outer globular clusters are metal-poor and have large half-light radii. Their metallicity shows a large spread at $R_{GC} <$ 30 kpc. The mean values of the metallicity show an anti-correlation with R_{GC} at $R_{GC} <$ 30 kpc, while they shows no correlation in the outer area. The metallicity distribution is bimodal: the metal-rich component in the bulge/thick disk, and the metal-poor component in the halo. The mean size of the globular clusters increases as R_{GC} increases. The globular clusters in the bulge group ($R_{GC}8 <$ 8 kpc) shows a strong age-[Fe/H] relation, while those in the halo ($R_{GC}8 <$ 8 kpc) shows a much weaker relation (Dotter et al. 2011). The globular clusters in the outer areas are considered to have an accretion-origin. So the globular clusters in the MWG were formed mostly within a short period of time, but not simultaneously, in the early days. The oldest globular clusters are located in the inner region of the MWG.

3.   Globular Clusters in Nearby Disk Galaxies

Recent wide field surveys found four extended globular clusters in the remote halos of NGC 6822 (Hwang et al. 2011). These clusters are probably old and metal-poor. Interestingly all they are located along the major axis of the NGC 6822 halo which is almost perpendicular to the disk. IC 10 is a famous starburst galaxy in the Local Group. The existence of young clusters in its main body has been known for long. Lim & Lee (2012, this conference) found a dozen of compact star clusters in the remote halo of this galaxy. Some of these clusters may be old and metal-poor. Similarly these old and metal-poor clusters were found in another famous starburst galaxy M82 in the M81 group (Lim et al. 2012, in preparation).

M31 has about 650 globular clusters (Lee et al. (2008), Lee et al. (2012, in preparation)). Ages and [Fe/H] for many of these were derived from the Lick line indices in comparison with the simple stellar population models. The kinematics of the M31 GCs in Fig. 2 show that both the metal-poor and metal-rich globular clusters show significant rotation and that the latter rotates faster than the former. So the halo of M31 is rotating, in contrast to the little rotating halo of the MWG. It is also noted that several globular clusters are not following the rotation, indicating that they have an external origin.

The age distribution of M31 globular clusters in Fig. 3 shows a strong peak at about 12 Gyr, similar to the case of the MW globular clusters. However it shows also a long tail in the young age range, which is not seen in the MWG. Both metal-poor and metal-rich globular clusters show a similar distribution. The metallicity distribution of the M31 globular clusters in Fig. 3 shows a broad distribution, while the MW globular clusters show a bimodal metallicity distribution. Younger globular clusters ($<$ 10 Gyr) have higher metallicity. These show that the globular clusters in M31 were formed in a much more extended period than the MW globular clusters.

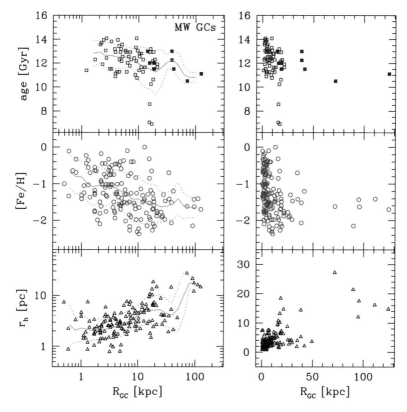

Figure 1.   Age, [Fe/H], and half-light radii (r_h) versus galactocentric distance (R_{GC}) in logarithmic (left panels) and linear (right panels) scales for MW globular clusters. Solid lines and dotted lines represent the mean values and 1σ, respectively.

4.   Globular Clusters in Giant Elliptical Galaxies

Giant elliptical galaxies (gEs) are rich in globular clusters. It has been known long that the globular clusters in gEs show a bimodal color distritribution, invoking several interesting scenarios to explain it. However the ages and metallicities of these globular clusters are relatively less known because of the difficulty in obtaining their spectra. Recently the data for age and [Fe/H] for globular clusters in several gEs in the literature were compiled by Park et al. (2012, ApJ, submitted), as shown in Fig. 4. The age distribution of metal-poor GCs in the combined sample shows a strong peak at about 12 Gyr and a weaker tail to the younger age. In contrast the metal-rich globular clusters show no old peak, but a much broader distribution. The metallicity distribution is clearly bimodal. Younger globular clusters (< 10 Gyr) shows a stronger metal-rich component, while older globular clusters (> 10 Gyr) shows a stronger metal-poor components. These show that globular clusters in gEs were formed in a much more extended period compared with the MWG globular clusters, and that the metal-rich ones were formed together with the stars, later than the metal-poor ones.

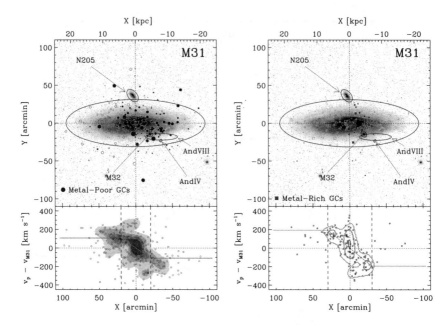

Figure 2.   Spatial distribution (upper panel) and radial velocity versus major axis of M31 (lower panel) for metal-poor (left) and metal-rich (right) globular clusters in M31. Contours in the lower panel represent the number density.

5.   Wandering Globular Clusters

Globular clusters are found not only in galaxies but also between galaxies in the M81 Group (Jang et al. 2012, in preparation), Virgo cluster (Lee et al. 2010a), Coma cluster (Peng et al. 2011), and Abell 1185 (West et al. 2011). Most of the intragroup/ intra-cluster or wandering globular clus are probably old and metal-poor, indicating that their origin may be dwarf galaxies (Lee et al. 2010a).

6.   Summary

Major recent findings are summarized as below. The Milky Way Galaxy is not typical, but unique in that its globular clusters are mostly very old and it lacks of young massive globular clusters. Starburst galaxies have not only young star clusters but also old globular clusters in their halo showing that they are also old. The kinematics of the metal-poor globular clusters in M31 show that the M31 halo is rotating. The globular clusters in gEs show a bimodal metallicity distribution and a broad age distribution. Intracluster globular clusters are mostly blue indicating that they are metal-poor. These observational clues for globular clusters are consistent with the mixture model (the bibimbap model) (Lee et al. 2010b). Every galaxy has a different evolution history, although they sometimes look similar in their morphology.

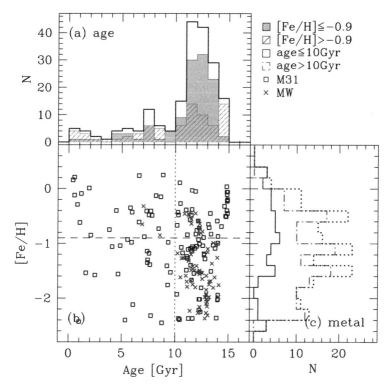

Figure 3. Age-[Fe/H] relation for globular clusters in M31. (a) Age distribution for metal-poor (filled histogram), metal-rich (hatched histogram), and all GCs (empty histogram) in M31. (b) Age-[Fe/H] relation for the globular clusters in M31 (open squares) and the MWG (crosses). (c) [Fe/H] distribution for young (solid line), old (dot-dashed line), and all GCs (dotted line).

Discussion

Ferguson: Could you comment on how you are finding globular clusters in the M81 Group since these objects must be almost unresolved from the ground?

Lee: Its hard to find them with the images taken with the ground-based telescopes. We used the HST images in the archive to find them.

Cohen: Two papers on globular clusters are about to be submitted: a) Jay Strader is leading a study of M87 globular clusters with about 750 spectroscopic velocities, and b) Janet Coluccis study of high dispersion spectra of about 20 globular clusters, including abundances of about 15 elements.

Lee: Thats wonderful.

Hensler: Super star clusters (SSCs) are formed in mergers's central peaks. They are supposed to develop to globular clusters. Do you see a possibility that SSCs are also formed in the tidal tails of mergers?

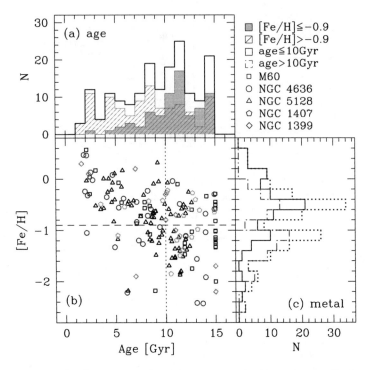

Figure 4.   Age-[Fe/H] relation for globular clusters in gEs a) Age distribution for metal-poor (filled histogram), metal-rich (hatched histogram), and all GCs (empty histogram). (b) Age-[Fe/H] relation for globular clusters in gEs. (c) [Fe/H] distribution for young (solid line), old (dot-dashed line), and all GCs (dotted line) in gEs.

Lee: We do not have mergers with tidal tails in the sample of our study. However, I think that SSCs will evolve to globular clusters when they get old.

Acknowledgments.   The author is grateful to his collaborators including Hong Soo Park, Sungsoon Lim, Insung Jang, Ho Seong Hwang, Narae Hwang, and Nobuo Arimoto. This was supported in part by Mid-career Research Program through the NRF grant funded by the MEST (no.2010-0013875).

References

Carretta, E. et al. 2010, A&A, 516, A55. 1003.1723
Dotter, A. et al. 2011, ApJ, 738, 74. 1106.4307
Harris, W. E. 1996, AJ, 112, 1487
Hwang, N. et al. 2011, ApJ, 738, 58. 1106.2878
Lee, M. G. et al. 2008, ApJ, 674, 886. 0711.1232
Lee, M. G. et al. 2010a, Science, 328, 334. 1003.2499
Lee, M. G. et al. 2010b, ApJ, 709, 1083. 0912.1728
Marín-Franch, A. 2009, ApJ, 694, 1498. 0812.4541
Peng, E. W. 2011, ApJ, 730, 23. 1101.1000
West, M. J. et al. 2011, A&A, 528, A115. 1101.5399

Galactic Archaeology: Near-Field Cosmology and the Formation of the Milky Way
ASP Conference Series, Vol. 458
W. Aoki, M. Ishigaki, T. Suda, T. Tsujimoto, N. Arimoto, eds.
©2012 Astronomical Society of the Pacific

Abundance Patterns and the Chemical Enrichment of Nearby Dwarf Galaxies

Vanessa Hill[1] and the DART collaboration

[1]*Laboratoire Lagrange, Universit de Nice Sophia-Antipolis, CNRS, Observatoire de la Côte d'Azur, BP 4229, 06304 Nice cedex 4*

Abstract. I review here the chemical abundances of individual stars in the nearest classical dwarf spheroidal galaxies, that have become available in increasing numbers (sample size and galaxies probed) in the last decade.

1. Introduction

The detailed chemical abundance patterns in individual stars of a stellar population provide a fossil record of chemical enrichment over different timescales. As generations of stars form and evolve, stars of various masses contribute different elements to the system, on timescales directly linked to their mass. These studies require precise measurements of elemental abundances in individual stars, only achievable with high-resolution and reasonably high signal-to-noise spectra. It is only very recently that this has become possible beyond our Galaxy. It is efficient high-resolution spectrographs on 8−10m telescopes that have made it possible to obtain high resolution (R>20000) spectra of RGB stars in nearby dwarf spheroidal galaxies (dSphs). After the pioneering works of Shetrone et al. (2001, 1998) and Bonifacio et al. (2000) in dSphs, samples have grown significantly in the last ten years, in particular thanks to multi-object high (R≥20,000, e.g. Tolstoy et al. 2006) and medium (R~7000, e.g. Kirby et al. 2009) resolution spectrographs. In the following, I will concentrate on the case of classical dSph galaxies, in which samples now reach samples sizes within in a given galaxy large enough to actually follow its chemical enrichment, down to the most primitive epochs of the chemical enrichment.

2. Alpha elements and star formation modes in dwarf galaxies

Alpha elements are essentially produced in massive stars and promptly released to the interstellar medium by core-collapse supernovae (SNII), while iron is also heavily produced by the longer-lived SNIa. Both are often used in conjunction, as a clock of star formation in stellar populations. In dwarf galaxies, the observed [α/Fe] ratios have been known to be lower than in the Milky-Way at the same metallicity, when probed from small samples drawn from the inner parts of these systems (Shetrone et al. 2001, 2003). More recently, thanks to multi-object high-resolution spectroscopy (R≥20,000), large samples of RGB stars in a few dwarf galaxies could be assembled, an effort to which the DART collaboration has contributed to a large extent (see e.g. Tolstoy et al. 2006, 2009). Even more recently, Kirby et al. (2009, 2011) have applied a new method to derive individual abundances from medium-resolution spectra (R~7000) to even larger samples of RGB stars in several dwarf galaxies. In Fig.1, we show the trend of the alpha elements (Mg and Ca) as a function of metallicity in a variety of nearby classical dwarf galaxies with different star formation histories : Sculptor (Mv=-11.1) and Sextans (Mv=-9.5) have predominantly old populations and no young stars, while Fornax (Mv=-13.2) and Sagittarius have a predominant intermediate age population in addition to their old population. This plot is quite revealing of the different loci occupied by the each galaxy (both in terms of metallicity ranges and elemental ratios), but also of the clear *internal chemical evolution within each system*, revealed by the narrow [α/Fe] trend as a function of metallicity.

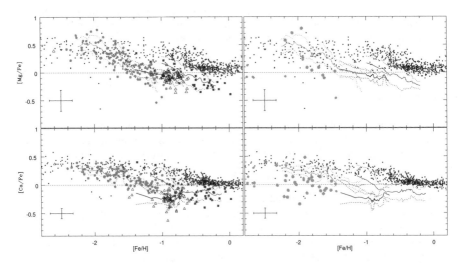

Figure 1.   The run of alpha elements (Mg and Ca) as a function of metallicity in a variety of nearby classical dwarf galaxies. *Left panel*: Sagitarius (red/gray filled squares: Sbordone et al. 2007; McWilliam & Smecker-Hane 2005), Fornax (blue/dark-gray open triangles: Letarte et al. 2010) and Sculptor (green/light-gray filled circles: Hill et al. 2012). *Right panel*: Sextans (orange/light-gray filled circles: Kirby et al. 2010; Aoki et al. 2009; Shetrone et al. 2003). In all panels, solid colored/gray lines are the running average (trend) and dotted lines are the corresponding σ-dispersion for each dwarf galaxy. The underlying small dots are the Milky-Way stars (Cayrel et al. (2004) for [Fe/H]< −2.5, and Venn et al. (2004) for [Fe/H]≥-2.5).

The α-elements knee: in each galaxy there seems to be a critical metallicity under which the abundance ratios overlay that of the Milky-Way halo. This critical metallicity is best defined in Sculptor where the sample probes nicely all metallicities above and below this point, the *knee* is located around [Fe/H] = −1.8 or −2. At metallicities below this *knee*, there seems to be no difference anymore between the Milky-Way halo and the dwarf galaxies, which in turn points toward a high mass Initial Mass Function (IMF) similar in all systems, despite the very different potential wells of the parent galaxies. The pioneering studies that were conducted a decade ago using single-slit spectrographs never sampled significantly this metal-poor component and therefore concluded that the dwarf galaxies always displayed lower α/Fe with respect to the Galactic halo.

Dependance of the knee position on galaxy luminosity: Furthermore, it is interesting to note that the location of this *knee* is related to the galaxy total luminosity, or to its mean metallicity (since both are related, see eg. Kirby et al. 2008, and references therein). This relationship can be expected if the galaxy total luminosity scales with its ability to retain the metals that its star formation episodes produce. In turn, this ability to retain metals must be linked to the system's potential well but also the star formation mode (strong activity versus sporadic bursts of small intensity). It is further interesting to note that the location of the *knee* in Sculptor coincides with the metallicity at which the stellar population in this galaxy change from the metal-rich, centrally concentrated and kinematically hotter population to the metal-poor, more extended, kinematically cooler population (Tolstoy et al. 2004; Battaglia et al. 2008). In Fornax also, two such populations exist (Battaglia et al. 2006), although the position of the *knee* is not established firmly enough to determine whether it also coincides with the kinematical and morphological separation.

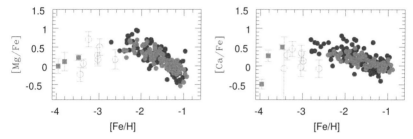

Figure 2.   Trend of the α-elements Mg and Ca seen at medium-resolution spectroscopy (red/gray filled circles Kirby et al. 2010, sorted to keep only the targets with low internal errors: error$_{[Fe/H]}$ < 0.15, error$_{[Mg/Fe]}$ < 0.3 or error$_{[Ca/Fe]}$ ≤ 0.4) compared with those seen at higher dispersion (green/light-gray filled circles: Hill et al. 2012), and complemented at the lowest metallicities by high resolution data (filled squares: Tafelmeyer et al. 2010; Frebel et al. 2010a) and the medium-resolution data obtained with X-shooter@VLT (open circles: Starkenburg et al., this volume).

How much dispersion is there ? In addition to the abundance ratio trends, the dispersion around these trends are a precious indication of how star formation has proceeded in these small galaxies. In the left-hand side panels of Fig. 1, the narrowness of the trends in Sculptor, Fornax and Sagittarius can be appreciated. In fact, the observed dispersion around the trend is fully compatible with the measurement error. On the other hand, the right-hand side panels of Fig. 1 shows that the lowest luminosity system probed here (Sextans) displays a larger dispersion than in the higher luminosity systems: this is expected (see for example the SPH simulations of isolated dwarf galaxies by Revaz et al. 2009; Revaz & Jablonka 2012) if the lowest luminosity systems only make stars in very low intensity sporadic bursts of star formation, leading to a succession of pockets of gas with distinctive abundances that produce a dispersion in the abundance ratios (in addition to very little age-metallicity relation in these systems). Carina, the prototypical galaxy with two separate burst of star formation, also shows a very large variety of abundance ratios at all metallicities (Koch et al. 2008b), although Lemasle et al. (2012) shows that the dispersion is minimal for stars that were made within the second burst of star formation with respect to the first (see Venn etal.

this volume for a thorough discussion of Carina). Simulated galaxies which end up with characteristics as of Carina (luminosity, mean metallicity and two well separated burst) in Revaz & Jablonka (2012) simulations also show a chemical dispersion at all metallicities.

Is there really a knee ? In the Sculptor dwarf galaxy, Kirby et al. (2011) claim that, while there is a hint of a flattening of the [Ca/Fe] (and [Ti/Fe]) at the lowest metallicities, the [Mg/Fe] ratios seem to keep on increasing as metallicity decreases with no break in the slope. However, Fig. 2 shows that selecting the best measured part of their sample yields a trend perfectly consistent with our (DART, R=20,000) data in Sculptor which does show a flattening of the [Mg/Fe] at low metallicity. Together with the dedicated follow-up of the lowest metallicity stars in Sculptor (Tafelmeyer et al. (2010), Starkenburg et al. this volume, and the star in Frebel et al. (2010a)) which all show normal α/Fe ratios, there is little room for any doubt as to the presence of a *knee* in Sculptor, and a *plateau* (or even a downturn at the very lowest metallicities < −3), rather than a steeply increasing Mg/Fe at low metallicity.

3. Bringing age and metallicity probes together: Sculptor

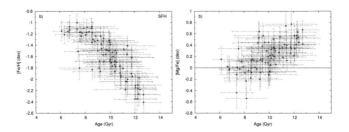

Figure 3.   Age-Metallicity relation (left panel) and the age dependence (right panel) of the [Mg/Fe] ratio in the Sculptor dwarf galaxy (de Boer et al. 2012).

Recently, de Boer et al. (2011) obtained deep BVI colour-magnitude diagrams (CMD) reaching the oldest turnoffs, over the whole face of Sculptor. It then becomes feasible to use the CMD (where the turnoff regions carries most of the age information) together with the spectroscopically measured metallicity distribution (MDF) of red giants to build a self-consistent picture of the star-formation history and metal-enrichment history of the galaxy, with no (or minimal) age-metallicity degeneracies. Such a combined approach was used successfully by de Boer et al. (2012) to produce a global star-formation history (as well as broken up in concentric annuli across the whole galaxy) for Sculptor, enlightening the well known main peak of star formation some ~ 12 Gyrs ago that lasted ~ 2 Gyrs, but also a low-level tail of star formation that lasted until ~5-6 Gyrs ago. Armed with this star formation history, one can then turn back to the RGB stars with spectroscopically measured metallicities and work out the most probable age for each star (based on its position in the CMD and its metallicity), given the underlying star formation history. The resulting age-metallicity relation and Mg/Fe-age relations are given in Fig.3: the age-metallicity relation is narrow and well defined (which is typically not the case when no underlying star formation history is assumed). The Mg/Fe-age relation can then be used to establish the timescale on which

SNIa started contributing to the chemical enrichment (position of the *knee* in age): in Sculptor, the Mg/Fe plateau lasted around 2 Gyrs.

4. Very metal-poor stars in dwarf galaxies

Using a new calibration of the Ca II infrared triplet, based on synthetic spectra, Starkenburg et al. (2010) showed that dSph contain, albeit in small numbers, extremely metal poor stars, at least down to ~ −4 metallicity (see also Starkenburg et al., this volume). There does not seem to be a clear difference between classical dSph galaxies and the ultra-faint dwarfs in this respect anymore (Kirby et al. 2008), and the fall-off both metallicity tails agree quantitatively with that of the galactic halo (Starkenburg et al. 2010).

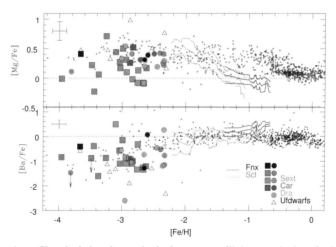

Figure 4.   Chemical abundances in the lowest metallicity stars in dwarf spheroidal galaxies: ultra-faint dwarfs (triangles, Koch et al. (2008b); Frebel et al. (2010b); Norris et al. (2010); Simon et al. (2010)); classical dwarfs (big squares and circles) Sculptor (Tafelmeyer et al. 2010; Frebel et al. 2010a, and Starkenburg et al. this volume), Fornax (Tafelmeyer et al. 2010), Sextans (Aoki et al. 2009; Tafelmeyer et al. 2010), Carina (Koch et al. 2008a; Venn et al. 2012), Draco CohenHuang:2009; Milky-Way comparisons symbols and running averages as of Fig.1

Thanks to the high-resolution follow-up of the extremely metal-poor candidates ([Fe/H] < −3) from classical and ultra-faint dSph galaxies, by the DART collaboration but also numerous other groups (see the figure caption for references) not only the metallicity, but also the detailed chemical composition of extremely metal poor stars can also be probed, and Fig. 4 shows Mg/Fe and Ba/Fe for a compilation of known stars in classical and ultra-faint dwarf galaxies below [Fe/H] < −2.3. There is a global agreement in the abundance ratios of extremely metal poor stars ([Fe/H] < −3) in dwarfs galaxies and the Milky-Way halo. However, it is also evident that the statistics in each system is still very poor, and much is needed before firm conclusions can be drawn on the true resemblence of extremely-metal poor stars in dwarf galaxies and the Milky-Way halo. Indeed, some elemental signatures may already be seen to differ slightly: among the 10 stars in Sculptor with [Fe/H]<-2.5 and observed carbon, none are carbon-rich while in the Milky-Wa ~ 25% have [C/Fe]>1, and in Sextans (Honda et al. 2011) and Bootes (Norris et al. 2010), such carbon-rich stars have been observed among many less candidates.

References

Aoki, W., Arimoto, N., Sadakane, K., Tolstoy, E., Battaglia, G., & al. 2009, A&A, 502, 569

Battaglia, G., Helmi, A., Tolstoy, E., Irwin, M., Hill, V., & Jablonka, P. 2008, ApJ, 681, L13

Battaglia, G., Tolstoy, E., Helmi, A., Irwin, M. J., Letarte, B., & al. 2006, A&A, 459, 423

Bonifacio, P., Hill, V., Molaro, P., Pasquini, L., Di Marcantonio, P., & Santin, P. 2000, A&A, 359, 663

Cayrel, R., Depagne, E., Spite, M., Hill, V., Spite, F., & al. 2004, A&A, 416, 1117

de Boer, T. J. L., Tolstoy, E., Hill, V., Saha, A., Olsen, K., Starkenburg, E., Lemalse, B., Irwin, M. J., & Battaglia, G. 2012, accepted for A&A. arXiv:astro-ph/1201.2408

de Boer, T. J. L., Tolstoy, E., Saha, A., Olsen, K., Irwin, M. J., & al. 2011, A&A, 528, A119

Frebel, A., Kirby, E. N., & Simon, J. D. 2010a, Nat, 464, 72

Frebel, A., Simon, J. D., Geha, M., & Willman, B. 2010b, ApJ, 708, 560

Hill, V., Venn, K., Tolstoy, E., & al. 2012, in preparation

Honda, S., Aoki, W., Arimoto, N., & Sadakane, K. 2011, PASJ, 63, 523

Kirby, E. N., Cohen, J. G., Smith, G. H., Majewski, S. R., Sohn, S. T., & Guhathakurta, P. 2011, ApJ, 727, 79

Kirby, E. N., Guhathakurta, P., Bolte, M., Sneden, C., & Geha, M. C. 2009, ApJ, 705, 328

Kirby, E. N., Guhathakurta, P., Simon, J. D., Geha, M. C., Rockosi, C. M., & al. 2010, ApJS, 191, 352

Kirby, E. N., Guhathakurta, P., & Sneden, C. 2008, ApJ, 682, 1217

Koch, A., Grebel, E. K., Gilmore, G. F., Wyse, R. F. G., Kleyna, J. T., & al. 2008a, AJ, 135, 1580

Koch, A., McWilliam, A., Grebel, E. K., Zucker, D. B., & Belokurov, V. 2008b, ApJ, 688, L13

Lemasle, B., Hill, V., Tolstoy, E., Venn, M., K. A. Shetrone, & al. 2012, accepted for A&A. arXiv:astro-ph/1112.0431

Letarte, B., Hill, V., Tolstoy, E., Jablonka, P., Shetrone, M., & al. 2010, A&A, 523, A17

McWilliam, A., & Smecker-Hane, T. A. 2005, in Cosmic Abundances as Records of Stellar Evolution and Nucleosynthesis, edited by T. G. Barnes III & F. N. Bash, vol. 336 of Astronomical Society of the Pacific Conference Series, 221

Norris, J. E., Yong, D., Gilmore, G., & Wyse, R. F. G. 2010, ApJ, 711, 350

Revaz, Y., & Jablonka, P. 2012, A&A, 538, A82

Revaz, Y., Jablonka, P., Sawala, T., Hill, V., Letarte, B., & al. 2009, A&A, 501, 189

Sbordone, L., Bonifacio, P., Buonanno, R., Marconi, G., Monaco, L., & Zaggia, S. 2007, A&A, 465, 815

Shetrone, M., Venn, K. A., Tolstoy, E., Primas, F., Hill, V., & Kaufer, A. 2003, AJ, 125, 684

Shetrone, M. D., Bolte, M., & Stetson, P. B. 1998, AJ, 115, 1888

Shetrone, M. D., Côté, P., & Sargent, W. L. W. 2001, ApJ, 548, 592

Simon, J. D., Frebel, A., McWilliam, A., Kirby, E. N., & Thompson, I. B. 2010, ApJ, 716, 446

Starkenburg, E., Hill, V., Tolstoy, E., González Hernández, J. I., Irwin, M., & al. 2010, A&A, 513, A34

Tafelmeyer, M., Jablonka, P., Hill, V., Shetrone, M., Tolstoy, E., & al. 2010, A&A, 524, A58

Tolstoy, E., Hill, V., Irwin, M., Helmi, A., Battaglia, G., & al. 2006, The Messenger, 123, 33

Tolstoy, E., Hill, V., & Tosi, M. 2009, ARA&A, 47, 371

Tolstoy, E., Irwin, M. J., Helmi, A., Battaglia, G., Jablonka, P., & al. 2004, ApJ, 617, L119

Venn, K., Shetrone, M., Irwin, M., Hill, V., Jablonka, P., & al. 2012, submitted to ApJ

Venn, K. A., Irwin, M., Shetrone, M. D., Tout, C. A., Hill, V., & Tolstoy, E. 2004, AJ, 128, 1177

Galactic Archaeology: Near-Field Cosmology and the Formation of the Milky Way
ASP Conference Series, Vol. 458
W. Aoki, M. Ishigaki, T. Suda, T. Tsujimoto, N. Arimoto, eds.
© 2012 Astronomical Society of the Pacific

The Inhomogeneous Chemical Evolution of the Carina Dwarf Galaxy

Kim Venn,[1] Bertrand Lemasle,[2] Matthew Shetrone,[3] Vanessa Hill,[4] Eline Tolstoy,[2] Mike Irwin [5]

[1] *University of Victoria, Dept. of Physics & Astronomy, Elliott Building, 3800 Finnerty Road, Victoria, BC, V8P 5C2, CANADA*

[2] *Kapteyn Astronomical Institute, University of Groningen, PO Box 800, 9700AV Groningen, The Netherlands*

[3] *McDonald Observatory, University of Texas at Austin, HC75 Box 1337-MCD, Fort Davis, TX, 79734*

[4] *Université de Nice Sophia-Antipolis, CNRS, Observatoire de la Côte d'Azur, Laboratoire Cassiopée, 06304, Nice Cedex 4, France*

[5] *Institute of Astronomy, University of Cambridge, Madingley Road, Cambridge CB3 0HA, UK*

1. Introduction

The Carina dSph galaxy has long been known to have an unusual and episodic star formation history, with distinct main sequence turnoffs clearly seen in its deep colour magnitude diagram (first shown by Smecker-Hane et al. 1996). Its star formation history is best described by an old population (10-12 Gyr), a dominant intermediate-aged population ($\sim$ 75% with ages 5-7 Gyr), and a trace young population (1-2 Gyr), separated by long quiescent periods (e.g., Bono et al. 2010, Lanfranchi et al. 2006, Monelli et al. 2003, Dolphin 2002). In spite of this punctuated star formation history, the Carina dSph has a very narrow red giant branch, most likely due to a fortuitous alignment in the age-metallicity degeneracy, but also partially due to the fact that the majority of stars are from the intermediate-aged population which may have a very small metallicity spread (Bono et al. 2010).

VLT FLAMES multi-fiber spectroscopy has been carried out for red giant branch stars in the inner region of the Carina dwarf galaxy. High resolution (R$\sim$45,000) UVES spectroscopy over a 2000 Å range has been obtained for 17 stars (Venn et al. 2012, Koch et al. 2008, Shetrone et al. 2003), while GIRAFFE (R$\sim$20,000) spectroscopy has been examined for an additional 35 stars over three shorter wavelength intervals (totalling $\sim$700Å; Lemasle et al. 2012). In addition to this, we have obtained high resolution (R$\sim$30,000) spectroscopy with the MIKE spectrograph at the Magellan telescope for three stars in the outer fields of Carina. The Magellan spectra also have the advantage of extending to very blue wavelengths ($\sim$3800 Å) where spectral lines of additional elements are located.

2. Metallicities

The metallicities of all of the stars observed spectroscopically are shown in Fig. 1. This includes over 400 RGB stars with metallicities determined from the Ca II triplet (Koch et al. 2006, Starkenburg et al. 2010), and 20 RGB stars with high resolution spectroscopic analyses by Venn et al. (2012), Lemasle et al. (2012), Koch et al. (2008), and Shetrone et al. (2003). The mean metallicity of the stars with high resolution spectroscopic analyses is higher than mean metallicity of the full distribution function; however this is most likely an observational bias. The only target selection criteria used in these projects were that the stars needed to be bright, red giants, and members of the Carina dSph. The slightly higher V magnitude associated with higher metallicities at the RGB tip may have contributed to the specific selections, but cannot have had a major effect since maximizing fiber placement was also a concern. Furthermore, while the three Magellan targets are located in the outer fields of Carina, they were purposely selected for their low metallicities, and therefore cannot be used (on their own) to suggest whether there is a population gradient between the inner and outer fields in Carina. Koch et al. (2006) found no significant difference in the mean metallicity of stars located in the inner versus outer fields of Carina. That the median metallicity ($\pm\sigma$) of the high resolution sample is the same as the mean metallicity predicted by Bono et al. (2010) for the intermediate aged population is interesting but not scientifically significant given our small sample.

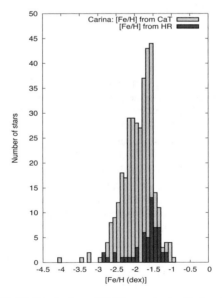

Figure 1. The [Fe/H] distribution of RGB stars in the Carina dSph. Metallicities for > 400 stars based on the CaT are shown in grey (Koch et al. 2006, Starkenburg et al. 2010), and those with high resolution spectroscopic metallicities are shown in red (Venn et al. 2012, Lemasle et al. 2012, Koch et al. 2008, and Shetrone et al. 2003).

3. Abundance Ratios

The abundances of up to 23 elements in 20 RGB stars are now available in the Carina dSph from high resolution, large wavelength coverage, spectroscopic analyses. A representative sample of elements are shown in Fig. 2 (the full sample is presented in Venn et al. 2012). In Fig. 2, the abundance ratios for these stars are separated into two age groups (old = red, young = blue). Ages are determined from isochrone fitting by Lemasle et al. (2012), accounting for the [Fe/H] and [α/Fe] determinations per star. The overlap in the [Mg/Fe] ratios at intermediate metallicities was interpreted by Lemasle et al. (2012) as evidence for infall of α-enriched metal-poor gas to trigger the second epoch of star formation in the Carina dSph.

The dispersion in the [Mg/Fe] ratios is larger than has been found in any other dSph galaxy, in particular stars in the Carina dSph show the lowest values of [Mg/Fe] yet found for their metallicities. In Car-5070 and other metal poor stars with [Fe/H]< −2, the low [Na/Fe] and [Mn/Fe] (also some neutron capture elements) suggest that these stars have *not* been enhanced by SNe Ia (Cescutti et al. 2008, Kobayashi & Nomoto 2009), nor by AGB stars (Herwig et al. 2004, Karakas 2010). This is important since a decrease in [α/Fe] with increasing [Fe/H] is usually interpreted as evidence for contributions from SNe Ia. In fact, the *knee* in this ratio is interpreted as the metallicity when SNe Ia begin to contribute to the chemical evolution of a galaxy (Tolstoy et al. 2009), however this only applies to simple homogeneous closed/leaky box models, which does not appear to be the case for Carina. The dispersion in [Mg/Fe] and other higher order abundance ratios, particularly in the old population, is more consistent with inhomogeneous mixing of the interstellar gas and stochastic statistical sampling of the SNe II yields during the formation of individual stars (e.g., Revaz & Jablonka 2011).

In addition, low [Mn/Fe] ratios and the low [Zn/Fe] limit for Car-5070 suggest that the metal poor stars may have formed from gas that is lacking contributions from hypernovae (Kobayashi & Nomoto 2009, Heger & Woosley 2010). This is further supported by the neutron capture ratios (see Venn et al. 2012) and suggests that the most massive SNe II progenitors did not form or that their gas was driven out in the SN II explosion. We also note that the chemistry of one star, Car-612 (labelled in Fig. 2) is very unusual, e.g., showing underabundances of nearly all ratios relative to iron, [X/Fe] (including Ni, but not Mn). We propose that this star has an overabundance of SN Ia/SN II contributions by a factor ∼5. Peculiar chemical abundances can affect the ages from isochrone fitting (Dotter et al. 2007), and so Car-612's age should be considered highly uncertain. If this star is younger than 10 Gyr, then this would significantly reduce the overlap in metallicity between the *old* and *intermediate aged* populations found by Lemasle et al. (2012). It may even suggest that the second epoch of star formation did arise from the existing chemically enriched gas, most likely an α-rich pocket, e.g., in the central region.

References

Bono, G., et al. 2010, PASP, 122, 651
Cescutti, G., Matteucci, F., Lanfranchi, G. A., & McWilliam, A. 2008, A&A, 491, 401
Dolphin A.E., 2002, MNRAS, 332, 91
Dotter A., et al. 2007, ApJ, 666, 403
Frebel A., 2010, Astronomische Nachrichten, 331, 474
Herwig F., 2004, ApJS, 155, 651

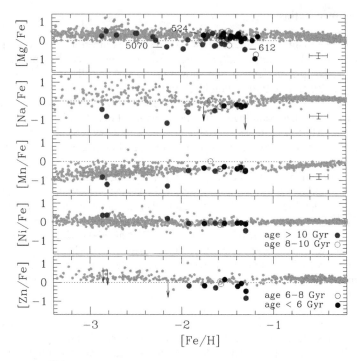

Figure 2.   (color online) Abundance ratios for stars in the Carina dSph separated into two age groups: stars >10 Gyr old are represented by red filled circles, stars <6 Gyr are respresented by blue filled circles. Stars at intermediate age ranges are represented by open circles (6–8 Gyr are blue, 8–10 Gyr are red). Carina abundance data is from Venn et al. (2012), Lemasle et al. (2012), Koch et al. (2008), and Shetrone et al. (2003); ages are from Lemasle et al. (2012). Galactic comparison stars are shown as small grey dots (including data from Venn et al. 2004, Frebel et al. 2010, Reddy et al. 2003, 2006).

Karakas A., 2010, MNRAS, 403, 1413
Karakas A., Lee H.Y., Lugaro M., Görres J., & Wiescher M., 2008, ApJ, 676, 1254
Kobayashi, C., & Nomoto, K. 2009, ApJ, 707, 1466
Koch A., Grebel E.K., Wyse R.F.G., Kleyna J.T., Wilkinson, M.I., Harbeck D.R., Gilmore G.F.,
        & Evans N.W., 2006, AJ, 131, 895
Koch A., Grebel E.K., Gilmore G.F., Wyse R.F.G., Kleyna J.T., Harbeck D.R., Wilkinson M.I.,
        Wyn & Evans, N., 2008, AJ, 135, 1580
Lanfranchi, G. A., Matteucci, F., & Cescutti, G. 2006, A&A, 453, 67
Lemasle B., et al. 2012, A&A, in press
Monelli M., Pulone L., Corsi C.E., Castellani M., et al. 2003 AJ, 126, 218
Reddy, B. E., Lambert, D. L., & Allende Prieto, C. 2006, MNRAS, 367, 1329
Reddy, B. E., Tomkin J., Lambert, D. L., & Allende Prieto, C. 2003, MNRAS, 340, 304
Revaz Y., & Jablonka P., 2011, A&A, in press
Shetrone M.D., Venn K.A., Tolstoy E., Primas F., Hill V., & Kaufer A., 2003, AJ, 125, 684
Smecker-Hane T.A., Stetson P.B., Hesser J.E., & Lehnert M.D., 1994, AJ, 108, 507
Starkenburg E., et al., 2010 A&A, 513, 34
Venn K.A., et al. 2012, ApJ, submitted
Venn K.A., Irwin M.J., Shetrone M.D., Tout C.A., Hill V., Tolstoy E., 2004 AJ, 128, 1177

Galactic Archaeology: Near-Field Cosmology and the Formation of the Milky Way
ASP Conference Series, Vol. 458
W. Aoki, M. Ishigaki, T. Suda, T. Tsujimoto, N. Arimoto, eds.
© *2012 Astronomical Society of the Pacific*

Heavy Neutron-Capture Elements in Extremely Metal-Poor Stars in Dwarf Galaxies

Satoshi Honda,[1] Wako Aoki,[2] Nobuo Arimoto,[2] and Kozo Sadakane[3]

[1] *Kwasan Observatory, Kyoto University, Ohmine-cho Kita Kazan, Yamashina-ku, Kyoto 607-8471, Japan*

[2] *National Astronomical Observatory of Japan, 2-21-1 Osawa, Mitaka, Tokyo 181-8588, Japan*

[3] *Astronomical Institute, Osaka Kyoiku University, 4-698-1 Asahigaoka, Kashiwara-shi, Osaka 582-8582, Japan*

Abstract.   Chemical abundance ratios of extremely metal-poor (EMP) stars in dwarf galaxies are key to understanding the early enrichment in such small systems as well as the early formation of the Milky Way (MW) halo structure. Abundance ratios of heavy neutron-capture elements with respect to iron show large star-to-star scatter in EMP stars in the MW halo, and will provide very useful constraints on the formation processes of low-mass stars in the early Galaxy. However, Ba abundances of dwarf galaxy stars in this metallicity range are quite low in general ([Ba/Fe] < −1). An exception is S 15-19 in the Sextans discovered by our previous study that has [Ba/Fe] =+0.5, which is similar to those of r-process-enhanced stars found in the field halo. Our new high resolution spectroscopy for this object for the blue region reveals, however, that no clear excess of r-process elements like Eu appears in this object. Moreover, a significant excess of carbon ([C/Fe] = +1.0) and deficiency of Sr ([Sr/Fe] = −1.4) are found for this object. Taking the variation of radial velocities measured at the two different epochs into consideration, the origin of the excesses of heavy neutron-capture elements in S 15-19 is not the r-process, but is the s-process in an asymptotic giant branch (AGB) star that was the binary companion (primary) of this object. Carbon- and s-process-enhanced material should have been transferred to the surface of S 15-19 across the binary system. As a result, no r-process-enhanced star is known in EMP stars in dwarf galaxies at present. The constraint is still weak because of the limited sample size, and further measurements of neutron-capture elements for dwarf galaxy stars are required.

1. Introduction

Chemical abundances of metal-poor stars are important to understand the galaxy formation and the origin of elements. Especially, Extremely Metal-Poor stars (EMP stars: [Fe/H] < −3) could be unique records of the early stage of the Galaxy. Chemical abundances of many EMP stars have been investigated by high dispersion spectroscopy (e.g., Cayrel et al. 2004; Honda et al. 2004), providing useful constraints on chemical evolution models (e.g., Kobayashi et al. 2006). In particular, overabundances of α-elements with respect to iron with little scatter in MW halo stars indicate that the dominant source of metals is core-collapse supernovae in the early Galaxy. In contrast,

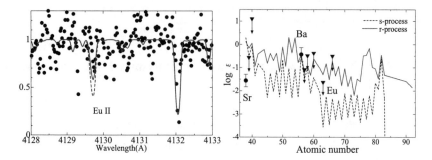

Figure 1.   Left : A portion of the spectrum around the Eu 4129 Å for S 15-19. The observed spectrum is shown by filled dot, and synthetic ones are shown by solid and dashed lines. The upper limit of the Eu abundance ([Eu/Fe] < 0.9) is estimated from this line. Right : Abundances of neutron-capture elements (filled circles), and upper limits (triangles), for S 15-19 as a function of atomic number. The dashed and solid lines are the solar s- and r-process abundance patterns normalized at Ba.

the abundances of neutron-capture elements show large dispersion in EMP stars (e.g., McWilliam et al. 1995). This dispersion should reflect the spatial inhomogeneity of the chemical composition of interstellar matter. Neutron-capture element-enhanced stars among them can be regarded as the result of individual nucleosynthesis processes. For instance, Sneden et al. (1996) found the neutron-capture-rich EMP star (CS 22892–052 : [Fe/H] = −3.1), showing the abundance pattern that agrees very well with that of the r-process component in solar-system material. The r-process is the dominant source of neutron-capture elements in EMP stars, while another source is also suggested to explain light neutron-capture elements in some EMP stars. The large scatter in abundance ratios indicate that neutron-capture elements are potentially useful probes of the formation processes of the Galactic halo and dwarf galaxies (e.g., Bland-Hawthorn et al. 2010).

2.   Observations of EMP stars in dwarf galaxies

Dwarf galaxies around the Milky Way (MW) are suggested to be the survivors of building blocks of the MW halo structure in the ΛCDM paradigm. If this is true, the metallicity distribution and abundance ratios of metal-poor stars in dwarf galaxies should agree with those of the MW halo. While differences in abundance ratios (e.g. [α/Fe]) are found between them, as reviewed by Tolstoy et al. (2009), some similarity is also suggested for extremely low metallicity. Hence, more detailed abundance studies of EMP stars in dwarf galaxies are urgently required.

Recently, EMP stars have been found in faint (or ultra-faint) dwarf galaxies by surveys based on low- and medium-resolution spectroscopy (e.g., Kirby et al. 2008), and follow-up high resolution studies have been conducted for some of them using 8-10m class telescopes. Among them, Aoki et al. (2009) carried out abundance measurements for candidate EMP stars in Sextans that were found by the DART program (Helmi et al. 2006). They confirm the existence of EMP stars and found that four of the six stars they studied show low Mg/Fe ratios in Sextans compared to field halo stars. Another inter-

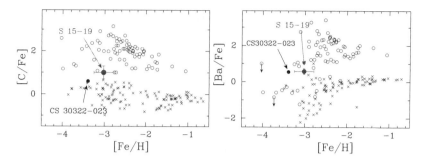

Figure 2.   [C/Fe] and [Ba/Fe] as a function of [Fe/H]. Carbon-enhanced stars are indicated by circles.

esting abundance feature found by Aoki et al. (2009) is that, while the Ba abundance is low in four stars, two objects have significantly high values. In particular, S 15-19 in their sample shows the highest value of Ba abundance ([Ba/Fe] = +0.5) in the EMP stars in dwarf galaxies known at present. If the origin of heavy elements of this object is the r-process, this is the first evidence for the existence of r-process enhanced EMP stars, which are known as r-II stars in the field halo (Beers & Christlieb 2005). In order to investigate the origin of heavy elements in this object, we performed abundance measurements for this object based on a newly obtained high resolution spectrum (Honda et al. 2011).

3.   Neutron-capture abundance of Sextans S 15-19

S 15-19 is a red giant with magnitude of V = 17.5. Our new observation was also carried out with Subaru/HDS as that of Aoki et al. (2009) but with a longer exposure (8 hours). The spectrum covers the blue range including lines of Sr, Eu, and CH molecular bands. We confirmed the metallicity and the high abundance of Ba by the new measurements. However, we could detect no Eu line even in the new spectrum (Figure. 1). The upper limit of [Eu/Fe] is 0.9. If the Ba of this star is made by r-process, [Eu/Fe] should be larger than 1.3 (c.f., Burris et al. 2000). This result indicates that Ba of this star is synthesized not only by the r-process, but is contributed by the s-process.

Moreover, the Sr of this object is deficient with respect to Ba, supporting that this star reflects the s-process at very low metallicity with very high ratios of neutrons to seed nuclei (Gallino et al. 1998). The strong feature of CH molecular band is also supportive for the contribution of the s-process in an AGB star. Variations of radial velocity (by 3 km s^{-1}) have been also found compared to the previous observation (Aoki et al. 2009). This fact suggests that S 15-19 belongs to a binary system.

4.   Summary and Discussion

We investigated the chemical composition of the Ba-rich EMP star S 15-19 in the Sextans dwarf galaxy. This EMP star has an excess of carbon ([C/Fe] = +1), but shows no clear excess of r-process elements ([Eu/Ba] < +0.5). We also found the variation of radial velocity. In conclusion, this star belongs to a binary system, and is affected by the s-process through mass transfer from an AGB star.

Such objects are known as Carbon-Enhanced Metal-Poor stars with s-process-excesses (CEMP-s stars) in the field halo (Beers & Christlieb 2005; Aoki et al. 2007). The excesses of carbon and Ba of S 15-19 are not very large in the distributions of these values of CEMP-s stars (Figure. 2). Among them, CS 30322-023 in the field halo has similar abundances to those of S 15-19 (Masseron et al. 2006; Aoki et al. 2007). While Masseron et al. (2006) suggests that this object is now on the thermally pulsing AGB stage, the binarity of this object supports the interpretation that mass transfer from an AGB star is the reason for the excesses of carbon and s-process elements.

Since S 15–19, which is a unique object having a large excess of Ba among EMP stars known for dwarf galaxies, is turned out to be a CEMP-s star, no r-process-enhanced EMP star is known in dwarf galaxies at present. This suggests that the enrichment of r-process elements, in particular its metallicity dependence, in dwarf galaxies is different from that in the MW halo. It should be noted that Ba abundances have been measured for about 20 stars with [Fe/H] < −2.5 in dwarf galaxies. The statistics is still insufficient, given the fact that about five percent of EMP stars in the field halo show large excesses of r-process elements (Barklem et al. 2005). However, if the difference of the abundance distributions is confirmed for r-process elements by future studies, that has an impact on the understanding of the relation between dwarf galaxies and the MW halo.

References

Aoki, W., et al. 2009, A&A, 502, 569
Aoki, W., Beers, T. C., Christlieb, N., Norris, J. E., Ryan, S. G., & Tsangarides, S. 2007, ApJ, 655, 492
Barklem, P. S., Christlieb, N., Beers, T. C., Hill, V., Bessell, M. S., Holmberg, J., Marsteller, B., Rossi, S., Zickgraf, F.-J., & Reimers, D. 2005, A&A, 439, 129
Beers, T. C., & Christlieb, N. 2005, ARA&A, 43, 531
Bland-Hawthorn, J., Karlsson, T., Sharma, S., Krumholz, M., & Silk, J. 2010, ApJ, 721, 582
Burris, D. L., Pilachowski, C. A., Armandroff, T. E., Sneden, C., Cowan, J. J., & Roe, H. 2000, ApJ, 544, 302
Cayrel, R., Depagne, E., Spite, M., Hill, V., Spite, F., François, P., Plez, B., Beers, T., Primas, F., Andersen, J., Barbuy, B., Bonifacio, P., Molaro, P., & Nordström, B. 2004, A&A, 416, 1117
Gallino, R., Arlandini, C., Busso, M., Lugaro, M., Travaglio, C., Straniero, O., Chieffi, A., & Limongi, M. 1998, ApJ, 497, 388
Helmi, A., et al. 2006, ApJ, 651, L121
Honda, S., Aoki, W., Arimoto, N., & Sadakane, K. 2011, PASJ, 63, 523
Honda, S., Aoki, W., Kajino, T., Ando, H., Beers, T. C., Izumiura, H., Sadakane, K., & Takada-Hidai, M. 2004, ApJ, 607, 474
Kirby, E. N., Simon, J. D., Geha, M., Guhathakurta, P., & Frebel, A. 2008, ApJ, 685, L43
Kobayashi, C., Umeda, H., Nomoto, K., Tominaga, N., & Ohkubo, T. 2006, ApJ, 653, 1145
Masseron, T., van Eck, S., Famaey, B., Goriely, S., Plez, B., Siess, L., Beers, T. C., Primas, F., & Jorissen, A. 2006, A&A, 455, 1059
McWilliam, A., Preston, G. W., Sneden, C., & Searle, L. 1995, AJ, 109, 2757
Sneden, C., McWilliam, A., Preston, G. W., Cowan, J. J., Burris, D. L., & Armosky, B. J. 1996, ApJ, 467, 819
Tolstoy, E., Hill, V., & Tosi, M. 2009, ARA&A, 47, 371

Galactic Archaeology: Near-Field Cosmology and the Formation of the Milky Way
ASP Conference Series, Vol. 458
W. Aoki, M. Ishigaki, T. Suda, T. Tsujimoto, N. Arimoto, eds.
© 2012 Astronomical Society of the Pacific

Extremely Low-Metallicity Stars in the Classical Dwarf Galaxies

Else Starkenburg[1,2] and the DART Team

[1]*Kapteyn Astronomical Institute, University of Groningen, PO Box 800, 9700 AV Groningen, the Netherlands*

[2]*Dept. of Physics and Astronomy, University of Victoria, PO Box 3055, STN CSC, Victoria BC V8W 3P6, Canada*

Abstract. After careful re-analysis of Ca II triplet calibration at low-metallicity, the classical satellites around the Milky Way are found not to be devoided of extremely low-metallicity stars and their (extremely) metal-poor tails are predicted to be much more in agreement with the Milky Way halo. A first follow-up study of 7 extremely metal-poor candidates within the Sculptor dwarf galaxy with X-shooter on ESO/VLT has further confirmed the new metallicity calibration for the Ca II triplet at low metallicities and provides abundances for many other elements in these stars. We will discuss the results of this study and show a comparison with the Galactic extremely metal-poor stars.

1. Introduction

The low-metallicity stars that still exist today must carry the imprint of only very few supernovae explosions and represent our closest observational approach to the epoch of the first stars, as no star completely without heavy elements has been found. An interesting puzzle in the field of nearby cosmology has been that no extremely metal-poor (EMP) candidates were found from initial Ca II triplet (CaT) surveys in the classical dwarf galaxies, in disagreement with the relative numbers of EMP stars discovered in the Galactic halo (Helmi et al. 2006). Starkenburg et al. (2010) however found that none of the existing CaT calibrations matched the metal-poor regime ([Fe/H]< -2.5) and determined a new calibration using synthetic spectra modeling and observations, to determine the metallicity for red giant branch (RGB) stars using the NIR CaT lines. Applying this new relation to the DART CaT datasets, consisting of ~2000 CaT spectra of stars in the Sculptor, Fornax, Carina and Sextans dwarf spheroidal galaxies, many new candidates for EMP stars were found. This prediction also brings the distribution of metal-poor stars in these dwarf galaxies in closer agreement with that of the Milky Way halo (Starkenburg et al. 2010).

Various EMP candidates are already discovered and followed up in many dwarf spheroidal satellites in other work, but the sample of known EMP stars outside the Milky Way is still small. The precise abundances for several different elements, as obtained through high-resolution studies, are important since they show the differences and similarities in the chemical evolution at the earliest times between the Galactic halo and its surrounding satellites.

2.   Observations and Analysis

In this study we selected seven new EMP targets from the DART CaT survey of RGB stars in the Sculptor galaxy (Battaglia et al. 2008) using the CaT calibration from Starkenburg et al. (2010). Observations were carried out with the X-shooter instrument on ESO's VLT. In addition three EMP halo stars from the sample of Cayrel et al. (2004) have been observed to test our analysis. In this work we focus on the spectra taken with the UVB and VIS arms, which have resolutions of R~6200 in the UVB and R~11000 in the VIS with our settings. The spectra were reduced using the X-shooter pipeline (Goldoni et al. 2006).

We use B, V and I photometry for our stars from a deep wide-field imaging project (de Boer et al. 2011), complemented with infrared photometry from the VISTA survey commissioning where possible, to derive temperatures and surface gravities (Ramírez & Meléndez 2005). The microturbulence velocities are estimated using a comparison of stellar parameters with the sample of Cayrel et al. (2004).

Our linelist was created starting from the compilation of Tafelmeyer et al. (2010). Equivalent widths were measured by fitting a Gaussian profile using *splot* in the IRAF package. For very strong lines and the CH band, the abundances are derived from a comparison with the modeled spectra. We use the *Turbospectrum* code (Alvarez & Plez 1998) and 1D spherical symmetric (OS)MARCS atmosphere models (e.g., Gustafsson et al. 2008), to synthesize the spectra and derive abundances from equivalent widths.

3.   Results

For the three EMP halo stars re-observed in our program, we find excellent agreement between our derived abundances and those from Cayrel et al. (2004). We will here briefly discuss the preliminary result for the Sculptor stars. A full description of the analysis, as well as more figures and tables will be published in Starkenburg et al., in preparation.

- *Iron:* Fe I abundances are determined from 18 to 30 lines in each spectrum. The [Fe/H] values found agree with the CaT-calibration predictions within error bars, as shown in Figure 1.

- *Carbon:* We measure the strength of the CH molecular band region around 4300 Å in comparison with synthetic spectra and find that all of the Sculptor targets are carbon-poor. For most targets the synthetic spectra fits suggest [C/Fe]~ −1.

- *Alpha elements:* Large samples of stars in dwarf galaxies and the Galactic halo have clearly demonstrated that the dwarfs show a lower [α/Fe] at metallicities [Fe/H]> −2 than the Galactic halo stars at similar metallicity (e.g., Venn et al. 2004). In our spectra we can measure Mg, Ca and Ti. Figure 2 shows their Mg abundances in comparison with the Cayrel et al. (2004) sample of EMPs in the Milky Way halo and other stars in the Sculptor dwarf galaxy. Our targets show agreement with the halo distribution at these EMP metallicities, but arguably a larger spread than the halo stars of similar metallicity, although not with very high significance. The abundances of Ca agree well with the CaT-derived predicted values from the calibration of Starkenburg et al. (2010) (see Figure 1).

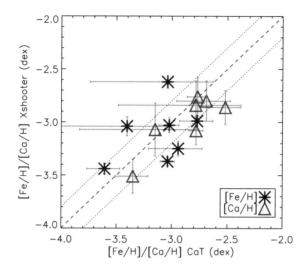

Figure 1. CaT predictions for both [Fe/H] and [Ca/H] versus their abundances derived from the X-shooter spectra.

- *Heavy elements:* Abundances for Ba and Sr measured are in agreement with the (spread in) Milky Way EMP stars.

- *Sodium:* We correct our Na abundances for non-LTE effects using results from Andrievsky et al. (2007) and find general agreement with Galactic trends. However, for two of our most metal-poor stars [Na/Fe] are significantly lower than the Galactic values.

4.   Discussion and conclusions

We have measured Fe, Na, Mg, Ca, Ti, Sr and Ba abundances in seven extremely metal-poor candidates in the Sculptor dwarf spheroidal which were selected from CaT samples. This work has clearly shown that the CaT lines can be used as a metallicity indicator down to the extremely metal-poor regime. Five stars have [Fe/H]< −3.0. In many cases, the observed abundances do follow the patterns observed in the Milky Way. Nonetheless we see that the dispersion at similar metallicities in alpha elements is larger than in halo stars, possibly indicating a more stochastic and less well mixed environment. The lack of carbon-rich stars in our sample is interesting when taking into account that many (∼ 20%) of the halo stars at this metallicity are enriched in carbon to a level of [C/Fe]>1.

Acknowledgments.   ES gratefully acknowledges financial support from the Netherlands Foundation for Scientific Research (NWO) as well as the Canadian Institute for Advanced Research (CIfAR) Junior Academy and a Canadian Institute for Theoretical Astrophysics (CITA) National Fellowship.

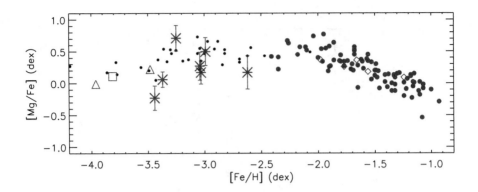

Figure 2.   [Mg/Fe] versus [Fe/H] abundances for our Sculptor targets (red asterisks). Other red symbols indicate Sculptor stars from Hill et al., in preparation (filled
circles), Shetrone et al. (2003) (diamonds), Tafelmeyer et al. (2010) (large open triangles) and Frebel et al. (2010) (large open square). Black small circles are the EMP
halo stars from Cayrel et al. (2004) as updated by Bonifacio et al. (2009).

References

Alvarez, R., & Plez, B. 1998, A&A, 330, 1109
Andrievsky, S. M., Spite, M., Korotin, S. A., Spite, F., Bonifacio, P., Cayrel, R., Hill, V., &
    François, P. 2007, A&A, 464, 1081
Battaglia, G., Helmi, A., Tolstoy, E., Irwin, M., Hill, V., & Jablonka, P. 2008, ApJ, 681, L13
Bonifacio, P., Spite, M., Cayrel, R., Hill, V., Spite, F., François, P., Plez, B., Ludwig, H.-G.,
    Caffau, E., Molaro, P., Depagne, E., Andersen, J., Barbuy, B., Beers, T. C., Nordström,
    B., & Primas, F. 2009, A&A, 501, 519
Cayrel, R., Depagne, E., Spite, M., Hill, V., Spite, F., François, P., Plez, B., Beers, T., Primas,
    F., Andersen, J., Barbuy, B., Bonifacio, P., Molaro, P., & Nordström, B. 2004, A&A,
    416, 1117
de Boer, T. J. L., Tolstoy, E., Saha, A., Olsen, K., Irwin, M. J., Battaglia, G., Hill, V., Shetrone,
    M. D., Fiorentino, G., & Cole, A. 2011, A&A, 528, A119+
Frebel, A., Kirby, E. N., & Simon, J. D. 2010, Nat, 464, 72
Goldoni, P., Royer, F., François, P., Horrobin, M., Blanc, G., Vernet, J., Modigliani, A., &
    Larsen, J. 2006, in Society of Photo-Optical Instrumentation Engineers (SPIE) Confer-
    ence Series, vol. 6269
Gustafsson, B., Edvardsson, B., Eriksson, K., Jørgensen, U. G., Nordlund, Å., & Plez, B. 2008,
    A&A, 486, 951
Helmi, A., Irwin, M. J., Tolstoy, E., Battaglia, G., Hill, V., Jablonka, P., Venn, K., Shetrone, M.,
    Letarte, B., Arimoto, N., Abel, T., Francois, P., Kaufer, A., Primas, F., Sadakane, K., &
    Szeifert, T. 2006, ApJ, 651, L121
Ramírez, I., & Meléndez, J. 2005, ApJ, 626, 465
Shetrone, M., Venn, K. A., Tolstoy, E., Primas, F., Hill, V., & Kaufer, A. 2003, AJ, 125, 684
Starkenburg, E., Hill, V., Tolstoy, E., González Hernández, J. I., Irwin, M., Helmi, A., Battaglia,
    G., Jablonka, P., Tafelmeyer, M., Shetrone, M., Venn, K., & de Boer, T. 2010, A&A,
    513, A34+
Tafelmeyer, M., Jablonka, P., Hill, V., Shetrone, M., Tolstoy, E., Irwin, M. J., Battaglia, G.,
    Helmi, A., Starkenburg, E., Venn, K. A., Abel, T., Francois, P., Kaufer, A., North, P.,
    Primas, F., & Szeifert, T. 2010, A&A, 524, A58+
Venn, K. A., Irwin, M., Shetrone, M. D., Tout, C. A., Hill, V., & Tolstoy, E. 2004, AJ, 128,
    1177

Galactic Archaeology: Near-Field Cosmology and the Formation of the Milky Way
ASP Conference Series, Vol. 458
W. Aoki, M. Ishigaki, T. Suda, T. Tsujimoto, N. Arimoto, eds.
© *2012 Astronomical Society of the Pacific*

The Star Formation History in the Far Outer Disc of M31: A Recent Burst Triggered by Interaction with M33?

E. J. Bernard, A. M. N. Ferguson, and M. K. Barker

Institute for Astronomy, Univ. of Edinburgh, Royal Obs., Edinburgh, UK

Abstract. We present the star formation history (SFH) of two fields located in the far outer discs of M31 and M33 based on HST/ACS color-magnitude diagrams (CMD) reaching the oldest main-sequence turn-offs. The SFHs were obtained using the CMD-fitting technique. We find that both galaxies underwent a significant burst of star formation 2 Gyr ago, that lasted ~1.5 Gyr and is responsible for about 25% of the total stellar mass in each field-of-view. In both galaxies, this burst is also accompanied by a decline in global metallicity, usually a clear signature of the inflow of metal-poor gas. Interestingly, dynamical models of the M31-M33 interaction favour ~2-3 Gyr ago as the last pericentric passage when the systems were within ~40 kpc of each other, which is coeval with the beginning of the burst. This suggests that the burst of star formation in the outer discs of both galaxies may have been triggered by the interaction.

1. Observations

The observations were carried out with the Advanced Camera for Surveys onboard the Hubble Space Telescope. The M31 and M33 fields were observed during 20 and 24 orbits, respectively, leading to total exposure times of 26,120 and 31,050 sec. The resulting CMDs reach the oldest main-sequence turn-offs, allowing us to reconstruct the SFH over the whole lifetimes of these galaxies with good accuracy.

2. Star Formation Histories

The SFHs of the M31 and M33 fields were calculated using the well-known CMD-fitting technique, in which the observed CMD is modelled as the sum of CMDs representing simple stellar populations. Here, we used the IAC-pop (Aparicio & Hidalgo 2009) and MinnIAC (Hidalgo et al. 2011) algorithms, and followed the method described in Monelli et al. (2010). The results for both fields are shown in Figure 1.

Both present a significant burst of star formation about 2 Gyr ago, that lasted ~1.5 Gyr and was accompanied by a decline in global metallicity. Interestingly, using realistic N-body simulations, McConnachie et al. (2009) were able to best reproduce the morphology of the outer substructure in M33 with orbits that brought the systems within ~40 kpc of each other 2-3 Gyr ago and that satisfy their current positions, distances, radial velocities, and M33's proper motion. These results are highly suggestive of an interaction between the two systems triggering inward flows of metal-poor gas and driving moderate bursts of star formation that created significant fractions of the total outer disc stellar mass (~25%).

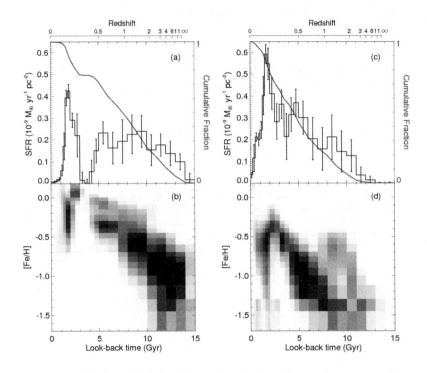

Figure 1.   Star formation rate (top) and chemical enrichment (bottom) as a function of look-back time for M31 (left) and M33 (right).

The main difference between the SF history of the outer discs of M31 and M33 is at older ages: we reliably trace star formation as far back as 12-13 Gyr ago in the outer disc of M31 while the onset of star formation occured about 2 Gyr later in M33, with median stellar ages of 7.5 Gyr and 4.5 Gyr, respectively.

Finally, another noteworthy feature of the SFHs is their well-defined and smoothly increasing age-metallicity relations, from the earliest epochs until about 2 Gyr ago. This suggests that the stellar populations observed in the far outer discs of both galaxies have largely formed in situ rather than migrated from smaller galactocentric radii.

A description of the data reduction and a detailed interpretation of the SFHs are presented in full in Bernard et al. (2012).

Acknowledgments.   We would like to thank the coauthors of our corresponding paper for their contributions.

References

Aparicio, A., & Hidalgo, S. L., 2009, AJ, 138, 558
Bernard, E. J., et al. 2012, MNRAS, *in press* (astro-ph/1111.5234)
Hidalgo, S. L., et al. 2011, ApJ, 730, 14
McConnachie, A. W., et al. 2009, Nature, 461, 66
Monelli, M., et al. 2010, ApJ, 720, 1225

Galactic Archaeology: Near-Field Cosmology and the Formation of the Milky Way
ASP Conference Series, Vol. 458
W. Aoki, M. Ishigaki, T. Suda, T. Tsujimoto, N. Arimoto, eds.
©2012 Astronomical Society of the Pacific

Outside-in Evolution of the Outer Large Magellanic Cloud Disk

R. Carrera[1,2]

[1]*Instituto de Astrofísica de Canarias, Spain*

[2]*Departamento de Astrofísica, Universidad de La Laguna, Spain*

Abstract. The outer Large Magellanic Cloud (LMC) have been studied in order to unveil clues about its formation and evolution using both deep color magnitude diagrams and low resolution spectroscopy of red giant branch stars in several fields which span a galactocentric range from 3 to 9 kpc. Our results point to an outside-in evolution scheme in opposition with the inside-out scenario predicted by ΛCDM cosmology for a galaxy like the LMC.

1. Introduction

The formation and evolution of stellar disks are still not well-understood proceses. Λ CDM predict an inside-out evolution in which the inner part of the disks form first and then they grow to reach their present size (e.g. White & Frenk 1991; Roškar et al. 2008). From an observational point of view, massive early-type spirals are bluer in their outer disks, in agreement with the inside-out scenario (e.g. Trujillo & Pohlen 2005). However, disks in late-type spirals and irregular galaxies have more puzzling behaviors (e.g. de Jong 1996). Some follow the same trends observed in early-type spirals but others become redder outward which is interpreted as the youngest populations are located in the innermost regions suggesting an outside-in scenario only predicted for less massive galaxies. The proximity of Large Magellanic Cloud (LMC) with a mass between large and dwarf galaxies offer an unique opportunity to investigate in detail the evolution of stellar disk in galaxies

2. Observational Data

We have obtained deep color magnitude diagrams, which reach at least two magnitudes bellow the oldest main sequence turn-off in 10 fields (Gallart et al. 2004, 2008; Carrera et al. 2011). These fields were selected to span a range of galactocentric distances from 3 to 9 kpc. In the same fields, low resolution spectra (R~7000) in the infrared Ca II triplet region (~8500Å) were obtained for red giant branch stars (Carrera et al. 2008; Carrera 2009; Carrera et al. 2011). For these stars, metallicities have been calculated from the equivalent widths of the Ca lines using the calibrations described by Carrera et al. (2007, 2011).

3. Discussion

The comparison of color-magnitude diagrams with isochrones shows that while the oldest populations are coeval in all fields, the age of the youngest ones gradually increases with radius. Assuming that the youngest stars were formed in-situ (e.g. there is no stellar migration), we are observing an outside-in quenching of star formation at recent times (Gallart et al. 2008; Carrera et al. 2011).

This age gradient observed across the LMC disk is not accompanied by a gradient in the mean metallicity, which is observed only for R<6 kpc. A gradient in the metallicity in the youngest objects cannot be excluded with our observations since they do not have counterparts in the red giant branch. This gradient in the mean metallicity from R~6 kpc is related to a varying proportion of stars of different ages in different fields since the chemical enrichment history has been the same over the LMC disk (Carrera et al. 2008). The LMC bar might be able to mix the stellar content of a disk within a certain radius. The age gradient observed at R<6 kpc can be explained by the fact that the galaxy has not had enough time to mix populations younger than 1 Gyr.

These results suggest an outside-in disk evolution scenario as opposed to the inside-out scenario predicted by ΛCDM cosmology and observed in more massive early-type spirals. The outside-in evolution scenario is qualitatively similar to that predicted by Stinson et al. (2009) for dwarf galaxies. However, for a galaxy like the LMC, the Stinson et al. (2009) models predict an inside-out scenario.

It is well known that the LMC forms an interacting system with the Small Magellanic Cloud and the Milky Way at the moment. However it is not clear if the same has happened in the past (e.g. Besla et al. 2010). Repeated encounters with one or more external systems might have erased, or at least weakened, any gradient. These results tend to support an evolution of the LMC in a more isolated environment.

Acknowledgments. I acknowledge funds from the Spanish Ministry of Science and Technology under the Juan de la Cierva fellowship and the Plan Nacional de Investigación Científica, Desarrollo, e Investigación Tecnológica (AYA2007-3E3507 and AYA2010-16717).

References

Besla, G., Kallivayalil, N., Hernquist, L., van der Marel, R. P., Cox, T. J., & Kere, D. 2010, ApJ, 721, L97
Carrera, R., Gallart, C., Pancino, E., & Zinn, R. 2007, AJ, 134, 1298
Carrera, R., Gallart, C., Hardy, E., Aparicio, A., & Zinn, R. 2008, AJ, 135, 836
Carrera, R. 2009, PASP, 121, 98
Carrera, R., Gallart, C., Aparicio, A., & Hardy, E. 2011, AJ, 142, 61
de Jong, R. S. 1996, A&A, 313, 377
Gallart, C., Stetson, P. B., Hardy, E., Pont, F., & Zinn, R. 2004, ApJ, 614, L109
Gallart, C., Stetson, P. B., Meschin, I. P., Pont, F., & Hardy, E. 2008, ApJ, 682, L89
Roškar, R., Debattista, V. P., Stinson, G. S., et al. 2008, ApJ, 675, L65
Stinson, G. S., Dalcanton, J. J., Quinn, T., et al. 2009, MNRAS, 395, 1455
Trujillo, I., & Pohlen, M. 2005, ApJ, 630, L17
White, S. D. M., & Frenk, C. S. 1991, ApJ, 379, 52

Galactic Archaeology: Near-Field Cosmology and the Formation of the Milky Way
ASP Conference Series, Vol. 458
W. Aoki, M. Ishigaki, T. Suda, T. Tsujimoto, N. Arimoto, eds.
© 2012 Astronomical Society of the Pacific

Andromeda and its Satellites: A Kinematic Perspective

Michelle L. M. Collins,[1] R. Mike Rich,[2] and Scott C. Chapman[3]

[1]*MPIA, Königstuhl 17, Heidelberg, 69117, Germany*

[2]*UCLA, Physics and Astronomy Building, 430 Portola Plaza, Box 951547 Los Angeles, CA 90095-1547, USA*

[3]*Institute of Astronomy, Madingley Rise, Cambridge, CB2 1ST, UK*

Abstract. Using spectroscopic data taken with Keck II DEIMOS by the Z-PAndAS team in the Andromeda-Triangulum region, I present a comparison of the disc and satellite systems of Andromeda with those of our own Galaxy. I discuss the observed discrepancies between the masses and scale radii of Andromeda dwarf spheroidal galaxies of a given luminosity with those of the Milky Way. I also present an analysis of the newly discovered M31 thick disc, which is measured to be hotter, more extended and thicker than that seen in the Milky Way.

1. The Thick Disc in Andromeda

Thick stellar discs are believed to represent an earlier epoch of galactic evolution than thin stellar discs. Understanding the properties of these structures is fundamental to our understanding of the evolution of large spiral galaxies. Until recently, no such component was detected in Andromeda, despite the belief that such structures are ubiquitous amongst spiral galaxies (Dalcanton & Bernstein 2002). We present a detection of a thick disc in the Andromeda galaxy (Collins et al. 2011a), isolating the component by identifying a significant population of stars that have velocities that lag behind the thin stellar disc, and are inconsistent with the Andromedean halo.

We have been able to measure the scale lengths of the discs. We measure $h_{r,thin}=$ 7.3 kpc and $h_{r,thick}=$ 8.0 kpc. Comparing these values with thick disc systems in external galaxies (Yoachim & Dalcanton 2006, YD06) we estimate the scale height of both components. We measure $z_{0,thin}=$ 1.1 kpc and $z_{0,thick}=$ 2.8 kpc. We co-add their spectra to ascertain the average metallicity of each component via the measurement of the equivalent widths of the Ca II triplet (Fig. 1). The thick disc has an intermediate metallicity of [Fe/H]= -1.0, more metal poor than the thin disc ([Fe/H]= -0.7) and more metal rich than the halo ([Fe/H]= -1.3).

2. The Dwarf Spheroidals of Andromeda

Dwarf spheroidal galaxies (dSphs) represent the smallest scales on which we are able to detect dark matter. 27 dSphs have been identified in the M31 halo, and while the relationship between the size and luminosity of these objects is consistent with the MW

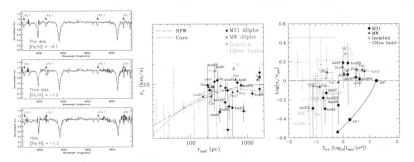

Figure 1.   (color online) **Left:** Composite spectra for the thin (top), thick disc (middle) and halo (bottom) populations in M31. These are chemically distinct, with the thick disc having a metallicity of [Fe/H]= −1.0. **Centre:** Velocity dispersion vs. half light radius for MW (red) M31 (blue) and isolated (light blue) dSphs. The best fit mass profiles of Walker et al. (2009) are overlaid. A number of M31 dSphs have lower velocity dispersions than expected. **Right:** Ratio of the measured : expected velocity dispersion from W09 NFW profile for Local Group dSphs vs. surface brightness. The M31 outliers are seen in the lower left corner. A tidal track from Peñarrubia et al. (2008) representing a dSph that has been stripped of 90 % of its mass is overplotted, and matches the observed trend.

dSphs (Brasseur et al. 2011), there are a number that are more extended than their MW counterparts (McConnachie & Irwin 2006; Richardson et al. 2011, Fig. 1).

Work by Walker et al. (2009) demonstrated that the MW dSphs were consistent with having formed in halos with identical dark matter profiles, suggesting that the evolution of the dark matter within these objects is the same, regardless of the size of the luminous component. Our group has been measuring the kinematics of the M31 dSphs (Chapman et al., 2005; Chapman et al. 2007; Collins et al. 2010, 2011b). We have discovered that these objects are not consistent with the MW population, as a number of them have lower velocity dispersions for a given half light radius when compared to the MW. These outliers are also typically the more extended M31 dSphs (Fig. 1), consistent with the effects of increased tidal stress from a more massive M31 disc (Peñarrubia et al. 2008, 2010).

References

Brasseur C. M., Martin, N. F. Maccio, A. V. Rix, H.-W. & Kang, X. 2011, ApJ, 743, 179.
Chapman, S. C. et al. 2005, ApJ, 632, 87.
Chapman, S. C.,et al. 2007, ApJ, 662, L79
Collins, M. L. M., et al. 2010, MNRAS, 407, 2411
Collins, M. L. M., et al. 2011a, MNRAS, 413, 1548.
Collins, M. L. M., et al. 2011b, MNRAS, 417, 1170.
Dalcanton, J. J. and Bernstein, R. A. 2002, AJ, 124 1328.
McConnachie, A. W. & Irwin, M. J. 2006, MNRAS, 365, 902.
Peñarrubia, J., Navarro, J. F., and McConnachie, A. W., 2008, ApJ, 673, 226.
Peñarrubia, J. et al. 2010, MNRAS, 406, 1290.
Richardson, J. C., et al. 2011, ApJ, 732, 76.
Walker, M. G. et al. 2009, ApJ, 704, 1274
Yoachim, P. & Dalcanton, J.J. 2006, AJ, 131, 226

Galactic Archaeology: Near-Field Cosmology and the Formation of the Milky Way
ASP Conference Series, Vol. 458
W. Aoki, M. Ishigaki, T. Suda, T. Tsujimoto, N. Arimoto, eds.
© *2012 Astronomical Society of the Pacific*

How Unique Is the Local Group? A Comparison to the Nearby Centaurus A Group

D. Crnojević,[1] E.K. Grebel,[2] A.M.N. Ferguson,[1] A.A. Cole,[3] A. Koch,[4] M. Rejkuba,[5] G. Da Costa,[6] H. Jerjen[6], and M.J. Irwin[7]

[1]*IfA/ROE, Blackford Hill, EH9 3HJ Edinburgh, UK*
[2]*ARI/ZAH, Mönchhofstr. 12-14, 69120 Heidelberg, Germany*
[3]*SMP/UTAS, Private Bag 37 Hobart, 7001 Tasmania, Australia*
[4]*LSW/ZAH, Königstuhl 12, 69117 Heidelberg, Germany*
[5]*ESO, Karl-Schwarzschild-Str. 2, D-85748 Garching, Germany*
[6]*RSAA/ANU, Cotter Road, Weston Creek, ACT 2611, Australia*
[7]*IoA, Madingley Road, CB3 0HA Cambridge, UK*

Abstract. The Local Group (LG) is the closest and thus most accessible place for seeking detailed information about the assembly and evolutionary history of dwarf and giant galaxies. However, in order to gain a broader and more complete view on these processes, we must step outside its boundaries and investigate different environments. The CenA/M83 group is a nearby (D~ 4 Mpc) dense complex dominated by a giant elliptical and a giant spiral, hosting more than 60 dwarf companions with a variety of morphological types and stellar contents. We study the resolved stellar populations of CenA and several satellite dwarf galaxies using optical and near-infrared data from space and ground based telescopes. In this contribution we outline the results from the analysis of their colour-magnitude diagrams (CMDs).

1. Dwarf Galaxies

We consider separately six dwarf spheroidal (dSph) and ten dwarf irregular (dIrr) galaxies in the CenA group.

For the former, a prominent red giant branch (RGB) in the optical (ACS/HST) colour-magnitude diagram (CMD) indicates a predominantly old ($\gtrsim$ 10 Gyr) population. In Crnojević et al. (2010) we derive photometric metallicity distribution functions (MDFs) via isochrone interpolation (assuming a single, old age), and find they all have a metal-poor content ([Fe/H]< -1.0) with an intrinsic metallicity dispersion. For these dSphs, the same luminosity-metallicity relation that holds for the Local Group (LG) dwarfs is valid. Moreover, we find statistically separated subpopulations in metallicity and in spatial distribution (with the metal-poorer populations more broadly distributed, while the metal-richer are centrally concentrated).

We also use near-infrared (ISAAC/VLT) CMDs in conjunction with the optical ones to make the separation between dwarf galaxies stars and Milky Way foreground stars easier, as explained in Crnojević et al. (2011b). From the number of luminous asymptotic giant branch stars (AGB, ~ 1 to 9 Gyr) we estimate the fraction of the intermediate-age populations and the last star formation (SF) epoch in the dSphs.

The optical CMDs of the dIrr galaxies show young (main sequence, blue-loop stars) and intermediate-age (AGB stars) populations besides the old RGB. We derive their recent SF histories (accurate for ages $\lesssim$ 1 Gyr) via synthetic CMD fitting (see Crnojević et al. 2011a; Crnojević et al. 2012a, in prep.). We find SF rates and metallicities that are typical for dIrrs, with a "gasping" SF mode (constant moderate SF with enhanced intensity peaks). The youngest populations are moreover found in clumpy, localized regions in the galaxies. Finally, the most recent SF ($\lesssim$ 500 Myr) appears to be quenched for dwarfs in dense group regions with respect to more isolated ones.

2. Centaurus A

We performed the first deep large-scale survey ($\sim$ 0.3 deg^2) of the outer resolved stellar halo ($\sim$ 35 up to $\sim$ 90 kpc) of the closest giant elliptical with VIMOS/VLT (Crnojević et al. 2012b, in prep.). We target each of the major and minor axes with two pointings, detecting a prominent RGB out to at least $\sim$ 80 kpc ($\sim$ 13 R_{eff}). We derive photometric MDFs for the predominantly old RGB, finding at most a mild radial metallicity gradient with a broad metallicity range (peaked at [Fe/H]$\sim$ -0.7).

In the radial density profiles of the RGB population, an excess of stars is seen along the major axis (at $\sim$ 40 kpc) with respect to the minor axis. This is most likely identified as tidal stellar debris from the outer parts of the gas rich accretion event visible in the middle of CenA.

3. Conclusions

The average properties of the studied dwarf galaxies (e.g., star formation histories and metallicity content) are similar to what is seen for LG members, thus pointing at internal processes regulating their evolution. However, we intriguingly discover that the intermediate age population fractions in dSphs around CenA are low with respect to those of Milky Way dSphs of similar luminosities, but comparable to those of low-mass M31 companions. This evidence suggests that environmental effects play a complementary role to internal processes in shaping the properties of the studied dwarfs in the dense CenA group.

We have also shown that the outer halo of the giant elliptical CenA is very extended and on average more metal-rich than any of its dwarf companions studied here. This suggests that the accretion of low-mass systems did not play a dominant role in building up the remote halo of CenA.

Acknowledgments.   DC and AMNF would like to thank the organizers for the enjoyable and stimulating conference.

References

Crnojević, D., Grebel, E. K., & Cole, A. A. 2011a, A&A, 530, A59
Crnojević, D., Grebel, E. K., & Koch, A. 2010, A&A, 516, A85
Crnojević, D., Rejkuba, M., Grebel, E. K., da Costa, G., & Jerjen, H. 2011b, A&A, 530, A58

Galactic Archaeology: Near-Field Cosmology and the Formation of the Milky Way
ASP Conference Series, Vol. 458
W. Aoki, M. Ishigaki, T. Suda, T. Tsujimoto, N. Arimoto, eds.
© *2012 Astronomical Society of the Pacific*

Extended Star Clusters: New Archaeological Tracers of Galaxy Evolution?

Narae Hwang

National Astronomical Observatory of Japan, Tokyo 181-8588, Japan

1. Introduction to Extended Star Clusters

Star clusters, especially globular clusters (GCs) have been used as valuable sources of information on the galaxy formation and evolutions by serving as tracers of stellar populations and kinematics. Extended star clusters (ESCs) are basically GC-like star clusters with systematically extended structure, usually larger than $7-10$ pc in half light radius R_h (c.f., size of typical GCs is $R_h = 2-5$ pc). The ESCs have not been noticed as a subpopulation of GCs until the recent observational reports of many 'peculiar' large GCs in nearby galaxies including M51 (see Hwang & Lee 2008, Fig. 13). Now, it is suspected that ESCs may inhabit in almost every type of galaxies, while relatively large population of ESCs tends to be observed only in the interacting galaxies.

2. Spatial Distribution: Key to Origin of ESCs?

The origin of ESCs has not been clearly understood yet although many observational and theoretical studies have worked on the issue, as discussed in Section 5.4 of Hwang et al. (2011). However, one notable feature of ESCs that can be helpful to reveal their origin is the spatial distribution, which is quite a contrast to that of typical GCs in the same galaxy. Faint Fuzzy clusters (FFs), a subpopulation of ESCs, in NGC 1023 (Larsen & Brodie 2000) and M51 or NGC 5195 (Hwang & Lee 2006, 2008) are some good examples suggesting that those ESCs may be peculiar disk populations or remnants of dynamical interactions of the host galaxies.

Even in the Milky Way Galaxy (MW), it has been known that many 'relatively large GCs' or MW-version of ESCs are found in the outer halo and they are aligned along with the so-called 'wall of dwarf galaxies', suggesting a possible correlation with nearby dwarf galaxies for their origins (Forbes et al. 2009; Metz et al. 2007). It is basically consistent with the conclusion made by Mackey & Gilmore (2004) that 'Young Halo (YH)' MW GCs with many extended or ESC-like ones may have come from the accretions of satellite galaxies, having different origin than the other MW GC populations. The situation seems similar in M31, another giant spiral galaxy in the Local Group. Roughly more than 20 ESCs have been discovered in the halo of M31 (Huxor et al. 2011) and many of them are argued to be associated with the adjacent stellar streams, implying that the ESCs and the stellar streams are remnants of satellite galaxy accretions (Mackey et al. 2010).

These observational findings suggest that ESCs, at least many of them, could have originated from dynamical events, mergers or accretions, that had happened to the host galaxies, and that the peculiar spatial distribution of ESCs may reveal the extent and, possibly, the path of dynamical events in the corresponding galaxies, making ESCs a tracer of dynamical galaxy evolutions.

3. Challenge: ESCs as Archaeological Tracers

Even though the usefulness of ESCs as a dynamical galaxy evolution tracer has not been tested or proved yet, there are a couple of positive developments in this regard.

First, the comparison with the theoretical simulations of M51 system hints that the FFs in M51 are preferentially aligned along the expected orbits of the companion galaxy NGC 5195: see Fig. 17 in Hwang & Lee (2008), and Fig. 4 in Dobbs et al. (2010). With the spectroscopic observation of these FFs in M51, this will provide an opportunity to test whether those FFs or ESCs are actually moving along the orbits expected from the theoretical modeling of M51 system, directly proving that FFs are actually part of interacting materials. This type of observational study will also help to improve the currently available models of galaxy interactions by providing detailed kinematical information of star clusters.

Second, a system of ESCs was discovered in nearby dwarf galaxy NGC 6822 where those ESCs are observed to lie in an alignment (Hwang et al. 2011). Moreover, these ESCs exhibit a systematic trend in their size and color along the galactocentric distance: ESCs are larger and bluer in the outer halo (see Hwang et al. 2011, Fig. 6). Assuming that the color of NGC 6822 ESCs represents their metallicity, this is consistent with the size and metallicity distribution of MW GCs although MW GC system is spatially too complex to exhibit a simple correlation such as observed in NGC 6822. The spectroscopic study of NGC 6822 ESCs is in progress and the result will provide a direct insight into the role of ESCs or ESC-like GCs in the accretion picture of galaxy evolution models, testing how reliably ESCs can be used as archaeological tracers of dynamical events in galaxies.

Acknowledgments.   I acknowledge invaluable collaborations with Myung Gyoon Lee, Hong Soo Park, Won-Kee Park, and Sang Chul Kim in the course of the ESC studies as well as numerous fruitful discussions with Nobuo Arimoto and Lee Spitler on star clusters and galaxy evolutions. I am also grateful to the organizers of the Subaru International Conference for their financial support and hospitality.

References

Dobbs, C. L., Theis, C., Pringle, J. E., & Bate, M. R. 2010, MNRAS, 403, 625
Forbes, D. A., Kroupa, P., Metz, M., & Spitler, L. 2009, Mercury, 38, 24
Huxor, A. P., Ferguson, A. M. N., Tanvir, N. R., Irwin, M. J., Mackey, A. D., Ibata, R. A., Bridges, T., Chapman, S. C., & Lewis, G. F. 2011, MNRAS, 414, 770
Hwang, N., & Lee, M. G. 2006, ApJ, 638, L79
— 2008, AJ, 135, 1567
Hwang, N., Lee, M. G., Lee, J. C., Park, W.-K., Park, H. S., Kim, S. C., & Park, J.-H. 2011, ApJ, 738, 58
Larsen, S. S., & Brodie, J. P. 2000, AJ, 120, 2938
Mackey, A. D., & Gilmore, G. F. 2004, MNRAS, 355, 504
Mackey, A. D., Huxor, A. P., Ferguson, A. M. N., Irwin, M. J., Tanvir, N. R., McConnachie, A. W., Ibata, R. A., Chapman, S. C., & Lewis, G. F. 2010, ApJ, 717, L11
Metz, M., Kroupa, P., & Jerjen, H. 2007, MNRAS, 374, 1125

Galactic Archaeology: Near-Field Cosmology and the Formation of the Milky Way
ASP Conference Series, Vol. 458
W. Aoki, M. Ishigaki, T. Suda, T. Tsujimoto, N. Arimoto, eds.
©*2012 Astronomical Society of the Pacific*

Hermes and the Sagittarius Dwarf: A Low Metallicity Goldmine?

Elaina A. Hyde,[1] D. B. Zucker,[1,2] M. Irwin,[3] J. Peñarrubia,[3,4]and A. Koch[5]

[1]*Department of Physics and Astronomy, Macquarie University, NSW 2109, AU*

[2]*Australian Astronomical Observatory, PO Box 296 Epping, NSW 1710, AU*

[3]*Institute of Astronomy, University of Cambridge, Cambridge CB3 0HA, UK*

[4]*IAA, Glorieta de la Astronomía s/n, 18008 Granada, ES*

[5]*ZAH, Landessternwarte, Königstuhl 12, 69117 Heidelberg, DE*

Abstract.   The Sagittarius dwarf galaxy and its vast associated stellar stream represent the most dramatic example of a satellite accreting onto the Milky Way in the past few billion years. We present an in-depth characterisation of the Sagittarius core using spectra of over 7,000 red giant stars taken with AAOmega on the AAT, and show the first results of stream and core data together. Future observations with HERMES will yield detailed abundances to compare with models of chemical enrichment.

1. The Sagittarius Dwarf Survey

With AAOmega at the Anglo-Australian Telescope (AAT), we obtained multi-object spectroscopy for 20 fields on the Sagittarius (Sgr) dwarf, representing the largest such data set since the initial discovery by Ibata et al. (1994, 1995). Spatial distributions of the fields and stellar velocities vs. metallicities are shown in Figure 1.

Data reduction was carried out with *2dfdr* and *IRAF* packages. We obtained velocity measurements from the Ca triplet line, and metallicities were derived (following Koch et al. (2008)) from Ca line equivalent widths and V magnitudes estimated from 2MASS data. For this we use the formulae from Rutledge et al. (1997a,b) and assuming a horizontal branch magnitude of $V_{HB} \sim 18$ (Monaco et al. 2003). Combining metallicities with the radial velocities for each star, we obtain a clear Sgr dwarf grouping, shown in Figure 1. Recently we have expanded our sample to include Sgr stream data as well, finding that the lowest metallicity objects, i.e. those with [Fe/H] $\lesssim -2.0$, are found throughout the Sgr dwarf as well as in the stream.

2. Conclusions and Future Work

Our data set now includes fields along the extended Sgr stellar stream (e.g., Martínez-Delgado et al. 2004, 2001), and we will soon have metallicities and velocities for Sgr stars spanning 300 degrees on the sky. As noted above, low metallicity stars ([Fe/H] $\lesssim$

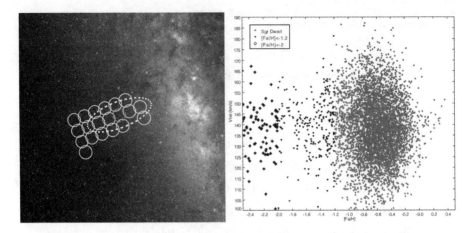

Figure 1.   Left: Sgr dwarf fields observed, with the central field as dashed light grey, other observed fields in solid white, and the outline of the general shape of the Sgr dwarf shown in the dashed oval outline. Background image from Mellinger (2009). Right: Velocity distribution for different metallicity ranges in the Sgr dwarf fields; V_hel is heliocentric velocity in kms^{-1} and [Fe/H] is estimated from Ca line equivalent widths.

−2.0) appear to be spread throughout the core and stream of Sgr. We also find that the puzzling bifurcation of the stream cannot be explained by a rotating progenitor (Peñarrubia et al. 2011). New, more sophisticated dynamical models are necessary to reproduce all the available data for the Sgr dwarf and its stream. The planned HERMES Galactic Archaeology survey will provide multi-element abundances and velocities for a million stars, many of which will overlap with our own survey of the Sgr dwarf and stream. Expanding our stream study and obtaining detailed abundances and precision radial velocities with the upcoming HERMES high-resolution spectrograph on the AAT will greatly advance our understanding of this system.

Acknowledgments.   We thank the Astronomical Society of Australia for overseas travel support and the Subaru Conference LOC for registration and internal travel support. The authors would like to thank G. Lewis and G. Gilmore for helpful discussions.

References

Ibata et al. 1994, Nature, 370, 194
— 1995, MNRAS, 277, 781
Koch et al. 2008, ApJ, 689, 958
Martínez-Delgado et al. 2001, ApJ, 549, L199
— 2004, ApJ, 601, 242
Mellinger 2009, PASP, 121, 1180
Monaco et al. 2003, ApJ, 597, L25
Peñarrubia et al. 2011, ApJ, 727, L2
Rutledge et al. 1997a, PASP, 109, 883
— 1997b, PASP, 109, 907

Galactic Archaeology: Near-Field Cosmology and the Formation of the Milky Way
ASP Conference Series, Vol. 458
W. Aoki, M. Ishigaki, T. Suda, T. Tsujimoto, N. Arimoto, eds.
© *2012 Astronomical Society of the Pacific*

Metallicity of Low Surface Brightness Galaxies

Ji Hoon Kim[1] and Stacy McGaugh[2]

[1]*Center for the Exploration of the Origin of the Universe, Seoul National University*

[2]*Department of Astronomy, University of Maryland, College Park*

Abstract. Low surface brightness galaxies (LSBGs) are an idiosyncratic population: blue colors, low metallicity, low stellar and gas surface density, low dust content, and high gas-to-star mass ratio. Allegedly having low star formation activity due to low gas surface density with relatively large gas reservoirs, LSBGs have very intriguing formation epochs and star formation histories (SFHs). Based on Hα photometry, near-infrared photometry and amount of neutral hydrogen, Kim (2007) show that LSBGs have ephemeral SFHs and suggest that LSBGs may experience late gas infall due to large specific angular momentum. Measuring both stellar and gas metallicity across disks can provide crucial information on how these LSB disks were formed and evolved. 8-m class telescopes, including Subaru, can nail down this issue.

1. Metallicity Gradient as a Probe for Galaxy Evolution

Radial color gradient of disk galaxies has been a key tool for diagnosing the ages and metallicities of the stars and gas of these galaxies, and thus, the formation process of these disks. In many cases, observational data support the 'inside-out' picture of disk galaxy formation proposed by Larson (1976) (Matteucci & Francois 1989; Boissier & Prantzos 1999). In this scenario, gas within dark matter halos cools and accretes on to the outer disk while enhancing star formation in the disk. Recent discoveries of "extended ultra-viloet" (XUV) disks also show that majority of disk galaxy experience active star formation within out disks where gas surface density is quite low (Thilker et al. 2007; Gil de Paz et al. 2007).

However, neither gas, nor stars stay put within galaxies. They rather migrate into bulges, disperse throughout galaxies, or flow into and out of galaxies via various mechanisms. There have been a few notable studies to investigate how radial star formation and metal abundance gradients vary across populations of disk galaxies systematically (Vila-Costas & Edmunds 1992; Zaritsky et al. 1994). However, the mechanisms driving gas transport are still poorly understood.

2. Star Formation at Low Surface Density Regime

The SFH of LSBGs are interesting but poorly constrained. These objects tend to be rather blue, contradicting the initial impression that they may simply be faded remnants of higher surface brightness galaxies whose star formation has finished. With low star formation rates (SFR) and relatively large amount of gas reservoirs, their formation epochs and SFHs are likely very unique. Using near-infrared broadband photometry and Hα photometry of a large sample of LSBGs to measure the current and the time-averaged SFR in order to constrain their SFHs, Kim (2007) found that the current SFRs of LSBGs generally are higher than their past SFRs, suggesting that the mean age of their stellar population is relatively young. This may stem from either a late epoch of formation or a sluggish evolution. In the latter case, the star formation efficiency may be an increasing function of time, perhaps due in part to the slow build up of metals and dust. Nevertheless, star formation remains sporadic and is generally not well organized across the disk. Kim (2007) also found a strong correlation between the ratio of current to past average SFR and the gas mass fraction. Galaxies with large reservoirs of gas have relatively high current SFRs. The question of why LSBGs have these sporadic SFHs is very interesting, particularly after a seemingly long hiatus of massive star formation. Kaufmann et al. (2007) shows that cold gas confined within primordial halos with large specific angular momentum collapse late and dark matter dominated halos of LSBGs are similar to these high specific angular momentum halos. Thus large angular momentum prevents gas from falling into disks, then eventually prevents gas from turning into stars.

By measuring stellar and gas metallicity across disks of a large sample of LSBGs with 8-m class telescope, we can constrain the SFHs of LSBGs while searching for discrepancies between these two metallicities and their gradients.

Acknowledgments. This work was supported by Korean Research Foundation (KRF) grant funded by the Korean government (MEST), No. 2010–0000712.

References

Boissier, S., & Prantzos, N. 1999, MNRAS, 307, 857. arXiv:astro-ph/9902148
Gil de Paz, A., Boissier, S., Madore, B. F., Seibert, M., Joe, Y. H., Boselli, A., Wyder, T. K., Thilker, D., Bianchi, L., Rey, S.-C., Rich, R. M., Barlow, T. A., Conrow, T., Forster, K., Friedman, P. G., Martin, D. C., Morrissey, P., Neff, S. G., Schiminovich, D., Small, T., Donas, J., Heckman, T. M., Lee, Y.-W., Milliard, B., Szalay, A. S., & Yi, S. 2007, ApJS, 173, 185. arXiv:astro-ph/0606440
Kaufmann, T., Mayer, L., Wadsley, J., Stadel, J., & Moore, B. 2007, MNRAS, 375, 53. arXiv:astro-ph/0601115
Kim, J. H. 2007, Ph.D. thesis, University of Maryland, College Park
Larson, R. B. 1976, MNRAS, 176, 31
Matteucci, F., & Francois, P. 1989, MNRAS, 239, 885
Thilker, D. A., Bianchi, L., Meurer, G., Gil de Paz, A., Boissier, S., Madore, B. F., Boselli, A., Ferguson, A. M. N., Muñoz-Mateos, J. C., Madsen, G. J., Hameed, S., Overzier, R. A., Forster, K., Friedman, P. G., Martin, D. C., Morrissey, P., Neff, S. G., Schiminovich, D., Seibert, M., Small, T., Wyder, T. K., Donas, J., Heckman, T. M., Lee, Y.-W., Milliard, B., Rich, R. M., Szalay, A. S., Welsh, B. Y., & Yi, S. K. 2007, ApJS, 173, 538. 0712.3555
Vila-Costas, M. B., & Edmunds, M. G. 1992, MNRAS, 259, 121
Zaritsky, D., Kennicutt, R. C., Jr., & Huchra, J. P. 1994, ApJ, 420, 87

Galactic Archaeology: Near-Field Cosmology and the Formation of the Milky Way
ASP Conference Series, Vol. 458
W. Aoki, M. Ishigaki, T. Suda, T. Tsujimoto, N. Arimoto, eds.
© 2012 Astronomical Society of the Pacific

The Chemical Evolution of Milky Way Satellite Galaxies from Keck/DEIMOS Multi-Element Abundance Measurements

Evan N. Kirby and Judith G. Cohen

California Institute of Technology, 1200 E. California Blvd., MC 249-17, Pasadena, CA 91125, USA

Abstract. A Keck/DEIMOS spectroscopic campaign of eight Milky Way (MW) dwarf spheroidal (dSph) satellite galaxies has generated spectral synthesis-based abundance measurements for nearly 3000 stars. The elements measured are Fe and the α elements Mg, Si, Ca, and Ti. The dSph metallicity distributions show that the histories of the less luminous dSphs were marked by massive amounts of gas loss. The $[\alpha/\text{Fe}]$ distributions indicate that the early star formation histories of most dSphs were very similar and that Type Ia supernova ejecta contributed to the abundances of all but the most metal-poor ($[\text{Fe}/\text{H}] < -2.5$) stars.

1. The Keck/DEIMOS Spectroscopic Sample

We obtained Keck/DEIMOS spectra of about 3000 red giants in eight MW dSphs. From these spectra, we measured Mg, Si, Ca, Ti, and Fe abundances from neutral absorption lines. The resulting catalog was published by Kirby et al. (2010).

2. Metal Loss from Dwarf Galaxies

The mass of metals a galaxy produces (M_{produced}) may be estimated from its stellar mass, an assumed initial mass function, and theoretical supernova yields. Our Keck/DEIMOS campaign has targeted eight MW dSphs, and the resulting spectra have allowed us to measure the detailed metallicity distribution for each galaxy. The integral of the metallicity distribution is the mass of metals remaining in the galaxy (M_{retained}). The difference between M_{produced} and M_{retained} is the amount of metals lost. It turns out that smaller galaxies lose a larger fraction of their metals. Fornax lost 96% of the iron it produced, and Ursa Minor lost 99.8%, as shown in Figure 1. Please refer to Kirby et al. (2011b) for more details.

3. Star Formation Histories of Dwarf Galaxies

Figure 2 shows how different α elements change with $[\text{Fe}/\text{H}]$ in the dSphs. At $[\text{Fe}/\text{H}] < -1.2$, the $[\alpha/\text{Fe}]$ ratios follow nearly the same path in all dSphs, suggesting similar star formation histories at early times. Furthermore, with few exceptions, there are no $[\alpha/\text{Fe}]$ plateaus at $[\text{Fe}/\text{H}] > -2.5$, which indicates that Type Ia supernova ejecta contributed to all but the most metal-poor stars. Please refer to Kirby et al. (2011a) for more details.

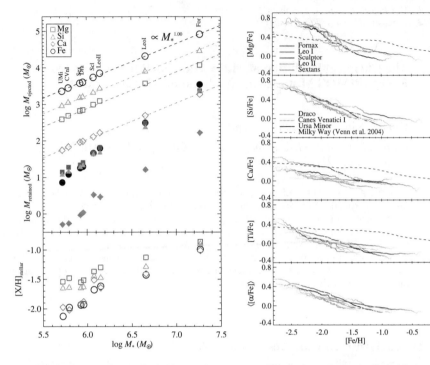

Figure 1. (color online) For each of the eight MW dSphs we observed with DEIMOS, $M_{retained}$ is shown as a filled point in the top panel. The colors and shapes of the points denote the element measured. The difference between $M_{produced}$ and $M_{retained}$ is the amount of metals lost (hollow points). The bottom panel shows the mass-metallicity relation.

Figure 2. (color online) Moving averages of the [α/Fe] ratios in MW dSphs. The figure legend lists the dSphs in order of decreasing luminosity.

Acknowledgments. Support for this work was provided by NASA through Hubble Fellowship grant 51256.01 awarded to ENK by the Space Telescope Science Institute, which is operated by the Association of Universities for Research in Astronomy, Inc., for NASA, under contract NAS 5-26555.

References

Kirby, E. N., Cohen, J. G., Smith, G. H., Majewski, S. R., Sohn, S. T., & Guhathakurta, P. 2011a, ApJ, 727, 79
Kirby, E. N., Guhathakurta, P., Simon, J. D., Geha, M. C., Rockosi, C. M., Sneden, C., Cohen, J. G., Sohn, S. T., Majewski, S. R., & Siegel, M. 2010, ApJS, 191, 352
Kirby, E. N., Martin, C. L., & Finlator, K. 2011b, ApJ, 742, L25
Venn, K. A., Irwin, M., Shetrone, M. D., Tout, C. A., Hill, V., & Tolstoy, E. 2004, AJ, 128, 1177

Galactic Archaeology: Near-Field Cosmology and the Formation of the Milky Way
ASP Conference Series, Vol. 458
W. Aoki, M. Ishigaki, T. Suda, T. Tsujimoto, N. Arimoto, eds.
© *2012 Astronomical Society of the Pacific*

A Study of Star Clusters in IC10 using SUBARU Suprime-Cam and MOIRCS Data

Sungsoon Lim and Myung Gyoon Lee

Department of Physics and Astronomy, Seoul National University, Korea

Abstract.
We present a photometric study of the star clusters in IC10. We find fifteen new star clusters from the inspection of SUBARU/Suprime-Cam images in the archive, while fifty seven star clusters are found from HST images in previous studies. We derive JHKs integrated photometry of these star clusters from the images taken with SUBARU/MOIRCS. We combine this with optical photometry derived from archive images. Then we derive age and mass of these star clusters using the spectral energy distribution fitting with the simple stellar population models. We fine that the age distribution has two dominant peaks at about 20 Myr and 1 Gyr. The recent peak at 20 Myr shows that recent starburst lasted since 20 Myr ago. The peak at 1 Gyr suggests that IC10 had strong starburst at 1 Gyr ago.

1. Introduction

IC10 is the nearest starbusrt galaxy. The intense star formation processes are revealed by the integrated spectroscopy (Hunter & Gallagher 1985). The star formation rate of this galaxy is the one of the highest values in the irregular galaxies (Hunter 1997). Star clusters (SCs) in IC10 are studied by several previous studies (Karachentsev & Tikhonov 1993; Hunter 2001; Tikhonov & Galazutdinova 2009). Although the previous studies investigated SCs in IC10, the survey area is still small which covered only main body of IC10. In this study, we present wide-field and multi-wavelength study for SCs in IC10.

2. Data & Methods

We used UBVRI images from the Local Group Survey (Massey et al. 2007), and JHKs images obtained with Subaru/MOIRCS for UBVRIJHKs photometry and Subaru/ Suprime-Cam R-band images from SMOKA (Baba et al. 2002) were used for the visual inspection. Source Extractor (Bertin & Arnouts 1996) was employed for source detection and photometry. We selected SC candidates by the criteria determined with known star clusters in various parameter spaces, such as $17.5 < m_V < 22$, $0.5 < (V - I) < 2.8$, stellarity < 0.8, and ellipticity < 0.7. These candidates were chosen as SCs by the visual inspection. Ages of SCs were estimated with Spectral Energy Distribution (SED) fitting method compared with simple stellar population models from Bruzual & Charlot (2003)

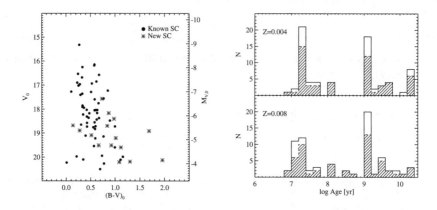

Figure 1.   (*Left*):Color-magnitude diagram of SCs.Filled circles and asterisks indicate known SCs in previous studies and newly found SCs in this study, repectively. (*Right*):Age distributions of SCs. Upper and lower panels show the results of SED fit assumed with Z= 0.004 and Z= 0.008, respectively. Shades histograms represent good fit results.

3. Result & Discussion

We found new fifteen SCs in IC10, and obtained UBVRI photometry of 72 SCs including new SCs. SCs which are found in this study are mostly fainter and redder then previosly known SCs. We also found new SCs outside the main body of IC10 while most SCs which were known in previous study are located on the main body. Most distant SCs is about 10 arcmin far from center of IC10. The age distribution of SCs shows two dominant peaks at ~ 20 Myr and ~ 1 Gyr. Wilcots & Miller (1998) suggested that IC10 was struck by HI clouds at $2 - 3 \times 10^7$ yrs ago. This epoch is consistent with the peak at ~ 20 Myr. The SC formation history suggests that strong star formation occurred at ~ 1 Gyr ago. Most young SCs (< 1Gyr) are located at the main body, while old SCs (> 2 Gyr) are mostly distributed outside the main body.

References

Baba, H., Yasuda, N., Ichikawa, S.-I., Yagi, M., Iwamoto, N., Takata, T., Horaguchi, T., Taga, M., Watanabe, M., Ozawa, T., & Hamabe, M. 2002, in Astronomical Data Analysis Software and Systems XI, edited by D. A. Bohlender, D. Durand, & T. H. Handley, vol. 281 of Astronomical Society of the Pacific Conference Series, 298
Bertin, E., & Arnouts, S. 1996, A&AS, 117, 393
Bruzual, G., & Charlot, S. 2003, MNRAS, 344, 1000. arXiv:astro-ph/0309134
Hunter, D. 1997, PASP, 109, 937
Hunter, D. A. 2001, ApJ, 559, 225. arXiv:astro-ph/0105456
Hunter, D. A., & Gallagher, J. S., III 1985, ApJS, 58, 533
Karachentsev, I. D., & Tikhonov, N. A. 1993, A&AS, 100, 227
Massey, P., Olsen, K. A. G., Hodge, P. W., Jacoby, G. H., McNeill, R. T., Smith, R. C., & Strong, S. B. 2007, AJ, 133, 2393. arXiv:astro-ph/0702236
Tikhonov, N. A., & Galazutdinova, O. A. 2009, Astronomy Letters, 35, 748
Wilcots, E. M., & Miller, B. W. 1998, AJ, 116, 2363

Galactic Archaeology: Near-Field Cosmology and the Formation of the Milky Way
ASP Conference Series, Vol. 458
W. Aoki, M. Ishigaki, T. Suda, T. Tsujimoto, N. Arimoto, eds.
©*2012 Astronomical Society of the Pacific*

Spatially Resolved Spectroscopic Observations of a Possible E+A Progenitor SDSS J160241.00+521426.9

Kazuya Matsubayashi

Research Center for Space and Cosmic Evolution, Ehime University, 2-5 Bunkyo-cho, Matsuyama, Ehime 790-8577, Japan

Abstract. In order to investigate the evolution of E+A galaxies, we observed a galaxy SDSS J160241.00+521426.9, a possible E+A progenitor which shows both emission and strong Balmer absorptions, and its neighbor galaxy. We used the integral field spectroscopic mode of the Kyoto Tridimensional Spectrograph (Kyoto3DII), mounted on the University of Hawaii 88-inch telescope located on Mauna Kea, and the slit-spectroscopic mode of the Faint Object Camera and Spectrograph (FOCAS) on the Subaru Telescope. We found a strong Balmer absorption region in the center of the galaxy and an emission-line region located 2 kpc from the center, in the direction of its neighbor galaxy. Comparing observed Lick indices of Balmer lines and color indices with those predicted from stellar population synthesis models, we find that a suddenly quenched star-formation scenario is plausible for the star-formation history of the central region.

1. Introduction

E+A galaxies are understood as post-starburst galaxies due to the presence of strong Balmer absorption lines (Hβ, Hγ, Hδ) and the lack of emission lines (Poggianti et al. 1999; Goto 2005). In this work, we carried out an integral field spectroscopic (IFS) and a slit-spectroscopic observations for a possible progenitor of an E+A galaxy, SDSS J160241.00+521426.9 (J1602). Through detailed analysis, we attempted to understand the underlying physical process that caused the simultaneous presence of post-starburst and current starburst regions in this galaxy. The results shown here are mainly based on Matsubayashi et al. (2011).

2. Observations and Data Reduction

We selected a target galaxy, J1602, which has both strong post-starburst and starburst properties, based on its line ratios from an Hδ strong galaxies catalog (Goto 2005) produced from the spectra of the Sloan Digital Sky Survey Data Release 2 (SDSS DR2: Abazajian et al. 2004). The 3″-fiber spectra from the SDSS show an interesting combination of very strong Balmer absorption lines and emission lines. We observed J1602 and its companion using the IFS mode of the Kyoto3DII (Sugai et al. 2010) mounted on the University of Hawaii 88-inch (2.2m) telescope at Mauna Kea. We also carried out a slit-spectroscopic observation using FOCAS (Kashikawa et al. 2002) on the Subaru Telescope.

3. Results and Discussion

Figure 1 shows the continuum, Hγ, and [OIII]λ5007 images obtained from Kyoto3DII IFS data. Two galaxies fall within our FOV: a brighter northern galaxy and a fainter southern one. Strong Balmer absorption lines and no emission line were found at the center of J1602 (PS1 hereafter), which indicates that PS1 is a post-starburst region. We also found from FOCAS data that strong Balmer absorption regions extends to ~ 6 kpc from the center. At 2 kpc southwest from PS1 (SB1 hereafter), many nebular emission lines were detected. Therefore, J1602 has both starburst and post-starburst regions in one galaxy.

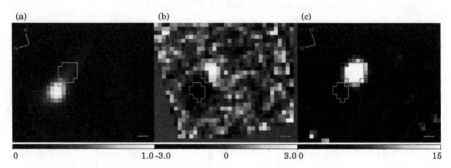

Figure 1.   (color online) (a) Continuum flux (4600 – 5000 Å in the observed frame), (b) Hγ flux, and (c) [OIII]λ5007 flux maps of J1602 and the companion galaxy observed with Kyoto3DII.

We compared Lick indices of the $H\gamma_A$ and $H\delta_A$ and the color indices in the rest-frame with predictions taken from star-formation models (Bruzual & Charlot 2003). The best-fit model was 200 Myr in the SSP model for $Z = 0.004$ and 0.008. The lowest χ^2 values for the SSP model are one order of magnitude lower than those of the other star-formation histories. Burst model, which has a constant starburst with a duration of 1 Gyr at the beginning and no star formation thereafter, can produce large $H\gamma_A$ index as observed. Thus, we consider that a suddenly quenched star formation history is plausible for E+A galaxies.

Acknowledgments.   We thank the staff at the UH 2.2-m telescope and the Subaru Telescope for their help during the observation. Use of the UH 2.2-m telescope for our observations was supported by National Astronomical Observatory of Japan. This work is based in part on data collected at Subaru Telescope, which is operated by the National Astronomical Observatory of Japan.

References

Abazajian, K., et al., 2004, AJ, 128, 502. arXiv:astro-ph/0403325
Bruzual, G., & Charlot, S. 2003, MNRAS, 344, 1000. arXiv:astro-ph/0309134
Goto, T. 2005, MNRAS, 357, 937. arXiv:astro-ph/0503088
Kashikawa, N., et al., 2002, PASJ, 54, 819
Matsubayashi, K., et al., 2011, ApJ, 729, 29. 1101.4933
Poggianti, B. M., et al., 1999, ApJ, 518, 576. arXiv:astro-ph/9901264
Sugai, H., et al., 2010, PASP, 122, 103

Galactic Archaeology: Near-Field Cosmology and the Formation of the Milky Way
ASP Conference Series, Vol. 458
W. Aoki, M. Ishigaki, T. Suda, T. Tsujimoto, N. Arimoto, eds.
©2012 Astronomical Society of the Pacific

Interaction between M31 and the Progenitor Dwarf Galaxy of the Andromeda Stellar Stream

Yohei Miki,[1] Masao Mori,[1] Toshihiro Kawaguchi,[1] and R. Michael Rich[2]

[1]*University of Tsukuba, Center for Computational Sciences, 1-1-1,Tennodai Tsukuba, Ibaraki 305-8577, Japan*

[2]*University of California at Los Angeles, Physics and Astronomy Building, 430 Portola Plaza, Box 951547 Los Angeles, CA 90095-1547, USA*

Abstract. Using N-body simulations of the interaction between an accreting satellite and M31, we have successfully reproduced observed distribution of the Andromeda stellar stream, and find physical constraints about the progenitor dwarf galaxy. Furthermore, we show such interaction suspends the AGN activity of galaxies due to stripping of a torus as a mass reservoir of the AGN.

1. Galaxy collision and abundant stellar structures

Recent progress in observational studies of the Andromeda galaxy (M31) revealed a wealth of substructures: a giant stellar stream to the south of M31, as well as giant stellar shells to the east and west of M31's center (Ibata et al. 2001, 2005, 2007; Ferguson et al. 2002; McConnachie et al. 2009). So far, theoretical studies via N-body simulations of the interaction between an infalling satellite dwarf galaxy and M31 demonstrate that the stream and shells are the tidal debris of the satellite on a radial orbit (Fardal et al. 2007; Mori & Rich 2008). These models successfully determine the orbit and mass range of the progenitor. However, possible effects of the size and the mass distribution of the satellite to the observed structures have never been considered.

Assuming a King sphere as a model of the progenitor galaxy, we performed parameter study about total mass, tidal radius and concentration parameter using $65,536$ particles. The orbit of the satellite and the potential model of M31 are same with Fardal et al. (2007). As a result of the simulation, we found the critical condition to reproduce the observed structures. If the satellite galaxy is a loosely-bound system, it is totally disrupted by a tidal force of the M31, and the debris no longer reproduces the observed features such as the Andromeda stream and the shells. In case of the tightly-bound system, the satellite galaxy is almost free of influence from M31. Therefore, we found that the degree of the binding energy of the satellite galaxy is the most important physical property to the shapes of the observed structures.

2. Galaxy collision and hungry black hole

Galaxy collisions have been so far considered enhancing the activity of Active Galactic Nuclei (AGN), by triggering mass fueling to the central super massive black hole

(SMBH) due to angular momentum transfer (e.g., Sanders et al. 1988). However, we show that galaxy collisions suppress the AGN activity in a certain condition: if mass reservoir of the central SMBH is swept away by galaxy collisions, then the AGN activity must be turn off due to lack of fueling sources. Such a possible process has never been considered.

M31 has a central SMBH ($M_{BH} = 1.4 \times 10^8 M_\odot$: Bender et al. (2005)), however, its X-ray luminosity is quite small ($L_{0.3-0.7keV} \leq 10^{-10} L_{Edd}$: Li et al. (2009)). The origin of its extremely low activity is still unknown, which motivate us to explore the possible mechanism as the shutdown of the AGN activity.

Since the progenitor of the stream blankets the central region of M31 for its crossing time of 1.1 Myr, the gas of the infalling satellite is modeled as gas inflow for 1.1 Myr. The gas fraction of the satellite, f_{gas}, is a parameter: $10^{-3} \leq f_{gas} \leq 1$ (Conselice et al. 2003). We assume an AGN torus is the fueling source of the SMBH. The torus is modeled as steady, axisymmetric polytrope gas under a spherical gravitational field (e.g., Okada et al. 1989). The mass of the torus gas M_{torus} is also a parameter: $10^{-3} \leq M_{torus}/M_{BH} \leq 1$ (e.g., Mor et al. 2009).

We have performed three dimensional hydrodynamic simulations: local simulations for (200 pc^3) box around the center of M31, gravitational potential of SMBH and bulge are modeled as a fixed potential. We have performed 12 runs of 256^3 grids for parameter study, a run of 1024^3 grids for convergence check, and a run of twice larger torus model (512^3 grids).

Numerical simulations show that the most important parameter is the gas column density ratio, $x \equiv f_{gas}/(M_{torus}/M_{BH})$. If the column density of the torus gas is smaller than that of the satellite galaxy, large amount of the torus gas is swept out. In such case ($x \gtrsim 100$), the AGN activity must be turn off due to lack of the fueling sources. In contrast, if the column density of the torus gas is large enough, there is a little effect on the structure of the torus. We find that the critical condition to suspend the AGN activity by galactic mergers due to stripping of fueling source is the gas column density ratio.

Acknowledgments.   Numerical Simulations have been performed with FIRST cluster and T2K-Tsukuba at University of Tsukuba. This work was supported in part by the FIRST project based on Grants-in-Aid for Specially Promoted Research by MEXT (16002003) and Grant-in-Aid for Scientific Research (S) by JSPS (20224002), (A) by JSPS (21244013), and (C) by JSPS (18540242).

References

Bender, R. et al. 2005, ApJ, 631, 280
Conselice, C. J., O'Neil, K., Gallagher, J. S., & Wyse, R. F. G. 2003, ApJ, 591, 167
Fardal, M. A. et al. 2007, MNRAS, 380, 15
Li, Z., Wang, Q. D., & Wakker, B. P. 2009, MNRAS, 397, 148
McConnachie, A. W. et al. 2009, Nat, 461, 66
Mor, R., Netzer, H., & Elitzur, M. 2009, ApJ, 705, 298
Mori, M., & Rich, R. M. 2008, ApJ, 674, L77
Okada, R., Fukue, J., & Matsumoto, R. 1989, PASJ, 41, 133
Sanders, D. B. et al. 1988, ApJ, 325, 74

Galactic Archaeology: Near-Field Cosmology and the Formation of the Milky Way
ASP Conference Series, Vol. 458
W. Aoki, M. Ishigaki, T. Suda, T. Tsujimoto, N. Arimoto, eds.
©2012 Astronomical Society of the Pacific

Near-Infrared Spectroscopy of Passively Evolving Galaxies at $z > 1.4$ with Subaru/MOIRCS

Masato Onodera

ETH Zürich, Wolfgang-Pauli-Strasse 27, 8093, Zürich, Switzerland

Abstract. We present the results of near-IR spectroscopic observations of passive galaxies at $z \gtrsim 1.4$ in the COSMOS field. The observations have been conducted with Subaru/MOIRCS, and have resulted in absorption lines and/or continuum detection for 16 out of 17 objects down to $K_{AB} = 21$ (18 of 34 in total), then allowing us the measurement of their spectroscopic redshifts. COSMOS photometric redshifts are found in fair agreement overall with the spectroscopic redshifts, with a standard deviation of $\simeq 0.05$, but including $\sim 30\%$ of outliers for which they are systematically underestimated. All galaxies fall in four distinct redshift spikes at $z = 1.43$, 1.53, 1.67 and 1.82, with this latter one including 7 galaxies. SED fits to broad-band fluxes indicate stellar masses in the range of $\sim 4 - 40 \times 10^{10} \, M_\odot$, and that star formation was quenched ~ 1 Gyr before the cosmic epoch at which they are observed. The spectra of individual galaxies have allowed us to measure $H\delta_F$ indices and the strength of the 4000 Å break, which confirms the passive nature of the program galaxies.

1. Introduction

Passively evolving galaxies (PEGs) tend to be located in the highest density environment in the universe, hence trace important parts of the large scale structure. This galaxy population is also interesting and important as they have already experienced the quenching of star formation which might be the most dramatic event in the evolution of galaxies. However, since they are very faint in optical, these galaxy population at $z > 1.4$, where the significant increase of comoving number density of such galaxy populations has been observed (e.g., Kong et al. 2006), has been largely missed in the current optical spectroscopic survey. Instead of optical, near-IR spectroscopy can observe the wavelength at > 4000 Å where PEGs are much brighter and have stronger spectral features which allow us redshift determination and investigation of their stellar populations.

2. Data

We have observed 34 passive BzK -selected galaxies (Daddi et al. 2004) with $19.4 < K_{AB} < 21.9$ selected from K-selected catalog for the COSMOS field (McCracken et al. 2010). We have also given the priority to those with (i) MIPS 24 μm non-detection, (ii) red $m(3.8\,\mu m) - m(4.5\,\mu m)$ color, (iii) photometric redshift higher than 1.4, (iv) high projected concentration of pBzKs , and (v) the 12 brightest pBzKs in the COSMOS field studied by Mancini et al. (2010). Observations have been carried out with Subaru/MOIRCS using the zJ500 grism and 0.7 arcsec width slit which covers 9000–17500 Å with a resolution of $R \simeq 500$. Three masks were observed with integration time of 7–9 hours.

We have identified 18 of them either by rest-frame absorption lines or by continuum shape, in particular, characterized by 4000 Å break. The identification is nearly complete down to $K_{AB} = 21$ as 16 of 17 observed are identified and all of pBzKs with $K_{AB} < 21$ were observed in three FoVs. The results for one of them has been already presented in Onodera et al. (2010).

3. Results

This is virtually the first attempt to systematically test the COSMOS 30-band photometric redshift (Ilbert et al. 2009) against measured spectroscopic redshift of PEGs at $z > 1.4$. A majority of the objects show fairly good agreement between them, but several outliers (up to $\sim 30\%$) which have underestimated photometric redshifts. More quantitatively, the average offset is $\langle z_{spec} - z_{phot}/(1 + z_{spec}) \rangle = 0.04$ and the standard deviation of $(z_{spec} - z_{phot})/(1 + z_{spec})$ is 0.053. The standard deviation is similar to those derived for faint star-forming galaxies at $1.5 < z < 3$ (Ilbert et al. 2009), whereas no catastrophic failure defined as $|z_{spec} - z_{phot}|/(1 + z_{spec}) > 0.15$ are found.

The redshift distribution of spectroscopically identified objects are found to fall in four distinct redshift spikes at $z = 1.43, 1.53, 1.67$ and 1.82, with this latter one including 7 galaxies and extending $\simeq 6$ Mpc in diameter and $\Delta z = 0.006$. To our knowledge this is the first spectroscopically confirmed overdensity of PEGs at such high redshift.

Fitting the evolutionary stellar population synthesis models to the broad-band photometry from u-band to Spitzer/IRAC bands have resulted in the stellar masses in the range of 4–$40 \times 10^{10} M_\odot$ and the SED ages of 1–3 Gyrs that is typically $\simeq 10$ times longer than the best-fit e-folding time of star formation, which confirms the passive nature of our sample.

Spectral indices of absorption features, namely $H\delta_F$ for the 4 brightest objects and Dn4000 for all the objects. The Dn4000 shows bimodality that about 40% of them have large Dn4000 ($\simeq 2$) indicating that they have been quenched relatively long time ago, and the rest of them have Dn4000 $\simeq 1.5$ typical of early stage of post-starburst (Balogh et al. 1999). However, $H\delta_F$ indices of large Dn4000 objects are found to be also large, $\simeq 6$, which could be due to recent episode of star formation, but is quite difficult to reproduce with commonly considered star formation history. On the other hand, $H\delta_F$ of the objects with Dn4000 $\simeq 1.5$ are about 3, which is fully consistent with recently quenched post-starburst with $\simeq 1$ Gyr stellar population.

References

Balogh, M. L., et al. 1999, ApJ, 527, 54
Daddi, E., et al. 2004, ApJ, 617, 746
Ilbert, O., et al. 2009, ApJ, 690, 1236
Kong, X., et al. 2006, ApJ, 638, 72
Mancini, C., et al. 2010, MNRAS, 401, 933
McCracken, H. J., et al. 2010, ApJ, 708, 202
Onodera, M., et al. 2010, ApJ, 715, L6. 1004.2120

Galactic Archaeology: Near-Field Cosmology and the Formation of the Milky Way
ASP Conference Series, Vol. 458
W. Aoki, M. Ishigaki, T. Suda, T. Tsujimoto, N. Arimoto, eds.
© 2012 Astronomical Society of the Pacific

Blue Stragglers in Milky Way Satellites

F. A. Santana,[1,2] R. R. Muñoz,[1,2] M. Geha,[2] P. Côté,[3] P. Stetson,[3] J. Simon[4] and S. G. Djorgovski[5]

[1]*Departamento de Astronomía, Universidad de Chile, Camino el Observatorio 1515, Las Condes, Santiago, Chile (fsantanar@das.uchile.cl, rmunoz@das.uchile.cl)*

[2]*Astronomy Department, Yale University, New Haven, CT 06520, USA (marga.geha@yale.edu)*

[3]*Herzberg Institute of Astrophysics, National Research Council of Canada, Victoria, BC, V9E 2E7, Canada*

[4]*Observatories of the Carnegie Institution of Washington, 813 Santa Barbara St., Pasadena, CA 91101, USA*

[5]*Astronomy Department, California Institute of Technology, Pasadena, CA, 91125, USA*

Abstract.   We have studied blue straggler stars (BSS) in a variety of Milky Way satellites: outer halo globular clusters, classical dwarf galaxies and the newly found ultra-faint dwarf galaxies and found BSS to be ubiquitous among all of them. Moreover, we study the likelihood that our BSS candidates correspond to young stars by analysing correlations between BSS frequencies and satellite parameters (such as absolute magnitude and collision time), and BSS distributions compared to those of simulated young stars. We find that the observed BSS seem to be genuine and likely formed by mass transfer in close binaries.

1.   Introduction

Blue Straggler Stars are those members of a given stellar population positioned blueward and above the main-sequence turnoff point, thus mimicking a younger population. They have been widely found in globular clusters (GCs) and increasingly in resolved dwarf galaxies, in which they can be confused with young stars. BSS are proposed to be formed either by direct collisions between stars (Hills & Day 1976) or by mass transfer between close binaries (McCrea 1964). In this context, the main goal of this study is to sample BSS in a variety of host environments in order to (1) shed light on their star formation histories by differentiating young stars from genuine BSS and (2) learn about the relationship between stellar evolution and dynamics by elucidating the formation mechanism responsible for BSS in these Galactic satellites.

2. Results

Our most important results can be summarized as follows:

1. BSSs are found to be ubiquitous, not just among GC, but also in dSphs.

2. An anti-correlation between BSS frequency and absolute magnitude has been found in the outer halo GCs, a result possibly explained by mass-transfer BSSs. On the other hand, no correlation between BSS frequency and collision time was detected for neither clusters nor dwarf galaxies (see Fig. 1).

3. Both radial and magnitude distributions of BSSs point to a binary origin. The radial distributions show no BSS central concentration, opposite to what would be expected for collisionally-formed BSSs. We can also rule out a significant contribution of young stars to our BSS counts by looking at the magnitude distributions, which are inconsistent with those of simulated young stars.

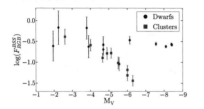 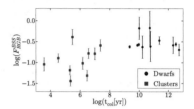

Figure 1.   Frequency of Blue Stragglers against absolute magnitude (left) and collision time (right). Circles represent dwarf galaxies while squares represent globular clusters.

3. Conclusion

We have systematically analyzed BSSs in globular clusters and dSphs. By using genuine BSSs in globular clusters (where we know there is no significant young star contribution) as a control sample, we can study BSS candidates in dwarf galaxies, which allows us to test the BSS formation mechanisms in the most diffuse systems and put constrains in the BSS/young star degeneracy. The fact that BSSs were found to be ubiquitous among dwarf galaxies, despite their extremely low stellar densities and lack of gas (especially true for the ultra faints), points to genuine BSSs formed by mass-transfer in close binaries, an interpretation also supported by the BSS magnitude and radial distributions for all satellites and the anti-correlation of their frequency and absolute magnitude found for clusters.

Acknowledgments.   We acknowledge support from the FONDAP astrophysics project N° 15010003.

References

Hills, J. G., & Day, C. A. 1976, ApJ, 17, 87
McCrea, W. H. 1964, MNRAS, 128, 147

Galactic Archaeology: Near-Field Cosmology and the Formation of the Milky Way
ASP Conference Series, Vol. 458
W. Aoki, M. Ishigaki, T. Suda, T. Tsujimoto, N. Arimoto, eds.
© *2012 Astronomical Society of the Pacific*

A New Method of Determining the Pattern Speed of the LMC

T. Shimizu and Y. Yoshii

Insititute of Astromony, Graduate School of Science, the University of Tokyo,
2-21-1 Osawa, Mitaka, Tokyo 181-0015 Japan (shimizu@ioa.s-tokyo.ac.jp)

Abstract. We focus on the idea proposed by de Vaucouleurs that constellation III would be regarded as the Lagrange point in a rotating non-axisymmetric bar potential. Based on this idea, we identify the center of constellation III with the Lagrange point L4 and have determined the pattern speed of the LMC as 21 ± 3km/s/kpc. Using this pattern speed, we estimate the velocity with which the constellation III captures matter around, and we find that the estimated value of velocity is consistent with the observation. In this presentation, using the LMC we describe our method of determining a pattern speed and present the dynamics around each of the Lagrange points in detail.

1. Introduction

In galactic dynamics, one of the fundamental parameters is a pattern speed that describes the angular speed of rotation of a bar or spiral arms. So far, many authors proposed methods to estimate the pattern speed of galaxies, based on various assumptions. Tremaine & Weinberg (1984) proposed an analytic form of the pattern speed as a function of velocity and surface brightness (or mass), assuming that they satisfy the continuity equation in the disk. Canzian (1993) showed how to determine the corotation radius through the change in residual velocity field if the spiral density wave is present. However, these methods cannot be applied straightforwardly to the LMC, because active star-forming regions are distributed irregularly and the spiral structure in this galaxy does not play a major role on the velocity field. In this work, based on simple dynamics we developed a new method for determining the pattern speed and applied it to the LMC.

2. Method and Discussion

Our method is based on the fact that the location of Lagrange points related to the pattern speed. We consider a non-axisymmetric potential composed by the disk and the bar rotating with the pattern speed Ω_p. Figure 1 (Left) shows contours of the effective potential in corotating frame, which is characterized by five equilibrium points called Lagrange points. The linear perturbation analysis shows that the Coriolis force makes L_4 and L_5 stable (Binney & Tremaine 2008) , so that gases are likely to gather, which triggers star formation. A star forming region far away from the bar may be explained by this scenario, and if so, finding such regions will reveal the location of Lagrange points. Let V_L and r_L denote the rotation speed at the Lagrange point and the distance

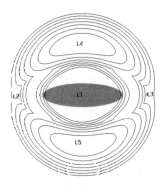 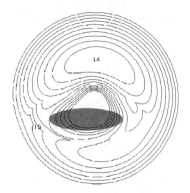

Figure 1.   Contours of the effective potential of asymmetric galaxy for two case:
the co-centered bar with the disk (Left) and the off-centered bar with the disk (Right).
The points marked L are Lagrange points.

between dynamical center and the Lagrange point, respectively. Since L_4 and L_5 are
corotating, we have $V_L = r_L \Omega_p$.

The LMC, composed of prominent bar and disk, has active star formation, and a
region of the highest star formation is located far from the bar, which is called Constellation III. One of the important features of the LMC is the off-centered bar from the
dynamical center(de Vaucouleurs 1973). Figure 1 (Right) shows the effective potential
of a LMC-like galaxy with an off-centered bar. In this case, L5 becomes unstable, so
that a star formation would occur only on the one side of the bar, which is reminiscent
to the situation in the LMC if we regard Constellation III as L_4. Based on this idea, we
can determine the pattern speed of the LMC as 21±3 km/s from the 21 cm observation
(Luks 1992).

We also examined the motion of gas around the stable Lagrange point, where the
Coriolis force and centrifugal force are balanced. As a result, we found a relation
between the size of gas and its rotational velocity. In the cases of Constellation III,
the observed radius of ~0.5kpc implies that the velocity of trapped gas cannot exceed
~20km/sec. Dopita et al. (1985) reported three peaks in the spectrum of Constellation
III, which are interpreted as Doppler shifted HI lines due to expanding star formation
region. If Constellation III is actually rotationally supported, three peaks indicate rotational velocity of ~ 18km/sec, which is close to our above estimation. Application of
our method to other Magellanic-type galaxies is now in progress.

References

Binney, J., & Tremaine, S. 2008, Galactic Dynamics (Prenceton University Press)
Canzian, B. 1993, Apj, 414, 487
de Vaucouleurs, C., G. K Freeman 1973, Structure and Dynamics of Barred Spiral galaxies, in
        paticular of the Magellanic Type (Pergamon Press)
Dopita, M. A., Mathewson, D. S., & Ford, V. L. 1985, Apj, 297, 41
Luks, T. 1992, A&A, 263, 41
Tremaine, S., & Weinberg, M. D. 1984, ApJ, 282, L5

Galactic Archaeology: Near-Field Cosmology and the Formation of the Milky Way
ASP Conference Series, Vol. 458
W. Aoki, M. Ishigaki, T. Suda, T. Tsujimoto, N. Arimoto, eds.
©2012 Astronomical Society of the Pacific

A Formation of Stephan's Quintet based on Star Clusters

Jubee Sohn, Sungsoon Lim, and Myung Gyoon Lee

Astronomy Program, Department of Physics and Astronomy, Seoul National University, Gwanak-gu, Seoul 151-742, Korea

Abstract. We present a study of star clusters in Stephan's Quintet based on the F438W, F606W, and F814W images taken with Wide Field Camera3 (WFC3) of the Hubble Space Telescope (HST). We detected 1,087 star cluster candidates with V < 26.3 mag through the visual inspection. Color magnitude diagrams of the star clusters show that the star clusters are mostly divided into two groups: blue clusters with B-V < 0.7 and red clusters with B-V > 0.7. Both blue and red clusters are found in the NGC 7318 system (E2+SBbc pec) and NGC 7319 (SBbc), while only red clusters are detected in NGC 7317 (E4). We derive the ages of the star clusters by comparing photometric data with theoretical synthesis population model. NGC 7317 clusters are all old (age > 1 Gyr). On the other hand, NGC 7318 and NGC 7319 have both old clusters and young clusters. The cluster age distributions in NGC 7318 and NGC 7319 show peaks at different position, the former at ~ 1.2 − 2 Gyr, the later at ~ 400 Myr.

1. Introduction

Stephan's Quintet (hereafter, SQ) is one of the most famous compact group which is composed of five galaxies and complicated tidal features. Complex structures of SQ indicate that SQ have suffered strong dynamical galaxy interactions. Among the various methods to probe the formation of SQ, star clusters are an ideal tool. Because they are usually formed during galaxy interactions. Then, galaxy interactions which occurred in different epoch might form star clusters with different ages. Therefore, star clusters can be used as a tracer of galaxy interaction history.

2. Data & Star Cluster Selection

We detected star cluster candidates (hereafter, clusters) using F438W (B_{438}), F606W (V_{606}), and F814W (I_{814}) band images of SQ taken with HST/WFC3. At the distance of SQ, *i.e.* 91 Mpc, images of typical clusters are seen like point sources. However, images of some clusters in high backgrounds appear to be slightly extended. Therefore, we selected clusters from both point and extended sources in HST/WFC3 images.

To select clusters, we firstly chose sources that are found in all 3-band images and brighter than $V_{606} = 26.3$. Secondly, we performed the visual inspection for each sources to eliminate spurious sources. Thirdly, we removed the contamination by foreground stars by imposing the color cuts of $B_{438} − V_{606} > 1.6$ and $V_{606} − I_{814} > 1.0$. Finally, we selected 1,087 clusters in the three galaxy regions, and 152 sources in the control fields.

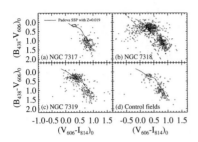 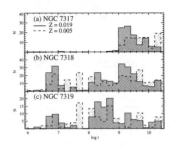

Figure 1.   (*Left*): $(B_{438} - V_{606})_0$ vs. $(V_{606} - I_{814})_0$ color-color diagrams of SQ clusters. The overlaid solid lines show the single stellar population model of Marigo et al. (2008) for the Z=0.005. (*Right*): Age distributions of clusters in the three galaxy regions and the control fields. The shaded and hatched histograms represent the SED fitting result assumed with Z= 0.019 and Z= 0.005, respectively.

We estimated the ages of the clusters by comparing the $B_{438}, V_{606}, I_{814}$ photometry with the SSP models (Bruzual & Charlot 2003). We assumed two metallicity cases of Z=0.005 and Z= 0.019 and applied only foreground reddening. The fitting result with $\chi^2 < 3.0$ are accepted to trace the cluster formation epoch.

3.   Result & Discussion

Figure 1 shows color-color diagrams and age distributions of clusters of three member galaxies and sources in the control fields. In the NGC 7317 region, we detected only red and old (> 1 Gyr) clusters. From this, we imply that NGC 7317 has not been involved galaxy interactions.

We noticed that there are three groups of clusters in the NGC 7318 region. One group of cluster is red and old, so they are considered to be globular clusters or earlier formed clusters during the NGC 7318 pair interaction (Hwang et al. 2012). Another group contains blue and young clusters located at the spiral arms and star-forming regions Clusters in the third group have abnormal colors, blue in $V_{606} - I_{814}$, but red in $B_{438} - V_{606}$. These are the youngest clusters that are still embedded in their natal gas, and the emission from natal gas brighten the V_{606} luminosity.

The NGC 7319 region contains both blue and red clusters; the former might be formed due to the interaction between NGC 7319 and NGC 7320c, and the later are mainly globular clusters. The age distribution of NGC 7319 shows peak at earlier epoch compared to that of NGC 7318 clusters. It mildly indicates that NGC 7319 underwent major galaxy interaction later than NGC 7318 pair.

References

Bruzual, G., & Charlot, S. 2003, MNRAS, 344, 1000
Hwang, J.-S., Struck, C., Renaud, F., & Appleton, P. N. 2012, MNRAS, 419, 1780
Marigo, P., Girardi, L., Bressan, A., Groenewegen, M. A. T., Silva, L., & Granato, G. L. 2008, A&A, 482, 883

Galactic Archaeology: Near-Field Cosmology and the Formation of the Milky Way
ASP Conference Series, Vol. 458
W. Aoki, M. Ishigaki, T. Suda, T. Tsujimoto, N. Arimoto, eds.
© 2012 Astronomical Society of the Pacific

Reducing Multi-Pointing Poor Galaxy Groups Optical Images Using THELI Pipeline

Soroush Sotoudeh and Rouhollah Joveini

Sharif University of Technology, Tehran, Iran

Abstract. In this paper we demonstrate the resaults of reducing galaxy group images using THELI (Erben & Schirmer 2005), an image processing pipeline. The observation was performed using the INT 2.54m telescope WFC camera in U, B, R and I band. Science frames mostly consist of Hickson Compact Galaxies (HCGs). Emphasis is mainly placed on photometric calibration which is of great interest to us due to our scientific case. Based on the cross-association of the extracted catalog against a reference catalog of stellar magnitudes, zeropoint calibration is performed.

1. Introduction

Majority of galaxies reside in galaxy groups. Groups are important cosmological tools and environments where galaxies interact more efficiently compared to clusters due to their low velocity dispersion. A key science objective of this analysis is to obtain galaxy luminosity function of a dozen of rich galaxy groups and compare those with poorer and richer systems. The group members will be identified through their colors and the background will be subtracted statistically, therefore multi-color catalogs are the key products of our data reduction and analysis. Several instrumental effects must be eliminated before raw CCD images become suitable for scientific analysis.

2. THELI pipeline

The THELI (Transforming HEavenly Light into Image)[1] pipeline was initially developed for WFI cameras mounted on the ESO 2.2 meter Max Planck telescope. It has a modular design that allows it to be adapted to other single or multi-chip cameras with considerable ease. The pipeline consists of shell scripts that can be easily modified, omitted or added for certain purposes or instruments. Through the course of the data reduction process the THELI pipeline uses well-tested astronomical software. This allows for easy exchange whenever a new algorithm or a better implementation becomes available.

---

[1] to be obtained from `http://astro.uni-bonn.de/~mischa/theli.html`

3. Results and Qualifications

After using THELI, with the final COADD images along with their WEIGHTs in hand in B, R and I filters one can produce several qualification plots. For photometry , as shown in Fig.1 we have plotted R-I color against B-R color for stars in the field of NGC3923. Stars have been separated from galaxies using `SExtractor`'s `CLASS_STAR` parameter larger than 0.95. 7 outliers have been removed by hand since they were only round-shaped galaxies. We have plotted Pickels colors as comparison also. As seen

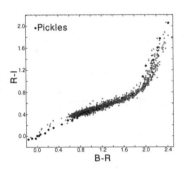 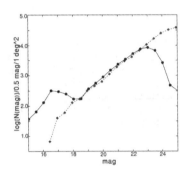

Figure 1.   Qualification Plots for NGC3923 Image Reduction: [Left: In these figure the accuracy of photometery has been tested by comparing color-color diagram of NGC3923 stars with those of standard stars from Pickels' standard stellar magnitude. Right: Galaxy count diagram for NGC3923 field of galaxies (circles, full line) vs. Brodwin et al. (2004) reference catalog (diamonds, dashed line).]

in Fig.1 (left) the consistency between our data points and those of standard stellar magnitudes is so that the reference points are within the scatter of our data points. In Fig.1 (right) we have plotted a galaxy count for NGC3923 field together with Brodwin et al. (2004) diagram. To derive the diagram we note that every object occupies an area, using isophote above detection threshold (`SExtractor`'s `ISO0`) for each object. Our galaxy count starts dropping dramatically at magnitude 23 because of limiting magnitude of the telescope. Seeing[2] associated with the individual pointings (in R band) ranged from 0.75 to 1.1 arcsec, and the average seeing of the coadded image has been measured to be 0.89 arcsec.

Acknowledgments.   The authors acknowledge IPM for providing computational facilities and also Prof. Mansouri, Dr. Khosroshahi, Mr. Molaei Nezhad and Mr. Roozrokh for useful discussions and guidance.

References

Brodwin, M., Lilly, S. J., Porciani, C., McCracken, H. J., Fevre, O. L., Crampton, D., Foucaud, S., Eisenhardt, P. R., & Stern, D. 2004, Bulletin of the American Astronomical Society, 36

Erben, T., & Schirmer, M. 2005, Astronomische Nachrichten, 326, 432464

---

[2]calculated using FWHM in an area around image center

Galactic Archaeology: Near-Field Cosmology and the Formation of the Milky Way
ASP Conference Series, Vol. 458
W. Aoki, M. Ishigaki, T. Suda, T. Tsujimoto, N. Arimoto, eds.
© *2012 Astronomical Society of the Pacific*

α-Elements Abundances in the Large Magellanic Cloud Bar

Mathieu Van der Swaelmen,[1,2] Vanessa Hill,[1] and Francesca Primas[2]

[1]*Université de Nice Sophia-Antipolis, Laboratoire Lagrange, UMR 7293, Observatoire de la Côte d'Azur, CNRS, Bd. de l'Observatoire BP 4229, F-06304, Nice cedex 4*

[2]*European Southern Observatory, Karl Schwarzschild Str. 2, 85748 Garching b. München, Germany*

Abstract. We carried out a spectroscopy survey of about 110 stars located in the bar of the Large Magellanic Cloud (LMC) that combined with photometry already available allowed us to derive photometric temperatures, surface gravities, microturbulence velocity, overall metallicity, [Fe/H] and [α/Fe] ratios. We compare our results to Galactic stellar populations and to the LMC inner disc sample.

1. Introduction

The LMC is one of the closest satellites of the Milky Way (MW), located at only 50kpc. This low-mass disc galaxy showing a prominent stellar bar is almost face-on, which gives us the possibility to easily distinguish these different components. The LMC is believed to have had an irregular star formation history (SFH). Especially, the central parts that are showing a stronger star formation 2-5 Gyrs ago, maybe related to the formation of the bar (Smecker-Hane et al. 2002). Dynamical simulations by Bekki et al. (2004) and Bekki & Chiba (2005, 2007) are able to explain the increase in star formation activity (new start of star formation, formation of the bar, formation of the Magellanic Stream) with the first close encounter with the Small Magellanic Cloud about 4 Gyr ago.

To investigate the relation between the bar and the disc, we obtained spectra of 110 stars located in the LMC bar at the ESO/VLT with the FLAMES multifibre spectrograph ($R \sim 20,000$) in 3 different wavelength regions covering a total of 600 Å, complementing a similar dataset in the LMC disc, $\sim$ 2 kpc from the center (Pompéia et al. 2008). Equivalent widths (EW) measured with DAOSPEC (Stetson & Pancino 2008) were translated into abundances with *turbospectrum* (Alvarez & Plez 1998) using OSMARCS spherical atmosphere models (Gustafsson et al. 2008). The sample of Pompéia et al. (2008) was reanalysed in exactly the same fashion to insure a homogeneous comparison of bar and disc fields.

2. Results and conclusions

Figure 1 shows that the LMC bar has experienced a chemical enrichment different from that of the Milky Way (MW) disc, with a slower SFH (left panel): 1) while metal-

poor LMC stars possess alpha abundances similar to those of MW halo stars, stars
with [Fe/H] ≥ −1 have [α/Fe] smaller than that of the MW; 2) the transition between
the SNe II-dominated regime and SNe Ia-dominated regime seems to occur at a lower
metallicity in the LMC bar than in the MW. The fields of the bar and the inner disc
(Pompéia et al. 2008) show similar [α/Fe] pattern at low metallicity (right plot). Nevertheless, there is a hint that for −0.3 ≤ [Fe/H] ≤ −0.6, the [α/Fe] ratio is higher in the
inner disc than in the bar, which is also shown by the steeper decrease of the running
average of the bar data.

The right panel shows the α age-metallicity relation (AMR) of our two LMC fields.
While abundance ratios of the bar and the inner disc are similar for old ages, they become differentiated for intermediate ages, the α-AMR of the bar being surprisingly flat
between 1 and 6 Gyr. Theoretical AMRs' proposed by Pagel & Tautvaisiene (1998) are
shown for a bursting and a continuous SFH. The smooth model systematically predicts
higher abundances than observed, while the bursting model gives ratios closer to our
measurements: it suggests that the inner disc has experienced a continuous SFH while
the bar has experienced a bursting SFH, with a weak activity at intermediate ages.

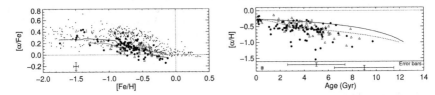

Figure 1.   Filled black circles: LMC bar (this work), empty blue triangles: LMC
inner disc, small black dots: MW thin and thick disc (Bensby et al. 2005; Reddy
et al. 2003, 2006), and halo (Fulbright 2000; Stephens & Boesgaard 2002). [α/Fe] =
1/3([O/Fe] + [Mg/Fe] + [Si/Fe]). Left panel: the data were smoothed with a box-
car average (black and blue continuous lines). Right panel: dashed line: AMR for
bursting SFH (bursts 3 and 12 Gyr ago), continuous line: AMR for continuous SFH
(Pagel & Tautvaisiene 1998). Typical error bars are given for the bar abundances.

References

Alvarez, R., & Plez, B. 1998, A&A, 330, 1109
Bekki, K., & Chiba, M. 2005, MNRAS, 356, 680
— 2007, MNRAS, 381, L16
Bekki, K., Couch, W. J., Beasley, M. A., Forbes, D. A., Chiba, M., & Da Costa, G. S. 2004,
      ApJ, 610, L93
Bensby, T., Feltzing, S., Lundström, I., & Ilyin, I. 2005, A&A, 433, 185
Fulbright, J. P. 2000, AJ, 120, 1841
Gustafsson, B., Edvardsson, B., Eriksson, K., Jørgensen, U. G., Nordlund, Å., & Plez, B. 2008,
      A&A, 486, 951
Pagel, B. E. J., & Tautvaisiene, G. 1998, MNRAS, 299, 535
Pompéia, L., Hill, V., Spite, M., Cole, A., Primas, F., Romaniello, M., Pasquini, L., Cioni,
      M.-R., & Smecker Hane, T. 2008, A&A, 480, 379
Reddy, B. E., Lambert, D. L., & Allende Prieto, C. 2006, MNRAS, 367, 1329
Reddy, B. E., Tomkin, J., Lambert, D. L., & Allende Prieto, C. 2003, MNRAS, 340, 304
Smecker-Hane, T. A., Cole, A. A., Gallagher, J. S., III, & Stetson, P. B. 2002, ApJ, 566, 239
Stephens, A., & Boesgaard, A. M. 2002, AJ, 123, 1647
Stetson, P. B., & Pancino, E. 2008, PASP, 120, 1332

Galactic Archaeology: Near-Field Cosmology and the Formation of the Milky Way
ASP Conference Series, Vol. 458
W. Aoki, M. Ishigaki, T. Suda, T. Tsujimoto, N. Arimoto, eds.
©2012 Astronomical Society of the Pacific

Blue Straggler Stars in Dwarf Spheroidal Galaxies

Z. Zhao,[1,2] S. Okamoto,[3] N. Arimoto,[1,2] W. Aoki,[2] and T. Kodama[2,4]

[1]*Department of Astronomical Science, Graduate University for Advanced Studies, Hayama, Kanagawa 240-0193, Japan*

[2]*National Astronomical Observatory of Japan, Mitaka, Tokyo 181-8588, Japan*

[3]*Kavli Institute for Astronomy and Astrophysics, Peking University, Beijing 100871, China*

[4]*Subaru Telescope, National Astronomical Observatory of Japan, 650 North Aohoku Place, Hilo, HI 96720, USA*

Abstract. With our homogeneous photometric data of 8 dwarf spheroidal galaxies (dSphs, $-9.5 < M_V < -4.9$) obtained by Subaru / Suprime-Cam, we have confirmed the anti-correlation between F_{BSS} and M_V found by Momany et al. (2007). We have also derived luminosity functions and radial distributions of blue straggler stars (BSSs) of three classical dSphs, Draco, Ursa Minor (UMi) and Sextans. The results suggest that BSSs in these dSphs were mainly formed from mass transfer in primordial binaries.

1. F_{BSS} Vs. M_V anti-correlation

Although BSSs have been discovered in many dSphs, we are still faced with the problem that it is hard to distinguish a young MS and an old BS population among the blue plume stars of dSphs. Momany et al. (2007) found an anti-correlation between F_{BSS} (=N_{BSS}/N_{HB}, where HB means Horizontal Branch stars) and M_V in dSphs and mentioned that it could be a powerful tool to discriminate galaxies hosting only genuine BSS from those also hosting young MSs. However, in view of the small range of luminosity of their samples and the heterogeneity of their sources, we used homogeneously observed 8 dSphs (Okamoto et al. 2008, 2012) in order to confirm this relation. Using our samples, we confirmed the anti-correlation between F_{BSS} and M_V (see Fig. 1). Most interestingly, the anti-correlation for ultra faint dwarfs (UFDs) seem to be more consistent with the general GCs than with the classical dwarf galaxies. Although the origin of these correlations is not understood clearly, theoretical studies aimed at explaining them will be useful to understand the dominant physical mechanisms for the formation of BSSs in different star systems.

2. Radial distribution and Luminosity function

Collisions are unlikely to occur due to very low stellar density of dSphs. Instead, BSSs in there should be mainly formed by mass transfer in primordial binaries. Indeed, the observed radial distributions of BSSs in several dSphs are consistent with model predictions with mass trasfer scenario (Mapelli et al. 2007, 2009; Monelli et al. 2012). However, the number of current observations is insufficient for drawing a definite conclusion as to the origin of BSSs in dSphs. We therefore derived radial distributions (upper) and luminosity distributions (lower) of BSSs in Draco (left), UMi (central) and Sextans (right) (see Fig. 2). In the case that the BSSs were formed via collisions or that the blue plume is made of young MSs, we expect a central peak in the radial distribution of BSSs, as well as for the more luminous BSSs to be more centrally concentrated than the fainter BSSs. As shown in Fig. 2, the lack of a strong central peak in the radial distribution and the independence of the luminosity distribution on radius are obvious. All of these results imply that in these dSphs, the blue plume stars are most likely real BSSs formed mainly by mass transfer in primordial binaries.

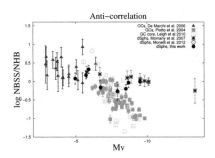

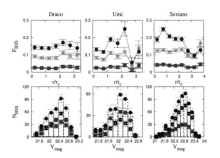

Figure 1. Anti-correlation between F_{BSS} and M_V. Data: de Marchi et al. (2006) (OCs, triangles), Piotto et al. (2004) and Leigh et al. (2011) (GCs, full and open squares), Momany et al. (2007), Monelli et al. (2012) and ours (dSphs, asterisks, open and full circles, respectively).

Figure 2. Upper panel: ratios of the number of BSSs with respect of MS (squares), SGB (asterisks), and RGB (circles) stars; Lower panel: luminosity function of BSSs, the different signs refer to all the BSSs (circles), BSSs inside (squares) and outside (asterisks) $1 \times r_c$ from the center.

Acknowledgments.   The authors thank the observatory staff of the Subaru Telescope. Works by S.O. were supported by grants Nos. 19540245 and 218816 from the Japanese Ministry of Education, Culture, Sports, Science and Technology (MEXT).

References

de Marchi, F., de Angeli, F., Piotto, G., Carraro, G., & Davies, M. B. 2006, A&A, 459, 489
Leigh, N., Sills, A., & Knigge, C. 2011, MNRAS, 415, 3771
Mapelli, M., Ripamonti, E., Battaglia, G., Tolstoy, E., Irwin, M. J., Moore, B., & Sigurdsson, S. 2009, MNRAS, 396, 1771
Mapelli, M., Ripamonti, E., Tolstoy, E., Sigurdsson, S., Irwin, M. J., & Battaglia, G. 2007, MARSA, 380, 1127
Momany, Y., Held, E. V., Saviane, I., Zaggia, S., Rizzi, L., & Gullieuszik, M. 2007, A&A, 468, 973
Monelli, M., Cassisi, S., Mapelli, M., Bernard, E. J., Aparicio, A., Skillman, E. D., Stetson, P. B., Gallart, C., Hidalgo, S. L., Mayer, L., & Tolstoy, E. 2012, ApJ, 744, 157
Okamoto, S., Arimoto, N., Yamada, Y., & Onodera, M. 2008, A&A, 487, 103
— 2012, ApJ, 744, 96
Piotto, G., De Angeli, F., King, I. R., Djorgovski, S. G., Bono, G., Cassisi, S., Meylan, G., Recio-Blanco, A., Rich, R. M., & Davies, M. B. 2004, ApJL, 604, 109

Part VI

Dark Matter

Galactic Archaeology: Near-Field Cosmology and the Formation of the Milky Way
ASP Conference Series, Vol. 458
W. Aoki, M. Ishigaki, T. Suda, T. Tsujimoto, N. Arimoto, eds.

Direct Detection of Dark Matter

Shigetaka Moriyama

Kamioka Observatory, Institute of Cosmic Ray Research, the University of Tokyo, Kamioka cho, Hida city, Gifu prefecture, Japan

Abstract. The principles and some important features of the direct detection of dark matter are introduced, and recent experimental progress is reported. In particular, the XMASS experiment, which is a large-scale dark-matter experiment in Japan, is explained in detail.

1. Introduction

At present, the existence of dark matter is widely recognized and accepted. One of the most important subjects in astrophysics and elementary particle physics is the identification of dark matter properties. According to the recent cosmological observations, more than 80 % of dark matter is not ordinary matter such as baryons (Komatsu et al. 2011). Direct dark-matter experiments aim to detect dark-matter particles directly in a laboratory. Positive evidence would prove that the dark matter is composed of particles and allow us to study their properties in detail. Such detailed studies are important for the elementary particles physics because they will stimulate the rise of a new field beyond the standard model of particle physics.

2. Principles of Direct Detection

2.1. Expected Interaction

Direct dark-matter experiments expect the dark-matter particles to interact with ordinary matter such as nucleons. This is a reasonable assumption if we assume that dark-matter particles were thermally produced in the early universe, decreased through annihilations into ordinary matter, and were frozen in number density in a comoving volume. Figure 1 shows schematically how interactions lead to annihilation into ordinary matter such as quarks. This interaction implies the existence of the scattering of dark matter with the ordinary matter as shown by the vertical arrow in the figure. Since the interaction is expected to be weak, these particles are called weakly interacting massive particles (WIMPs). They must be massive because any massless particles cannot behave as matter does.

2.2. Amount of Dark Matter Around Us

The frequency of interaction depends on how many WIMPs exist and on how fast they are moving. From the observed rotational curve of the galaxy, the local mass density and their mean velocity can be derived. The former is expected to be $0.3\,\mathrm{GeV\,cc^{-1}}$

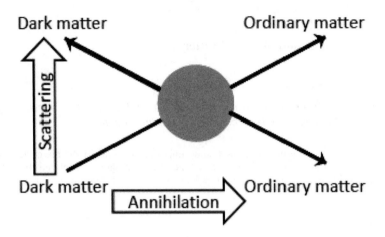

Figure 1.   Dark-matter particles thermally generated in the early universe are considered to annihilate into ordinary matter. This assumption implies the existence of an interaction between dark-matter particles and ordinary matter, as shown in the figure.

to within a factor of two to three (Nakamura et al. 2010) and the latter is expected to be around 230 km s^{-1} (Lewin & Smith 1996). From these numbers, the expected number density and flux, which are inversely proportional to the mass of WIMPs, can be calculated.

2.3.   Signals After Interaction

The interaction between WIMPs and ordinary matter causes energy transfer. The typical kinetic energy after the energy transfer is $1/2m\beta^2$, where m is the mass of the ordinary matter and $\beta = v/c \sim 10^{-3}$. Because of this, we usually look for nuclear-recoil signals instead of electron-recoil signals. Thus, nuclei of mass similar to that of the WIMPs are the best choice from the point of view of kinematics.

Once the energy transfer occurs, various signal channels can be expected, such as scintillation light, phonon signals, ionization signals, and bubble generation. Multiple signals are useful for reducing various types of common background, such as background caused by gamma rays. By utilizing these signals, each experimental group strives to minimize background and maximize signal.

2.4.   Expected Energy Spectrum

If one makes assumptions such as the Maxwell distribution for the velocity of WIMPs in the rest frame of the galaxy, the recoil energy spectrum can be calculated. One important aspect to consider in calculations is the coherence of the interaction. Since the interaction amplitude can be calculated by summing the wave function of the mediating particle at each nucleon, a small momentum transfer (long wavelength) causes an amplitude proportional to the number of nucleons. Since the interaction cross section is proportional to the square of the amplitude, a large enhancement can be expected for spin-independent interactions. A more detailed treatment can be found elsewhere (Lewin & Smith 1996).

 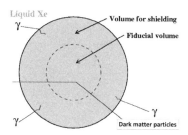

Figure 2.   Structure of the 800-kg detector (left). Liquid xenon fills the central part and is surrounded by 642 photomultiplier tubes. Since the dominant background is caused by gamma rays from the PMTs, which can be absorbed by the exterior layer of the liquid xenon, a low-background experiment would be possible if the inner radioactivity was shown to be low (right).

2.5.   Annual Modulation and Directional Distribution of Recoil Nuclei

Although we assumed a Maxwell distribution for the WIMP velocity, our targets in laboratories are moving in the galaxy with the sun and the earth. Since the sun is moving at 230 km s^{-1} in the galaxy and the earth is moving at 30 km s^{-1} around the sun, the velocity of the target in the galaxy changes as a function of time over a sidereal year. This is expected to cause a variation in the event rate as well in the nuclear-recoil spectrum. Such an effect would not be large but would be considered an important finding in support of the interpretation of positive signals.

Another important expectation is the directionality of nuclear recoils. Since we usually assume isotropic scattering in the center-of-mass frame, nuclear recoils in forward angles are expected. If the detector is sensitive to the nuclear-recoil direction, it can give "smoking gun" evidence. Since this requires a very fine track readout (as short as 0.1 μm in LXe and longer in gas targets), development of better detectors is necessary.

3.   Direct-Detection Experiments

Over 30 experiments are ongoing around the world– collecting data, or preparing their detectors to search for positive signals from dark-matter particles. Here, I categorize the positive signals into three types: (1) a significant excess over known background, (2) an annual modulation, and (3) an observed of directionality. To date, no positive evidence of a type-3 signal has been observed because it requires reading out nuclear-recoil tracks under very low background. However, results are available for type-1 signals from CRESST-II (Angloher et al. 2011) and type-2 signals from DAMA/LIBRA (Savage et al. 2009) and CoGeNT (Aalseth et al. 2011). Conversely, XENON10/XENON100 (Aprile et al. 2011), CDMS (Ahmed et al. 2010), and EDELWEISS (Armengaud &

collaboration 2011) report negative results. Many efforts are ongoing to check the consistency between these experiments (Censier 2011) but, for now, further experimental studies remain indispensable.

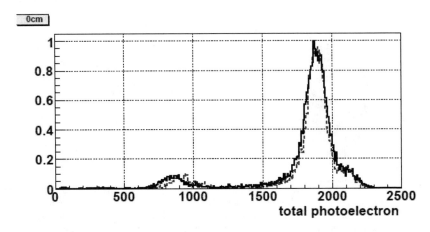

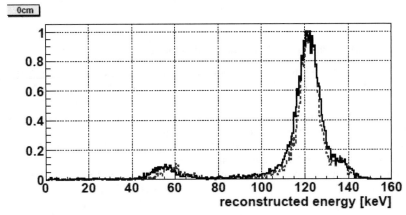

Figure 3.   Observed total photoelectron distribution and reconstructed energy spectrum for ^{57}Co source (122 keV and 136 keV from ^{57}Co and 60 keV from X-rays from tungsten inside the source) at center of detector. The solid histogram is for the data and the dashed histogram is for the Monte Carlo simulation, and the two agree reasonably well. The photoelectron yield is ~15 p.e./keV which is larger than expected.

4.   XMASS Experiment

The XMASS experiment aims to construct multipurpose, low-background detectors for astroparticle physics and to detect signals from low-energy solar neutrinos, neutrinoless double beta decay, and dark matter in the universe (Suzuki 2000). In the first phase of the experiment, a detector was constructed in the Kamioka mine, Japan, which required 800 kg of liquid xenon (fiducial volume 100 kg) for dark-matter searching. As shown in Fig. 2 (left), the central part (liquid xenon) is surrounded by 642 hexagonal photomultiplier tubes (PMTs) arranged spherically. Photocathodes cover 62% of the inner surface of this sphere. Figure 2 (right) depicts the interaction of gamma rays and WIMPs. A dominant background due to gamma rays from the PMTs are absorbed at the surface of the liquid xenon. However, WIMPs would interact uniformly inside the detector. If we could extract only the inner events, the dark-matter search could be done in a low-background environment. To locate a given interaction the events must be reconstructed, which can be done based on the observed photoelectron pattern. By comparing the observed pattern with expected results at various positions in the detector, we can determine the interaction vertex.

For this reason, it is important to demonstrate event reconstruction, and we have prepared gamma-ray sources that can be inserted into the detector for such a purpose. Figure 3 shows the reconstructed energy spectrum of a ^{57}Co source as well as the one from our simulation. The energy resolution and the vertex resolution for the 122-keV gamma ray were found to be 4% and 1 cm, respectively, which is a satisfactory result.

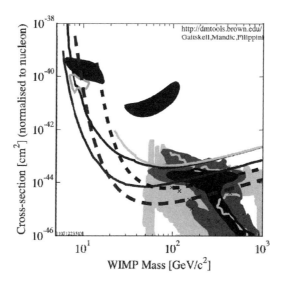

Figure 4. Sensitivity of XMASS experiment. The two dashed lines represent the 100 days data for our sensitivity, with 5- and 2-keV electron-equivalent-energy thresholds. Solid lines give results of other experiments. We can expect a large improvement in the sensitivity of detecting dark matter. The two shaded areas above show DAMA results. The area around 10 GeV and 10^{-40} cm^2 shows CoGeNT results. The areas at the bottom right are predictions from supersymmetry models. Except for the dashed lines, the plots are generated by Gaitskell & Mandic (2004).

The 800-kg detector was successfully constructed and is currently in the commissioning phase. All the parameters related to the reconstruction are being tuned, the detector performance is being confirmed, and an investigation of background properties is underway. We expect the dark-matter searches to begin very soon. Figure 4 shows the expected sensitivity for the dark-matter search, which constitutes an order of magnitude improvement in sensitivity.

5. Summary

Direct detection of dark matter is expected to reveal the nature of this material. Numerous experiments around the world are currently dedicated to the search, and these represent significant improvements in the sensitivity of detecting dark matter. Although some groups have claimed positive evidence of dark matter, the results are still controversial and so must be clarified by new experimental data. The XMASS experiment utilizes a very massive 800-kg detector and has entered its commissioning phase, so it will soon begin contributing to the search for dark matter.

References

Aalseth, C. E., et al. 2011, Phys. Rev. Lett., 107, 141301. 1106.0650
Ahmed, Z., et al. (The CDMS-II) 2010, Science, 327, 1619. 0912.3592
Angloher, G., et al. 2011. 1109.0702
Aprile, E., et al. (XENON100) 2011, Phys. Rev. Lett., 107, 131302. 1104.2549
Armengaud, E., & collaboration, f. t. E. 2011, PoS, IDM2010, 012. 1011.2319
Censier, B. 2011. 1110.0191
Gaitskell, R., & Mandic, V. 2004, Dark matter direct detection results plotter. URL http://dmtools.brown.edu/
Komatsu, E., Smith, K. M., Dunkley, J., Bennett, C. L., Gold, B., Hinshaw, G., Jarosik, N., Larson, D., Nolta, M. R., Page, L., Spergel, D. N., Halpern, M., Hill, R. S., Kogut, A., Limon, M., Meyer, S. S., Odegard, N., Tucker, G. S., Weiland, J. L., Wollack, E., & Wright, E. L. 2011, ApJS, 192, 18. 1001.4538
Lewin, J. D., & Smith, P. F. 1996, Astropart. Phys., 6, 87
Nakamura, K., et al. (Particle Data Group) 2010, J. Phys., G37, 075021
Savage, C., Gelmini, G., Gondolo, P., & Freese, K. 2009, JCAP, 0904, 010. 0808.3607
Suzuki, Y. (XMASS) 2000. hep-ph/0008296

Galactic Archaeology: Near-Field Cosmology and the Formation of the Milky Way
ASP Conference Series, Vol. 458
W. Aoki, M. Ishigaki, T. Suda, T. Tsujimoto, N. Arimoto, eds.
©2012 Astronomical Society of the Pacific

Probing the Formation of the Milk Way

Brian W. O'Shea,[1] Facundo Gomez,[1] Chris Coleman-Smith,[2] Ivan Minchev,[3] Jason Tumlinson,[4] Young Sun Lee,[1] Timothy Beers,[5,1] and Deokkeun An[6]

[1] *Department of Physics and Astronomy and JINA, Michigan State University, East Lansing, MI 48824, USA*

[2] *Department of Physics, Duke University, Durham, NC 27708, USA*

[3] *Leibniz-Institut für Astrophysik Potsdam (AIP), An der Sternwarte 16, D-14482, Potsdam, Germany*

[4] *Space Telescope Science Institute, Baltimore, MD 21218, USA*

[5] *National Optical Astronomy Observatory, Tucson, AZ 85719 USA*

[6] *Department of Science Education, Ewha Womans University, Seoul 120-750, Republic of Korea.*

Abstract. We explore two consequences of hierarchical structure formation on galaxy evolution: the effect that a particular Milky Way-sized galaxy's merger history has on the properties of its stellar halo and dwarf galaxy population, and the signatures of minor mergers in the thick disk of the Milky Way. In the first case, we use semi-analytical models (which include phenomenological descriptions of the evolution of stellar populations coupled to N-body produced merger trees) to demonstrate that the formation history of galaxies of approximately equal mass can significantly affect bulk properties of the dwarf galaxy population, but that the galaxy's stellar halo metallicity is much more robust. In the second project, we show that a carefully-chosen sample of Solar neighborhood thick disk stars exhibit distributions of energies that are consistent with the predictions of a minor-merger event that corresponds to recent models of Sagittarius' interactions with the disk of the Milky Way.

1. Introduction

The formation of the Milky Way, as with all galaxies, was an incredibly dynamic process. According to the dominant paradigm of cosmological structure formation, the fundamental driver of this sequence of events, gravitational potential energy, drove the merger of ever-larger dark matter halos and their accompanying baryonic components, resulting in the population of galaxies that we see today. While the general concepts behind the hierarchical formation of galaxies is well-supported observationally, many of the details remain to be worked out. The explosion of observations of our own galaxy in the past decade, most notably by the Sloan Digital Sky Survey (York & SDSS Collaboration 2000), has provided ever-larger and more accurate datasets that can be used to test and falsify theoretical models of structure formation.

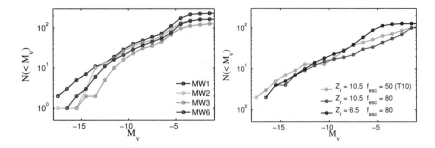

Figure 1.   (color online) Left panel: Cumulative dwarf galaxy luminosity function for four different galaxies (i.e., merger histories) but using the same ChemTreeN model parameters. Right: The same plot, but for a single galaxy's merger history using three different sets of model parameters.

In this proceedings we present the results of two projects that attempt to understand the dynamical history of our own galaxy. In Section 2, we explore theoretically how the observable properties of the Milky Way stellar halo and satellites are affected by both the merger history of the galaxy and by variations in model parameters that control bulk baryonic properties of the gas and stars in dark matter halos. In Section 3, we show that a carefully-chosen sample of nearby thick disk stars show a distributions of total energy that is consistent with the predictions of a minor-merger event that corresponds to recent models of Sagittarius' interactions with the Milky Way. Given space limitations, we provide an abbreviated description of each project, and direct the interested reader to Gomez et al. 2012a (ApJ, submitted) and 2012b (MNRAS, submitted) for the work described in Section 2 and Section 3, respectively.

2.   The effect of formation history on bulk stellar properties

In this project, we examine how the observable properties of the the Milky Way's stellar halo and dwarf galaxy population depend on the galaxy's formation history and on the model parameters that control bulk properties of the gas and stars in these objects over the course of their evolution. To do this, we use the ChemTreeN semi-analytical model (Tumlinson 2006, 2010), which combines N-body cosmological simulations with a phenomenological model for the evolution of the stellar and gas components of the dark matter halos. ChemTreeN works by advancing in time through a galaxy's merger history, tagging individual dark matter particles (which can be traced over time via a unique identifier) with stellar populations and the resulting metal-enriched gas. In this project, we use four cosmological simulations that all form approximately Milky Way-sized galaxies at $z = 0$, but which have significantly different merger histories. We also vary three model parameters: i) z_r, which controls the redshift of reionization (suppressing star formation in low-mass galaxies), ii) f_{esc}, which controls the mass of gas entrained in galactic winds and thus removed from the halo, and iii) f_{bary}, the baryonic mass fraction in all halos before reionization, and in high-mass halos after reionization (thus controlling the reservoir of gas available for star formation).

Figures 1 and 2 show the effects that varying the merger history of a galaxy and the ChemTreeN model parameters have on the dwarf galaxy luminosity function and

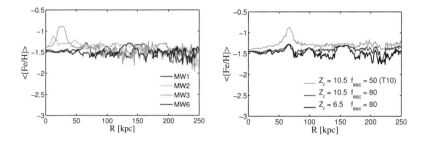

Figure 2.   (color online) Left panel: Mean metallicity of the parent galaxy's stellar halo as a function of galactocentric radius for four different galaxies (i.e.., merger histories) but using the same ChemTreeN model parameters. Right: The same plot, but for a single galaxy's merger history using three different sets of model parameters.

the metallicity of the stellar halo, respectively. Figure 1 shows that the number of bright dwarf galaxies are the most sensitive to the merger history of the parent halo, though there is a significant (factor of two) halo-to-halo variation in the overall number of dwarf galaxies between simulations, even when using the same model parameters. The most luminous dwarfs are relatively insensitive to model parameters, due primarily to their early formation times and deep potential wells. Figure 2 shows only small differences in the mean metallicity of stars in the galactic halo as a result of formation history or model parameters. This is likely due to the halo being formed by the stripping or destruction of stars in many dwarf galaxies over time, which serves to smear out differences. We note, however, that the data snown on both of these plots are in rough agreement with the metallicity of the M31 stellar halo, but are roughly half a dex too high for the Milky Way's halo.

Figure 3 shows one of the most important results coming from this study. By using a moderate number (~ 200) of ChemTreeN models to create an "emulator" that provides a reasonably accurate estimate of observational outputs as a function of model inputs, we can begin to understand the sensitivity of various observable quantities to parameters in the model (and thus to the physical processes important to galaxy formation). While constructing the emulator, we hold back one ChemTreeN model, which we choose to be the "real" observation we are attempting to match, and we quantify how accurately we can match this model. The top left, top right, and bottom left panels of Figure 3 show the sensitivity of the number of most and least luminous dwarf galaxies and the dwarf galaxy metallicity-luminosity relation to the three parameters we are allowing to vary, with the "correct" model indicated in each. The number of the most luminous dwarf galaxies are quite insensitive to the epoch of reionization and the amount of gas ejected from the halo, but are very sensitive to the overall amount of baryons available for star formation. In stark contrast, however, the least luminous galaxies are highly sensitive to the redshift of reionization, but relatively insensitive to the other parameters, likely because their stellar populations are formed in one burst of star formation, rather than over an extended period of time. The luminosity-metallicity relation for the entire population of dwarf galaxies has a much more complex relation-

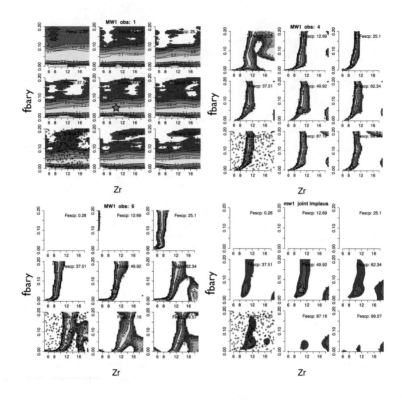

Figure 3.   (color online) Top left: sensitivity of the number of the most luminous dwarf galaxies ($M_v < -16$) to the model parameters f_{bary}, z_r, and f_{esc}. Top right: sensitivity of the number of ultra-faint dwarf galaxies ($M_v > -16$) to the same set of parameters. Bottom left: sensitivity of the slow of the dwarf galaxy M_v-[Fe/H] relation to the same set of parameters. Bottom right: confidence intervals for a simultaneous fit to all observable quantities under consideration. In all four panels, the "correct" model is shown by a star, and confidence intervals are shown by both colors and contours. Each set of nine panels is arranged with f_{bary} on the y-axis, z_r on the x-axis, and stepping through f_{escp}. All models use the same underlying N-body simulation, and thus the same merger history.

ship with the model parameters. The bottom-right panel of Figure 3 shows the result of a joint fit to all of the observable quantities. As can be seen, our model captures the "real" observation quite well.

Another important result of this project (which we lack the space to show here) demonstrates the dependence of observational properties on the formation history of the galaxy. For example, we can create an emulator using one of the four cosmological simulations described here (e.g., MW1), and use it to fit mock observations produced by running ChemTreeN on another of the simulations (e.g., MW6). In general, we find that it is unlikely the most likely match obtains the correct model parameters for our second galaxy by this process, even if the merger histories of the galaxies are relatively similar. This suggests that it will be quite difficult to understand the processes of galaxy

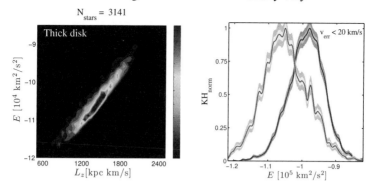

Figure 4. (color online) Left panel: $E - L_z$ distribution of likely thick-disk stars located within 2 kpc of the Sun, obtained from our SDSS G-dwarf sample. The different colours (contours) indicate different numbers of stars. Right panel: kernel histogram of E, obtained from both the thick-disc (red solid line) and the thin-disc (blue solid line) stellar subsamples. The shaded areas indicate errors associated with poor sampling of the underlying distributions. For both plots, only stars with total errors in velocity $V_{err} < 20$ km s^{-1} are considered.

formation solely by examining the Milky Way and its satellites – rather, we will need to use a significant number of large galaxies and their satellite halos to obtain statistically meaningful results. We direct the interested reader to Gomez et al. 2012 (ApJ, submitted) for more information on this result and any other results described in this section.

3. Signatures of minor mergers in the thick disk

In this section, we demonstrate that a local sample of likely thick disk stars, taken from the Sloan Digital Sky Survey's SEGUE project and the Schuster et al. (2006) stellar sample, shows structure in its phase-space distribution that is suggestive of a minor merger in the Milky Way's recent past.

The left panel of Figure 4 shows the total energy-angular momentum distribution of a sample of 3141 stars located within 2 kpc of the Sun, obtained from the SDSS G-dwarf sample (Lee et al. 2011). The stars in this sample have high values of [α/Fe] and are likely to belong to the thick disk. Note the presence of a series of high-density features, especially at large energy values. The right panel in this figure shows the kernel histogram of energy, obtained from both the thick disk (red line) and thin disk (blue line) stellar subsamples. The shaded areas indicate error estimates calculated using the bootstrap method. The high-density features observed in the left panel correspond to peaks in the kernel histogram. Note that the thin-disk subsample exhibits a smoother distribution relative to the thick disk. This result is in consistent with the hypothesis that features associated with minor-mergers should last longer in the thick disc. Thick disc stars spend relatively little time near the Galactic plane, where heating from self-gravitating spiral arms or the bar and scattering by giant molecular clouds is most vigorous.

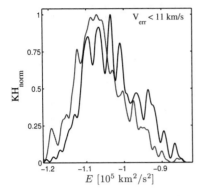 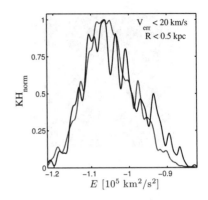

Figure 5.   (color online) Left panel: Kernel histogram of total energy obtained from the SCH06 sample of disk stars with total velocity error $V_{err} < 11$ km s^{-1}, shown with a black solid line. Right panel: As in the left panel, for a sample of disk stars with total velocity error $V_{err} < 20$ km s^{-1}. In both panels, the red line is the energy distribution from the SDSS G-dwarf sample described in the text.

Figure 5 shows the energy distributions of both the Schuster et al. (2006) sample (black line) and the SDSS local G-dwarf sample (red line), shown with two different cuts in velocity error and (for the SDSS sample) radial distance. The Schuster et al. sample includes stars located within 80 pc of the Sun, and was chosen in a manner that is independent of the method used for the SDSS sample. It is important to note the large number of peaks located at very similar values of E as in the kernel histogram of the G-dwarf subsample. The slight shift between these two distributions can by accounted for by the different volumes probed by the samples (see text), as well as poor sampling of the underlying energy distribution. The subsample of the Schuster et al. data shown in the left panel contains a total of 603 stars; that shown in the right panel, with less stringent requirements for velocity errors, contains 813 stars.

It seems clear from Figures 4 and 5 that the features seen in the energy distributions are real – but what are they? To answer this question, we analyzed two simulations from Purcell et al. (2011) that model the merger of a light ($10^{10.5}$ M$_\odot$) and heavy (10^{11} M$_\odot$) Sagittarius-like dwarf galaxy merging with the Milky Way, and examine the resulting impact that these mergers will have on the stellar populations in the simulated disk. This work shows that, when the phase space distributions of the stars in several different Solar neighborhood-like volumes are examined, one sees features that are strikingly similar to those that we see in the observational data, with the locations of these peaks depending strongly on both the exact location of the Solar-like volume and the mass of the merging galaxy. While not conclusive, this suggests strongly that the features observed in our local stellar samples are likely to be related to the merger of a Sagittarius-sized dwarf galaxy with the Milky Way.

Acknowledgments.   The authors would like to thank James Bullock, Chris Purcell, Alvaro Villalobos, the National Science Foundation, the Department of Energy, MSU's Institute for Cyber-Enabled Research, and the Joint Institute for Nuclear Astrophysics for funding the work described in this paper. The stellar data described was provided by the Sloan Digital Sky Survey.

References

Lee, Y. S., Beers, T. C., An, D., Ivezić, Ž., Just, A., Rockosi, C. M., Morrison, H. L., Johnson, J. A., Schönrich, R., Bird, J., Yanny, B., & Rocha-Pinto, H. J. 2011, ApJ, 738, 187
Purcell, C. W., Bullock, J. S., Tollerud, E. J., Rocha, M., & Chakrabarti, S. 2011, Nat, 477, 301
Schuster, W. J., Moitinho, A., Márquez, A., Parrao, L., & Covarrubias, E. 2006, A&A, 445, 939
Tumlinson, J. 2006, ApJ, 641, 1
— 2010, ApJ, 708, 1398
York, D. G., & SDSS Collaboration 2000, AJ, 120, 1579

Mt. Fuji from the conference room.

Galactic Archaeology: Near-Field Cosmology and the Formation of the Milky Way
ASP Conference Series, Vol. 458
W. Aoki, M. Ishigaki, T. Suda, T. Tsujimoto, N. Arimoto, eds.
©2012 Astronomical Society of the Pacific

Early Evolution of the Milky Way Satellite System

Gerhard Hensler and Mykola Petrov

University of Vienna, Institute of Astrophysics, Tuerkenschanzst. 17,
1180 Vienna, Austria; email: gerhard.hensler@univie.ac.at

Abstract. The dwarf spheroidal galaxies around the Milky Way (MW) belong to the most poorly understood class of astronomical objects and serve as the most challenging targets of astrophysical research for the reasons of cosmology, evolution of satellite galaxies, faintest dwarf galaxies, and accretion history of the MW. In order to yield a deeper insight into these perspectives, numerical simulations from cosmological to galactic scales and semi-analytical galaxy models have been undertaken by numerous authors which are discussed here. Furthermore, a new comprehensive chemodynamical approach is presented and its results are highlighted.

1. Introduction

Cold Dark Matter (CDM) simulations of cosmological structure and galaxy formation predict the existence of a large number of small CDM subhaloes surrounding massive DM gravitational potentials, i.e. galaxies such as the Milky Way (MW) and M31 (Moore et al. 1999; Diemand et al. 2008; Springel et al. 2008; Stadel et al. 2009). These subhaloes should serve as the DM progenitors of dwarf galaxies (DGs). Indeed, the Local Group (LG) is permeated by DGs of different morphology. Except the Magellanic clouds, irregular DGs in the LG exist with significant gas fractions to account for star formation (SF) only at larger distances from the MW.

Most DGs around the MW are less luminous and gas-free with elliptically shaped stellar distribution, therefore called dwarf spheroidal galaxies (dSphs), and extend to the fainter end of dwarf ellipticals. Because of their low surface brightness μ though even close to the MW, only a few of these dSphs could be observed up to now in the range of $M_V = -14^m$ to -10^m. Their location in the $M_V - \mu$ parameter space separates them clearly from Globular Clusters (Tolstoy et al. 2009). Their number of detections increased over the last years due to improving sensitivity and thanks to systematic surveys like SDSS so that their brightness could be shifted to almost -5^m for the recently discovered ultra-faint dwarf galaxies (UFDs) (Belokurov et al. 2006, 2007; Martin et al. 2006; Zucker et al. 2006a,b; Irwin et al. 2007; Walsh et al. 2007; Simon & Geha 2007).

Although DGs serve as cornerstone for the validity of the cosmological CDM concordance model, the faint low-mass regime can at present only be tested around the MW. The significant lack of observed objects (Grebel & Gallagher 2004; Mateo et al. 2008), so-called missing satellite problem (Moore et al. 1999; Kravtsov 2002), and the peculiar spatial distribution, namely, the concentration of dSph around the MW and M31 into a disk-of-satellites (DoS) (Metz et al. 2009; Kroupa et al. 2010) raise serious challenges to the cosmological CDM hypothesis and our understanding of very low-mass galaxies in the environment of a major galaxy. Whether these facts make the CDM cosmology invalid or reflect that dSphs represent only the peak of the iceberg of subhalos, namely those which have retained their baryons while various processes must have emptied by far the most DM subhalos (Kravtsov et al. 2004) is a matter of intensive debate.

From the astrophysical points of view further burning questions are addressed jointly with structural properties of dSphs: Did re-ionization (Robertson et al. 2005; Font et al. 2006; Strigari et al. 2007) suppress the SF in the low-mass DM progenitor haloes at the early epoch? At what redshifts did SF commence and was it the same for all dSphs? How are stellar populations distributed in dSphs? How do they relate to the observed populations of surviving dSphs? When and how did the observed UFDs and "classical" dSphs form and evolve since the time of rapid accretion onto the Galaxy? What fraction of dSph-like galaxies did contribute to the built-up of the Galactic stellar halo and what is the chemical distribution of their stellar components? Can the distribution of the dSphs give an indication of the possibility of morphological transformation of DGs? How does the existence of a host galaxy affect the DG evolution by means of tides and its halo gas?

Understanding the evolution of the luminous content of small subhalos needs to exploit in detail the stellar populations, their stellar ages and fractions, i.e. the SF epochs, and chemical abundances. And indeed, both is performed observationally and by numerical models. While observational campaigns are of increasing intensity, as e.g. DART, APOGEE, etc. are providing overwhelming data and informations, the theoretical modelling is more slowly advancing and cannot yet be complete and provide a coherent picture, because the widely differing scales and processes allow to focus on particular aspects only.

The most recent and comprehensive review of the state-of-the-art LG galaxies' research by Tolstoy et al. (2009) summarized new facts since the review by Mateo (1998) and shows for the gas-free dSphs also how stellar populations and element abundances are deconvolved. As main issue which demonstrates the diversity of their evolution is the stellar populations: in all dSphs there is an early onset of SF in some with a strong decline and death, but others experience a SF continuation with varying rates, as e.g. Carina, and some with increasing SF rates. Sculptor has produced stars at least until 5 Gyrs ago, producing two chemically and kinematically distinct stellar populations. Though gas-free, Sculptor is sitting in a bath of HI clouds of the same radial velocity. From the stellar kinematics it was early derived that the luminous mass of dSphs is much lower than the dynamical one, leading to very high mass-to-light ratios M/L increasing to fainter dSphs (Mateo 1998).

The metal enrichment of most satellite galaxies can be easily understood when their stars are self-enriched at first by type II supernovae (SNeII) leading to constant ratio of α elements to iron α/Fe. Continuous SF at low efficiency then leads to a decline of this ratio at lower than solar Fe abundance in most dSphs. Considering their general metallicity Z, the LG DGs fit into the mass-Z relation (Grebel et al. 2003). Although the CDM merging hypothesis requires the infall and accumulation of the MW mass by DM subhalos and gas, also their stars are "mining" the halo (Salvadori et al. 2008). If this happened in the very early epoch with the first stars only, no differences at the low-Z end will provide an insight, because both halo and dSphs' stars are systematically at the constant value of SNII enrichment while the knee of α/Fe deviates from MW stars (Shetrone et al. 2003; Tolstoy et al. 2003; Venn et al. 2004; Koch et al. 2008).

This fact allows to pin-down that progenitors of present-day dSphs are not the expected builing blocks of the galactic halo and to explain the lack of expected numerous stellar streams. From the kinematics of halo stars, however, a dichotomy is found (Bell et al. 2008; Carollo et al. 2007), one regular population in the inner region out to 10 kpc radius and an outer-most heterogeneous and decoupled halo population most plausibly accreted from disrupted satellites.

The metallicity distribution function (MDF) of the UFDs suggests that these tiny systems contain a larger fraction of extremely metal-poor stars than the MW halo does (Kirby et al 2008) and retain the chemical imprint of the interstellar medium (ISM) when the Universe was less than 1 Gyr old.

2. Modeling dwarf satellite galaxies

Since DGs are most efficiently affected by energetic processes and environmental effects, simple non-dynamical considerations as performed to understand the chemical evolution (Lanfranchi et al. 2006; Lanfranchi & Matteucci 2010; Carigi & Hernandez 2008; Prantzos 2008; Kirby et al. 2011a,b) provide only a very limited understanding of the real evolution of DGs. Dynamical models concerning the formation and evolution of the satellite galaxies can be devided into 4 categories:

1. CDM simulations with additional semi-analytical evolutionary tools (Salvadori et al. 2008; Font et al. 2011; Cooper et al. 2010);
2. CDM models with baryon physics but high mass resolution to allow for faint dSphs (e.g. Maschenko et al. 2008);
3. N-body simulations of individual units in the tidal field of the MW (Johnston et al. 2008; Peñarrarubia et al. 2009; Peñarrarubia et al. 2010);
4. Gasdynamical simulations of isolated DGs with SF, stellar feedback, and chemical abundances (e.g. Hensler et al. 2004; Marcolini at al. 2006; Stinson et al. 2006; Marcolini at al. 2008; Stinson et al. 2009; Revaz et al. 2009; Sawala et al. 2010).

Although the gasdynamical simulations advanced from 1D *chemo-dynamical* models (Hensler et al. 2004) to 3D hydrodynamics (see e.g. Marcolini at al. 2008; Revaz et al. 2009), they still lack of a self-consistent treatment of various processes All these simulations are differently focussed and yield results that do not deviate too much from observational data, however, the system of satellites experience a whole bunch of processes, internally, gas processes by means of SF, heating, and cooling, as well as externally, ram-pressure (Mayer et al. 2007) and tidal (Read et al. 2006a) stripping, gas accretion, and further more. If these external facts are not taken into account but simulations are limited to isolation the models do not allow the trace-back of the evolution of any dSph galaxy.

Although the advancement to a two-phase ISM treatment in SPH is not trivial and implies various numerical problems, but is not impossible (Berczik et al. 2003; Harfst et al. 2006; Scannapieco et al. 2006), such treatment would be absolutely necessary in order to approach reality and to achieve reliable results. In addition, the *chemo-dynamical* interaction processes must be applied (Hensler 2009).

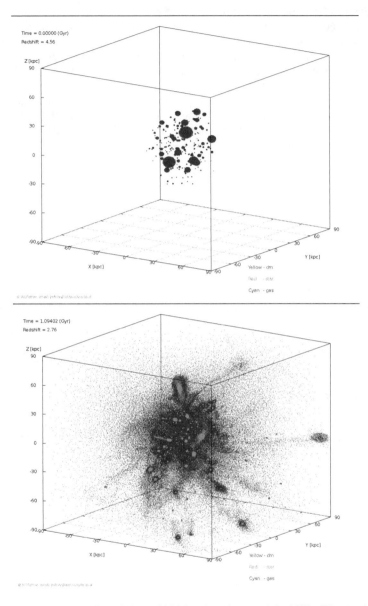

Figure 1.   (color online) Cubes of 200 kpc length around the Milky Way (at their
center). *upper panel:* Initial conditions of the Milky Way's satellite system: Distribution of Dark Matter (DM) subhalos within a sphere of 40 kpc radius around the
Milky Way at redshift z=4.56. *lower panel:* Snapshot of the satellites' dynamical
evolution 1 Gyr after the numerical onset, i.e. at redshift z=2.76. The DM subhalos
are filled with baryonic gas of mass fraction of 17%, form stars, and lose mass of all
constituents due to tidal interactions among the satellite system.

3. Modeling the Milky Way satellite system

To model instead of isolated subhalos the evolution of the system of dSphs in the gravitational field of the MW for which the accretion by the host galaxy is probable over the Hubble time, the cosmological ΛCDM simulation Via Lactea II (Diemand et al. 2008) is used. For the simulations an advanced version of the single-gas chemo-dynamical Smooth-particle Hydrodyamics (SPH)/N-body code is applied, treating the production and chemical evolution of 11 elements (Petrov & Hensler 2012).

Since an acceptable computational time limits the number of gas particles to two million and the DM particles to the same and, in order to reach a mass resolution of $10^3 M_\odot$ per SPH particle, only 250 subhaloes as DM progenitors of dSphs in the total-mass range of $10^6 < M_{sat}/M_\odot < 6 \cdot 10^8$ from $z = 4.56$ could be followed. Unfortunately, this fact limits the radius of consideration to 40 kpc around the MW's center of mass. In order to study the construction of the MW halo by accretion of subhalos with both gas and stars, as a first step, the *chemo-dynamical* evolution of the dSph system is followed for the first Gyr (Petrov & Hensler 2012), i.e. until redshift $z = 2.76$ (see Fig.1).

Starting with a 10^4 K warm gas of 17% of the subhalo masses in virial equilibrium and under the assumption that re-ionization is improbable to have affected the LG dSphs (Grebel & Gallagher 2004), cooling allows the gas particles to achieve SF conditions in all satellites, but its efficiency directly depends on the mass of a satellite and its dynamical history (e.g. merging with other satellites or disruption by the MW gravitational potential).

4. Results

For the first 0.1 Gyrs of the simulation there is a considerable variance of stellar oxygen abundance in the whole system ($-5. \leq$ [O/H] ≤ -0.5) reflecting the very inhomogeneous production and distribution of enriched gas. After 0.1 Gyrs the merging of satellites' ISM promotes the mixing of heavy elements. Finally, almost completely recycling of the gas erases the abundance inhomogeneities so that O in stars converges to $-1. \leq$[O/H]≤ 0. with a small dispersion.

Further results will be published in comprehensive papers by Petrov & Hensler by more detailed analyses, e.g. concern the SF history, which starts in all subhalos equally, then ceases for the lowest mass objects while it continues in more massive ones with fluctuations due to gas exchange and merging with low-mass dSphs. dSphs develop their stellar components and element abundances dependent on the distance from the MW. Gas is pushed out from low-mass dSphs by their internal stellar energy release and lost from more massive dSphs by the tidal force, both effects feeding the MW gas halo by pre-processed hot gas. Inherently as an additional effect, dSphs also get rid of their gas by their motion within their own bath of lost hot gas.

The observed common mass scale (Strigari et al. 2008) cannot be reproduced by our model but agree with the L_{tot} - $M(r_{300})$ relation expected within the CDM framework (Kroupa et al. 2010). Last but not least, it must be emphasized that all low-mass subhalos survive with an old stellar component and would be observable with their surface brightness still today in the SDSS. These disagreements on small scales of observations to the expectations within the cosmological "concordance" models from the evolution of dSphs and the MW halo in the early universe are presented in a comprehensive paper and will be discussed with their implications for our cosmological picture.

Acknowledgments. The authors are grateful to Pavel Kroupa and Simone Recchi for their contributions and continuous discussions to this field. G.H. would like to the thank the conference organizers for their invitation, the excellent science presentations, and the friendly atmosphere. This work was supported by Initiative College IK538001 and by the Austrian Science Foundation FWF under project no. P21097-N16.

References

Bell, E.F., Zucker, D.B., Belokurov, V., et al. 2008, ApJ, 680, 295
Belokurov, V., Zucker, D.B., Evans, N.W., et al., 2006, ApJ, 647, L111
Belokurov, V., Zucker, D.B., Evans, N.W., et al., 2007, ApJ, 654, 897
Berczik, P., Hensler, G., Theis, C., & Spurzem, R. 2003, Astrophys. Space Sci., 284, 865
Carigi, L. & Hernandez, X. 2008, MNRAS, 390, 582
Carollo, D., Beers, T.C., Lee, Y.S., et al. 2007 Nat, 450, 1020
Cooper, A.P., Cole, S., Frenk, C.S., et al. 2010, MNRAS, 407, 744
Diemand, J., Kuhlen, M., Madau, P., et al. 2008, Nat, 454, 735
Font, A.S., Johnston, K.V., Bullock, J.S., & Robertson, B.E. 2006, ApJ, 638, 585
Font, A.S., Benson, A.J., Bower, R.G., et al. 2011, MNRAS, 417, 1260
Grebel, E.K., Gallagher, J.S., & Harbeck, D. 2003, AJ, 125, 1966
Grebel, E.K. & Gallagher, J.S. 2004, ApJ, 610, L89
Harfst, S., Theis, C., & Hensler, G. 2006, A&A, 449, 509
Hensler, G. 2009, Proceed. IAU Symp. No. 254, J. Andersen et al. (eds.), Cambridge Univ. Press, p. 269
Hensler, G., Theis, C., & Gallagher, J.S. 2004, A&A, 426, 25
Irwin, M.J., Belokurov, V., Evans, N.W., et al. 2007, ApJ, 656, L13
Johnston, K.V., Bullock J.S., Sharma S., et al. 2008, ApJ, 689, 936
Katz, N., Weinberg, D.H., & Hernquist, L. 1996, ApJS, 105, 19
Kirby E.N., Simon, J.D., Geha, M., et al. 2008, ApJ, 685, L43
Kirby, E.N., Lanfranchi G.A., Simon J.D., et al. 2011, ApJ, 727, 78
Kirby, E.N., Cohen, J.G., Smith, G.H, et al. 2011, ApJ, 727, 79
Koch, A., Grebel, E.K., Gilmore, G.F., et al. 2008, AJ, 135, 1580
Kravtsov, A.V. 2002, A&A, 396, 117
Kravtsov, A.V., Gnedin, O.Y., & Klypin, A.A. 2004, ApJ, 609, 482
Kroupa, P., Famaey, B., de Boer, K.S., et al. 2010, A&A, 523, A32
Lanfranchi, G.A., Matteucci, F., & Cescutti, G. 2006, A&A, 453, 67
Lanfranchi, G.A., & Matteucci, F. 2010, A&A, 512, A85
Marcolini, A., D'Ercole, A., Brighenti, F., & Recchi, S. 2006, MNRAS, 371, 643
Marcolini, A., D'Ercole, A., Battaglia, G., & Gibson, B.K. 2008, MNRAS, 386, 2173
Martin, N. F., Ibata, R. A., Irwin, M. J., et al. 2006, MNRAS, 371, 1983
Mashchenko, S., Wadsley, J., & Couchman, H.M.P., 2008, Science, 319, 174
Mateo, M. 1998, ARA&A, 36, 435
Mateo, M., Olszewski, E.W., & Walker, M.G. 2008, AJ, 675, 201
Mayer, L., Kazantzidis, S., Mastropietro, C., & Wadsley, J. 2007, Nat, 445, 738
Metz M., Kroupa P., Theis C., Hensler G., & Jerjen H., 2009, ApJ, 697, 269
Moore, B., Ghigna, S., Governato, F., et al. 1999, ApJ, 524, L19
Peñarrubia, J., Navarro, J.F., McConnachie, A.W., & Martin, N.F. 2009, ApJ, 698, 222
Peñaarrubia, J., Benson, A.J., Walker, M.G., et al. 2010, MNRAS, 406, 1290
Petrov, M. & Hensler, G. 2012, ApJ, submitted
Prantzos N. 2008, A&A, 489, 525
Read, J.I., Wilkinson, M.I., Evans, N.W., et al. 2006a, MNRAS, 366, 429
Read, J.I., Pontzen, A.P., & Viel, M. 2006b, MNRAS, 371, 885

Revaz, Y., Jablonka P., Sawala T., et al. 2009, A&A, 501, 189
Robertson, B., Bullock, J.S., Font, A.S., et al. 2005, ApJ, 632, 872
Salvadori, S., Ferrara, A., & Schneider, R. 2008, MNRAS, 386, 348
Sawala, T., Scannapieco, C., Maio, U., & White, S., 2010, MNRAS, 402, 1599
Scannapieco, C., Tissera, P.B., White, S.D.M.,& Springel, V. 2006, MNRAS, 371, 1125
Shetrone, M, Venn, K.A., Tolstoy, E, et al., 2003. AJ, 125, 688
Simon, J.D., & Geha, M. 2007, ApJ, 670, 313
Seabroke, G.M., Gilmore, G., Siebert, A., et al. 2008, MNRAS, 384, 11
Springel V., Wang J., Vogelsberger M., et al. 2008, MNRAS, 391, 1685
Stadel J., Potter D., Moore B., et al. 2009, MNRAS, 398, L21
Stinson, G.S., Seth, A., Katz, N., et al. 2006, MNRAS, 373, 1074
Stinson, G.S., Dalcanton, J.J., Quinn, T., et al. 2007, ApJ, 667, 170
Stinson, G.S., Dalcanton, J.J., T. Quinn, T., et al. 2009, MNRAS, 395, 1455
Strigari, L.E., Bullock, J.S., Kaplinghat, M., et al. 2007, ApJ, 669, 676
Strigari, L.E., Bullock, J.S., Kaplinghat M., et al. 2008, Nat, 454, 1096
Tolstoy, E., Venn, K.A., Shetrone, M., et al. 2003, AJ, 125, 707
Tolstoy, E., Hill, V., & Tosi, M. 2009, ARA&A, 47, 371
Venn, K.A., Irwin, M, Shetrone, M.D., et al. 2004. AJ, 128, 1177
Walsh, S.M., Jerjen, H., & Willman, B. 2007, ApJ, 662, L83
Zucker, D.B., Belokurov, V., Evans, N.W., et al. 2006a, ApJ, 643, L103
Zucker, D.B., Belokurov, V., Evans, N.W., et al, 2006b, ApJ, 650, L41

Excursion to Jogasaki coast on November 3rd. Learning structure formation in Japan.

Galactic Archaeology: Near-Field Cosmology and the Formation of the Milky Way
ASP Conference Series, Vol. 458
W. Aoki, M. Ishigaki, T. Suda, T. Tsujimoto, N. Arimoto, eds.
© 2012 Astronomical Society of the Pacific

Accurate Stellar Kinematics at Faint Magnitudes: Application to the Boötes I Dwarf Spheroidal Galaxy

Sergey Koposov

Institute of Astronomy, University of Cambridge, CB3 OHA, UK

Abstract. We develop, implement and characterise an enhanced data reduction approach which delivers precise, accurate, radial velocities from moderate resolution spectroscopy with the fibre-fed VLT/FLAMES+GIRAFFE facility. The repeated measurements let us reliably calibrate our individual velocity errors ($0.2 \leq \delta_V \leq 5$ km s^{-1}) and directly detect stars with variable radial velocities. We show, by application to the Boötes I dwarf spheroidal, that the intrinsic velocity dispersion of this system is significantly below 6.5 km s^{-1} reported by previous studies. Our data favor a two-population model of Boötes I, consisting of a majority 'cold' stellar component, with velocity dispersion $2.4^{+0.9}_{-0.5}$ km s^{-1}, and a minority 'hot' stellar component, with velocity dispersion ~ 9 km s^{-1}, although we can not completely rule out a single component distribution with velocity dispersion $4.6^{+0.8}_{-0.6}$ km s^{-1}.

1. Introduction

There is continuing interest in analysis of the number, nature, masses, and evolutionary histories of the dwarf spheroidal (dSph) satellite galaxies, found in moderate numbers around both the Milky Way Galaxy and M31 in the Local Group. They have typical half-light radii greater than 100pc, low surface brightnesses (~ 25-30 mag arcsec^{-2}), and central velocity dispersions of several km s^{-1}, implying that the luminous component is embedded in a dominant extended dark matter halo ($M/L_V \sim 10 - 100 M/L_{V,\odot}$). Therefore measuring precise velocity dispersions in these galaxies and therefore their masses represent a task of extreme importance.

In this study (Koposov et al. 2011) We have two ambitions. The first is to study one particular dSph galaxy: Boötes I, which was one of the first new dSphs discovered using the SDSS photometric survey and seems representative of the group of newly-discovered intrinsically-faint dSph galaxies. And the second aim is to improve our knowledge of how reliably and accurately we can measure radial velocities of faint dSph member stars.

2. Velocity Determination and Spectral Fitting

The standard approach used for the measurement of stellar velocities has been to cross-correlate against a template spectrum. Although simple and computationally fast, cross-correlation is known not to perform optimally. In fact direct pixel-fitting methods have been widely employed for more than a decade in spectroscopic studies of unresolved stellar populations. Methods based on direct pixel fitting provide more realistic error-

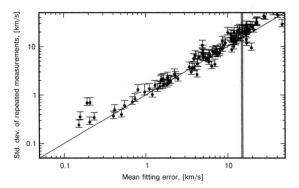

Figure 1. Comparison of the mean velocity error determined from the fitting procedure and the estimated standard deviation of the repeatedly measured velocities. Error bars show 68% confidence limits for the estimated standard deviations. The solid black line shows the one-to-one relation. The grey line shows the approximate velocity where the one-to-one relation between the mean error and the estimated standard deviation is expected to fail due to non-Gaussianity of the probability distributions.

bars and give a better way to treat multiple templates and continuum levels. And that is the method we employ for this work. One of the most important checks on the validity of our results—as well as a check on the effectiveness of our reduction method—is the confirmation that the velocity errors that we determine from individual observations of specific (non-variable) stars are not systematically larger or smaller than the scatter between individual repeated measurements. Figure 1 compares the standard deviation determined from repeated measurements to the mean error determined by our fitting procedure. With reassuringly few exceptions, the data points in Figure 1 scatter about the one-to-one line. There is a slight apparent systematic tendency for the data points to be scattered more above the one-to-one line than below it, expected given that the error-bars on the standard deviation are significantly asymmetric. The one-to-one relation extends in general down to a precision of a few hundred m s^{-1}, confirming that our derived error-bars are reliable down to $0.1-0.2$ km s^{-1}.

3. Velocity Dispersion Measurement

Equipped with the high quality radial velocity measurements and their error-bars and after rejecting from the sample the stars which seems to have a variable radial velocities, we can proceed to the modeling of the velocity distribution. Figure 2 shows the observed radial velocity distribution of Boötes I galaxy and the comparison with the estimate of velocity dispersion from previous works illustrating that the stellar velocity dispersion which we measure is noticeably smaller. The modeling of the velocity distribution by a single Gaussian gives an estimate of the velocity dispersion of the system $4.6^{+0.8}_{-0.6}$ km s^{-1}.

If we make the assumption that the Boötes I velocity distribution consists of two Gaussians (as slightly suggested by the data), where one Gaussian has higher dispersion than the other we get the following estimates: the velocity dispersion of the lower

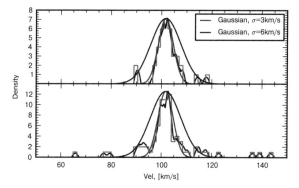

Figure 2.   (color online) The distribution of stellar velocities in Boötes I. The black line shows the distribution of velocities estimated using the Epanechnikov kernel with a bandwidth of 1.5 km s^{-1}, the grey line shows a standard histogram with bin size of 1.5 km s^{-1}. The red and blue lines are overplotted Gaussians with sigma of 3 and 6 km s^{-1}; respectively; 6 km s^{-1} is the smaller of the previously published determinations of the Boötes I internal velocity dispersion. The top panel shows the velocity distribution for our sample of 37 stars which are highly probable Boötes I members, i.e., those with [Fe/H]<-1.5, log g <3.5, small velocity error σ_v <2.5 km s^{-1} and no significant velocity variability. The bottom panel shows the velocity distribution for all 100 of our stars with non-varying radial velocity.

dispersion component is then $2.4^{+0.9}_{-0.5}$ km s^{-1}, while the velocity dispersion of the other component is not very well determined, but is around 9 km s^{-1}. The fraction of stars belonging to the higher dispersion component according to the MCMC fit is around 30%. The corresponding Gaussian distributions are overlaid on the kinematic data on Figure 3. In order to assess the probability that the Boötes I velocity distribution is indeed described by two Gaussians instead of one we measure the likelihood ratio for these two hypotheses and this test favours with ~98% confidence favours the double Gaussian hypothesis.

4.   Conclusion

In this work we have developed and implemented a thorough analysis of low-moderate spectral resolution (R = 6500) VLT/FLAMES stellar spectra taken in the CaT wavelength region near 860nm. We optimised a data reduction methodology which delivers very accurate radial velocities, and very reliable uncertainties on those radial velocities. We set up an optimised observational proof of methodology, targeting faint candidate RGB stars in the very metal-poor Boötes I dwarf spheroidal galaxy. By making 16 individual repeat observations over six weeks, with a wide dynamic range in each observational data set, we have reached several goals: most importantly, we have been able to properly assess the errors of our radial velocity measurements; our delivered radial velocity precision, for faint extremely weak-lined stars, is better than 1 km s^{-1} for the combined exposures. Second, we have been able to identify and reject stars that show significant radial velocity variability.

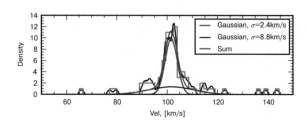

Figure 3.   (color online) The model for the probability distributions of radial velocities as determined from an MCMC fit to our 100-star non-variable velocity data, when the velocity distribution is assumed to be consistent with two Gaussians. The histogram shows the data. The MCMC analysis allocated 70% of the stars to the 2.4 km s^{-1} dispersion component, and 30% of the stars to the 9 km s^{-1} dispersion component.

Comparing our derived velocity dispersion, and individual velocities, with literature studies (Muñoz et al. 2006; Martin et al. 2007), shows that previous studies have substantially overestimated the velocity dispersion of Boötes I. It is possible that earlier studies underestimate their velocity errors, and hence overestimate the velocity distribution which is deconvolved from those errors. By exploiting the spectrograph stability to build integrations on times from days to years, we can detect many radial velocity variables, whose unrecognised presence would inflate erroneously a derived velocity dispersion. Importantly, from repeated observations, we can quantify reliably our velocity accuracy. We are currently applying this observational technique to several other dSph galaxies.

We have useful radial velocity measurements for 100 non-variable RGB candidate stars, all within one half-light radius (12.5arcmin, 240pc) of the centre of Boötes I. Approximately 60-70 stars are likely members from our full sample. Implementing a general MCMC analysis, which includes separate Boötes I-member and background distribution functions of our derived stellar parameters log g, [Fe/H], and of the member and background velocity distributions, we show that the distribution function of stellar radial velocities in Boötes I which we measure can be described in two ways. The less likely is that the distribution is Gaussian, with a velocity dispersion of $4.6^{+0.8}_{-0.6}$ km s^{-1}. The more likely is that the distribution consists of two components: a "colder" component, containing 70% of the member stars, which has a projected radial velocity dispersion of $2.4^{+0.9}_{-0.5}$ km s^{-1}, and a "hotter" component, containing 30% of the member stars, which has a projected radial velocity dispersion of 9 km s^{-1}. The data favor, with 98% confidence, the two component model.

References

Koposov, S. E., Gilmore, G., Walker, M. G., Belokurov, V., Wyn Evans, N., Fellhauer, M., Gieren, W., Geisler, D., Monaco, L., Norris, J. E., Okamoto, S., Peñarrubia, J., Wilkinson, M., Wyse, R. F. G., & Zucker, D. B. 2011, ApJ, 736, 146. 1105.4102
Martin, N. F., Ibata, R. A., Chapman, S. C., Irwin, M., & Lewis, G. F. 2007, MNRAS, 380, 281. 0705.4622
Muñoz, R. R., Carlin, J. L., Frinchaboy, P. M., Nidever, D. L., Majewski, S. R., & Patterson, R. J. 2006, ApJ, 650, L51. arXiv:astro-ph/0606271

Galactic Archaeology: Near-Field Cosmology and the Formation of the Milky Way
ASP Conference Series, Vol. 458
W. Aoki, M. Ishigaki, T. Suda, T. Tsujimoto, N. Arimoto, eds.
© 2012 Astronomical Society of the Pacific

Counting Dark Sub-halos with Star Stream Gaps

Raymond G. Carlberg

*Department of Astronomy & Astrophysics, University of Toronto, Toronto, ON,
M5S 3H4, Canada.* `raymond.carlberg@utoronto.ca`

Abstract. The Cold Dark Matter paradigm predicts vast numbers of dark matter sub-halos to be orbiting in galactic halos. The sub-halos are detectable through the gaps they create gaps in stellar streams. The gap-rate is an integral over the density of sub-halos, their mass function, velocity distribution and the dynamical age of the stream. The rate of *visible* gap creation is a function of the width of the stream. The available data for four streams: the NW stream of M31, the Pal 5 stream, the Orphan Stream and the Eastern Banded Structure, are compared to the LCDM predicted relation. We find a remarkably good agreement, although there remains much to be done to improve the quality of the result. The narrower streams require that there is a total population of order 10^5 sub-halos above $10^5 M_\odot$ to create the gaps.

1. Introduction

LCDM simulations predict about 10^4 sub-halos more massive than $10^6 M_\odot$ in a steeply rising mass function that constitutes nearly 10% of a typical galaxy's dark halo (Springel et al. 2008; Diemand et al. 2007; Stadel et al. 2009). The large population of sub-halos is not detected in stars, gas, or in any currently detectable annihilation radiation. Logically there are three broad possibilities for the deficiency: dark matter sub-halos never formed with the LCDM predicted abundance, or, the dark matter sub-halos did form and through subsequent evolution were severely depleted, or, the dark matter sub-halos do exist but only a few are populated with visible baryons. Any one of these solutions has significant implications for galaxy formation theory and cosmology.

Here we develop a statistical method to count dark matter sub-halos. The gravitational field of a sub-halo induces orbital deflections in stellar streams that are potentially observable as either velocity or positional disturbances (Ibata et al. 2002; Siegal-Gaskins & Valluri 2008; Yoon et al. 2011; Carlberg et al. 2011). In particular, close passages create gaps which are detectable in measurements of the density along a star stream. We provide an expression for the average rate at which gaps are created in star streams that are populated with the full LCDM population of dark matter sub-halos. Combining this with the predicted length of the gaps gives a predicted relationship between two observable quantities, the gap creation rate and the width of a star stream.

2. The Gap-Rate vs Width Relation

The rate per unit length at which sub-halos cross the stream at velocity $v_\perp$ to create gaps is,

$$\mathcal{R}_\cup(r) = \int_M \int_{v_\perp} \int_0^{b_{max}} n(r)N(M)v_\perp f(v_\perp)\pi\, db\, dv_\perp\, dM, \qquad (1)$$

where b_{max} is the biggest impact parameter that can create a visible gap. The various factors in Equation 1 are evaluated with numerical simulations. We take the sub-halo mass function $N(M)$ and radial distribution $n(r)$ from Springel et al. (2008). We perform a large set of simulations of rings with single halo fly-bys to determine the depth and length of the gap that a sub-halo induces. It is quickly apparent that only encounters where the sub-halo partially passes through the star stream lead to a noticeable density dip. We describe the relation as a step function at $b \le \alpha R_s(M)$ where $R_s(M)$ is the scale radius of the sub-halo. We use the Springel et al. (2008) measurement for $n(r)$ (their Fig. 11) which finds that the sub-halo density at 100 kpc is 6 times the mean within the V_{50} volume. The simulations provide the necessary relations for the maximum effective impact parameter and length of the gap, as shown in Figure 1.

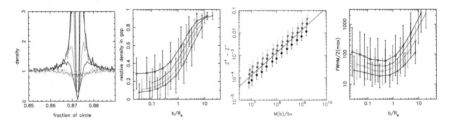

Figure 1.   First panel: The density at the location of closest passage, showing decreasing dip depth with increasing impact parameter. Second panel: The depth of the density dip as a function of the impact parameter ratioed to the sub-halo scale radius for masses increasing from 10^6 to $10^9 M_\odot$. Third panel: The vertical extent of the loop for rings at 30, 60 and 90 kpc with the impact approximation prediction for 60 kpc is shown as the line. Fourth panel: The ratio of the gap length to the vertical extent, again for masses increasing from 10^6 to $10^9 M_\odot$.

The width of the stream is set by the velocity dispersion around a mean guiding center motion of the stream. The epicyclic motion of stars around the guiding center means that to a good approximation that any gap narrower than the stream width will be blurred out by the random motion in the stream. Therefore the stream width is the minimum visible gap size and we can eliminate $\hat{M}$ from our equations through $w = l(\hat{M})$. Putting all these factors together gives gap creation rate as a function of the width of stream,

$$\mathcal{R}_\cup(w, r) = 0.059 \left(\frac{n(r)/n_0}{6}\right)\left(\frac{r}{100\,\text{kpc}}\right)^{0.55} w^{-0.85} \text{ kpc}^{-1}\text{Gyr}^{-1}, \qquad (2)$$

for w in kpc. Equation 2 provides a straightforward testable prediction of the CDM halo substructure model, effectively counting sub-halos.

Table 1.   Gap Statistics and Widths of Star Streams

Stream	Gaps #	Length [kpc]	Width [kpc]	Age [Gyr]	R_{GC} [kpc]	n/n_0
M31-NW[1]	12	200	5.0	10	100	6
Pal 5[2]	5	6.5	0.11	7	19	24
EBS[3]	8	4.7	0.17	7	15	30
Orphan[4]	2	30	1.0	3.9	30	20

References: [1]Carlberg et al. (2011); [2]Grillmair & Dionatos (2006); [3] Grillmair (2011);[4]Newberg et al. (2010)

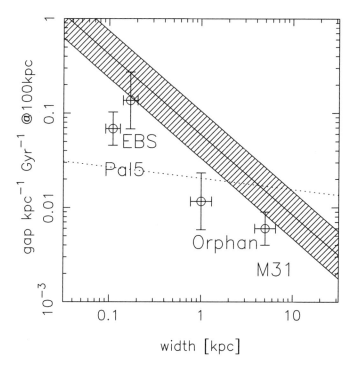

Figure 2.   The estimated gap rate vs stream width relation for M31 NW, Pal 5, the EBS and the CDM halo prediction. All data have been normalized to 100 kpc. Predictions for an arbitrary alternative mass functions, $N(M) \propto M^{-1.6}$ normalized to have the same number, 33, halos above $10^9 M_\odot$ as the standard distribution, is shown with a dotted line. The predicted relation has a width due to the width of the fitted relationships, as well as a halo-to-halo variance.

3.   Comparison of Predictions and Observations

The observed stream gap rate and width estimates are summarized in Table 1. The results of this paper are largely encapsulated in Figure 2, which plots the measured and predicted gap rates against the widths of the streams. The data have been scaled for plotting to a galacto-centric distance of 100 kpc using $n(r)/n_0$ and r in Equation 2. Comparison of the CDM based prediction of the gap rate-width relation with the published density data for four streams shows generally good agreement within the fairly generous measurement errors. The result is a statistical argument that the vast predicted population of sub-halos is indeed present in the halos of galaxies like M31 and the Milky Way.

Discussion

Rich: Doesn't the existence of wide binaries limit the number of sub-halos that can be present in a galactic halo?

Carlberg: Probably not. The distribution of wide binaries is said to be an inverse power (Opik's) law (Longhitano & Binggeli 2010) to the galactic tidal limit at 1pc, with no features. The origin of this distribution is unclear. Penarrubia etal (2010) have done some simulations of the survivability of wide binaries in the very low velocity dispersion environment of a dwarf galaxy, finding that wide binaries should be eroded to a roughly inverse square law beyond 10^4 to 10^5 au (i.e. nearly a parsec) depending on sub-halo fraction. Therefore it appears that the effect will cut in about where the distribution is depleted anyway, so at present there is no clear problem from wide-binaries. Carr & Sakellariadou considered this issue in a more general context and found the very hard potentials of globular clusters to be more of a problem.

Bland-Hawthorn: Could the stream clumps be due to "bead" instabilities?

Carlberg: This is a complex and controversial topic. Kupper, Heggie and others have pointed out that the first one or two clumps close to a globular cluster progenitor are likely the result of epicyclic pileup. Further down the stream our current full n-body simulations find no instabilities, but much depends on the dark matter content.

Acknowledgments.   The author thanks NSERC and the Canadian Institute for Advanced Research for support.

References

Carlberg, R. G., Richer, H. B., McConnachie, A. W., Irwin, M., Ibata, R. A., Dotter, A. L., Chapman, S., Fardal, M., Ferguson, A. M. N., Lewis, G. F., Navarro, J. F., Puzia, T. H., & Valls-Gabaud, D. 2011, ApJ, 731, 124. 1102.3501

Diemand, J., Kuhlen, M., & Madau, P. 2007, ApJ, 667, 859. arXiv:astro-ph/0703337

Grillmair, C. J. 2011, ApJ, 738, 98. 1107.5044

Grillmair, C. J., & Dionatos, O. 2006, ApJ, 641, L37. arXiv:astro-ph/0603062

Ibata, R. A., Lewis, G. F., Irwin, M. J., & Quinn, T. 2002, MNRAS, 332, 915. arXiv:astro-ph/0110690

Newberg, H. J., Willett, B. A., Yanny, B., & Xu, Y. 2010, ApJ, 711, 32. 1001.0576

Siegal-Gaskins, J. M., & Valluri, M. 2008, ApJ, 681, 40. 0710.0385

Springel, V., Wang, J., Vogelsberger, M., Ludlow, A., Jenkins, A., Helmi, A., Navarro, J. F., Frenk, C. S., & White, S. D. M. 2008, MNRAS, 391, 1685. 0809.0898

Stadel, J., Potter, D., Moore, B., Diemand, J., Madau, P., Zemp, M., Kuhlen, M., & Quilis, V. 2009, MNRAS, 398, L21. 0808.2981

Yoon, J. H., Johnston, K. V., & Hogg, D. W. 2011, ApJ, 731, 58. 1012.2884

Galactic Archaeology: Near-Field Cosmology and the Formation of the Milky Way
ASP Conference Series, Vol. 458
W. Aoki, M. Ishigaki, T. Suda, T. Tsujimoto, N. Arimoto, eds.
©*2012 Astronomical Society of the Pacific*

Dark Matter Profiles in Galactic Dwarf Satellites: Constraints from Non-Spherical Mass Models

Kohei Hayashi and Masashi Chiba

Astronomical Institute, Tohoku University, Aoba-ku, Sendai 980-8578, Japan

Abstract. Dwarf spheroidal (dSph) galaxies are ideal sites for studying the basic properties of dark matter halos, because such galaxies are largely dominated by dark matter, with mass-to-light ratios of 10 to 1000. Until now, most of mass models for dSphs have assumed spherical symmetry for simplicity, so the detailed comparisons with CDM models have yet been limited. However, luminous parts of dSphs are actually non-spherical and CDM models predict non-spherical virialized dark halos. We thus construct non-spherical mass models for dSphs to obtain more realistic and important limits on density profiles and shapes of dark halos. We first construct axisymmetric mass models based on the axisymmetric Jeans equations, where each of visible and halo density profiles has an axis ratio, and we also take into account a finite inclination angle with respect to the line of sight. Based on these models, we find characteristic features in the profiles of line of sight velocity dispersions for axisymmetric mass models and the application of these models to six dSphs in the Galaxy reveals that shapes of their dark halos deviate significantly from spherical symmetry.

1. Mass models for dSphs

We construct the following mass models. Surface brightness of stars in dSphs follows a Plummer model, $I(x,y) = L(\pi b_*^2)^{-1}[1 + m_*^2/b_*^2]^{-2}$, where $m_*^2 = x^2 + y^2/q'^2$, and q' is a projected axis ratio, which is related to a true axis ratio q and inclination of a galaxy i: $q'^2 = \cos^2 i + q^2 \sin^2 i$ (We here fix $i = 90°$; edge-on). For density profiles of dark halos, we assume the following power-law form

$$\rho(R, z) = \rho_0\Big(\frac{m}{b_{halo}}\Big)^{\alpha}\Big[1 + \Big(\frac{m}{b_{halo}}\Big)^2\Big]^{\delta},$$ (1)

where $m^2 = R^2 + z^2/Q^2$. Q is an axis ratio, b_{halo} is a scale length and ρ_0 is a density normalization. We then solve the axisymmetric Jeans equations (see Binney & Tremaine 2008, p. 354), where anisotropy of velocity dispersions with $(\overline{v_\phi^2}, \overline{v_R^2} = \overline{v_z^2})$ is fully taken into account, and determine the halo parameters (Q, b_{halo}, ρ_0) by fitting to the observed line of sight velocity dispersion. We apply these axisymmetric models to six dSphs (Carina, Fornax, Sculptor, Sextans, Draco, LeoI) to obtain their halo parameters. In contrast to previous work where stellar kinematics are spherically averaged (e.g., Walker et al. 2009; Strigari et al. 2010), we consider their systematic variation along major and minor axis. Detailed discussion will be presented in Hayashi & Chiba (2012, in preparation).

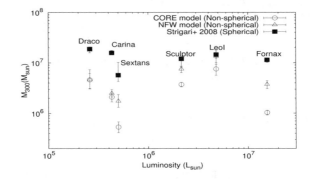

Figure 1.   The estimated total mass of six dSphs within their inner 0.3 kpc as a function of their total luminosity, in units of solar luminosities. Filled squares denote the results of Strigari et al. (2008), while open symbols are based on this work.

2.   Results

2.1.   Best fit models of dark halos

Based on chi-square fitting method, we examine the best fit parameters of dark halos (Q, b_{halo}, ρ_0) for each of six dSphs. In this work, we focus largely on shapes of dark halos, thus the two parameters which determine the profiles of dark halos (i.e. α, δ) are a priori fixed to NFW (Navarro et al. 1997) and CORE profile. As a result, we find that shapes of dark matter halos are not spherical (i.e. $Q \neq 1$) but significantly flattened $(0.3 < Q < 0.7)$, both for NFW and CORE models. Which model is more likely is however unclear from currently available data of stars.

2.2.   Mass within inner 300 pc radius

In order to compare spherical mass with non-spherical mass, we also estimate the total mass of six dSphs within inner 300 pc. Figure 1 illustrates the estimated total mass within a radius of 300 pc as a function of their total luminosity. It is clear that our axisymmetric mass models provide a different picture on this issue, namely the mass constancy within inner 300 pc as argued by spherical models is not the case. Therefore, we find that this mass estimate is rather sensitively dependent on the assumed mass profiles and shapes of dark matter halos in dSphs.

References

Binney, J., & Tremaine, S. 2008, Galactic Dynamics (Princeton: Princeton University Press), 2nd ed.
Navarro, J. F., Frenk, C. S., & White, S. D. 1997, ApJ, 490, 493
Plummer, H. C. 1911, MNRAS, 71, 460
Strigari, L. E., Bullock, J. S., Kaplinghat, M., Simon, J. D., Geha, M., Willman, B., & Walker, M. G. 2008, Nature, 454, 1096
Strigari, L. E., Frenk, C. S., & White, S. D. 2010, MNRAS, 408, 2364
Walker, M. G., Mateo, M., Olszewski, E. W., Penarrubia, J., Wyn Evans, N., & Gilmore, G. 2009, ApJ, 704, 1274

Galactic Archaeology: Near-Field Cosmology and the Formation of the Milky Way
ASP Conference Series, Vol. 458
W. Aoki, M. Ishigaki, T. Suda, T. Tsujimoto, N. Arimoto, eds.
© 2012 Astronomical Society of the Pacific

The Core-Cusp Problem in CDM Halos and Supernova Feedback

Go Ogiya and Masao Mori

Graduate School of Pure and Applied Science, University of Tsukuba, 1-1-1 Tennodai, Tsukuba 305-8577, Japan

Abstract. The Core-Cusp problem is one of the open questions on Cold Dark Matter (CDM) cosmology. It is a discrepancy about the mass-density distribution of a dark matter halo between theory and observation. We study about the dynamical response of a virialized system with a central cusp to the energy feedback driven by supernova explosions from the galaxy center using collisionless N-body simulations. Here, we focus on the timescale of gravitational potential change induced by supernova feedback. The simulations indicate that the timescale is one of important factors to determine the dynamical evolution of the DM halos.

1. Core-cusp problem

The Core – Cusp problem is a well known descrepancy between Cold Dark Matter (CDM) cosmology and observational results of nearby galaxies. CDM halos have power-law like mass-density profile at the center (e.g., Navarro et al. 1997), and this is called Cusp. However, less-massive galaxies in which dark matter dominated dynamically have constant density at their center (e.g., Moore 1994), and this is called Core. To solve this problem, gravitational effects from baryon components to a DM halo have been studied, since less-massive galaxies like dwarfs are more sensitive to stellar activities than giant ones because of their shallow potential well (e.g., Navarro et al. 1996; Pontzen & Governato 2011; Ogiya & Mori 2011). In this study, we investigate the dynamical response of DM halos to change of gravitational potential induced by motion of baryonic component using collisionless N-body simulations. We have studied about following two models; In the Mass-loss model, stellar feedbacks expel a significant amount of the baryon component from galaxies at one time. In the Oscillation model, depending on the star formation and feedback cycles, the baryonic system in the CDM halo repeats expansion and contraction.

2. Numerical model

In this paper, we simulate the dynamical response of a DM halo with the virial mass $10^9 M_\odot$, the virial radius 10 kpc, and the scale length 2 kpc. Total number of particles is 1,048,576, the tolerance parameter of the Barnes–Hut tree algorithm is 0.8 and the softening parameter is 0.008 kpc. We assume DM halos have Navarro–Frenk–White density profile (Navarro et al. 1997), initially.

To represent a baryon component, we add the external Hernquist potential into the N-body systems. In the Mass-loss model, the total mass of baryon decreases in a given

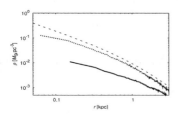

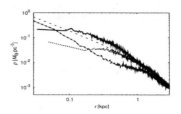

Figure 1. The density profile of DM halos in quasi-equilibrium state after the mass-loss. Dashed line shows the initial condition for NFW model. Solid and dotted lines represents T_{out} = 10 Myr, and 500 Myr, respectively. T_{out} is the mass-loss time-scale.

Figure 2. The density profile of DM halos after several oscillations of the external potential. Dashed line shows the initial condition for NFW model. Solid, dotted, and dot-dashed lines represents T_{osc} = 10 Myr, 30 Myr and 100 Myr, respectively, where T_{osc} is the period of the oscillation of the external potential.

time scale. On the other hand, the scale length of the baryon component oscillates in a given frequency for the Oscillation model.

3. Results

Fig. 1 shows the results of the Mass-loss model. The central cusp is made flatter when the mass-loss occurs over a short time-scale than when it occurs over a long time-scale. However, it is still steeper than typical observational density structure of dwarf galaxies. Fig. 2 demonstrates the results of the Oscillation model. The resultant core-scale depends on the period of the oscillation. Here, the dynamical time of DM halos at the center is ∼ 10Myr. We found that the Landau resonance between DM particles and density waves in CDM halo induced by the stellar feedback plays a role to the cusp-core transition of the DM halo.

4. Summary

We have studied the dynamical response of the DM halos against the mass-loss of the baryonic system from the galaxy center or the oscillation of the baryonic system, especially focused on the timescale of the stellar feedback. We have demonstrated that the results strongly depend on the time-scale of the stellar feedback. In other words, the density structure of DM halos correlate with star formation activities directly. In the forthcoming works, we will study the relation between the star formation histories of galaxies and the structures of DM halos.

Acknowledgments. This work was supported by the Grant-in-Aid for Scientific Research (A)(21244013).

References

Moore, B. 1994, Nat, 370, 629

Navarro, J. F., Eke, V. R., & Frenk, C. S. 1996, MNRAS, 283, L72
Navarro, J. F., Frenk, C. S., & White, S. D. M. 1997, ApJ, 490, 493
Ogiya, G., & Mori, M. 2011, ApJ, 736, L2
Pontzen, A., & Governato, F. 2011, arXiv:1106.0499

Coffee break. M. Ishigaki (left) and B. Nortström.

Galactic Archaeology: Near-Field Cosmology and the Formation of the Milky Way
ASP Conference Series, Vol. 458
W. Aoki, M. Ishigaki, T. Suda, T. Tsujimoto, N. Arimoto, eds.
©*2012 Astronomical Society of the Pacific*

Grand Rotation Curve, Dark Halo, and Baryon Fraction in the Milky Way Galaxy

Yoshiaki Sofue[1,2]

[1]*Dept. Physics, Meisei University, Hino, Tokyo, Japan*

[2]*Inst. Astronomy, University of Tokyo, Mitaka, Tokyo, Japan*
Email: sofue@ioa.s.u-tokyo.ac.jp

Abstract.   Grand rotation curve of the Milky Way Galaxy was constructed, which covers from the Galactic Center to Local Group ($\sim$ 1 Mpc). Least-sq. fit by bulge, disk and NFW dark halo resulted Galactic parameters in table 1, leading to local dark matter density of $\sim$ 0.235 $\pm$ 0.030 GeV cm^{-3}. We obtain stellar baryon fraction M(b+d) / M(b+d+h) = 0.072 $\pm$ 0.018, smaler than those in the universe (WMAP: 17%) or groups of galaxies ($\sim$ 12%). Missing baryons ($\sim$ 5%) may exist as hot gas of $\sim$ 10^6 K and $EM \sim 10^{-5}$ pc cm^{-6}, sharing a small fraction of X-ray background.

1. Introduction

We compiled large-scale data for rotation curves of the Milky Way, and radial velocities of globular clusters and member balaxies of the Local Group. The radial velocities of the non-disk objects were multiplied by $\sqrt{2}$ to approximate Virial velocity, and combined with the rotation curve. They are further running-averaged to yield a Grand Rotation Curve (GRC) shown in Figure 1, where the rotation velocities are plotted against the galactocentric distance in logarithmic scaling. The declining part of the NFW rotation velocity was clearly detected for the first time.

The GRC was deconvolved into de Vaucouleur bulge, exponential disk and NFW halo by least-squares fitting, resulting in the best-fit Galactic parameters in table 1. The local dark matter density is $\sim$ 0.235 $\pm$ 0.030 GeV cm^{-3}, consistent with the current values. We obtain a stellar baryon fraction of M_{b+d}/M_{b+d+h} = 0.072 $\pm$ 0.018, which may be compared with expected baryon fraction in the Local Group ($\sim$ 12%). We suggest that baryons in the form of hot gas are filling the dark halo with temperature of $\sim$ 10^{6}K and emission measure $\sim$ 10^{-5} pc cm^{-6}. Such hot halo gas may share a small fraction of the observed X-ray background emission ($\sim$ 10$^{-2\sim-3}$ pc cm^{-6}).

References

Sofue, Y. 2012, PASJ 64, No2.

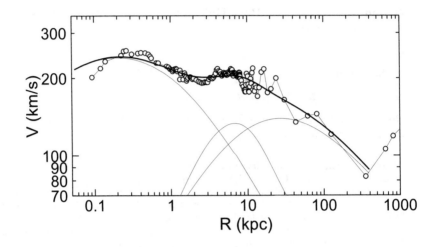

Figure 1.   Grand rotation curve of the Milky Way (dots), best-fitted by de Vaucouleurs bulge, expontial disk, and NFW dark halo with parameters in table 1.

Table 1.   Best-fit Galactic parameters

Mass component	Mass/Density	Scale Radius
dV Bulge	$M_b = (1.652 \pm 0.083) \times 10^{10} M_\odot$	$a_b = 0.522 \pm 0.037$ kpc
Expo. Disk	$M_d = (3.41 \pm 0.41) \times 10^{10} M_\odot$	$a_d = 3.19 \pm 0.35$ kpc
B+D Mass	$M_{b+d} = (5.06 \pm 0.97) \times 10^{10} M_\odot$	
B/D ratio	$M_b/M_d = 0.48 \pm 0.09$	
NFW Dark Halo	$\rho_0 = (1.06 \pm 0.14) \times 10^{-2} M_\odot pc^{-3}$	$h = 12.53 \pm 0.88$ kpc
	$= 0.403 \pm 0.051$ GeV cm^{-3}	
Local DM dens.	$\rho_0^\odot = (6.12 \pm 0.80) \times 10^{-3} M_\odot pc^{-3}$	
at $R_0 = 8$ kpc	$= 0.235 \pm 0.030$ GeV cm^{-3}	
DH Mass‡	$M_h(\leq 8\mathrm{kpc}) = (2.71 \pm 0.42) \times 10^{10} M_\odot$	
	$M_h^*(\leq h) = (5.05 \pm 0.78) \times 10^{10} M_\odot$	
	$M_h(\leq 20\mathrm{kpc}) = (8.87 \pm 1.37) \times 10^{10} M_\odot$	
	$M_h(\leq 385\mathrm{kpc}) = (6.52 \pm 1.01) \times 10^{11} M_\odot$	
Galaxy Mass	$M_{b+d+h} = (7.03 \pm 1.01) \times 10^{11} M_\odot$	$(R \leq 385$ kpc$)$
Baryon Fraction	$M_{b+d}/(M_{b+d+h}) = \mathbf{0.072 \pm 0.018}$	

Part VII

Future Prospects

Galactic Archaeology: Near-Field Cosmology and the Formation of the Milky Way
ASP Conference Series, Vol. 458
W. Aoki, M. Ishigaki, T. Suda, T. Tsujimoto, N. Arimoto, eds.
©2012 Astronomical Society of the Pacific

The HERMES Project: Reconstructing Galaxy Formation

K.C. Freeman

RSAA, Australian National University, Mount Stromlo Observatory, Cotter Road, Weston Creek, Canberra, ACT 2611, Australia.

Abstract. The primary driver for the HERMES multi-object high resolution spectrometer on the AAT is a Galactic archaeology survey of about a million stars with $V < 14$. I will give a brief overview of the instrument, Galactic archaeology and chemical tagging, and then describe the goals and plans for the GALAH survey.

1. Introduction

HERMES is a new high-resolution fiber-fed multi-object spectrometer on the AAT. The spectral resolution is about 28,000, and there is also an $R = 45,000$ mode using a slit mask. The spectrometer is fed via about 400 fibres distributed over π square degrees of sky. It has four simultaneous non-contiguous spectral bands centered at $4800, 5761, 6610$ and 7740Å, covering a total of about 1000Å. First light is expected late in 2012. The main driver for the instrument is the GALAH survey (Galactic Archaeology with HERMES) with about 40 team members, mostly from Australian institutions. Many are here today in Shuzenji.

2. Galactic Archaeology

In Galactic archaeology, we seek signatures or fossils from the epoch of Galaxy formation, to give us insight about the processes that took place as the Galaxy formed. We would like to reconstruct the star-forming aggregates that built up the disk, bulge and halo of the Galaxy. Some of these dispersed aggregates can be still recognised kinematically as stellar moving groups. For most, however, their dynamical identity has been lost through disk heating and mixing processes, but they are still recognizable by their chemical signatures.

We would like to find the debris of groups of stars, now dispersed, that were associated at birth, either because they were born together in a single Galactic star-forming event, or because they came into the Milky Way from a common accreted dwarf galaxy. CDM theory predicts a high level of merger activity which conflicts with some observed properties of disk galaxies. A major goal of Galactic Archaeology is to evaluate how important mergers and accretion events were in building up the Galactic disk and the bulge.

The Galactic halo shows kinematical substructure which is believed to be the remains of accreted objects that built up the halo. The Galactic disk also shows kinematical substructure, usually called moving stellar groups. The stars of the moving groups are all around us: they are not identifiable as a concentration of stars on the sky, but only in velocity space. The groups appear as clumps in the (U, V) velocity space, where U is the radial component of a star's motion relative to the Local Standard of Rest, and V is the azimuthal component.

Some of the moving groups are generated by dynamical resonances with the Galactic bar or spiral structure. The Hercules moving group is an example: it is believed to be associated with local resonant kinematic disturbances by the inner bar (Dehnen 1999). Some moving groups are debris of star-forming aggregates in the disk (eg the HR1614 and Wolf 630 groups), which are now partly dispersed into extended regions of the Galaxy. Others may be debris of infalling objects, as seen in ΛCDM simulations: e.g. Abadi et al. (2003). The Arcturus group was believed to be an example (Navarro et al. 2004).

The nature of each moving group can be assessed from its chemical properties. For example, the chemical abundance distribution of the Hercules Group stars cannot be distinguished from those of the field stars (Bensby et al. 2007). This reinforces the identification of the Hercules Group as a dynamical (resonant) group, and not as the relic of a star forming event. On the other hand, the stars of the HR1614 moving group (coeval age $\sim$ 2 Gyr, [Fe/H] = +0.2) are chemically identical at the level of accuracy to which abundances can be measured. We know that the stars of open star clusters are chemically homogeneous, so the HR1614 group is probably the dispersed relic of an old star forming event (De Silva et al. 2007).

Although the disk does show some surviving kinematic substructure in the form of these moving stellar groups, a lot of dynamical information was lost in the heating and radial mixing by spiral arms and giant molecular clouds after their parent clusters were disrupted. Most dispersed aggregates would not now be recognizable dynamically. However, we are not restricted to dynamical techniques. Much fossil information is locked up in the detailed distribution of chemical elements in stars.

3. Chemical Tagging

The idea of chemical tagging is to use the detailed chemical abundances of stars to tag or associate them to common ancient star-forming aggregates with similar abundance patterns (e.g. Freeman & Bland-Hawthorn 2002). The detailed abundance patterns reflect the chemical evolution of the gas from which the aggregates formed.

Chemical studies of the old disk stars in the Galaxy can help to identify disk stars that are the debris of common dispersed star-forming aggregates, and also those that came in from outside in disrupting satellites. We expect that the debris of satellites will be recognizable by their chemical properties. The detailed abundance patterns of stars in surviving satellites (the dwarf spheroidal galaxies) vary from satellite to satellite, and are different from the overall patterns of the Galactic disk stars. The different evolution of element abundances reflects their different star formation histories.

With HERMES we expect to measure abundances of about 25 elements. We can think of a chemical space whose coordinates are the abundances of these elements. The elements do not all vary independently from star to star. Ting et al. (2011) showed that the number of independent dimensions of the chemical space is between 8 and 9. Most disk stars inhabit a sub-region of this C-space. Stars from chemically homogeneous aggregates, like disrupted open clusters in which the stars were born together, will lie in tight clumps in C-space[1]. Stars which came in from satellites may be different enough to stand out from the rest of the disk stars in chemical space.With this chemical tagging approach, we may be able to detect or put observational limits on the satellite accretion history of the galactic disk. Wylie-de Boer et al. (2010) have already used the chemical peculiarities of the globular cluster ω Centauri to identify metal-poor halo stars that were probably stripped from the cluster or its parent dwarf galaxy when it was accreted by the Milky Way.

For chemical tagging to work in reconstructing the star formation history of the disk, a few conditions are necessary:

- stars form in large aggregates. This is believed to be true

- aggregates are chemically homogenous

- aggregates have unique chemical signatures defined by several elements which do not vary in lockstep from one aggregate to another. A sufficient spread in abundances is needed from aggregate to aggregate so that chemical signatures can be distinguished with the achievable measurement accuracy (~ 0.05 dex differentially).

The last two conditions appear to be true: see De Silva et al. (2009) and Ting et al. (2011).

We note that chemical tagging is not just assigning stars chemically to a particular population (thin disk, thick disk, halo). Chemical tagging is intended to assign stars chemically to a common origin in substructure which is no longer detectable kinematically. Chemical tagging needs a high resolution spectroscopic survey of about a million stars, homogeneously observed and analysed: e.g. Bland-Hawthorn & Freeman (2004). This is a prime science driver for HERMES.

3.1. The Thick Disk

The Galactic thick disk could be particularly rewarding for chemical tagging. Thick disks are very common in other galaxies: they provide about 10% of the disk mass in large spirals, and their stars are old (> 8 Gyr) and moderately metal-poor. The formation of thick disks is not yet understood. Some possible formation routes include

- heating of the early stellar disk by accretion events or minor mergers

- stellar debris of ancient merger events

- star formation associated with early large gaseous accretion events

- dissolution of giant clumps in high-z galaxies

If the fourth option (giant clumps) is correct for the thick disk of our Galaxy, then we may be able to demonstrate this via chemical tagging.

Many high-z galaxies   (the clump cluster galaxies)   show massive starbursting clumps. These clumps have masses up to about 10^9 M$_\odot$ and star formation rates of up

---

[1] Although some authors prefer to use the term "chemical fingerprinting", we note that human siblings and even identical twins have different fingerprints.

to $\sim 20\,M_\odot\,yr^{-1}$: e.g. Genzel et al. (2011). These clumps are believed to be short-lived ($< 10^8$ yr) and may disperse to form the thick disk: e.g. Kroupa (2002) and Bournaud et al. (2009). If this is correct, the thick disk would have formed from a relatively small number of clumps. If these clumps were chemically homogenous (Bland-Hawthorn et al. 2010), then it would be fairly easy to identify the debris of a small number of homogeneous clumps from their distribution in chemical C-space.

4. Galactic Archaeology with HERMES

The GALAH survey is planned to give detailed chemical abundances for about 1.2×10^6 stars down to $V = 14$. At this magnitude, the stellar density matches the fiber density at intermediate galactic latitudes. The survey will cover half the southern sky at $|b| > 20$ in about 3000 pointings. At $V = 14$ and resolution $R = 28,000$, we expect a SNR of 100 per resolution element in about 60 minutes. This would be a bright time program, observing about 8 fields per night for 400 clear nights. The *Galaxia* Galaxy model and survey tool (Sharma et al. 2011) will be used to choose fields with high enough stellar density and low enough stellar reddening. The chemical pipeline by Wylie de Boer and Sneden will give spectroscopic stellar parameters and detailed abundances for about 25 elements (Li, C, O, Na, Al, K; Mg, Si, Ca, Ti; Sc, V, Cr, Mn, Fe, Co, N, Cu, Zn; Y, Zr, Ba, La, Nd, Eu). We expect that the sample of stars down to $V = 14$ will be about 78% thin disk stars (58% dwarfs, 20% giants), 17% thick disk stars (10, 7) and 5% halo stars (2, 3). The old disk dwarfs will lie within about 1 kpc of the sun, the old disk giants within about 5 kpc and the halo giants within 15 kpc.

About 9% of the Galactic thick disk stars and about 14% of the thin disk stars pass through our 1 kpc dwarf horizon. We now assume that the debris of all of their disrupted formation aggregates has azimuthally mixed right around the Galaxy, each in some annular zone, so that all of their formation sites are represented within our horizon. Simulations by Bland-Hawthorn & Freeman (2004) and Bland-Hawthorn et al. (2010) show that a complete random sample of 1.2×10^6 stars with $V < 14$ would allow detection of about 20 thick disk dwarfs from each of about 4,500 star formation sites, and about 10 thin disk dwarfs from each of about 35,000 star formation sites. We note that a smaller survey would mean less stars from a similar number of sites.

Is it possible to detect $\sim 35,000$ different disk sites using chemical tagging techniques? We believe so: about 7 independent chemical element groups would be needed, each with 5 measurable abundance levels, to get enough independent cells (5^7) in chemical space (4^8 would also do).

Are there 7 independent elements or element groups ? Yes: Ting et al. (2011) used principal component analysis techniques to make a detailed study of abundance patterns in existing abundance surveys of metal poor stars, metal rich stars, star clusters, and the Fornax dwarf spheroidal galaxy. They find that the dimensionality of chemical space is between 8 and 9. The number of independent components is similar for metal rich and metal poor stars, although the nature of the independent components is different because of the very different star formation history and chemical evolution of the metal rich and metal poor stars. In the context of earlier talks by Nomoto and by Kobayashi, it is interesting to note that both the metal rich and metal poor samples show a principal component involving the elements Mn and Cr.

For the open clusters, which cover a much larger range of galactocentric radii (from 6 to 20 kpc) than the mostly nearby stars analysed by Ting et al. (2011), the C-space has about one more dimension than for the metal-rich solar neighborhood stars. In the Fornax galaxy, the dimensionality of the C-space is again a little higher than for the halo and disk stars; one can see the effects of the slow star formation rate on the structure of the PCA components involving the light and heavy s-process elements that come from AGB stars of different masses.

It is possible to interpret the first few of the stronger principal components in terms of nucleosynthesis. For example, for the metal poor stars (excluding the carbon-enhanced stars), the first (strongest) component includes all of the n-capture elements and the alpha elements. It is probably related to core-collapse SN producing alpha elements plus the r-process contribution to n-capture elements. The second component shows an anticorrelation of alpha elements with Fe-peak and n-capture elements; it may be related to normal core-collapse SN which do not contribute to the r-process.

4.1. Chemical tagging in the Inner Galactic Disk

The old (> 1 Gyr) surviving open clusters are almost all in the outer Galaxy, beyond a radius of 8 kpc. Young open clusters are seen in the inner Galaxy but do not appear to survive for long against the interaction with the giant molecular clouds and the Galactic tidal field. We therefore expect to find the debris of many broken open (and globular) clusters in the inner disk. The GALAH sample will include about $200,000$ survey giants in the inner region of the Galaxy. These giants will be good for chemical tagging recovery of the disrupted clusters. The radial extent of the recovered debris for individual clusters of different ages should provide an acute test of radial mixing theory. We note also that the Na/O anticorrelation is ubiquitous and unique to globular clusters, and will help to identify the debris of disrupted globular clusters throughout the Galaxy.

5. HERMES and Gaia

The GALAH survey will benefit greatly from Gaia. For stars of $V = 14$, the Gaia parallax and proper motion precisions are about 10 μas and 10 μas yr^{-1} respectively. This is Gaia at its best; it corresponds to 1% distance errors at 1 kpc and 0.7 km s^{-1} velocity errors at 15 kpc. The HERMES radial velocity errors will also be < 1 km s^{-1}. When the Gaia data are available, we can expect to have accurate distances and 3-D velocities for all the stars in the GALAH survey sample. This will allow us to derive an accurate color-(absolute magnitude) diagram for all of the survey stars, providing an independent check that the chemically tagged groups of stars do in fact have common ages.

Acknowledgments. It is a pleasure to acknowledge collaborations with Joss Bland-Hawthorn and the contributions of the GALAH working groups. The HERMES instrument is under construction by the Australian Astronomical Observatory (AAO).

References

Abadi, M. G., Navarro, J. F., Steinmetz, M., & Eke, V. R. 2003, ApJ, 597, 21. arXiv: astro-ph/0212282

Bensby, T., Oey, M. S., Feltzing, S., & Gustafsson, B. 2007, ApJ, 655, L89. arXiv:astro-ph/0612658

Bland-Hawthorn, J., & Freeman, K. C. 2004, PASA, 21, 110. arXiv:astro-ph/0403700

Bland-Hawthorn, J., Karlsson, T., Sharma, S., Krumholz, M., & Silk, J. 2010, ApJ, 721, 582

Bournaud, F., Elmegreen, B. G., & Martig, M. 2009, ApJ, 707, L1. arXiv:astro-ph/0910.3677

De Silva, G. M., Freeman, K. C., & Bland-Hawthorn, J. 2009, PASA, 26, 11. arXiv:astroph/0810.2287

De Silva, G. M., Freeman, K. C., Bland-Hawthorn, J., Asplund, M., & Bessell, M. S. 2007, AJ, 133, 694. arXiv:astro-ph/0610041

Dehnen, W. 1999, ApJ, 524, L35. arXiv:astro-ph/9908105

Freeman, K., & Bland-Hawthorn, J. 2002, ARA&A, 40, 487. arXiv:astro-ph/0208106

Genzel, R., Newman, S., Jones, T., Förster Schreiber, N. M., Shapiro, K., Genel, S., Lilly, S. J., Renzini, A., Tacconi, L. J., Bouché, N., Burkert, A., Cresci, G., Buschkamp, P., Carollo, C. M., Ceverino, D., Davies, R., Dekel, A., Eisenhauer, F., Hicks, E., Kurk, J., Lutz, D., Mancini, C., Naab, T., Peng, Y., Sternberg, A., Vergani, D., & Zamorani, G. 2011, ApJ, 733, 101. arXiv:astro-ph/1011.5360

Kroupa, P. 2002, MNRAS, 330, 707. arXiv:astro-ph/0111175

Navarro, J. F., Helmi, A., & Freeman, K. C. 2004, ApJ, 601, L43. arXiv:astro-ph/0311107

Sharma, S., Bland-Hawthorn, J., Johnston, K. V., & Binney, J. 2011, ApJ, 730, 3. arXiv:astro-ph/1101.3561

Ting, Y., Freeman, K., Kobayashi, C., de Silva, G., & Bland-Hawthorn, J. 2011. arXiv:astro-ph/1112.3207

Wylie-de Boer, E., Freeman, K., & Williams, M. 2010, AJ, 139, 636. arXiv:astro-ph/0910.3735

Galactic Archaeology: Near-Field Cosmology and the Formation of the Milky Way
ASP Conference Series, Vol. 458
W. Aoki, M. Ishigaki, T. Suda, T. Tsujimoto, N. Arimoto, eds.
© 2012 Astronomical Society of the Pacific

Galactic Archaeology with Subaru: Prospects for Wide-Field Surveys

Masashi Chiba

Astronomical Institute, Tohoku University, Sendai 980-8578, Japan

Abstract. Having a very wide field of view at prime focus, Subaru is distinguished and uniquely positioned to do wide-field surveys for Galactic Archaeology (GA) science cases requiring its large aperture. Here we present our plan for such wide-field GA surveys using a wide-field imager, Hyper Suprime-Cam (HSC), and a wide-field multi-object spectrograph, Prime Focus Spectrograph (PFS). HSC will see first light in 2012. The basic concept of PFS has been approved in the Subaru community and its commissioning will be in around 2015. The primary scientific driver for both of these wide-field instruments is cosmology, but they will offer us important opportunities to conduct strategic GA surveys as well, especially in synergy with Gaia and other upcoming projects related to GA in the next decade.

1. Background

Unraveling how galaxies like the Milky Way, Andromeda and other Local Group galaxies formed in the expanding Universe is our ultimate science goal in near-field cosmology (Freeman & Bland-Hawthorn 2002), because such nearby galaxies offer us our most detailed views of galactic structure and evolution through their resolved stars. In particular, ancient galactic components such as extended thick disks and stellar halos provide invaluable information on early chemo-dynamical evolution of disk galaxies more than 10 billion years ago, i.e., well before luminous thin disk components appeared. For instance, stars spread over the vast reaches of the Milky Way halo are characterized by low metal abundance and high velocity dispersion. This extreme nature of halo stars compared to disk ones reflects the dynamical and chemical evolution of the Galaxy at early epochs when its appearance differed significantly from what we see today. In particular, recent growing observational evidence as provided by the Sloan Digital Sky Survey (SDSS) suggests that the halo may have formed, in part, from an assembly process of many subsystems, such as dwarf galaxies. Indeed, the idea of an assembly process for halo formation is in perfect accord with the modern theory of galaxy formation based on hierarchical clustering of sub-galactic building-block systems in the Cold Dark Matter (CDM) model. Thus, detailed studies of ancient stellar populations in the Milky Way and nearby galaxies provide us with important clues to understanding galaxy formation.

The Subaru 8.2-meter telescope, being distinguished for having the widest field of view at prime focus of all 8 to 10-meter class telescopes, is uniquely positioned to offer us wide-field studies of near-field cosmology requiring this large aperture. Further advantage of Subaru is that superb images better than 0.7 arcsec (FWHM) are routinely obtained, owing to the precision optics and mechanism built by Japanese firms. Here we introduce the currently developed instruments to be mounted on the prime focus of Subaru, HSC and PFS, and describe primary GA science subjects to be explored with these wide field of view imager and spectrograph in the next decade.

2. HSC

2.1. Summary of HSC

HSC is an upgrade prime focus camera of Suprime-Cam, where the latter has played a leading role in wide-field imaging astronomy since Subaru started its operation. The field size of HSC is expanded nearly 10 times larger than that of Suprime-Cam while maintaining its equivalent image quality. This camera will thus offer us great opportunities to explore unique and legacy surveys including GA science cases.

Main characteristics of HSC are summarized as follows.

☐ Funding started in 2006 (PI: H. Karoji).

☐ Developed based on international collaboration: Japan (NAOJ, IPMU, Tokyo, Tohoku, Nagoya), Princeton and Taiwan.

☐ Field of view is 1.77 deg^2 (1.5 deg in diameter), which corresponds to about 10 times larger than FOV of Suprime-Cam.

☐ Pixel scale: 0.17 arcsec/pix.

☐ Filters: grizy broad-band and several narrow-band filters.

☐ First light is scheduled in 2012.

2.2. GA with HSC

We are now preparing for the plan of a HSC imaging survey of Galactic and Andromeda stars in the framework of either the HSC/Subaru strategic proposal or other PI-led programs to be undertaken in 2012-2016. Our proposed HSC survey will be two-fold:

1. The Milky Way halo survey: searching new faint dwarf satellites and halo substructures in the outer part of the Galactic halo over 1,500 to 2,000 deg^2 of the sky with (g, r, i) down to ~ 26 mag, i.e., 3 mag fainter than SDSS. This survey fully utilizes the wide-field survey data of HSC dedicated to the weak-lensing science case.

2. The M31 halo survey: mapping Andromeda's stellar halo over ~ 200 deg^2, based on the separation of bright red giants with (g, r, i) of < 22.5 mag from foreground Galactic dwarfs using a narrow-band filter NB515.

Our primary aim of the Milky Way halo survey is to discover new faint dwarf satellites in the outer part of the Milky Way halo by identifying their main-sequence turn-off (MSTO) stars and also new halo stellar streams based on MSTO and brighter red giant branch (RGB) stars. We note that the known Galactic satellites are located at radii from 30 kpc (Ursa Major II) to 250 kpc (Leo I), thus we expect the MSTO stars of new satellites in the range of $g = 21.0 \sim 25.5$ mag. An exquisite image quality of

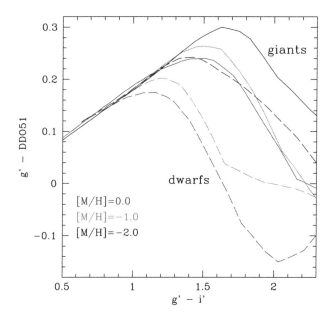

Figure 1.   Color-color diagram of $g' - DDO51$ (where $DDO51$ mag denotes a magnitude derived from our NB515 filter) vs. $g' - i'$ to distinguish giants (solid curve) from dwarfs (dashed curve). Metallicity [M/H] for each curve is 0.0, −1.0 and −2.0 from bottom to top. This plot is made in collaboration with Mikito Tanaka.

HSC will thus enable us to identify yet missing, ~ 20 or more faint satellites as well as some 3 to 4 new stellar streams and additional ~ 10 faint streams associated with tidal debris of Galactic globular clusters over the proposed survey area of 1,500 to 2,000 deg^2. Also, this imaging survey provides us with basic photometric data including $g - r$ colors for PFS follow-up observations as described below.

The M31 halo survey is dedicated to mapping bright RGB stars in the M31 halo, similarly to the PAndAS survey (Richardson et al. 2011), but our survey will be distinguished by the use of a newly designed narrow-band filter (NB515 filter with CW = 5145 Å and BW = 80 Å). This NB515 filter covers a series of magnesium hydride absorption lines which are sensitive to surface gravity; these lines are strong in dwarfs and weak in giants, thus enabling us efficiently to remove the Galactic dwarfs in the foreground and to derive the intrinsic halo structures of M31 (Figure 1). Thus, these imaging samples will become an important source of targets in our PFS survey as described below.

3.   PFS

3.1.   Summary of PFS

The PFS concept reflects the previously planned Wide Field Multi-Object Spectrograph (WFMOS) in collaboration with the Gemini community, which was eventually canceled by the Gemini board in 2009 because of mounting cost for it. The idea of a

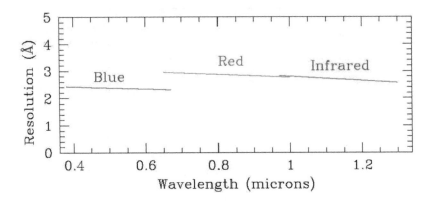

Figure 2.   Design resolution for each of the three arms of the PFS (taken from the PFS white paper released in 2011).

wide-field spectrograph for Subaru had continued even after the cancelation of WF-MOS, and in 2009 a proposal for developing this type of instrument was approved, which is actually based on the joint project using both HSC and PFS, named SUbaru Measurement of Images and REdshifts ("SUMIRE", the Japanese word for "violet").

Main characteristics of PFS are summarized as follows.

☐ Funding started in 2010 (PI: H. Murayama).

☐ Developed based on international collaboration: all Japan (led by IPMU, University of Tokyo), Caltech/JPL, Princeton, JHU, LAM, UK, Brazil and Taiwan.

☐ Field of view is 1.3 deg in diameter.

☐ Number of fibers: 2400.

☐ Spectrograph: 3-arm design to cover 0.38-1.3 μm simultaneously, i.e., blue (3800-6700 Å), red (6500-10000 Å) and IR arms (9700-13000 Å). The current design is based on the resolution of $\Delta\lambda = 2.5$ to 3.0 Å (see Figure 2).

☐ Upgrade plan to a higher-resolution mode for GA science is under discussion.

☐ First light: tentatively scheduled in 2016.

3.2. GA with PFS

Our primary science goal with PFS is to clarify the formation history of galactic structures, especially in light of the hierarchical merging scenario of the CDM model. Resolved ancient stars in Local Group galaxies including the Milky Way are ideal targets for this study, because such stars hold fossil records of galaxy formation through their kinematics and chemical abundances. Kinematics of stars reflect past galaxy collapse and/or merging events, as their relaxation time via two-body stellar encounters is quite long compared to galaxy life, so that their distribution in phase space (as defined by

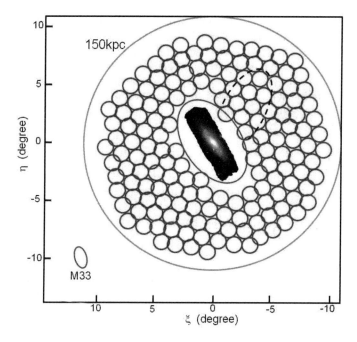

Figure 3. Proposed PFS pointings in the M31 halo over ~ 200 deg^2. Dashed line denotes the position of a narrow stellar stream discovered in the NW part of the halo.

integrals of motion such as angular momentum) remains basically unchanged. Chemical abundances of stars reflect star-formation history and chemical evolution over past years, possibly in association with dynamical state of proto-galactic clouds such as their collision and merging. Also, all of these processes are controlled by hierarchical clustering of CDM via self-gravity in galaxy scales. Thus, to assess what the CDM model predicts, it is of great importance to unravel the spatial distribution of dark-matter halos in the Galaxy. In this respect, stars are ideal tracers of the background gravitational field, provided that their full space motions are available, combined with precise measurements of distances and proper motions by Gaia. All of these requirements are indeed feasible with the planned PFS.

Our proposed PFS survey is summarized as follows:

1. The Milky Way survey: primary targets in this survey consists of two samples: (i) the Gaia sample and (ii) the Stream sample. For the Gaia sample with $V < 20$ mag, the survey is aimed at measuring radial velocities and metal abundances for millions of stars in synergy with the Gaia astrometric observations. For the Stream sample, we target the stars associated with halo substructures in the form of stellar streams (Sagittarius Stream and Orphan Stream) and those in the outskirts of some Galactic dwarf spheroidal galaxies, with magnitude limit of $V < 21.5$ mag.

2. The M31 halo survey: primary targets in this survey are bright red giants with $V \sim 21.5$ mag, i.e., stars around the tip of red giant branch, in the vast area of

the M31 halo (Figure 3). The pre-imaging observations and selection of targets will be provided by HSC/NB515 survey. This survey is aimed at identifying a general halo component, several stream-like features and their chemo-dynamical properties, by means of separation of genuine halo stars through spectrographic observations. In particular, identifying and separating stars in the NW stream will set important limits on the abundance of orbiting CDM subhalos through the density distribution along the stream (See Carlberg's contribution in this volume).

4. Further prospects

In addition to HSC and PFS, the Subaru community is planning to develop a next-generation Adaptive Optics (AO) instrument, possibly in the form of either Ground-Layer AO or Multi-Object AO. This will offer us important capabilities to study dense stellar systems in the Galactic disk and bulge. Also, Japanese astronomical community is going to join the Thirty Meter Telescope (TMT). For the purpose of distributing the importance of TMT inside Japan, the domestic TMT project office organized five science working groups to address key science subjects with TMT in each field of research. Our group led by W. Aoki covered "Stars and the Local Group" and summarized key science goals in the framework of (i) Exploring stellar activities and explosions and (ii) Clarifying galaxy formation with resolved stars. The combination of TMT with Subaru will provide the unique and legacy data in the field of GA.

Discussion

Martin: Will it be possible to quickly shift between the instruments (HSC and PFS)?

Chiba: Probably not. But actually PFS will be commissioning after the main survey using HSC is completed, namely in 2016. So, this quick shift between HSC and PFS would not be required.

Bland-Hawthorn: We were all greatly saddened by the events at Sendai. We wish you every success in getting life back to normal. I would like to ask what is the driving design of the PFS instruments, near field or far field cosmology?

Chiba: The main science driver of the PFS is far field cosmology. However, since the instrument is found to be useful for other science cases including near field cosmology, the design of the spectrograph has been carefully examined to match several science requirements.

Andersen: In 2005 the European funding agencies formed ASTRONET to introduce coordination in European astronomy including now to specialize the 2-8m telescopes on the most challenging problems. This is now happening on a global scale – great!

References

Freeman, K., & Bland-Hawthorn, J. 2002, ARA&A, 40, 487. arXiv:astro-ph/0208106
Richardson, J. C., Irwin, M. J., McConnachie, A. W., Martin, N. F., Dotter, A. L., Ferguson, A. M. N., Ibata, R. A., Chapman, S. C., Lewis, G. F., Tanvir, N. R., & Rich, R. M. 2011, ApJ, 732, 76. 1102.2902

Galactic Archaeology: Near-Field Cosmology and the Formation of the Milky Way
ASP Conference Series, Vol. 458
W. Aoki, M. Ishigaki, T. Suda, T. Tsujimoto, N. Arimoto, eds.
©2012 Astronomical Society of the Pacific

The LAMOST Spectroscopic Survey of Milky Way Stars (LEGUE)

Heidi Jo Newberg,[1] Jeffrey L. Carlin,[1] Li Chen,[2] Licai Deng,[3] Sébastien Lépine,[4] Xiaowei Liu,[5,6] Fan Yang,[3] Hai-Bo Yuan,[5] Haotong Zhang,[3] Yueyang Zhang,[3] the LEGUE Working Group and the LAMOST-PLUS Partnership

[1] *Physics Department, Rensselaer Poly. Inst., 110 8th Street, Troy, NY 12180, USA heidi@rpi.edu*

[2] *Shanghai Astronomical Observatory, Chinese Academy of Sciences, 80 Nandan Road, Shanghai, 200030, China*

[3] *National Astronomical Observatories, Chinese Academy of Sciences, 20A Datun Road, Chaoyang District, Beijing, 100012, China*

[4] *Division of Physical Sciences, Department of Astrophysics, American Museum of Natural History, Central Park West at 79th Street, New York, NY 10024, USA*

[5] *Department of Astronomy, Peking University, Beijing 100871, China*

[6] *Kavli Institute for Astronomy and Astrophysics, Peking University, Beijing 100871, China*

Abstract. The Guo Shoujing Telescope (GSJT, formerly LAMOST) pilot survey started in October 2011 and will run through April 2012. We report on the footprint and selection algorithms for the stellar portion of the survey (LEGUE).

1. The Guo Shuojing Telescope

The Guo Shoujing Telescope (GSJT, formerly the Large Sky Area Multi-Object Fiber Spectroscopic Telescope, LAMOST) project is one of the National Major Scientific Projects undertaken by the Chinese Academy of Science. LAMOST is a 4m class telescope with 4000 fibers in a 5° field of view (Wang et al. 1996; Su et al. 1998; Xing et al. 1998; Zhu et al. 2006; Su & Cui 2004; Wu et al. 2011). Spectra of objects as faint as 20m.5 will be obtained in 1.5 hours. The scientific survey is planned to start in late 2012. More information can be found at http://www.lamost.org/website/en/ and http://www.lamost.us/.

2. The Pilot Survey

A pilot survey was begun October 24, 2011, and will run through April 2012, using most of the available observing time during that period. A smaller part of the time is devoted to engineering tests to improve the system performance, in particular the fiber positioning and temperature control (dome seeing) are contributing to current performance that is below what is required for the final system. The pilot survey includes targets selected by both the Lamost ExtraGAlactic Survey (LEGAS) and the Lamost Experiment for Galactic Understanding and Exploration (LEGUE) working groups. There are also separate input target lists for clear, dark nights and for nights that either have poor transparency or brighter moon. The target selection in the pilot survey approximates the algorithms we expect to use in regular survey operations, including different selection criteria for stars in different regions of the Galaxy.

Figure 1 shows the area of the sky from which faint and bright pilot survey targets will be selected. The survey regions were chosen to cover a large range of right ascension, so that there will be fields to observe at all times of the night, during the entire observing season. The declination range was chosen because the telescope performance is good near $\delta = 30°$ or to cover a particularly interesting region of the sky. The middle panel of Figure 1 shows the typical number of hours of good observing per night as a function of season of the year. The seasons have been lined up with the plot of sky coverage to show which parts of the sky are up at which times. Remember that the Guo Shoujing Telescope can only operate near the meridian.

3. Target Selection Algorithms

The LEGAS (extragalactic) targets included color-selected QSO candidates, and galaxies with $17.5 < r < 18$. This magnitude range pushes slightly fainter than SDSS. Unused fibers are placed on stars using the spheroid selection algorithm.

Spheroid (blue, red and yellow faint regions): We use a weighting function in r, $(g - r)$, and $(r - i)$ to randomly select 600 stars per sq. degree (three times the LAMOST fiber density), to a limiting magnitude of $r < 19.5$. The first stars selected have priority 1, and the last stars selected have priority 80. Since we select a higher fraction of rare stars, and therefore run out of rare stars before the selection is finished, the priority 1 stars include more rare stars and are placed on the plate design with higher priority. The plate design algorithm needs three times as many stars as will be eventually targetted in order to fill all of the fibers, but we want to assign the rare stars with higher priority since we want to target more than a third of these stars. In the blue region, we additionally select stars with the colors and apparent magnitude of the halo stellar stream GD-1 (Grillmair & Dionatos 2006). These are targetted with the highest priority, zero.

Anticenter (green faint region): Stars in this region of the sky were selected from the Xuyi Schmidt Photometric Survey. This survey covers over five thousand square degrees near the Galactic anticenter, including M31 and the Triangulum Pinwheel Galaxy, in SDSS g, r, and i. We divide stars by magnitude ($14 < i < 16, 16 < i < 18, 18 < i < 19$). For each magnitude range, we select a uniform distribution in i, $(g - i)$ space (if possible). Since there are multiple fields selected at each sky position, the first plates selected might have a uniform distribution of stars in color and magnitude, and plates selected later might have more stars in more common regions of the color-magnitude diagram. The exposure time is longer for the fainter plates than the brighter plates.

M31 (cyan region): Special objects around M31 and the Triangulum Pinwheel Galaxy are observed, including QSOs, planetary nebulae, globular clusters, etc.

Disk (magenta bright region): We select stars with $11.3 < I < 16.3, -1.5 < (B - I) < 4.5$ from the PPMXL proper motion catalog. Stars that are members of

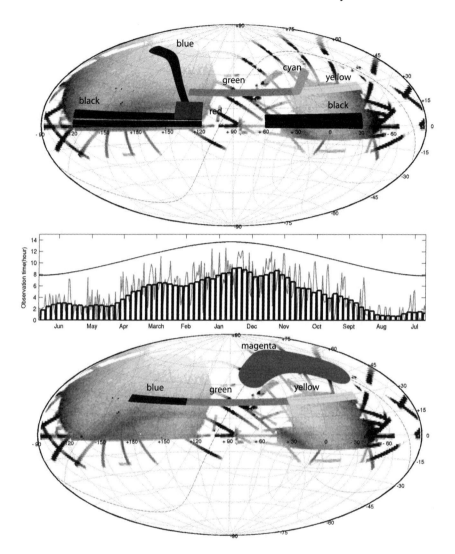

Figure 1. The Guo Shoujing Pilot Survey footprint. The top panel shows the footprint for faint plates taken on clear, dark nights. The bottom panel shows the footprint for bright plates taken in bright moon or low atmospheric transparency. The central panel shows the average number of hours of clear weather, averaged over a four year period, as a function of day of the year. The black stripes on the Celestial equator are the LEGAS portion of the survey, though stars are selected on any unused fibers (typically half of the fibers on each plate) using the spheroid target selection. The spheroid target selection is used for black, dark blue, red and yellow areas. Faint plates in the yellow region will only be observed if there are no LEGAS fields available. The anticenter target selection is used in the green region. The target selection in the cyan region is designed for early science on M31, targeting QSOs, planetary nebulae, globular clusters, etc. Disk target selection is used in the magenta region. Note that the best weather is when the Galactic anticenter is near the meridian, and the Galactic center is virtually unobservable from GSJT.

open clusters are given the highest priority in targetting (typically < 100 targets per plate, with more than one open cluster on each plate). Cluster stars must be more than 5" from another star; field stars must be > 6" from another star. The proper motion limit is PM< 100 mas/yr. Each plate is observed five times, including three bright (11.3 < I < 14.3) and three faint (14.3 < I < 16.3) pointings.

Bright Spheroid (blue and yellow bright regions): Bright survey targets were selected from 2MASS JHK magnitudes. We supplemented the catalogs with SDSS stars having (g < 16, r < 16, i < 16, *or* z < 16) that are not in 2MASS.

4. Results

There are already 255 abstracts on the NASA ADS that refer to LAMOST. Most are technical papers, but a few are science results from commissioning data. Results include discoveries of planetary nebulae, discoveries of QSOs, and a study of stellar populations in the Andromeda galaxy. Given the much larger number of stars and better quality of the pilot survey data, we expect more early science results in the coming year. The LEGUE survey will use similar target selection algorithms and produce a catalog of millions of Galactic stars.

Discussion

Bland-Hawthorn: Does the 2° rise in temperature due to the 8000 motors [in the focal plane] degrade the seeing?

Newberg: Yes. It might also change the fiber positions. These issues are being addressed.

Acknowledgments.   Guoshoujing Telescope (the Large Sky Area Multi-Object Fiber Spectroscopic Telescope LAMOST) is a National Major Scientific Project built by the Chinese Academy of Sciences. Funding for the project has been provided by the National Development and Reform Commission. LAMOST is operated and managed by the National Astronomical Observatories, Chinese Academy of Sciences. Work on the input catalog was supported by the National Astronomical Observatory of China, and also by NSF grant AST-09-37523, and NSFC grants 10973015, 11061120454, and 11073038.

References

Grillmair, C. J., & Dionatos, O. 2006, ApJ, 643, L17. arXiv:astro-ph/0604332
Su, D. Q., Cui, X., Wang, Y., & Yao, Z. 1998, in Society of Photo-Optical Instrumentation Engineers (SPIE) Conference Series, edited by L. M. Stepp, 3352, 76
Su, D.-Q., & Cui, X.-Q. 2004, Chinese Journal of Astronomy & Astrophysics, 4, 1
Wang, S.-G., Su, D.-Q., Chu, Y.-Q., Cui, X., & Wang, Y.-N. 1996, Appl.Optics, 35, 5155
Wu, Y. et al. 2011, Research in Astronomy and Astrophysics, 11, 924. 1105.2681
Xing, X., Zhai, C., Du, H., Li, W., Hu, H., Wang, R., & Shi, D. 1998, in Society of Photo-Optical Instrumentation Engineers (SPIE) Conference Series, edited by L. M. Stepp, 3352, 839
Zhu, Y. et al. 2006, in Society of Photo-Optical Instrumentation Engineers (SPIE) Conference Series, 6269

Galactic Archaeology: Near-Field Cosmology and the Formation of the Milky Way
ASP Conference Series, Vol. 458
W. Aoki, M. Ishigaki, T. Suda, T. Tsujimoto, N. Arimoto, eds.
© *2012 Astronomical Society of the Pacific*

SkyMapper and Galactic Archaeology

Stefan C. Keller,[1] and the SkyMapper and AEGIS teams

[1] *Research School of Astronomy and Astrophysics, Australian National University*

Abstract. We briefly outline the SkyMapper Southern Sky Survey and its use in the development of a series of programs designed to constrain the structure and evolution of the Milky Way. The coming decade will see a number of large programs for galactic archaeology, amongst them the HERMES program and the Gaia-ESO survey. Through a unique filter set optimised for stellar astrophysics, SkyMapper will provide input to the observing plans of both major programs. In these proceedings we demonstrate with follow-up spectroscopy of metal-poor star candidates the ability of SkyMapper to find these rare targets.

1. Introduction

SkyMapper a 1.3m survey telescope with a digital camera providing a 5.7 square degree field of view. It has been built and is operated by the Australian National University from Siding Spring Observatory. It is an automated facility that pursues a nightly observation plan and delivers the obtained data the next day for processing on ANU campus. It has been in commissioning operation since July 2011. The data we report on in these proceedings are based upon these early commissioning data. Over the next five years of operation, SkyMapper will conduct the Southern Sky Survey, the first digital optical map of the southern sky. The survey will image the entire southern sky in six colors and six times in each color. The expected survey limits will be similar to those of the Sloan Digital Sky Survey (SDSS, York et al. 2000).

The focal plane of the imager consists of a mosaic of 32 2048×4096 pixel CCDs manufactured by E2V. This provides a 268-mega pixel camera. Each pixel projects to 0.5" on sky providing sky coverage of 2.3 degrees on each side. The pixel scale of 0.5" is appropriate for the seeing typically obtained at the site (median seeing of 1.5"). We have utilized the detector controller technology from the University of Hawaii's Pan-STARRS program. This allows us to readout the array in 15 seconds.

2. A survey optimized for stellar astrophysics

Figure 1 shows a comparison of the filter set from SkyMapper and SDSS surveys. In devising the filter set for SkyMapper we sought to find a series of filters that enable us to optimally resolve the fundamental stellar characteristics (namely, temperature, surface gravity, and metallicity) with the minimal number of filters. Our filter set shows three modifications over the SDSS design. We have truncated the red side of the u filter

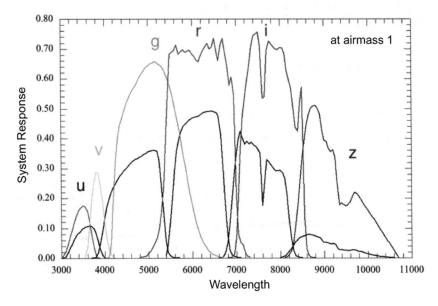

Figure 1.   The filter set of SkyMapper compared to that of the Sloan Digital Sky Survey.

and the blue side of the g filter and interposed an intermediate bandpass filter v. As shown in our program summary (Keller et al. 2007), the u and v filters are either side of the Balmer Jump and provide superior surface gravity sensitivity. These two filters also provide a measure of metal line blanketing of the continuum that gives SkyMapper improved metallicity sensitivity at spectral types F-K.

2.1. Demonstration: finding metal-poor stars

In Figure 2 we show preliminary data from SkyMapper (it is uncalibrated in an absolute sense). In this color-color diagram we see raw $(g-i)$, representing temperature, plotted against raw $(v-g)$, which measures the level of line blanketing due to the stellar metallicity. The lower the metallicity of a star the bluer its $(v-g)$ color. This SkyMapper field has also been the target of intermediate resolution spectroscopy with AAOmega on the Anglo-Australian Telescope. These spectra have been analysed to determine metallicity by Melissa Ness (see these proceedings) and are shown as the bold colored circles in the figure. The metallicity discrimination of SkyMapper's filter set is clear:- we can discern metal-poor stars of [Fe/H]< −2 within these galactic bulge fields.

3. SkyMapper: supporting Galactic archaeological efforts

3.1. The Aaomega Evolution of GalactIc Structure (AEGIS) survey

We are carrying out a long term program of multi-object spectroscopy at the Anglo-Australian Telescope (AAT) following up on SkyMapper detections of key indicators of Galactic structure and evolution. The AEGIS survey uses SkyMapper candidate

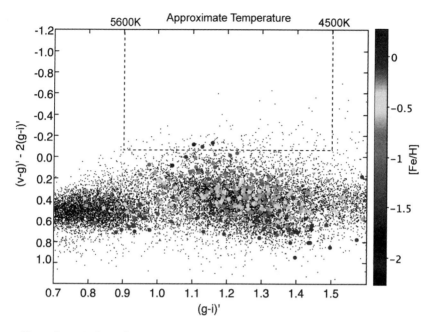

Figure 2.   (color online) A color-color diagram for one SkyMapper field directed towards the Galactic bulge. The small points show the position of stars within the SkyMapper field of view. Spectra for small subset of stars in this field have been analysed by Melissa Ness (these proceedings). The metallicities derived are shown as colored circles. This demonstrates our ability to draw metal-poor stars from within very crowded fields.

extremely metal-poor stars, blue horizontal branch stars, red clump, and K giant stars as input to the 392 fibre MOS, AAOmega. The goals for AEGIS are to explore the low metallicity tail of the halo and the thick disk. It will provide radial velocities and abundances for on order 50,000 stars with which to explore the extent and substructure of the halo and to constrain formation scenarios for the thick disk.

3.2.   The HERMES Galactic Archaeology (GALAH) program

HERMES is the Australian Astronomical Observatory's headline new instrumentation. It is expected to be commissioned in the later quarter of 2012. It will seek to observe at high spectral resolution, of the order of 1 million stars in the thin and thick disk. The goals are elucidated by Freeman in these proceedings. The input catalog is derived from the 2MASS point source catalog (Skrutskie et al. 2006) and is designed to avoid metallicity bias. It is hoped that SkyMapper photometry will expedite the analysis of these spectra by supplying temperature, surface gravity and metallicity priors.

3.3.   The Gaia-ESO survey

The Gaia-ESO survey was established by a large consortium of astronomers, largely from Europe. This survey has been allocated 300 nights over three years to conduct multi-object spectroscopy of stars in the bulge, disk (open clusters), thick disk, and halo using GIRAFFE/UVES on VLT. SkyMapper will supplement the input catalog for Gaia-ESO (which is unbiased in terms of metallicity) with spatially rare targets that are key for studies of galactic structure and evolution. These objects, metal-poor stars, blue horizontal branch, and K giant stars, will account for up to 20% of the targets in a Gaia-ESO field.

Discussion

Grillmair: Will the observations in the Galactic plane be subject to special handling?

Keller: Yes, we understand that we will reach confusion limits sooner there so we will be aiming for a brighter limit in the galactic plane regions of $g \sim 19 - 20$.

References

Keller, S.C. et al. 2007, Pub. Astron. Soc. Australia, 24, 1.
Skrutskie, M.F. et al. 2006, AJ, 131, 1163.
York, D.G. et al. 2000, AJ, 120, 1579.

Galactic Archaeology: Near-Field Cosmology and the Formation of the Milky Way
ASP Conference Series, Vol. 458
W. Aoki, M. Ishigaki, T. Suda, T. Tsujimoto, N. Arimoto, eds.
© *2012 Astronomical Society of the Pacific*

SkyMapper and AEGIS: Tracing the Structure and Evolution of the Galaxy

A. R. Casey,[1] S. C. Keller,[1] M. K. Ness,[1] the AEGIS collaboration, and the SkyMapper team.

[1]*Research School of Astronomy & Astrophysics, Australian National University, Mount Stromlo Observatory via Cotter Road, Weston, ACT 2611, Australia.*

Abstract. The AAOmega Evolution of Galactic Structure (AEGIS) program aims to constrain the chemodynamical evolution of the Milky Way through the study of the halo and the outer thick disk. The AEGIS survey will determine the metal content, kinematics and chemical abundance ratios for 70,000 stars over 4,900 deg^2 using the AAOmega multi-object spectrograph on the 3.9m Australian Astronomical Telescope. With such a vast survey area, AEGIS benefits by allocating fibres to very rare high impact classes of objects such as globular cluster tidal tails, white dwarfs, hyper-velocity stars, QSOs, and extremely metal-poor (EMP) stars. Here we present the progress of the AEGIS survey and highlight the efficiency in using SkyMapper photometry to select rare EMP candidates.

1. The AEGIS Survey: Key Science Goals

The AEGIS survey will address three specific questions about the formation and evolution of the Milky Way disk and halo system:

- **The contribution of substructure:** What fraction of halo and thick disk stars were accreted in mergers, and how does this vary as a function of Galactocentric radius?

- **Characterising substructure:** What were the masses, star formation histories of accreted systems, and for how long did these systems undergo isolated chemical evolution?

- **The formation and evolution of the thick disk:** What is the importance of dynamical heating from accretion in the formation of the thick disk? How do secular evolution, radial migration, and early in situ star formation create/modify metallicity and [alpha/Fe] gradients in the thick disk?

In order to address the key science goals of AEGIS effectively, diagnostic classes of old stellar populations are targeted. SkyMapper commissioning photometry is used to accurately select these populations for the AEGIS program and identify rare, high-impact objects.

2. Identifying EMP candidate stars using SkyMapper photometry

The SkyMapper telescope has a unique filter set which has been designed for stellar astrophysics (Keller et al. 2007). SkyMapper will perform the Southern Sky Survey; imaging the entire southern sky over multiple epochs in six filters. SkyMapper is currently in commissioning phase and is regularly taking preliminary scientific data. SkyMapper's capability in efficiently identifying extremely metal-poor stars is shown in Figure 1.

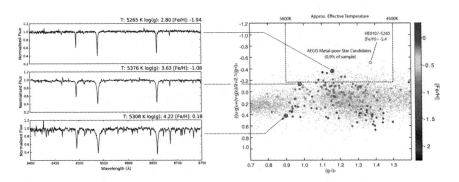

Figure 1. SkyMapper photometry (right) with a subset coloured by their spectroscopically determined abundances (Ness et al 2012, in prep.) and selected spectra (left).

This diagram combines SkyMapper photometry and spectroscopically-determined metallicities for giants in the Galactic bulge (Ness et al 2012, in prep.). The spectroscopic metallicity is tightly correlated with the preliminary SkyMapper metallicity index, $((u - g)_0 + (v - g)_0)/2 + 2.1(g - i)_0$. The ultra metal-poor star HE0107-5240 with [Fe/H] $= -5.4$ (Christlieb et al. 2002) is illustrated and falls well within the AEGIS metal-poor star selection criteria. The stars shown within the selection box in Figure 1 represent only 0.9% of the total AEGIS metal-poor star candidates.

3. Observing Progress

The AEGIS program has been allocated 45 nights on the AAT over three semesters, concluding in 2012B. As of November 2011 with two observing runs complete, 26 fields (13%) have been spectroscopically observed and data analysis is underway.

References

Christlieb, N., Bessell, M. S., Beers, T. C., Gustafsson, B., Korn, A., Barklem, P. S., Karlsson, T., Mizuno-Wiedner, M., & Rossi, S. 2002, Nature, 419, 904
Keller, S. C., Schmidt, B. P., Bessell, M. S., Conroy, P. G., Francis, P., Granlund, A., Kowald, E., Oates, A. P., Martin-Jones, T., Preston, T., Tisserand, P., Vaccarella, A., & Waterson, M. F. 2007, PASA, 24, 1

Galactic Archaeology: Near-Field Cosmology and the Formation of the Milky Way
ASP Conference Series, Vol. 458
W. Aoki, M. Ishigaki, T. Suda, T. Tsujimoto, N. Arimoto, eds.
© 2012 Astronomical Society of the Pacific

Design and Capabilities of the AAT/HERMES Spectrograph

G.M. De Silva,[1] J. Heijmans,[1] L. Gers,[1] D. Zucker,[1,2] and
the AAO HERMES team

[1]*Australian Astronomical Observatory*

[2]*Macquarie University*

Abstract. The High Efficiency and Resolution Multi-Element spectrograph (HERMES) currently under construction at the Australian Astronomical Observatory will be the next major instrument for the Anglo-Australian Telescope. It will provide a unique and powerful new facility for multi-object spectroscopy. HERMES uses the 2dF fibre positioning system to provide up to 392 multiplex capability over a 2 degree field of view. The spectrograph design includes 4 wavelength channels, each with VPH-gratings providing a nominal spectral resolving power of 28,000 and a high-resolution mode of 50,000. The initial wavelength channels are tailored for determining a large range of chemical elements suitable for chemical tagging, but allow for grating upgrades reconfigurable between 370 - 1000 nm. An overview of the project and expected performance based on the HERMES simulated data is presented.

1. Introduction

The HERMES Spectrograph is the next major instrument for the 3.9m Anglo-Australian Telescope (AAT), currently under construction at the Australian Astronomical Observatory (AAO). It will provide a unique and powerful new facility for high resolution multi-object spectroscopy. HERMES is expected to be available for science use in 2013.

2. Overview of spectrograph design

HERMES uses the existing 2dF robotic fibre positioning facility of the AAT to provide up to 392 multiple capability (plus 8 guide fibres) over a 2 degree field of view, with each fibre covering 2 arcsecs on sky. 2dF currently feeds the low resolution AAOmega spectrograph. An improved throughput fibre feed, with dual fibre buttons will connect 2dF to both HERMES and AAOmega spectrographs.

The 4 channel design of HERMES includes an off-axis collimator and three beam splitters. The useable wavelength in each channel is 370-502nm in the Blue, 560-593nm in the Green, 643-679nm in the Red, and 754 - 1000nm in the Red and Infrared channel. Each channel has a VPH-grating operated at a high angle of incidence (67deg) providing a nominal spectral resolution of 28,000. Higher resolution of $\approx$ 50,000 can be achieved using a slit-mask with approximately 50% light loss. Each channel has four

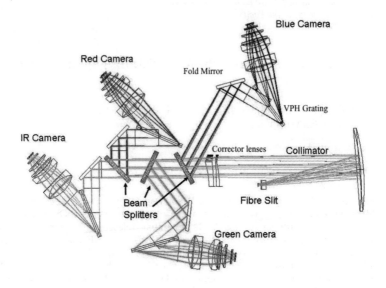

Figure 1.   The four channel optical design of the AAT/HERMES spectrograph.

cameras optimized for the respective wavelengths.

With the current grating configurations, the observable wavelengths in each channel are 470-489nm in the Blue, 564 - 587nm in the Green, 648 - 674nm in the Red and 759-789nm in the IR channel. These wavelength regions were selected in order observe spectral lines of a large range of chemical elements, that includes light (Li), odd-z (Na, Al), alpha (O, Mg, Si, Ca, Ti), Fe-peak (Cr, Mn, Fe, Co, Ni, Zn), light s-process (Y, Zr), heavy s-process (Ba, La) and r-process (Eu) elements. The spectrograph design allows for grating and beamsplitter upgrades in order to observe other wavelength regions.

3.   HERMES Detectors

HERMES detectors are 4K x 4K grade o devices by E2V, with peak quantum efficiencies between 85 - 93 %. A bulk silicone device will be used for the IR channel to minimize fringing. The AAO in-house built controllers allow a combination of ultra-fast, fast, normal, and slow readout using 1-4 amplifiers. Normal readout time using 2 amplifiers is ~ 140sec, with a gain of 1.8 and readout noise of 3e.

4.   Data Simulator results

The HERMES Data Simulator software generates detector images incorporating the atmosphere, telescope, fibre feed, spectrograph and detector specifications. Based on the simulator, one hour exposure of a V = 14 magnitude solar-type star provides spectra with a signal to noise ratio of ~100 in the Blue channel, and higher in the other channels.

Galactic Archaeology: Near-Field Cosmology and the Formation of the Milky Way
ASP Conference Series, Vol. 458
W. Aoki, M. Ishigaki, T. Suda, T. Tsujimoto, N. Arimoto, eds.
© *2012 Astronomical Society of the Pacific*

Infrared Space Astrometry Missions ~ JASMINE Missions ~

Naoteru Gouda

National Astronomical Observatory of Japan, 2-21-1 Osawa, Mitaka, Tokyo
181-8588, Japan

Abstract. "JASMINE" is an abbreviation of Japan Astrometry Satellite Mission for Infrared Exploration. Three satellites are planned as a series of JASMINE missions, as a step-by-step approach, to overcome technical issues and promote scientific results. These are Nano-JASMINE, Small-JASMINE and (medium-sized) JASMINE. JASMINE missions provide the positions and proper motions of celestial objects. Nano-JASMINE uses a very small nano-satellite and is scheduled to be launched in 2013. Nano-JASMINE will operate in zw-band (~ 0.8μm) to perform an all sky survey with an accuracy of 3 milli-arcseconds for position and parallaxes. Small-JASMINE will observe towards a region around the Galactic center and other small regions, which include interesting scientific targets, with accuracies of 10 to 50 μ-arcseconds in an infrared Hw-band (~ 1.7μm). The target launch date is around 2017. (Medium-sized) JASMINE is an extended mission of Small-JASMINE, which will observe towards almost the whole region of the Galactic bulge with accuracies of ~ 10μ arcseconds in Kw-band (~ 2.0μ m). The target launch date is the first half of the 2020s.

1. Nano-JASMINE

The Nano-JASMINE project is planned to demonstrate for the first time the capability for space astrometry in Japan and to perform experiments for verifications of techniques and operations planned for Small-JASMINE and JASMINE (Gouda 2011). Nano-JASMINE is a nano-size satellite of which the size and weight are (50cm)^3 and about 35 kg, respectively . Nano-JASMINE will operate in the zw-band (0.6 ~ 1.0μm). Nano-JASMINE will provide 3 mill-accuracies of the positions and parallaxes of the stars brighter than zw=7.5 mag. The number of the stars brighter than zw=7.5 mag is estimated to be about 200,000 by using cataloged stars in the Guide Star Catalogue version 2.3, the Hipparcos and the Tycho catalogue (Gouda 2011; Kobayashi et al. 2011). Moreover high-accuracy proper motions (~ 0.1 milli-arcseconds/year) can be obtained by combining the Nano-JASMINE catalogue with the Hipparcos catalogue because the decrease in the error of the proper motions is proportional to the inverse of the epoch difference between the two catalogues. The epocch difference will exceed 20 years. The flight model of the Nano-JASMINE satellite has been already furnished. Nano-JASMINE will be launched in 2013 at the Alcantara space center in Brazil by a Cyclone-4 rocket developed in Ukraine. The orbit of Nano-JASMINE is a Sun-synchronized orbit with the altitude of about 800km.

2. Small-JASMINE

Small-JASMINE will operate in Hw-band(1.1 ~ 1.7μm). Infrared space astrometry has an advantage when observing towards the Galactic plane, especially towards the Galactic center, which is hidden by the interstellar dust when observing at visual wavelengths. Also the very interesting star formation regions, surrounded by much interstellar dust, are of great interest.

Small-JASMINE will determine positions and parallaxes accurate to 10 ~ 50μ-arcseconds for stars towards a region (3 $^\circ$ × 3°) around the Galactic center and other small regions which include scientifically interesting target stars, brighter than Hw=11.5 mag (Gouda 2011). Proper motions of between 10 and 50 μ-arcseconds/year are expected. The survey will be done with a single beam telescope of which the diameter of the primary mirror is about 30 cm (Yano et al. 2011). The target launch date is around 2017. JASMINE team aims at a proposal for the Small-JASMINE mission to JAXA, to get launch approval in the near future.

The main science objective of Small-JASMINE is to clarify the structure formation model of the Galactic bulge, star formation histories around the Galactic center, and the evolution of the super massive black hole located at the center of the Galaxy (Gouda 2011). To clarify the structure of the Galactic bulge is an important element in understanding the Galaxy formation history. Next to this primary goal, Small-JASMINE will have many other scientific targets. For example, the orbital elements of the star accompanying Cygnus X-1 can be resolved by Small-JASMINE. Small-JASMINE will provide useful data of distances and tangential velocities of stars in the Galactic bulge which are complemented by measurements of radial velocities and chemical compositions of bulge stars obtained by spectroscopic surveys (e.g., APOGEE (Majewski et al. 2010) and BRAVA (Howard et al. 2008)).

3. (Medium-sized)JASMINE

JASMINE is an extended version of the Small-JASMINE mission (Gouda 2011). It is designed to perform a survey towards the whole Galactic bulge region (20° × 10°) field around the Galactic center with a single-beam telescope of which the diameter of the primary mirror is about 80 cm. Positions and parallaxes are expected to be determined to an accuracy up to 10 μ arcseconds for stars brighter than Kw=11 mag (Kw-band: 1.5 ~ 2.5μ m), and proper motion accuracies of 4 μ arcseconds/year. The target launch date is the first half of the 2020s.

Acknowledgments.   I would like to thank member of JAMINE team for discussions on development of JASMINE missions.

References

Howard, C.D., et al. 2008, Astrophysical Journal, 688, 1060
Gouda, 2011, Scholarpedia, 6(10),12021 http://www.scholarpedia.org/article/JASMINE
Kobayashi, Y., et al., 2011, ESA publication series (Gaia: At the Frontiers of astrometry), 45, 401
Majewski, S.R., et al., 2010, Proceedings of IAU symposium, 265, 480
Yano, T., et al.,2011, ESA publication series (Gaia: At the Frontiers of Astrometry), 45, 449

Galactic Archaeology: Near-Field Cosmology and the Formation of the Milky Way
ASP Conference Series, Vol. 458
W. Aoki, M. Ishigaki, T. Suda, T. Tsujimoto, N. Arimoto, eds.
©*2012 Astronomical Society of the Pacific*

Gaia: Mapping The Milky Way

N. A. Walton,[1] T. Prusti,[2] A. G. A. Brown,[3] C. Jordi,[4] S. A. Klioner,[5] L. Lindegren,[6] F. Mignard,[7] S. Randich,[8] and C. Soubiran[9]

[1]*Institute of Astronomy, University of Cambridge, Madingley Road, Cambridge, CB3 0HA, UK*

[2]*RSSD, European Space Agency (ESTEC), P.O. Box 299, 2200 AG Noordwijk, The Netherlands*

[3]*Leiden Observatory, Leiden University, PO Box 9513, 2300 RA Leiden, the Netherlands*

[4]*Dept. d'Astronomia i Meteorologia, Institut de Ciéncies del Cosmos (ICC), Universitat de Barcelona (IEEC-UB), Martí Franquès 1, 08028, Barcelona, Spain*

[5]*Lohrmann-Observatorium, Technische Universität Dresden, 01062 Dresden, Germany*

[6]*Lund Observatory, Lund University, Box 43, 22100 Lund, Sweden*

[7]*Laboratoire Lagrange, UMR7293, UNS, CNRS, Observatoire de la Côte d'Azur, Le Mont Gros, BP 4229, 06304 Nice Cedex 4, France*

[8]*INAF - Osservatorio Astrofisico di Arcetri, Largo E. Fermi 5, 50125, Firenze, Italy*

[9]*Laboratoire d'Astrophysique de Bordeaux, UMR 5804, CNRS, Université Bordeaux, 33370 Floirac, France*

Abstract.   Gaia is an ESA cornerstone mission set to revolutionise our understanding of the Milky Way. Gaia is scheduled for launch in 2013, and is designed to map over one billion stars with three instruments to collect astrometric, photometric and spectroscopic data on stars in the Milky Way and in galaxies belonging to the Local Group, distant galaxies, quasars and solar system objects. Gaia builds on the expertise established in Europe through the successful ESA Hipparcos mission. This contribution provides updated information on the Gaia mission and notes the science performance capability of the mission. The GREAT (Gaia Research for European Astronomy Training) research network, which is taking a role in promoting scientific networking of the community building awareness and readiness in advance of the Gaia launch, is discussed.

1. Gaia Performance

2011 saw the completion of a significant milestone in the development of Gaia, with the successful completion of the final critical design reviews at sub-system and system level, culminating in the final Mission review. With the completion of these, the science performance estimates of Gaia were revised to reflect expected spacecraft and instrument performance. In general terms these performance meet or in some cases surpass the original requirements. As an example, the predicted end-of-mission parallax standard errors, averaged over the sky for a uniform distribution, are given:

	B1V	G2V	M6V
V–I_C (mag)	−0.22	0.75	3.85
Bright stars	5–14 μas (6 mag < V < 12 mag)	5–14 μas (6 mag < V < 12 mag)	5–14 μas (6 mag < V < 14 mag)
V = 15 mag	26 μas	24 μas	9 μas
V = 20 mag	330 μas	290 μas	100 μas

The complete description of Gaia expected science performance is given at http: //www.rssd.esa.int/index.php?project=GAIA&page=Science_Performance.

At the time of writing (Jan. 2012), the launch date is scheduled for August 2013. After a short commissioning and initialisation phase, full scientific operation will begin in early 2014.

2. GREAT: Gaia Research for European Astronomy Training

The Gaia Research for European Astronomy Training (GREAT) network begun in 2009, as an initiative from the Gaia Science Team and the Data Processing and Analysis Consortium Executive[1], with the intention to strengthen the scientific community aiming to exploit the Gaia data products. The GREAT network is organised into a number of working groups, addressing the full range of science areas where Gaia will have a major impact. Thus these working groups cover topics from models to relativity, from exoplanets to extragalactic objects, the open clusters, the local group and so forth. The full list of the GREAT working groups is available at http://great.ast.cam.ac. uk/Greatwiki/CategoryWorkgroups

In addition to the community input, GREAT receives specific funding through two European level programmes: (a) The GREAT European Science Foundation Research Network Programme (GREAT-ESF - see http://www.esf.org/great) which runs over the period 2009–2015. It provides financial support to community programmes such as conferences, workshops, training schools and exchange visits. There have been a significant number of scientific activities funded, full details of which can be found at http://great.ast.cam.ac.uk/Greatwiki/GaiaScienceMeetings. (b) The GREAT EC FP7 Initial Training Network (GREAT-ITN - see http://www. great-itn.eu). This is a four year programme 2011–2015) focused on training early stage researchers in science topics related to the science of Gaia.

Acknowledgments.   Gaia is a large and complex endeavour where many are playing a vital role in ensuring its success. The reader is referred to the ESA Gaia 'who's who' at http://www.rssd.esa.int/index.php?project=GAIA&page=Whos_who which list this community of people and institutions working on the Gaia mission.

---

[1] see http://www.rssd.esa.int/gaia/dpac

Galactic Archaeology: Near-Field Cosmology and the Formation of the Milky Way
ASP Conference Series, Vol. 458
W. Aoki, M. Ishigaki, T. Suda, T. Tsujimoto, N. Arimoto, eds.
©*2012 Astronomical Society of the Pacific*

The Galactic Archaeology with HERMES Survey

D.B. Zucker,[1,2] G. De Silva,[2] K. Freeman,[3] J. Bland-Hawthorn[4] and
the HERMES Team

[1]*Department of Physics and Astronomy, Macquarie University, NSW 2109,
Australia*

[2]*Australian Astronomical Observatory, PO Box 296 Epping, NSW 1710,
Australia*

[3]*Research School of Astronomy & Astrophysics, Australian National
University, Cotter Road, Weston Creek, ACT 2611, Australia*

[4]*Sydney Institute for Astronomy, School of Physics, University of Sydney,
Camperdown, NSW 2006, Australia*

Abstract. HERMES is a multi-fibre spectrograph being built for the AAT 3.9m telescope, designed to simultaneously obtain high resolution ($R \sim 28000$) spectra for ~ 400
stars over a 2° field of view. The Galactic Archaeology with HERMES (GALAH) Survey is a major Australian-led project to obtain detailed elemental abundances for a
million stars, with the goal of using chemical tagging to decipher the formation history
of the Milky Way. For the GALAH Survey, $\sim 10^6$ stars (down to $V \sim 14$, at S/N ~ 100
/ resolution element) will be observed in four passbands, selected to include elements
from all major independently-varying element groups, thus allowing direct determination of abundances for each star. The survey will also be directly complementary to
wide-area photometric surveys such as Skymapper, and the multidimensional dataset
which will come from ESA's Gaia mission.

1. Introduction

The goal of Galactic Archaeology (GA) is to disentangle the formation history of the
Milky Way by recovering the building blocks of the disk and halo, i.e., the remnants
of star formation and accretion events. Traces of these building blocks survive to the
present day in the abundance patterns of low-mass stars, and can be revealed by the
technique of chemical tagging (Freeman & Bland-Hawthorn 2002). HERMES, the
High Efficiency and Resolution Multi-Element Spectrograph, is a new instrument being
built for GA on the 3.9m Anglo-Australian Telescope (AAT). Using the 2dF top end,
HERMES will be able to position ~ 400 fibres over a 2° field of view, obtaining spectra
at a resolution $R \sim 28,000$ (or a higher resolution mode: $\sim 45,000$) in 4 channels, for
a total λ coverage of ~ 1000 Å. HERMES will have $\sim 10\%$ efficiency, to achieve SNR
~ 100 at $V = 14$ in 1 hour, and will be commissioned in the 1st quarter of 2013.

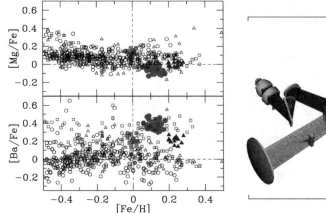

Figure 1.   (color online) Left: Chemical Tagging in action – [Ba/Fe] and [Mg/Fe] for two star clusters, Collinder 261 (green squares) and the Hyades (red circles), and one moving group, HR1614 (blue triangles), compared to field stars (De Silva et al. 2009). Right: A 3D schematic of HERMES, showing the four wavelength channels (blue, green, red and infrared).

2. The GALAH Survey

The GALAH Survey, a large observing programme for chemical tagging, is designed to reconstruct the lost stellar substructures of the proto-Galaxy, and obtain a detailed physical picture of the formation and evolution of the Galaxy. An Australian-led project with international collaborators, GALAH will obtain spectra of $\sim 10^6$ stars, complete down to $V \sim 14$; with ~ 3000 plate configurations (~ 400 stars / field) it can be carried out in ~ 400 nights of bright time, giving a survey duration of 5 years. An automated abundance pipeline will use spectral synthesis to derive over 20 elemental abundances per star from 7 independent element groups, with a relative accuracy of $0.05 - 0.1$ dex.

GALAH is designed to address basic questions about the formation and evolution of the Milky Way: What were the conditions of star formation during Galaxy assembly? When and where were the major episodes of star formation in the disk and what drove them? To what extent are the Galactic thin and thick disks composed of stars from merger events? In what conditions and types of systems did accreted stars form? How have the stars that formed in situ in the disk evolved dynamically?

The GALAH dataset will also have powerful synergies with major upcoming surveys/projects. Skymapper will map the Southern sky in 5 bandpasses; HERMES will yield abundances and radial velocities for Skymapper discoveries. Gaia will measure proper motions and parallaxes for $\sim 10^9$ stars; these 6-D phase space data, in combination with detailed HERMES abundances, will help to disentangle the formation history of the Milky Way (e.g., distinguishing "real" phase-space substructures from artefacts).

References

De Silva, G. M., Freeman, K. C., & Bland-Hawthorn, J. 2009, PASA, 26, 11
Freeman, K., & Bland-Hawthorn, J. 2002, ARAA, 40, 487

Part VIII

Closing

Galactic Archaeology: Near-Field Cosmology and the Formation of the Milky Way
ASP Conference Series, Vol. 458
W. Aoki, M. Ishigaki, T. Suda, T. Tsujimoto, N. Arimoto, eds.
©*2012 Astronomical Society of the Pacific*

Conference Summary

Alvio Renzini

INAF – Osservatorio Astronomico di Padova, Italy

1. Ages, Lookback Times, Redshifts

I wish to start this conference closing talk by paying due tribute to the Subaru Telescope and its three unique instruments, namely the Suprime Camera, MOIRCS and FMOS, so far unparalleled at other 8-10 m class telescopes. As demonstrated by the Subaru Conferences, this instrumentation has placed Subaru in the position to play a leading role in several areas of current astrophysical and cosmological research. Such a leading role is likely to be further expanded by the advent of the next generation of Subaru instruments, namely HSC and PFS.

An extremely wide range of astrophysical and cosmological issues have been addressed at this meeting, which would make it impossible to mention individual contributions in the short space of this summary. Thus, the SOC has suggested me to look at the grand themes of this Conference in the perspective of the developments we may expect to happen in the not too distant future.

In following this recommendation, I will cursorily look to the major topics discussed at the various sessions of the meeting by adopting one particular point of view: the age-redshift connection. Galactic Archaeology aims to recover the evolutionary history of galaxies from their present stellar content, by measuring ages, chemical compositions and kinematics for (very) large numbers of stars. Stellar ages are lookback times to formation, and lookback times immediately translate into redshifts, where we can look to the formation processes themselves. Thus, to each local galaxy or galactic component for which ages are estimated we can associate a redshift interval where to look for analog objects to form before our eyes. There is indeed a great deal of complementarity between local *archaeological* studies and high redshift ones, and their combination offers to us the best opportunity to understand the formation and evolution of galaxies and their components.

2. Extremely metal poor stars, and more

This local to high-redshift connection was particularly evident in the session on extremely metal poor stars, those which must have been among the first to form in the Universe. Ages and lookback times in excess of $\sim 12 - 13$ Gyr bring us to extremely high redshifts, in excess of ~ 6 or so, thus well into the *reionization* epoch, i.e., in the epoch of Pop III stars, first supernovae and the beginning of chemical evolution.

Our knowledge of the $6 \lesssim z \lesssim 1000$ Universe is currently limited to a few (metal rich!) QSOs, some Ly-α emitters and DLAs, and a few Lyman-break galaxies (LBG). This is currently not enough to properly understand the reionization process, including the unambiguous identification of the sources of such reionization. This is why extremely metal poor stars in the local Universe offer a valuable and complementary diagnostics to explore the reionization era. Major astronomical projects, such as JWST, E-ELT and TMT, are deliberately designed to probe into this cosmic epoch, i.e., into the end of the *Dark Ages* and the dawn of galaxies. With these new instruments it should be possible to directly see first supernovae and hypernovae at extremely high redshifts, and possibly resolve their young host galaxies.

3. Globular clusters

Globular clusters are perhaps the objects for which ages have been most accurately measured. With most estimates clustering around ~ 12 Gyr, the formation epoch of globular clusters corresponds to $z \sim 3 - 4$. This is today a far better explored slice of the early Universe, with lots of LBGs and QSOs, when galaxies were growing near exponentially in mass and star formation rate, while supporting widespread galactic winds enriching the intergalactic medium.

   The formation of globular clusters was never properly understood, and the problem has recently turned much more complex than ever suspected before. The widespread presence of multiple populations within individual globulars, with some of them highly enriched in helium, has revolutionized our view of these objects, and possibly of their role in galaxy evolution.

   Tomorrow, with JWST and the ELTs, it should become possible to see individual globular clusters forming within or around $z = 3 - 4$ galaxies and/or see their young (~ 0.1 Gyr) *precursors*. Indeed, the presence of multiple populations has suggested that such precursors may well have been ten or more times more massive than today survivors, hence must have been very bright at formation, which may facilitate their direct detection in very distant galaxies.

4. Galactic Bulge and Thick Disk

Age dating of both Galactic bulge and thick disk stars indicate ages of ~ 10 Gyr or more for the bulk population of these Milky Way components, which bring us to $z \sim 2$. At these redshifts galaxies are at the peak of their star formation and AGN activity, meanwhile quenching of star formation in massive galaxies and morphological differentiation are already well underway.

   As of today, lots of data have been accumulated on $z \sim 2$ galaxies, both from the ground and from space. Thus, we should be able to witness directly bulges and thick disks being formed in such galaxies. Indeed, many $z \sim 2$ galaxies appear to be large, rotating disks which differ from those of local spirals in several ways: they are extremely gas rich (gas fraction $\sim 50\%$ or more), clumpy, and with high velocity dispersion ($\sigma \simeq 50 - 100$ km s^{-1}). Such disks appear to be unstable, prone to fragment in massive star-forming clumps that in turn can migrate via dynamical friction to finally coalesce at the center. Disks with high velocity dispersion may well be thick, and coalescence of clumps may well result in bulge formation. Thus, we may have already witnessed bulge and thick disk formation in high-redshift galaxies.

   Tomorrow, with the superior resolution of JWST and especially the ELTs, we should reach close to produce "megapixel posters" of $z \sim 2$ galaxies, with bulges in various stages of development, and surrounded by their halo of young globular clusters.

Besides disky star-forming galaxies, the $z \sim 2$ Universe has already started to be populated by the first massive ellipticals, which could then be studied in exquisite detail. Thus, we can hope that the very high resolution observations of star forming and quenched galaxies at these redshift may shed light on the physical processes able to quench star formation in massive galaxies and change their morphology, two crucial events in galaxy evolution which existing observations are still unable to clarify.

5. Thin Disk

Stars in the Galactic thin disk span a full range of ages, from 0 to $\sim$ 10 Gyr, corresponding to the redshift range from 0 to $\sim$ 2. This is the epoch dominated by the peaceful growth of disks, with also several of the less massive galaxies being quenched, with the final morphological differentiation, and with the growth of large structures where environmental effect become an additional driver in galaxy evolution.

As of today, lots, lots of observational data have illustrated the evolution of galaxy scaling relation through this cosmic times, including the evolution of the so called *Main Sequence* of star-forming galaxies (the tight relation between stellar mass and star formation rate). On local galaxies, the disks of Milky Way and M31 are prime target for Galactic Archaeology, and age-dating large numbers of stars is used to infer the star formation history of such disks. In turn, this is a fully complementary exercise to the direct mapping of the evolution of the star formation rate of disk galaxies from $z \sim 2$ to $z \sim 0$.

Not far into the future, Gaia and its ground-based complements will give us a detailed history of the Milky Way, of its production of new stars through cosmic times as well as of the capture and dissolution of minor galaxies that may have merged with it. Indeed, an impressive fraction of the $\sim$ 200 billion stars of our home Galaxy will be accurately located in the Galactic phase space and chemically tagged, in an ultimate achievement of Galactic Archaeology.

6. Dwarfs

Local dwarf galaxies, such as dwarf spheroidals (DSph) and ultra faint dwarfs (UFD), contain stars in a broad age range, from a few to $\sim$ 13 Gyr, which corresponds to the broad redshift range from $z \sim 0.4$ to over $\sim$ 6. Though all such galaxies appear to harbor a very old stellar component, each of them is characterized by its own specific star formation history, often characterized by a few separate star formation episodes. For some time the notion has been entertained according to which DSph's may be the original *building blocks* for the formation of the Milky Way halo. Nowadays this does not appear to be the case: their chemical tagging (set of abundance rations) is different from that of the stars in the MW halo, hence DSph's do not qualify as viable building blocks. Maybe UFDs will? This remains to be seen, though perhaps as many of $\sim$ 100 thousand UFDs would be needed to make up the mass of the stellar halo. If so many were needed, while so few survivors remain? There seems to be a persisting shortage of adequate building blocks ....

Extremely deep high redshift observations, especially with the next generation of major facilities, promise to solve this dilemma. Indeed, the direct detection and count of the star-forming precursors of DSph's (and perhaps of UFDs) should become possible, thus mapping the build up of the stellar halos of galaxies such as the Milky Way and M31.

7. Shifting Paradigms

Theoretical efforts of modelling galaxy formation and evolution did not have a major share at this conference, but influential theoretical ideas still offer guidance to many of the studies that were presented. In this context, it seems to me worth emphasizing that in recent years some important *paradigm shifts* have taken place as to the nature of the major drivers of galaxy evolution. For example, for quite a long time galaxy merging and merging driven starbursts have been regarded as the major drivers. Nowadays, the interest has rather shifted towards quasi-steady accretion, in the form of *cold streams* of gas feeding galaxies to maintain their quasi-steady star formation activity, with starbursts and major mergers playing only a minor role. If such shifts are for the better, one may expect a diminished role for accretion of mainly stellar satellites, in favor of *in situ* star formation for all galactic components (disks and bulge), with the exception perhaps of the outer stellar halo.

Finally, worth mentioning is that theoreticians have started to look at alternatives to the classical ΛCDM paradigm, perhaps driven by enduring difficulties of of some predictions of the model, such as overabundance of minihalos and the cuspy cores of DM halos. This shift may indeed be required, but it would come at the expense of a loss of elegance and conciseness to add new parameters for the dark matter to the many already in use to describe the oddities of the baryons. This would not be a reassuring message for the perspective of understanding galaxy evolution via models constructed from first physical principles.

So, it looks that shifts of interests are under way from hot to cold baryons, and from cold to warm WIMPs. Stay tuned

————OOO————

In closing this summary, I wish to remember my friend Bob Rood, who so prematurely passed away early in the week of the Conference, and was so dear to me and to many of the participants to this Conference.

Conference summary by A. Renzini.

Conference poster with an optical image of IC 10 obtained with the Subaru/Suprime-Cam and Hokusai's "Asakusa Torigoe".

Author Index

ASTRONOMICAL SOCIETY OF THE PACIFIC

THE ASTRONOMICAL SOCIETY OF THE PACIFIC is an international, nonprofit, scientific, and educational organization. Some 120 years ago, on a chilly February evening in San Francisco, astronomers from Lick Observatory and members of the Pacific Coast Amateur Photographic Association—fresh from viewing the New Year's Day total solar eclipse of 1889 a little to the north of the city—met to share pictures and experiences. Edward Holden, Lick's first director, complimented the amateurs on their service to science and proposed to continue the good fellowship through the founding of a Society "to advance the Science of Astronomy, and to diffuse information concerning it." The Astronomical Society of the Pacific (ASP) was born.

The ASP's purpose is to increase the understanding and appreciation of astronomy by engaging scientists, educators, enthusiasts, and the public to advance science and science literacy. The ASP has become the largest general astronomy society in the world, with members from over 70 nations.

The ASP's professional astronomer members are a key component of the Society. Their desire to share with the public the rich rewards of their work permits the ASP to act as a bridge, explaining the mysteries of the universe. For these members, the ASP publishes the Publications of the Astronomical Society of the Pacific (PASP), a well-respected monthly scientific journal. In 1988, Dr. Harold McNamara, the PASP editor at the time, founded the ASP Conference Series at Brigham Young University. The ASP Conference Series shares recent developments in astronomy and astrophysics with the professional astronomy community.

To learn how to join the ASP or to make a donation, please visit http://www.astrosociety.org.

ASTRONOMICAL SOCIETY OF THE PACIFIC
MONOGRAPH SERIES

Published by the Astronomical Society of the Pacific

The ASP Monograph series was established in 1995 to publish select reference titles.
For electronic versions of ASP Monographs, please see
http://www.aspmonographs.org.

INFRARED ATLAS OF THE ARCTURUS SPECTRUM, 0.9-5.3μm
eds. Kenneth Hinkle, Lloyd Wallace, and William Livingston (1995)
ISBN: 1-886733-04-X, e-book ISBN: 978-1-58381-687-5

**VISIBLE AND NEAR INFRARED ATLAS
OF THE ARCTURUS SPECTRUM 3727-9300Å**
eds. Kenneth Hinkle, Lloyd Wallace, Jeff Valenti, and Dianne Harmer (2000)
ISBN: 1-58381-037-4, e-book ISBN: 978-1-58381-688-2

ULTRAVIOLET ATLAS OF THE ARCTURUS SPECTRUM 1150-3800Å
eds. Kenneth Hinkle, Lloyd Wallace, Jeff Valenti, and Thomas Ayres (2005)
ISBN: 1-58381-204-0, e-book ISBN: 978-1-58381-689-9

**HANDBOOK OF STAR FORMING REGIONS: VOLUME I
THE NORTHERN SKY**
ed. Bo Reipurth (2008)
ISBN: 978-1-58381-670-7, e-book ISBN: 978-1-58381-677-6

**HANDBOOK OF STAR FORMING REGIONS: VOLUME II
THE SOUTHERN SKY**
ed. Bo Reipurth (2008)
ISBN: 978-1-58381-671-4, e-book ISBN: 978-1-58381-678-3

A complete list and electronic versions of ASPCS volumes may be found at
http://www.aspbooks.org.

All book orders or inquiries concerning the ASP Conference Series, ASP
Monographs, or International Astronomical Union Volumes published by the ASP
should be directed to:

Astronomical Society of the Pacific
390 Ashton Avenue
San Francisco, CA 94112-1722 USA
Phone: 800-335-2624 (within the USA)
Phone: 415-337-2126
Fax: 415-337-5205
Email: service@astrosociety.org

For a complete list of ASP publications, please visit
http://www.astrosociety.org.